P9-AZV-102

Fundamental Equations of Statics and Mechanics of Materials

Cartesian Vector

$$\mathbf{A} = A_x\mathbf{i} + A_y\mathbf{j} + A_z\mathbf{k}$$

Magnitude

$$A = \sqrt{A_x^2 + A_y^2 + A_z^2}$$

Directions

$$\mathbf{u}_A = \frac{\mathbf{A}}{A} = \frac{A_x}{A}\mathbf{i} + \frac{A_y}{A}\mathbf{j} + \frac{A_z}{A}\mathbf{k}$$
$$= \cos\alpha\mathbf{i} + \cos\beta\mathbf{j} + \cos\gamma\mathbf{k}$$
$$\cos^2\alpha + \cos^2\beta + \cos^2\gamma = 1$$

Dot Product

$$\mathbf{A}\cdot\mathbf{B} = AB\cos\theta = A_xB_x + A_yB_y + A_zB_z$$

Cross Product

$$\mathbf{C} = \mathbf{A}\times\mathbf{B} = \begin{vmatrix} \mathbf{i} & \mathbf{j} & \mathbf{k} \\ A_x & A_y & A_z \\ B_x & B_y & B_z \end{vmatrix}$$

Cartesian Position Vector

$$\mathbf{r} = (x_2 - x_1)\mathbf{i} + (y_2 - y_1)\mathbf{j} + (z_2 - z_1)\mathbf{k}$$

Cartesian Force Vector

$$\mathbf{F} = F\mathbf{u} = F\left(\frac{\mathbf{r}}{r}\right)$$

Moment of a Force

$$M_O = Fd$$
$$\mathbf{M}_O = \mathbf{r}\times\mathbf{F} = \begin{vmatrix} \mathbf{i} & \mathbf{j} & \mathbf{k} \\ r_x & r_y & r_z \\ F_x & F_y & F_z \end{vmatrix}$$

Moment of a Force About a Specified Axis

$$M_a = \mathbf{u}\cdot\mathbf{r}\times\mathbf{F} = \begin{vmatrix} u_x & u_y & u_z \\ r_x & r_y & r_z \\ F_x & F_y & F_z \end{vmatrix}$$

Simplification of a Force and Couple System

$$\mathbf{F}_R = \Sigma\mathbf{F}$$
$$(\mathbf{M}_R)_O = \Sigma\mathbf{M}_c + \Sigma\mathbf{M}_O$$

Equilibrium

Particle

$$\Sigma F_x = 0,\ \Sigma F_y = 0,\ \Sigma F_z = 0$$

Rigid Body—Two Dimensions

$$\Sigma F_x = 0,\ \Sigma F_y = 0,\ \Sigma M_O = 0$$

Rigid Body—Three Dimensions

$$\Sigma F_x = 0,\ \Sigma F_y = 0,\ \Sigma F_z = 0$$
$$\Sigma M_{x'} = 0,\ \Sigma M_{y'} = 0,\ \Sigma M_{z'} = 0$$

Friction

Static (maximum) $F_s = \mu_s N$

Kinetic $F_k = \mu_k N$

Center of Gravity

Particles or Discrete Parts

$$\bar{r} = \frac{\Sigma\tilde{r}W}{\Sigma W}$$

Body

$$\bar{r} = \frac{\int \tilde{r}\,dW}{\int dW}$$

Area and Mass Moments of Inertia

$$I = \int r^2\,dA \qquad I = \int r^2\,dm$$

Parallel-Axis Theorem

$$I = \bar{I} + Ad^2 \qquad I = \bar{I} + md^2$$

Radius of Gyration

$$k = \sqrt{\frac{I}{A}} \qquad k = \sqrt{\frac{I}{m}}$$

Axial Load

Normal Stress

$$\sigma = \frac{P}{A}$$

Displacement

$$\delta = \int_0^L \frac{P(x)dx}{A(x)E}$$
$$\delta = \Sigma\frac{PL}{AE}$$
$$\delta_T = \alpha\,\Delta TL$$

Torsion

Shear Stress in Circular Shaft

$$\tau = \frac{T\rho}{J}$$

where

$$J = \frac{\pi}{2}c^4 \text{ solid cross section}$$
$$J = \frac{\pi}{2}(c_o^4 - c_i^4) \text{ tubular cross section}$$

Power

$$P = T\omega = 2\pi fT$$

Angle of Twist

$$\phi = \int_0^L \frac{T(x)dx}{J(x)G}$$
$$\phi = \Sigma\frac{TL}{JG}$$

Average Shear Stress in a Thin-walled Tube

$$\tau_{avg} = \frac{T}{2tA_m}$$

Shear Flow

$$q = \tau_{avg}t = \frac{T}{2A_m}$$

Bending

Normal Stress

$$\sigma = \frac{My}{I}$$

Unsymmetric Bending

$$\sigma = -\frac{M_z y}{I_z} + \frac{M_y z}{I_y}, \qquad \tan\alpha = \frac{I_z}{I_y}\tan\theta$$

Shear

Average Direct Shear Stress

$$\tau_{avg} = \frac{V}{A}$$

Transverse Shear Stress

$$\tau = \frac{VQ}{It}$$

Shear Flow

$$q = \tau t = \frac{VQ}{I}$$

Stress in Thin-Walled Pressure Vessel

Cylinder

$$\sigma_1 = \frac{pr}{t} \qquad \sigma_2 = \frac{pr}{2t}$$

Sphere

$$\sigma_1 = \sigma_2 = \frac{pr}{2t}$$

Stress Transformation Equations

$$\sigma_{x'} = \frac{\sigma_x + \sigma_y}{2} + \frac{\sigma_x - \sigma_y}{2}\cos 2\theta + \tau_{xy}\sin 2\theta$$
$$\tau_{x'y'} = -\frac{\sigma_x - \sigma_y}{2}\sin 2\theta + \tau_{xy}\cos 2\theta$$

Principal Stress

$$\tan 2\theta_p = \frac{\tau_{xy}}{(\sigma_x - \sigma_y)/2}$$

$$\sigma_{1,2} = \frac{\sigma_x + \sigma_y}{2} \pm \sqrt{\left(\frac{\sigma_x - \sigma_y}{2}\right)^2 + \tau_{xy}^2}$$

Maximum In-Plane Shear Stress

$$\tan 2\theta_s = -\frac{(\sigma_x - \sigma_y)/2}{\tau_{xy}}$$

$$\tau_{\max} = \sqrt{\left(\frac{\sigma_x - \sigma_y}{2}\right)^2 + \tau_{xy}^2}$$

$$\sigma_{\text{avg}} = \frac{\sigma_x + \sigma_y}{2}$$

Absolute Maximum Shear Stress

$$\tau_{\substack{\text{abs}\\ \max}} = \frac{\sigma_{\max} - \sigma_{\min}}{2}$$

$$\sigma_{\text{avg}} = \frac{\sigma_{\max} + \sigma_{\min}}{2}$$

Material Property Relations

Poisson's Ratio

$$\nu = -\frac{\epsilon_{\text{lat}}}{\epsilon_{\text{long}}}$$

Generalized Hooke's Law

$$\epsilon_x = \frac{1}{E}\left[\sigma_x - \nu(\sigma_y + \sigma_z)\right]$$

$$\epsilon_y = \frac{1}{E}\left[\sigma_y - \nu(\sigma_x + \sigma_z)\right]$$

$$\epsilon_z = \frac{1}{E}\left[\sigma_z - \nu(\sigma_x + \sigma_y)\right]$$

$$\gamma_{xy} = \frac{1}{G}\tau_{xy}, \quad \gamma_{yz} = \frac{1}{G}\tau_{yz}, \quad \gamma_{zx} = \frac{1}{G}\tau_{zx}$$

where

$$G = \frac{E}{2(1 + \nu)}$$

Relations Between *w*, *V*, *M*

$$\frac{dV}{dx} = -w(x), \qquad \frac{dM}{dx} = V$$

Elastic Curve

$$\frac{1}{\rho} = \frac{M}{EI}$$

$$EI\frac{d^4v}{dx^4} = -w(x)$$

$$EI\frac{d^3v}{dx^3} = V(x)$$

$$EI\frac{d^2v}{dx^2} = M(x)$$

Buckling

Critical Axial Load

$$P_{\text{cr}} = \frac{\pi^2 EI}{(KL)^2}$$

Critical Stress

$$\sigma_{\text{cr}} = \frac{\pi^2 E}{(KL/r)^2}, \ r = \sqrt{I/A}$$

Secant Formula

$$\sigma_{\max} = \frac{P}{A}\left[1 + \frac{ec}{r^2}\sec\left(\frac{L}{2r}\sqrt{\frac{P}{EA}}\right)\right]$$

Geometric Properties of Area Elements

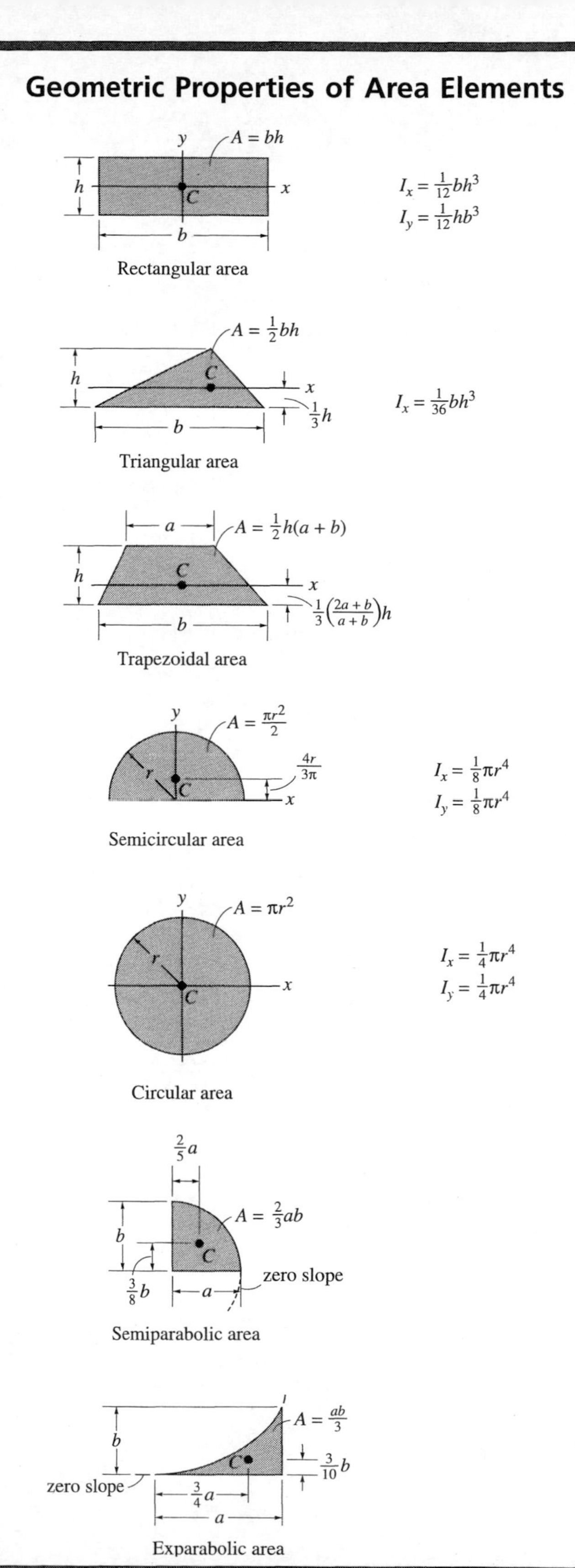

STATICS AND MECHANICS OF MATERIALS

STATICS AND MECHANICS OF MATERIALS

SI EDITION

R. C. HIBBELER

SI CONVERSION BY S.C. FRAN

CUSTOM EDITION FOR QUEEN'S UNIVERSITY

Taken from:
Statics and Mechanics of Materials, SI Edition
By R. C. Hibbeler

Cover image: courtesy of PhotoDisc/Getty Images.

Taken from:

Statics and Mechanics of Materials, SI Edition
By R. C. Hibbleler

Published by Prentice Hall
A Pearson Education Company
Upper Saddle River, New Jersey 07458

This special edition published in cooperation with Pearson Custom Publishing.

Printed in Canada

4 5 6 DPC 12 11 10

ISBN 0-536-49884-9

2007360766

SB

Please visit our web site at *www.pearsoncustom.com*

PEARSON CUSTOM PUBLISHING
501 Boylston Street, Suite 900, Boston, MA 02116
A Pearson Education Company

TO THE STUDENT

With the hope that this work will stimulate an interest in Engineering Mechanics and Mechanics of Materials and provide an acceptable guide to its understanding.

PREFACE

This book represents a combined abridged version of two of the author's books, namely *Engineering Mechanics: Statics, Third Edition* and *Mechanics of Materials*. It is intended for those students who do not need complete coverage of these subjects. Rather, it provides a clear and thorough presentation of both the theory and application of the important fundamental topics of this material, which is often used in many engineering disciplines. Understanding is based on explaining the physical behavior of materials under load and then modeling this behavior to develop the theory. The development emphasizes the importance of satisfying equilibrium, compatibility of deformation, and material behavior requirements. The hallmark of the book, however, remains the same as the author's unabridged versions, and that is, strong emphasis is placed on drawing a free-body diagram, and the importance of selecting an appropriate coordinate system and an associated sign convention is stressed when the equations of mechanics are applied. Throughout the book, many analysis and design applications are presented, which involve mechanical elements and structural members often encountered in engineering practice.

Organization and Approach

In order to aid both the instructor and the student, the contents of each chapter are organized into well-defined sections. Selected groups of sections contain an explanation of specific topics, followed by illustrative example problems and a set of homework problems. The topics within each section are often placed in subgroups denoted by boldface titles. The purpose of this is to present a structured method for introducing each new definition or concept and to make the book convenient for later reference and review.

As in the author's other textbooks, a "procedure for analysis" is used throughout the book, providing the student with a logical and orderly method to follow when applying the theory. The example problems are then solved using this outlined method in order to clarify its numerical application. It is to be understood, however, that once the relevant principles have been mastered and enough confidence and judgment have been acquired, the student can then develop his or her own procedures for solving problems. In most cases, it is felt that the first step in any procedure should be to draw a diagram. In doing so, the student forms the habit of tabulating the necessary data while focusing on the physical aspects of the problem and its associated geometry. If this step is correctly performed, applying the relevant equations becomes somewhat methodical, since the data can be taken directly from the diagram.

Contents

The book is divided into two parts, and the material is covered in the traditional manner.

Statics. The subject of statics is presented in 7 chapters. The text begins in Chapter 1 with an introduction to mechanics and a discussion of units. The notion of a vector and the properties of a concurrent force system are introduced in Chapter 2. Chapter 3 contains a general discussion of concentrated force systems and the methods used to simplify them. The principles of rigid-body equilibrium are developed in Chapter 4 and then applied to specific problems involving the equilibrium of trusses, frames, and machines in Chapter 5. Topics related to the center of gravity, centroid, and moment of inertia are treated in Chapter 6. Lastly, internal loadings in members is discussed in Chapter 7.

Mechanics of Materials. This portion of the text is covered in 10 chapters. Chapter 8 begins with a formal definition of both normal and shear stress, and a discussion of normal stress in axially loaded members and average shear stress caused by direct shear; finally, normal and shear strain are defined. In Chapter 9 a discussion of some of the important mechanical properties of materials is given. Separate treatments of axial load, torsion, bending, and transverse shear are presented in Chapters 10, 11, 12, and 13, respectively. Chapter 14 provides a partial review of the material covered in the previous chapters, in which the state of stress resulting from combined loadings is discussed. In Chapter 15 the concepts for transforming stress and strain are presented. Chapter 16 provides a means for a further summary and review of previous material by covering design applications of beams. Also, coverage is given for various methods for computing deflections of beams and finding the reactions on these members if they are statically indeterminate. Lastly, Chapter 17 provides a discussion of column buckling.

Sections of the book that contain more advanced material are indicated by a star (★). Time permitting, some of these topics may be included in the course. Furthermore, this material provides a suitable reference for basic principles when it is covered in other courses, and it can be used as a basis for assigning special projects.

Alternative Method for Coverage of Mechanics of Materials. Some instructors prefer to cover stress and strain transformations *first*, before discussing specific applications of axial load, torsion, bending, and shear. One possible method for doing this would be first to cover stress and strain and its transformations, Chapter 8 and Chapter 15. The discussion and example problems in Chapter 15 have been styled so that this is possible. Chapters 9 through 14 can then be covered with no loss in continuity.

Problems. Numerous problems in the book depict realistic situations encountered in engineering practice. It is hoped that this realism will both stimulate the student's interest in the subject and provide a means for developing the skill to reduce any such problem from its physical description to a model or symbolic representation to which the principles may be applied.

Throughout the text there is an approximate balance of problems using SI units. Furthermore, in any set, an attempt has been made to arrange the problems in order of increasing difficulty. The answers to all but every fourth problem are listed in the back of the book. To alert the user to a problem without a reported answer, an asterisk (*) is placed before the problem number. Answers are reported to three significant figures, even though the data for material properties may be known with less accuracy. Although this might appear to be poor practice, it is done simply to be consistent and to allow the student a better chance to validate his or her solution. All the problems and their solutions have been independently checked for accuracy.

Chapter Reviews. New chapter review sections summarize key points of the chapter, often in bulleted lists.

Instructor's Solutions CD—Provides complete solutions supported by problem statements and problem figures. All solutions appear on either one or two pages.

Acknowledgments

Preparation of the manuscript for this book has undergone several reviews and I owe the reviewers a personal debt of gratitude. As this text is a combination of my *Statics* and *Mechanics of Materials* books, I would like to thank the reviewers who helped with these editions. Their encouragement and willingness to provide constructive criticism are very much appreciated; in particular, Patrick Kwon of Michigan State University, Cliff Lissenden of Penn State University, Dahsin Liu of Michigan State University, Ting-Wen Wu of the University of Kentucky, Javad Hashemi of Texas Tech University, and Assimina Pelegri of Rutgers—The State University of New Jersey, Paul Heyliger of Colorado State University, Kenneth Sawyers of Lehigh University, John Oyler of University of Pittsburgh, Glenn Beltz of University of California, Johannes Gessler of Colorado State University, Wilfred Nixon of University of Iowa, Jonathan Russell of U.S. Coast Guard Academy, Robert Hinks of Arizona State University, Cap. Mark Orwat of U.S. Military Academy—West Point, Cetin Cetinyaka of Clarkson University, Jack Xin of Kansas State University, Pierre Julien of Colorado State University, Stephen Bechtel of Ohio State University, W. A. Curtain of Brown University, Robert Oakberg of Montana State University, Richard Bennett of University of Tennessee.

I would also like to thank all my students who have used the manuscript and the computer tutorial as well as their revisions, and made comments to improve their contents. A particular note of thanks goes to one of my former graduate students, Kai Beng Yap, who has been a great help to me in this regard. A special note of gratitude also goes to my editors and the staff at Pearson Education, who have all been very supportive in allowing me to have a more creative and artistic license in the design and execution of this book. It has been a pleasure to work with all of them. Finally, appreciation goes to my wife, Conny, who has been a source of encouragement and has helped with the details of preparing the manuscript for publication.

RUSSELL CHARLES HIBBELER

CONTENTS

Statics

1

General Principles

2

Force Vectors

3

Force System Resultants

4

Equilibrium of a Rigid Body

5

Structural Analysis

6

Geometric Properties and Distributed Loadings

7

Internal Loadings

Appendices

CHAPTER 1

General Principles

CHAPTER OBJECTIVES

- To provide an introduction to the basic quantities and idealizations of mechanics.
- To give a statement of Newton's Laws of Motion and Gravitation.
- To review the principles for applying the SI system of units.
- To examine the standard procedures for performing numerical calculations.
- To present a general guide for solving problems.

1.1 Mechanics

Mechanics can be defined as that branch of the physical sciences concerned with the state of rest or motion of bodies that are subjected to the action of forces. In general, this subject is subdivided into three branches: *rigid-body mechanics, deformable-body mechanics*, and *fluid mechanics*. This book treats only rigid-body mechanics since it forms a suitable basis for the design and analysis of many types of structural, mechanical, or electrical devices encountered in engineering. Also, rigid-body mechanics provides part of the necessary background for the study of the mechanics of deformable bodies and the mechanics of fluids.

Rigid-body mechanics is divided into two areas: statics and dynamics. *Statics* deals with the equilibrium of bodies, that is, those that are either at rest or move with a constant velocity; whereas *dynamics* is concerned with the accelerated motion of bodies. Although statics can be considered as a special case of dynamics, in which the acceleration is zero, statics deserves separate treatment in engineering education since many objects are designed with the intention that they remain in equilibrium.

Historical Development. The subject of statics developed very early in history because the principles involved could be formulated simply from measurements of geometry and force. For example, the writings of Archimedes (287–212 B.C.) deal with the principle of the lever. Studies of the pulley, inclined plane, and wrench are also recorded in ancient writings—at times when the requirements of engineering were limited primarily to building construction.

Since the principles of dynamics depend on an accurate measurement of time, this subject developed much later. Galileo Galilei (1564–1642) was one of the first major contributors to this field. His work consisted of experiments using pendulums and falling bodies. The most significant contributions in dynamics, however, were made by Issac Newton (1642–1727), who is noted for his formulation of the three fundamental laws of motion and the law of universal gravitational attraction. Shortly after these laws were postulated, important techniques for their application were developed by Euler, D'Alembert, Lagrange, and others.

1.2 Fundamental Concepts

Before we begin our study of engineering mechanics, it is important to understand the meaning of certain fundamental concepts and principles.

Basic Quantities. The following four quantities are used throughout mechanics.

Length. *Length* is needed to locate the position of a point in space and thereby describe the size of a physical system. Once a standard unit of length is defined, one can then quantitatively define distances and geometric properties of a body as multiples of the unit length.

Time. *Time* is conceived as a succession of events. Although the principles of statics are time independent, this quantity does play an important role in the study of dynamics.

Mass. *Mass* is a property of matter by which we can compare the action of one body with that of another. This property manifests itself as a gravitational attraction between two bodies and provides a quantitative measure of the resistance of matter to a change in velocity.

Force. In general, *force* is considered as a "push" or "pull" exerted by one body on another. This interaction can occur when there is direct contact between the bodies, such as a person pushing on a wall, or it can occur through a distance when the bodies are physically separated. Examples of the latter type include gravitational, electrical, and magnetic forces. In any case, a force is completely characterized by its magnitude, direction, and point of application.

Idealizations. Models or idealizations are used in mechanics in order to simplify application of the theory. A few of the more important idealizations will now be defined. Others that are noteworthy will be discussed at points where they are needed.

Particle. A *particle* has a mass, but a size that can be neglected. For example, the size of the earth is insignificant compared to the size of its orbit, and therefore the earth can be modeled as a particle when studying its orbital motion. When a body is idealized as a particle, the principles of mechanics reduce to a rather simplified form since the geometry of the body will not be involved in the analysis of the problem.

Rigid Body. A *rigid body* can be considered as a combination of a large number of particles in which all the particles remain at a fixed distance from one another both before and after applying a load. As a result, the material properties of any body that is assumed to be rigid will not have to be considered when analyzing the forces acting on the body. In most cases the actual deformations occurring in structures, machines, mechanisms, and the like are relatively small, and the rigid-body assumption is suitable for analysis.

Concentrated Force. A *concentrated force* represents the effect of a loading which is assumed to act at a point on a body. We can represent a load by a concentrated force, provided the area over which the load is applied is very small compared to the overall size of the body. An example would be the contact force between a wheel and the ground.

Newton's Three Laws of Motion. The entire subject of rigid-body mechanics is formulated on the basis of Newton's three laws of motion, the validity of which is based on experimental observation. They apply to the motion of a particle as measured from a nonaccelerating reference frame. With reference to Fig. 1–1, they may be briefly stated as follows.

First Law. A particle originally at rest, or moving in a straight line with constant velocity, will remain in this state provided the particle is *not* subjected to an unbalanced force.

Second Law. A particle acted upon by an *unbalanced force* **F** experiences an acceleration **a** that has the same direction as the force and a magnitude that is directly proportional to the force.* If **F** is applied to a particle of mass m, this law may be expressed mathematically as

$$\mathbf{F} = m\mathbf{a} \qquad (1\text{–}1)$$

Third Law. The mutual forces of action and reaction between two particles are equal, opposite, and collinear.

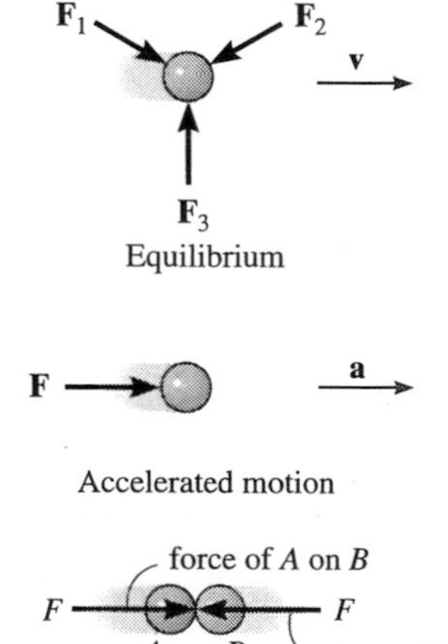

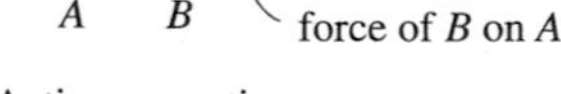

Fig. 1–1

*Stated another way, the unbalanced force acting on the particle is proportional to the time rate of change of the particle's linear momentum.

Newton's Law of Gravitational Attraction. Shortly after formulating his three laws of motion, Newton postulated a law governing the gravitational attraction between any two particles. Stated mathematically,

$$F = G\frac{m_1 m_2}{r^2} \tag{1–2}$$

where
F = force of gravitation between the two particles
G = universal constant of gravitation; according to experimental evidence, $G = 66.73(10^{-12})\ \text{m}^3/(\text{kg}\cdot\text{s}^2)$
m_1, m_2 = mass of each of the two particles
r = distance between the two particles

Weight. According to Eq. 1–2, any two particles or bodies have a mutual attractive (gravitational) force acting between them. In the case of a particle located at or near the surface of the earth, however, the only gravitational force having any sizable magnitude is that between the earth and the particle. Consequently, this force, termed the *weight*, will be the only gravitational force considered in our study of mechanics.

From Eq. 1–2, we can develop an approximate expression for finding the weight W of a particle having a mass $m_1 = m$. If we assume the earth to be a nonrotating sphere of constant density and having a mass $m_2 = M_e$, then if r is the distance between the earth's center and the particle, we have

$$W = G\frac{mM_e}{r^2}$$

Letting $g = GM_e/r^2$ yields

$$\boxed{W = mg} \tag{1–3}$$

By comparison with $\mathbf{F} = m\mathbf{a}$, we term g the acceleration due to gravity. Since it depends on r, it can be seen that the weight of a body is *not* an absolute quantity. Instead, its magnitude is determined from where the measurement was made. For most engineering calculations, however, g is determined at sea level and at a latitude of 45°, which is considered the "standard location."

1.3 Units of Measurement

The four basic quantities—force, mass, length and time—are not all independent from one another; in fact, they are *related* by Newton's second law of motion, $\mathbf{F} = m\mathbf{a}$. Because of this, the *units* used to measure these quantities cannot *all* be selected arbitrarily. The equality $\mathbf{F} = m\mathbf{a}$ is maintained only if three of the four units, called *base units*, are *arbitrarily defined* and the fourth unit is then *derived* from the equation.

SI Units. The International System of units, abbreviated SI after the French "Système International d'Unités," is a modern version of the metric system which has received worldwide recognition. As shown in Table 1–1, the SI system specifies length in meters (m), time in seconds (s), and mass in kilograms (kg). The unit of force, called a newton (N), is *derived* from $\mathbf{F} = m\mathbf{a}$. Thus, 1 newton is equal to a force required to give 1 kilogram of mass an acceleration of 1 m/s^2 ($\text{N} = \text{kg} \cdot \text{m/s}^2$).

If the weight of a body located at the "standard location" is to be determined in newtons, then Eq. 1–3 must be applied. Here $g = 9.806\,65 \text{ m/s}^2$; however, for calculations, the value $g = 9.81 \text{ m/s}^2$ will be used. Thus,

$$W = mg \qquad (g = 9.81 \text{ m/s}^2) \tag{1–4}$$

Therefore, a body of mass 1 kg has a weight of 9.81 N, a 2-kg body weighs 19.62 N, and so on, Fig. 1–2.

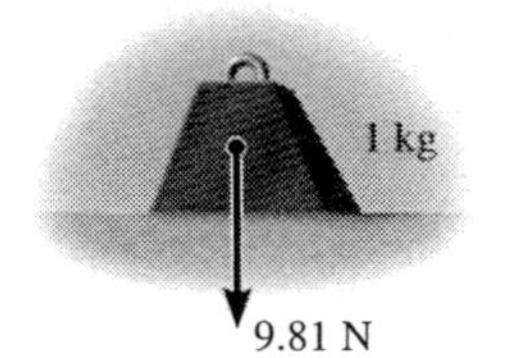

Fig. 1–2

TABLE 1–1 • System of Units

Name	Length	Time	Mass	Force
International System of Units (SI)	meter (m)	second (s)	kilogram (kg)	newton* (N) $\left(\frac{\text{kg} \cdot \text{m}}{\text{s}^2}\right)$

*Derived unit.

1.4 The International System of Units

The SI system of units is used extensively in this book since it is intended to become the worldwide standard for measurement. Consequently, the rules for its use and some of its terminology relevant to mechanics will now be presented.

Prefixes. When a numerical quantity is either very large or very small, the units used to define its size may be modified by using a prefix. Some of the prefixes used in the SI system are shown in Table 1–2. Each represents a multiple or submultiple of a unit which, if applied successively, moves the decimal point of a numerical quantity to every third place.* For example, 4 000 000 N = 4 000 kN(kilo-newton) = 4MN (mega-newton), or 0.005m = 5 mm (milli-meter). Notice that the SI system does not include the multiple deca (10) or the submultiple centi (0.01), which form part of the metric system. Except for some volume and area measurements, the use of these prefixes is to be avoided in science and engineering.

TABLE 1–2 • Prefixes

	Exponential Form	Prefix	SI Symbol
Multiple			
1 000 000 000	10^9	giga	G
1 000 000	10^6	mega	M
1 000	10^3	kilo	k
Submultiple			
0.001	10^{-3}	milli	m
0.000 001	10^{-6}	micro	μ
0.000 000 001	10^{-9}	nano	n

*The kilogram is the only base unit that is defined with a prefix.

Rules for Use. The following rules are given for the proper use of the various SI symbols:

1. A symbol is *never* written with a plural "s," since it may be confused with the unit for second (s).
2. Symbols are always written in lowercase letters, with the following exceptions: symbols for the two largest prefixes shown in Table 1–3, giga and mega, are capitalized as G and M, respectively; and symbols named after an individual are also capitalized, e.g., N.
3. Quantities defined by several units which are multiples of one another are separated by a *dot* to avoid confusion with prefix notation, as indicated by $N = kg \cdot m/s^2 = kg \cdot m \cdot s^{-2}$. Also, $m \cdot s$ (meter-second), whereas ms (milli-second).
4. The exponential power represented for a unit having a prefix refers to both the unit *and* its prefix. For example, $\mu N^2 = (\mu N)^2 = \mu N \cdot \mu N$. Likewise, mm^2 represents $(mm)^2 = mm \cdot mm$.
5. Physical constants or numbers having several digits on either side of the decimal point should be reported with a *space* between every three digits rather than with a comma; e.g., 73 569.213 427. In the case of four digits on either side of the decimal, the spacing is optional; e.g., 8537 or 8 537. Furthermore, always try to use decimals and avoid fractions; that is, write 15.25 *not* $15\frac{1}{4}$.

6. When performing calculations, represent the numbers in terms of their *base or derived units* by converting all prefixes to powers of 10. The final result should then be expressed using a *single prefix*. Also, after calculation, it is best to keep numerical values between 0.1 and 1000; otherwise, a suitable prefix should be chosen. For example,

$$\begin{aligned}(50\text{ kN})(60\text{ nm}) &= [50(10^3)\text{ N}][60(10^{-9})\text{ m}]\\ &= 3000(10^{-6})\text{ N}\cdot\text{m} = 3(10^{-3})\text{ N}\cdot\text{m} = 3\text{ mN}\cdot\text{m}\end{aligned}$$

7. Compound prefixes should not be used; e.g., kμs (kilo-micro-second) should be expressed as ms (milli-second) since $1\text{ k}\mu\text{s} = 1(10^3)(10^{-6})\text{ s} = 1(10^{-3})\text{ s} = 1\text{ ms}$.
8. With the exception of the base unit the kilogram, in general avoid the use of a prefix in the denominator of composite units. For example, do not write N/mm, but rather kN/m; also, m/mg should be written as Mm/kg.
9. Although not expressed in multiples of 10, the minute, hour, etc., are retained for practical purposes as multiples of the second. Furthermore, plane angular measurement is made using radians (rad). In this book, however, degrees will often be used, where $180° = \pi$ rad.

1.5 Numerical Calculations

Numerical work in engineering practice is most often performed by using handheld calculators and computers. It is important, however, that the answers to any problem be reported with both justifiable accuracy and appropriate significant figures. In this section we will discuss these topics together with some other important aspects involved in all engineering calculations.

Dimensional Homogeneity. The terms of any equation used to describe a physical process must be *dimensionally homogeneous;* that is, each term must be expressed in the same units. Provided this is the case, all the terms of an equation can then be combined if numerical values are substituted for the variables. Consider, for example, the equation $s = vt + \frac{1}{2}at^2$, where, in SI units, s is the position in meters, m, t is time in seconds, s, v is velocity in m/s, and a is acceleration in m/s^2. Regardless of how this equation is evaluated, it maintains its dimensional homogeneity. In the form stated, each of the three terms is expressed in meters

$[\text{m}, (\text{m}/\cancel{\text{s}})\cancel{\text{s}}, (\text{m}/\cancel{\text{s}^2})\cancel{\text{s}^2},]$ or solving for a, $a = 2s/t^2 - 2v/t$, the terms are each expressed in units of m/s^2 $[\text{m/s}^2, \text{m/s}^2, (\text{m/s})/\text{s}]$.

Since problems in mechanics involve the solution of dimensionally homogeneous equations, the fact that all terms of an equation are represented by a consistent set of units can be used as a partial check for algebraic manipulations of an equation.

Significant Figures. The accuracy of a number is specified by the number of significant figures it contains. A *significant figure* is any digit, including a zero, provided it is not used to specify the location of the decimal point for the number. For example, the numbers 5604 and 34.52 each have four significant figures. When numbers begin or end with zeros, however, it is difficult to tell how many significant figures are in the number. Consider the number 400. Does it have one (4), or perhaps two (40), or three (400) significant figures? In order to clarify this situation, the number should be reported using powers of 10. Using *engineering notation*, the exponent is displayed in multiples of three in order to facilitate conversion of SI units to those having an appropriate prefix. Thus, 400 expressed to one significant figure would be $0.4(10^3)$. Likewise, 2500 and 0.00546 expressed to three significant figures would be $2.50(10^3)$ and $5.46(10^{-3})$.

Computers are often used in engineering for advanced design and analysis.

Rounding Off Numbers. For numerical calculations, the accuracy obtained from the solution of a problem generally can never be better than the accuracy of the problem data. This is what is to be expected, but often handheld calculators or computers involve more figures in the answer than the number of significant figures used for the data. For this reason, a calculated result should always be "rounded off" to an appropriate number of significant figures.

To convey appropriate accuracy, the following rules for rounding off a number to n significant figures apply:

- If the $n + 1$ digit is *less than* 5, the $n + 1$ digit and others following it are dropped. For example, 2.326 and 0.451 rounded off to $n = 2$ significant figures would be 2.3 and 0.45.
- If the $n + 1$ digit is equal to 5 with zeros following it, then round off the nth digit to an *even number*. For example, $1.245(10^3)$ and 0.8655 rounded off to $n = 3$ significant figures become $1.24(10^3)$ and 0.866.
- If the $n + 1$ digit is *greater than* 5 or equal to 5 with any nonzero digits following it, then increase the nth digit by 1 and drop the $n + 1$ digit and others following it. For example, 0.723 87 and 565.500 3 rounded off to $n = 3$ significant figures become 0.724 and 566.

Calculations. As a general rule, to ensure accuracy of a final result when performing calculations on a pocket calculator, always retain a greater number of digits than the problem data. If possible, try to work out the computations so that numbers which are approximately equal are not subtracted since accuracy is often lost from this calculation.

In engineering we generally round off final answers to *three* significant figures since the data for geometry, loads, and other measurements are often reported with this accuracy.* Consequently, in this book the intermediate calculations for the examples are often worked out to four significant figures and the answers are generally reported to *three* significant figures.

*Of course, some numbers, such as π, e, or numbers used in derived formulas are exact and are therefore accurate to an infinite number of significant figures.

EXAMPLE 1.1

Evaluate each of the following and express with SI units having an appropriate prefix: (a) (50 mN)(6 GN), (b) $(400\ \text{mm})(0.6\ \text{MN})^2$, (c) $45\ \text{MN}^3/900\ \text{Gg}$.

Solution

First convert each number to base units, perform the indicated operations, then choose an appropriate prefix (see Rule 6 on p. 9).

Part (a)

$$
\begin{aligned}
(50\ \text{mN})(6\ \text{GN}) &= [50(10^{-3})\ \text{N}][6(10^{9})\ \text{N}] \\
&= 300(10^{6})\ \text{N}^2 \\
&= 300(10^{6})\ \cancel{\text{N}}^2\left(\frac{1\ \text{kN}}{10^3\ \cancel{\text{N}}}\right)\left(\frac{1\ \text{kN}}{10^3\ \cancel{\text{N}}}\right) \\
&= 300\ \text{kN}^2 \qquad\qquad \textit{Ans.}
\end{aligned}
$$

Note carefully the convention $\text{kN}^2 = (\text{kN})^2 = 10^6\ \text{N}^2$ (Rule 4 on p. 9).

Part (b)

$$
\begin{aligned}
(400\ \text{mm})(0.6\ \text{MN})^2 &= [400(10^{-3})\ \text{m}][0.6(10^{6})\ \text{N}]^2 \\
&= [400(10^{-3})\ \text{m}][0.36(10^{12})\ \text{N}^2] \\
&= 144(10^{9})\ \text{m}\cdot\text{N}^2 \\
&= 144\ \text{Gm}\cdot\text{N}^2 \qquad\qquad \textit{Ans.}
\end{aligned}
$$

We can also write

$$
\begin{aligned}
144(10^{9})\text{m}\cdot\text{N}^2 &= 144(10^{9})\text{m}\cdot\cancel{\text{N}}^2\left(\frac{1\ \text{MN}}{10^6\ \cancel{\text{N}}}\right)\left(\frac{1\ \text{MN}}{10^6\ \cancel{\text{N}}}\right) \\
&= 0.144\ \text{m}\cdot\text{MN}^2
\end{aligned}
$$

Part (c)

$$
\begin{aligned}
45\ \text{MN}^3/900\ \text{Gg} &= \frac{45(10^6\ \text{N})^3}{900(10^6)\ \text{kg}} \\
&= 0.05(10^{12})\ \text{N}^3/\text{kg} \\
&= 0.05(10^{12})\ \cancel{\text{N}}^3\left(\frac{1\ \text{kN}}{10^3\ \cancel{\text{N}}}\right)^3\frac{1}{\text{kg}} \\
&= 0.05(10^{3})\ \text{kN}^3/\text{kg} \\
&= 50\ \text{kN}^3/\text{kg} \qquad\qquad \textit{Ans.}
\end{aligned}
$$

Here we have used Rules 4 and 8 on p. 9.

1.6 General Procedure for Analysis

The most effective way of learning the principles of engineering mechanics is to *solve problems*. To be successful at this, it is important to always present the work in a *logical* and *orderly manner*, as suggested by the following sequence of steps:

1. Read the problem carefully and try to correlate the actual physical situation with the theory studied.
2. Draw any necessary diagrams and tabulate the problem data.
3. Apply the relevant principles, generally in mathematical form.
4. Solve the necessary equations algebraically as far as practical, then, making sure they are dimensionally homogeneous, use a consistent set of units and complete the solution numerically. Report the answer with no more significant figures than the accuracy of the given data.
5. Study the answer with technical judgment and common sense to determine whether or not it seems reasonable.

When solving problems, do the work as neatly as possible. Being neat generally stimulates clear and orderly thinking, and vice versa.

IMPORTANT POINTS

- Statics is the study of bodies that are at rest or move with constant velocity.
- A particle has a mass but a size that can be neglected.
- A rigid body does not deform under load.
- Concentrated forces are assumed to act at a point on a body.
- Newton's three laws of motion should be memorized.
- Mass is a property of matter that does not change from one location to another.
- Weight refers to the gravitational attraction of the earth on a body or quantity of mass. Its magnitude depends upon the elevation at which the mass is located.
- In the SI system the unit of force, the newton, is a derived unit. The meter, second, and kilogram are base units.
- Prefixes G, M, k, m, μ, n are used to represent large and small numerical quantities. Their exponential size should be known, along with the rules for using the SI units.
- Perform numerical calculations to several significant figures and then report the final answer to three significant figures.
- Algebraic manipulations of an equation can be checked in part by verifying that the equation remains dimensionally homogeneous.
- Know the rules for rounding off numbers.

PROBLEMS

1-1. Round off the following numbers to three significant figures: (a) 4.65735 m, (b) 55.578 s, (c) 4555 N, (d) 2768 kg.

1-2. Represent each of the following quantities in the correct SI form using an appropriate prefix: (a) 0.000431 kg, (b) $35.3(10^3)$ N, (c) 0.00532 km.

***1-3.** Represent each of the following combinations of units in the correct SI form using an appropriate prefix: (a) m/ms, (b) μkm, (c) ks/mg, and (d) km $\cdot$ μN.

1-4. Evaluate each of the following and express with an appropriate prefix: (a) $(430\text{ kg})^2$, (b) $(0.002\text{ mg})^2$, and (c) $(230\text{ m})^3$.

***1-5.** Represent each of the following combinations of units in the correct SI form: (a) kN/μs, (b) Mg/mN, and (c) MN/(kg $\cdot$ ms).

1-6. What is the weight in newtons of an object that has a mass of: (a) 10 kg, (b) 0.5 g, (c) 4.50 Mg? Express the result to three significant figures. Use an appropriate prefix.

1-7. Evaluate each of the following to three significant figures and express each answer in SI units using an appropriate prefix: (a) 354 mg(45 km)/(0.035 6 kN), (b) (.004 53 Mg)(201 ms), (c) 435 MN/23.2 mm.

***1-8.** Two particles have a mass of 8 kg and 12 kg, respectively. If they are 800 mm apart, determine the force of gravity acting between them. Compare this result with the weight of each particle.

1-9. Determine the mass of an object that has a weight of (a) 20 mN, (b) 150 kN, (c) 60 MN. Express the answer to three significant figures.

1-10. Using the base units of the SI system, show that Eq. 1–2 is a dimensionally homogeneous equation which gives F in newtons. Determine to three significant figures the gravitational force acting between two spheres that are touching each other. The mass of each sphere is 200 kg and the radius is 300 mm.

***1-11.** Evaluate each of the following to three significant figures and express each answer in SI units using an appropriate prefix: (a) $(0.631\text{ Mm}) / (8.60\text{ kg})^2$, (b) $(35\text{ mm})^2\,(48\text{ kg})^3$.

2.4 Addition of a System of Coplanar Forces

When the resultant of more than two forces has to be obtained, it is easier to find the components of each force along specified axes, add these components algebraically, and then form the resultant, rather than form the resultant of the forces by successive application of the parallelogram law as discussed in Sec. 2.3.

In this section we will resolve each force into its rectangular components $\mathbf{F}_x$ and $\mathbf{F}_y$, which lie along the x and y axes, respectively, Fig. 2–14*a*. Although the axes are horizontal and vertical, they may in general be directed at any inclination, as long as they remain perpendicular to one another, Fig. 2–14*b*. In either case, by the parallelogram law, we require

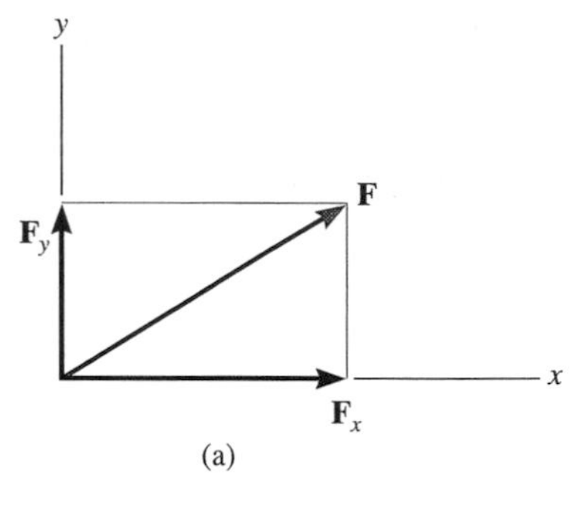

(a)

$$\mathbf{F} = \mathbf{F}_x + \mathbf{F}_y$$

and

$$\mathbf{F}' = \mathbf{F}'_x + \mathbf{F}'_y$$

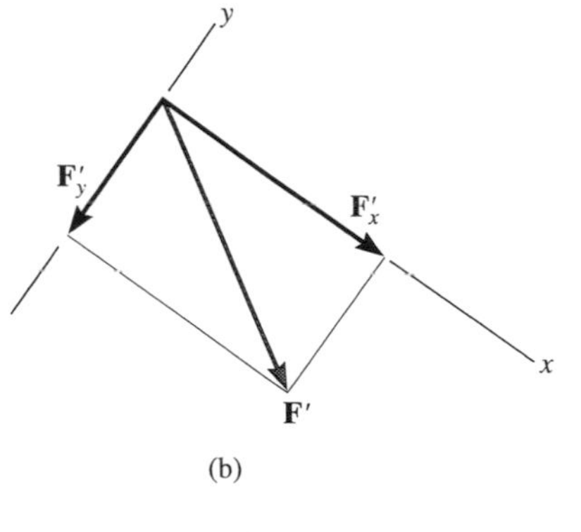

(b)

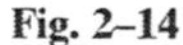
Fig. 2–14

As shown in Fig. 2–14, the sense of direction of each force component is represented *graphically* by the *arrowhead*. For *analytical* work, however, we must establish a notation for representing the directional sense of the rectangular components. This can be done in one of two ways.

Scalar Notation. Since the x and y axes have designated positive and negative directions, the magnitude and directional sense of the rectangular components of a force can be expressed in terms of *algebraic scalars*. For example, the components of **F** in Fig. 2–14*a* can be represented by positive scalars F_x and F_y since their sense of direction is along the *positive* x and y axes, respectively. In a similar manner, the components of **F′** in Fig. 2–14*b* are F'_x and $-F'_y$. Here the y component is negative, since $\mathbf{F}'_y$ is directed along the negative y axis.

It is important to keep in mind that this scalar notation is to be used only for computational purposes, not for graphical representations in figures. Throughout the book, the *head of a vector arrow* in any figure indicates the sense of the vector *graphically*; algebraic signs are not used for this purpose. Thus, the vectors in Figs. 2–14*a* and 2–14*b* are designated by using boldface (vector) notation.* Whenever italic symbols are written near vector arrows in figures, they indicate the *magnitude* of the vector, which is *always* a *positive* quantity.

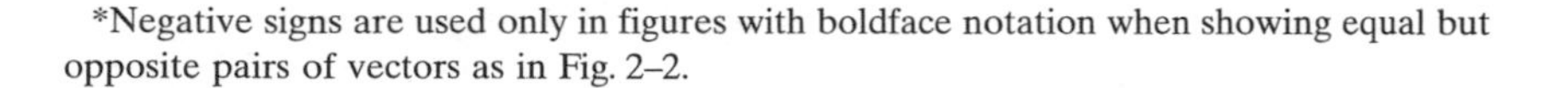
*Negative signs are used only in figures with boldface notation when showing equal but opposite pairs of vectors as in Fig. 2–2.

Cartesian Vector Notation. It is also possible to represent the components of a force in terms of Cartesian unit vectors. When we do this the methods of vector algebra are easier to apply, and we will see that this becomes particularly advantageous for solving problems in three dimensions.

In two dimensions the *Cartesian unit vectors* **i** and **j** are used to designate the *directions* of the x and y axes, respectively, Fig. 2–15*a*.* These vectors have a dimensionless magnitude of unity, and their sense (or arrowhead) will be described analytically by a plus or minus sign, depending on whether they are pointing along the positive or negative x or y axis.

As shown in Fig. 2–15*a*, the *magnitude* of each component of **F** is *always a positive quantity*, which is represented by the (positive) scalars F_x and F_y. Therefore, having established notation to represent the magnitude and the direction of each vector component, we can express **F** in Fig. 2–15*a* as the *Cartesian vector*,

$$\mathbf{F} = F_x\mathbf{i} + F_y\mathbf{j}$$

And in the same way, $\mathbf{F}'$ in Fig. 2–15*b* can be expressed as

$$\mathbf{F}' = F'_x\mathbf{i} + F'_y(-\mathbf{j})$$

or simply

$$\mathbf{F}' = F'_x\mathbf{i} - F'_y\mathbf{j}$$

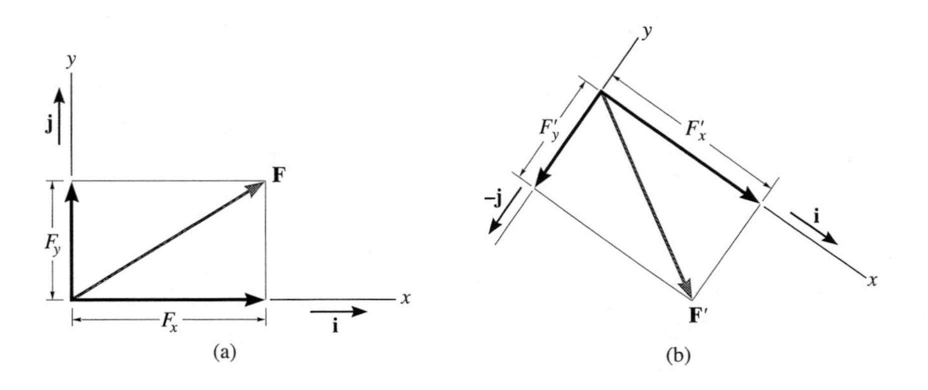

Fig. 2–15

*For handwritten work, unit vectors are usually indicated using a circumflex, e.g., $\hat{i}$ and $\hat{j}$.

Coplanar Force Resultants. Either of the two methods just described can be used to determine the resultant of several *coplanar forces*. To do this, each force is first resolved into its x and y components, and then the respective components are added using *scalar algebra* since they are collinear. The resultant force is then formed by adding the resultants of the x and y components using the parallelogram law. For example, consider the three concurrent forces in Fig. 2–16*a*, which have x and y components as shown in Fig. 2–16*b*. To solve this problem using *Cartesian vector notation*, each force is first represented as a Cartesian vector, i.e.,

$$\mathbf{F}_1 = F_{1x}\mathbf{i} + F_{1y}\mathbf{j}$$
$$\mathbf{F}_2 = -F_{2x}\mathbf{i} + F_{2y}\mathbf{j}$$
$$\mathbf{F}_3 = F_{3x}\mathbf{i} - F_{3y}\mathbf{j}$$

The vector resultant is therefore

$$\begin{aligned}\mathbf{F}_R &= \mathbf{F}_1 + \mathbf{F}_2 + \mathbf{F}_3 \\ &= F_{1x}\mathbf{i} + F_{1y}\mathbf{j} - F_{2x}\mathbf{i} + F_{2y}\mathbf{j} + F_{3x}\mathbf{i} - F_{3y}\mathbf{j} \\ &= (F_{1x} - F_{2x} + F_{3x})\mathbf{i} + (F_{1y} + F_{2y} - F_{3y})\mathbf{j} \\ &= (F_{Rx})\mathbf{i} + (F_{Ry})\mathbf{j}\end{aligned}$$

If *scalar notation* is used, then, from Fig. 2–16*b*, since x is positive to the right and y is positive upward, we have

$$\overset{+}{\rightarrow} \qquad F_{Rx} = F_{1x} - F_{2x} + F_{3x}$$
$$+\uparrow \qquad F_{Ry} = F_{1y} + F_{2y} - F_{3y}$$

These results are the *same* as the $\mathbf{i}$ and $\mathbf{j}$ components of $\mathbf{F}_R$ determined above.

In the general case, the x and y components of the resultant of any number of coplanar forces can be represented symbolically by the algebraic sum of the x and y components of all the forces, i.e.,

$$F_{Rx} = \Sigma F_x$$
$$F_{Ry} = \Sigma F_y \qquad (2\text{–}1)$$

When applying these equations, it is important to use the *sign convention* established for the components; and that is, components having a directional sense along the positive coordinate axes are considered positive scalars, whereas those having a directional sense along the negative coordinate axes are considered negative scalars. If this convention is followed, then the signs of the resultant components will specify the sense of these components. For example, a positive result indicates that the component has a directional sense which is in the positive coordinate direction.

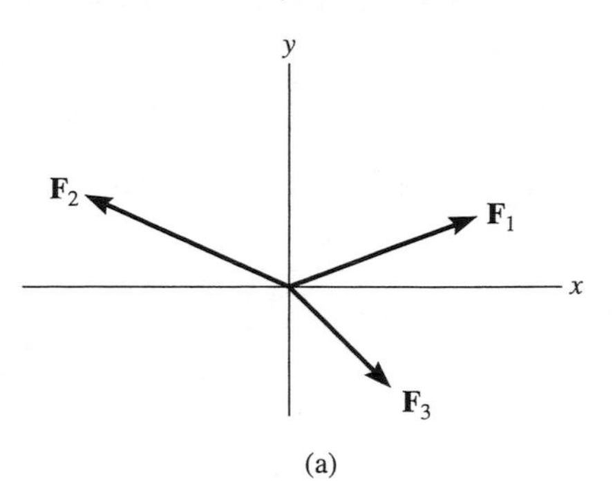

(a)

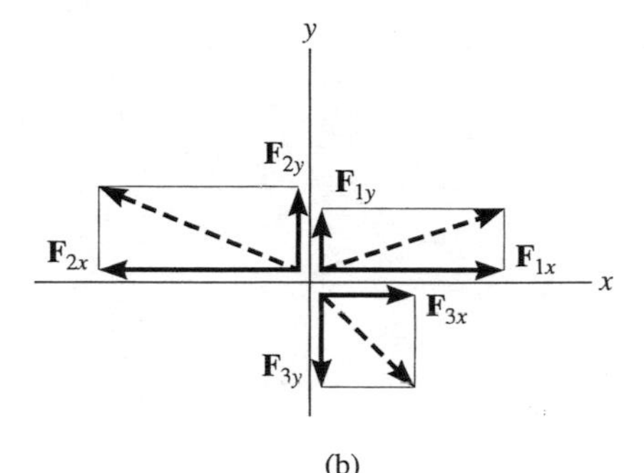

(b)

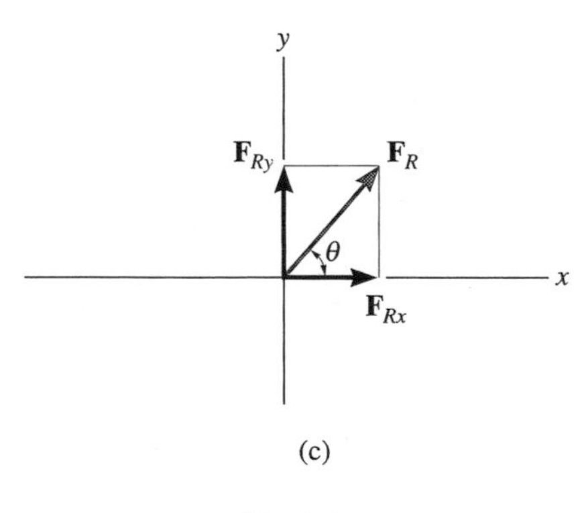

(c)

Fig. 2–16

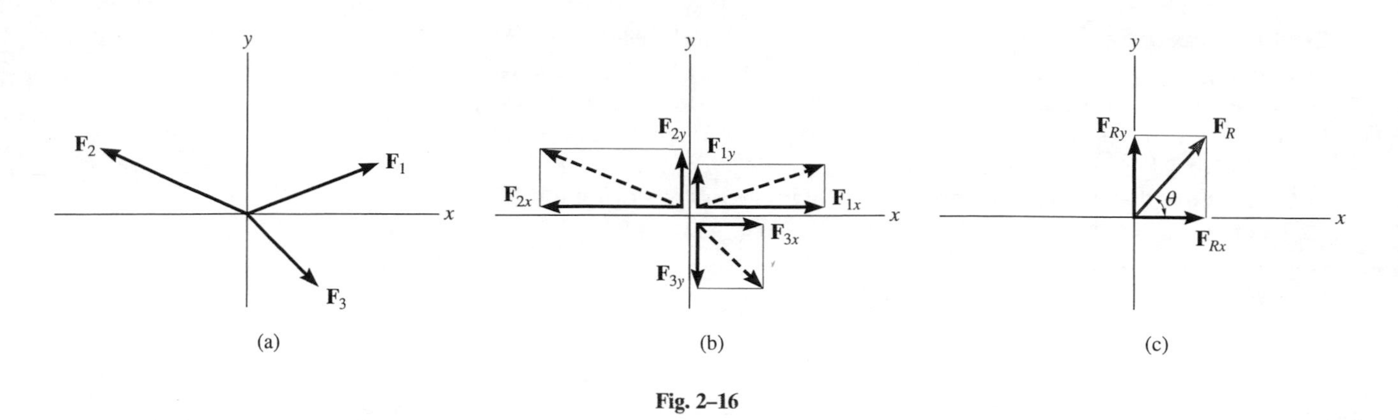

Fig. 2–16

The resultant force of the four cable forces acting on the supporting bracket can be determined by adding algebraically the separate x and y components of each cable force. This resultant $\mathbf{F}_R$ produces the *same pulling effect* on the bracket as all four cables.

Once the resultant components are determined, they may be sketched along the x and y axes in their proper directions, and the resultant force can be determined from vector addition, as shown in Fig. 2–16*c*. From this sketch, the magnitude of $\mathbf{F}_R$ is then found from the Pythagorean theorem; that is,

$$F_R = \sqrt{F_{Rx}^2 + F_{Ry}^2}$$

Also, the direction angle θ, which specifies the orientation of the force, is determined from trigonometry:

$$\theta = \tan^{-1}\left|\frac{F_{Ry}}{F_{Rx}}\right|$$

The above concepts are illustrated numerically in the examples which follow.

IMPORTANT POINTS

- The resultant of several coplanar forces can easily be determined if an x, y coordinate system is established and the forces are resolved along the axes.
- The direction of each force is specified by the angle its line of action makes with one of the axes, or by a sloped triangle.
- The orientation of the x and y axes is arbitrary, and their positive direction can be specified by the Cartesian unit vectors $\mathbf{i}$ and $\mathbf{j}$.
- The x and y components of the *resultant force* are simply the algebraic addition of the components of all the coplanar forces.
- The magnitude of the resultant force is determined from the Pythagorean theorem, and when the components are sketched on the x and y axes, the direction can be determined from trigonometry.

EXAMPLE 2.5

Determine the x and y components of $\mathbf{F}_1$ and $\mathbf{F}_2$ acting on the boom shown in Fig. 2–17a. Express each force as a Cartesian vector.

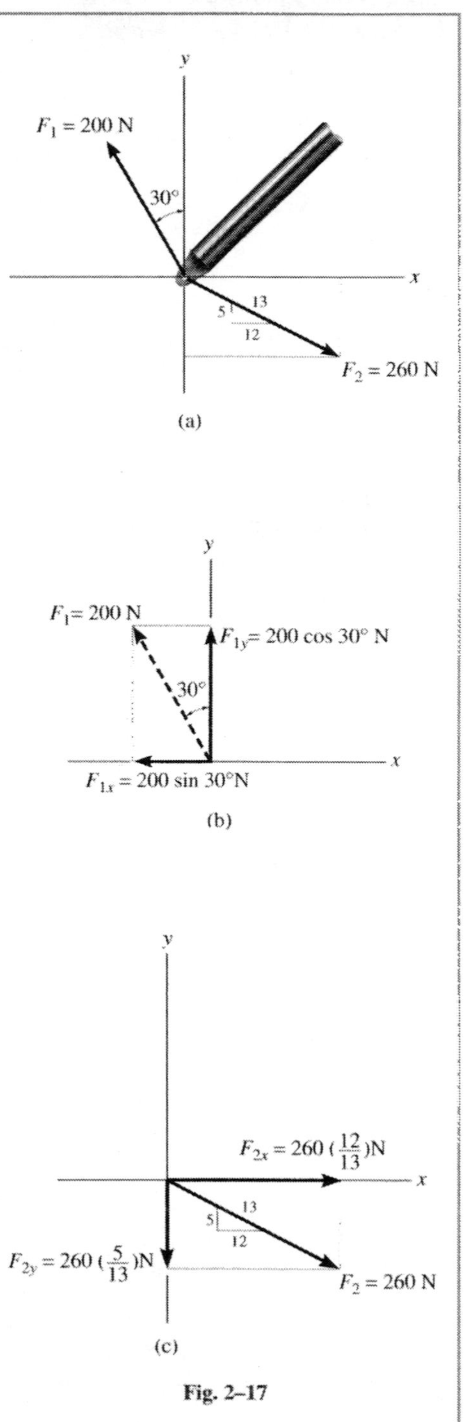

Fig. 2–17

Solution

Scalar Notation. By the parallelogram law, $\mathbf{F}_1$ is resolved into x and y components, Fig. 2–17b. The magnitude of each component is determined by trigonometry. Since $\mathbf{F}_{1x}$ acts in the $-x$ direction and $\mathbf{F}_{1y}$ acts in the $+y$ direction, we have

$$F_{1x} = -200 \sin 30° \text{ N} = -100 \text{ N} = 100 \text{ N} \leftarrow \qquad \textit{Ans.}$$

$$F_{1y} = 200 \cos 30° \text{ N} = 173 \text{ N} = 173 \text{ N}\uparrow \qquad \textit{Ans.}$$

The force $\mathbf{F}_2$ is resolved into its x and y components as shown in Fig. 2–17c. Here the *slope* of the line of action for the force is indicated. From this "slope triangle" we could obtain the angle θ, e.g., $\theta = \tan^{-1}(\frac{5}{12})$, and then proceed to determine the magnitudes of the components in the same manner as for $\mathbf{F}_1$. An easier method, however, consists of using proportional parts of similar triangles, i.e.,

$$\frac{F_{2x}}{260 \text{ N}} = \frac{12}{13} \qquad F_{2x} = 260 \text{ N}\left(\frac{12}{13}\right) = 240 \text{ N}$$

Similarly,

$$F_{2y} = 260 \text{ N}\left(\frac{5}{13}\right) = 100 \text{ N}$$

Notice that the magnitude of the *horizontal component*, F_{2x}, was obtained by multiplying the force magnitude by the ratio of the *horizontal leg* of the slope triangle divided by the hypotenuse; whereas the magnitude of the *vertical component*, F_{2y}, was obtained by multiplying the force magnitude by the ratio of the *vertical leg* divided by the hypotenuse. Hence, using scalar notation,

$$F_{2x} = 240 \text{ N} = 240 \text{ N} \rightarrow \qquad \textit{Ans.}$$

$$F_{2y} = -100 \text{ N} = 100 \text{ N}\downarrow \qquad \textit{Ans.}$$

Cartesian Vector Notation. Having determined the magnitudes and directions of the components of each force, we can express each force as a Cartesian vector.

$$\mathbf{F}_1 = \{-100\mathbf{i} + 173\mathbf{j}\} \text{ N} \qquad \textit{Ans.}$$

$$\mathbf{F}_2 = \{240\mathbf{i} - 100\mathbf{j}\} \text{ N} \qquad \textit{Ans.}$$

EXAMPLE 2.6

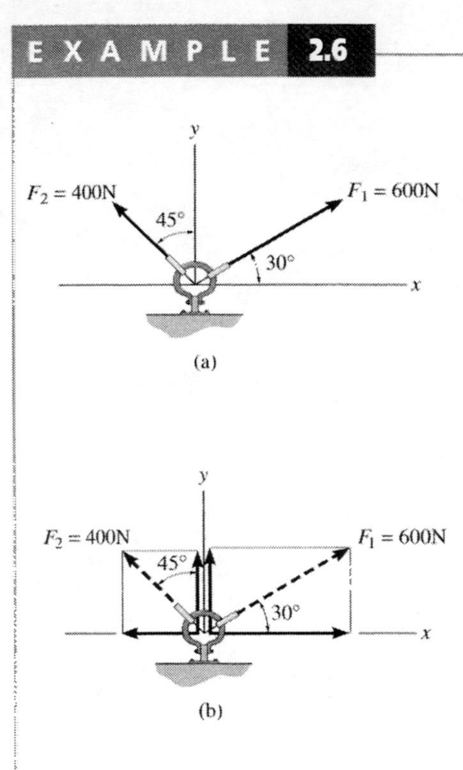

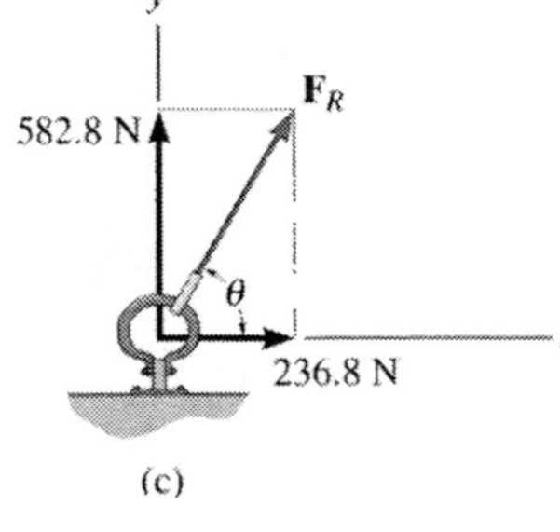

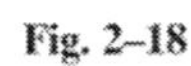
Fig. 2–18

The link in Fig. 2–18*a* is subjected to two forces $\mathbf{F}_1$ and $\mathbf{F}_2$. Determine the magnitude and orientation of the resultant force.

Solution I

Scalar Notation. This problem can be solved by using the parallelogram law; however, here we will resolve each force into its x and y components, Fig. 2–18*b*, and sum these components algebraically. Indicating the "positive" sense of the x and y force components alongside each equation, we have

$$\overset{+}{\rightarrow} F_{Rx} = \Sigma F_x; \qquad F_{Rx} = 600 \cos 30^\circ \text{ N} - 400 \sin 45^\circ \text{ N}$$
$$= 236.8 \text{ N} \rightarrow$$

$$+\uparrow F_{Ry} = \Sigma F_y; \qquad F_{Ry} = 600 \sin 30^\circ \text{ N} + 400 \cos 45^\circ \text{ N}$$
$$= 582.8 \text{ N}\uparrow$$

The resultant force, shown in Fig. 2–18*c*, has a *magnitude* of

$$F_R = \sqrt{(236.8 \text{ N})^2 + (582.8 \text{ N})^2}$$
$$= 629 \text{ N} \qquad \textit{Ans.}$$

From the vector addition, Fig. 2–18*c*, the direction angle θ is

$$\theta = \tan^{-1}\left(\frac{582.8\text{N}}{236.8\text{N}}\right) = 67.9^\circ \qquad \textit{Ans.}$$

Solution II

Cartesian Vector Notation. From Fig. 2–18*b*, each force is expressed as a Cartesian vector

$$\mathbf{F}_1 = \{600 \cos 30^\circ \mathbf{i} + 600 \sin 30^\circ \mathbf{j}\} \text{ N}$$
$$\mathbf{F}_2 = \{-400 \sin 45^\circ \mathbf{i} + 400 \cos 45^\circ \mathbf{j}\} \text{ N}$$

Thus,

$$\mathbf{F}_R = \mathbf{F}_1 + \mathbf{F}_2 = (600 \cos 30^\circ \text{ N} - 400 \sin 45^\circ \text{ N})\mathbf{i}$$
$$+ (600 \sin 30^\circ \text{ N} + 400 \cos 45^\circ \text{ N})\mathbf{j}$$
$$= \{236.8\mathbf{i} + 582.8\mathbf{j}\} \text{ N}$$

The magnitude and direction of $\mathbf{F}_R$ are determined in the same manner as shown above.

Comparing the two methods of solution, note that use of scalar notation is more efficient since the components can be found *directly*, without first having to express each force as a Cartesian vector before adding the components. Later we will show that Cartesian vector analysis is very beneficial for solving three-dimensional problems.

EXAMPLE 2.7

The end of the boom O in Fig. 2–19a is subjected to three concurrent and coplanar forces. Determine the magnitude and orientation of the resultant force.

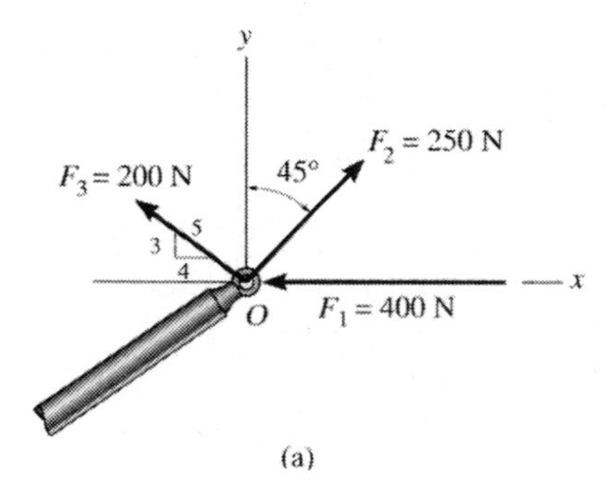

(a)

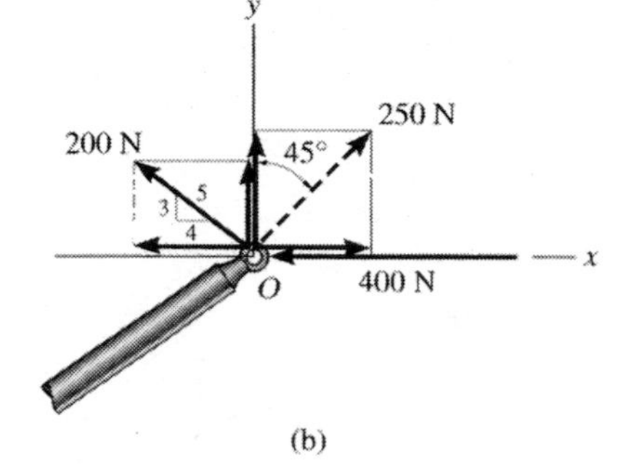

(b)

Fig. 2–19

Solution

Each force is resolved into its x and y components, Fig. 2–19b. Summing the x components, we have

$$\overset{+}{\rightarrow} F_{Rx} = \Sigma F_x; \qquad F_{Rx} = -400\text{ N} + 250\sin 45^\circ\text{ N} - 200(\tfrac{4}{5})\text{ N}$$
$$= -383.2\text{ N} = 383.2\text{ N}\leftarrow$$

The negative sign indicates that F_{Rx} acts to the left, i.e., in the negative x direction as noted by the small arrow. Summing the y components yields

$$+\uparrow F_{Ry} = \Sigma F_y; \qquad F_{Ry} = 250\cos 45^\circ\text{ N} + 200(\tfrac{3}{5})\text{ N}$$
$$= 296.8\text{ N}\uparrow$$

The resultant force, shown in Fig. 2–19c, has a *magnitude* of

$$F_R = \sqrt{(-383.2\text{N})^2 + (296.8\text{N})^2}$$
$$= 485\text{ N} \qquad \textit{Ans.}$$

From the vector addition in Fig. 2–19c, the direction angle θ is

$$\theta = \tan^{-1}\left(\frac{296.8}{383.2}\right) = 37.8^\circ \qquad \textit{Ans.}$$

Note how convenient it is to use this method, compared to two applications of the parallelogram law.

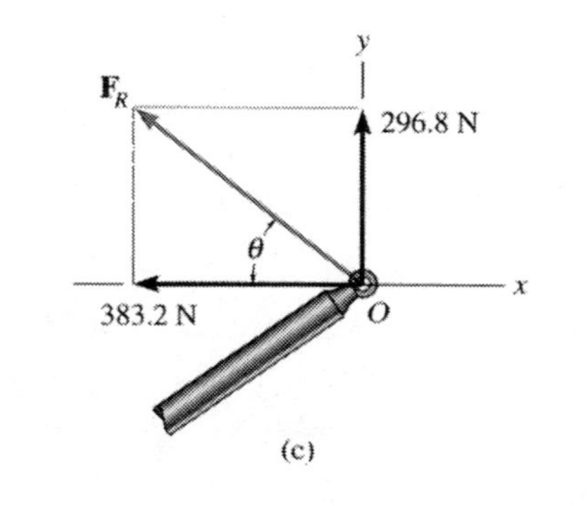

(c)

PROBLEMS

*2-20. Determine the magnitude of the resultant force and its direction, measured counterclockwise from the positive x axis.

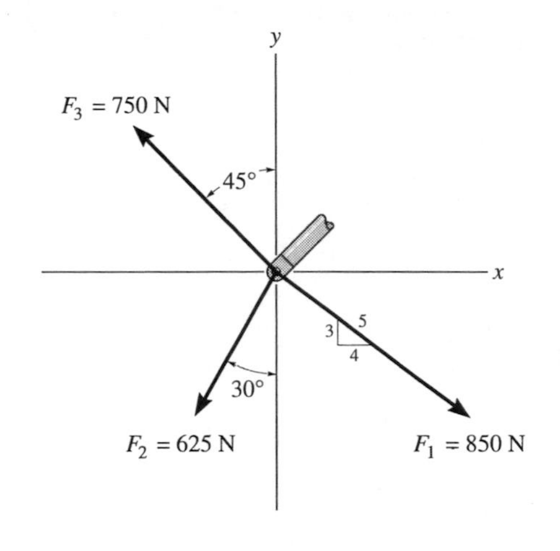

Prob. 2–20

2-21. Determine the magnitude and direction θ of $\mathbf{F}_1$ so that the resultant force is directed vertically upward and has a magnitude of 800 N.

2-22. Determine the magnitude and direction measured counterclockwise from the positive x axis of the resultant force of the three forces acting on the ring A. Take $F_1 = 500$ N and $\theta = 20°$.

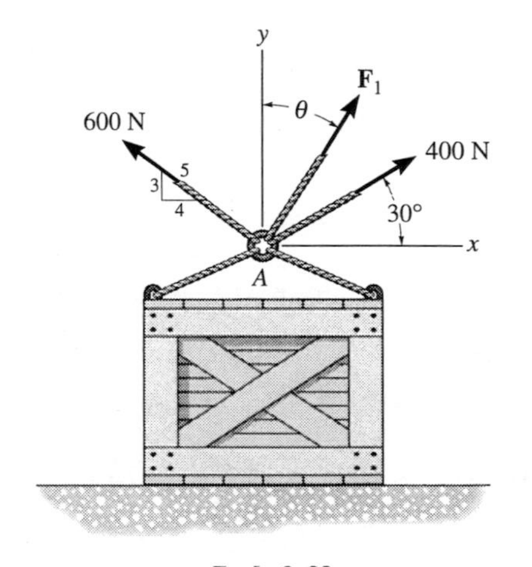

Prob. 2–22

2-23. Express $\mathbf{F}_1$ and $\mathbf{F}_2$ as Cartesian vectors.

***2-24.** Determine the magnitude of the resultant force and its direction measured counterclockwise from the positive x axis.

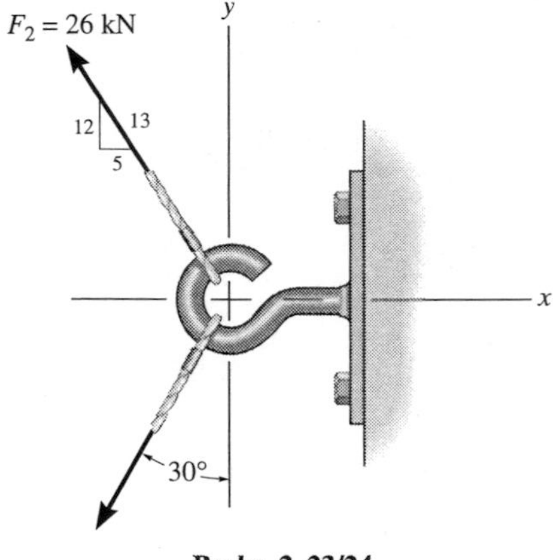

Probs. 2–23/24

2-25. Solve Prob. 2–1 by summing the rectangular or x, y components of the forces to obtain the resultant force.

2-26. Solve Prob. 2–22 by summing the rectangular or x, y components of the forces to obtain the resultant force.

2-27. Determine the magnitude and orientation θ of $\mathbf{F}_B$ so that the resultant force is directed along the positive y axis and has a magnitude of 1500 N.

***2-28.** Determine the magnitude and orientation, measured counterclockwise from the positive y axis, of the resultant force acting on the bracket, if $F_B = 600$ N and $\theta = 20°$.

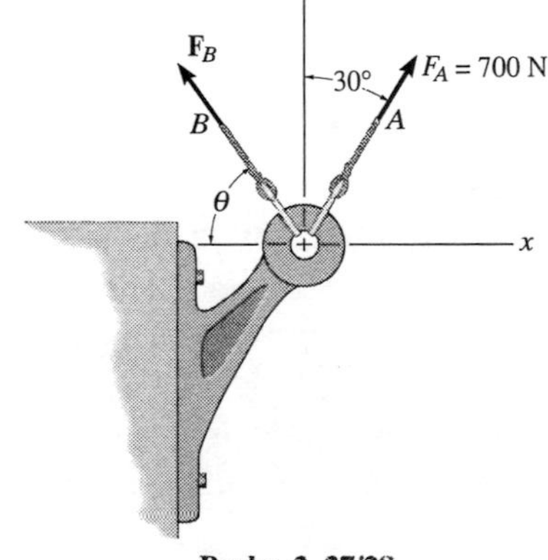

Probs. 2–27/28

2-29. Determine the x and y components of $\mathbf{F}_1$ and $\mathbf{F}_2$.

2-30. Determine the magnitude of the resultant force and its direction, measured counterclockwise from the positive x axis.

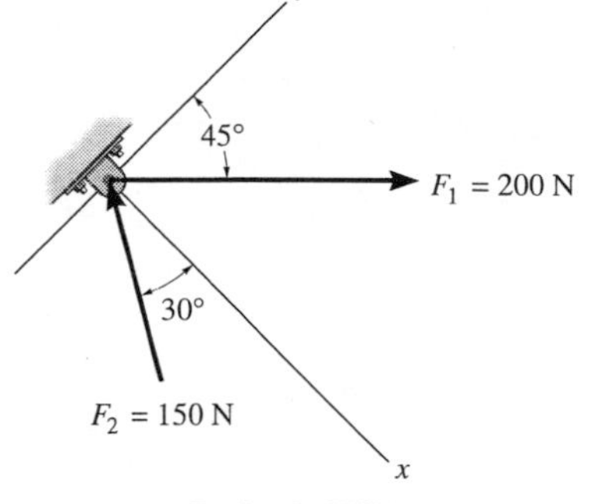

Probs. 2–29/30

2-31. Determine the x and y components of each force acting on the *gusset plate* of the bridge truss. Show that the resultant force is zero.

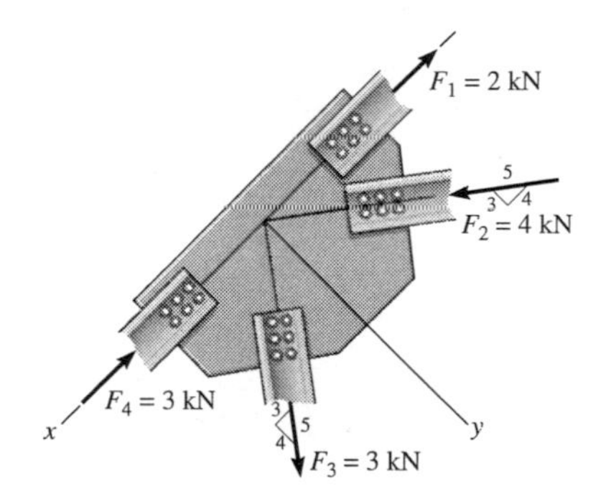

Prob. 2–31

***2-32.** If $\theta = 60°$ and $F = 20$ kN, determine the magnitude of the resultant force and its direction measured clockwise from the positive x axis.

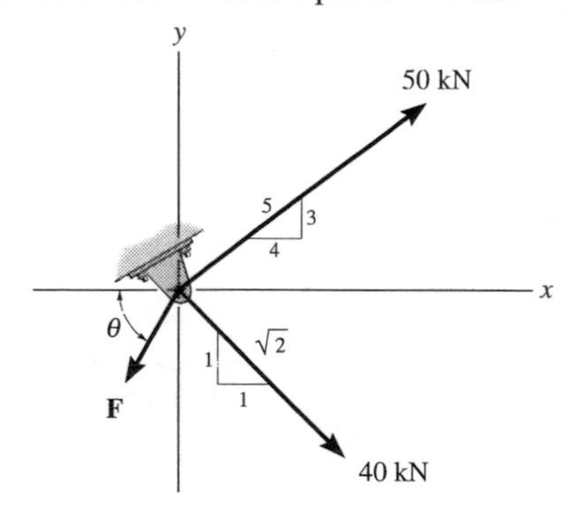

Prob. 2–32

2-33. Determine the magnitude and direction θ of $\mathbf{F}_A$ so that the resultant force is directed along the positive x axis and has a magnitude of 1250 N.

2-34. Determine the magnitude and direction, measured counterclockwise from the positive x axis, of the resultant force acting on the ring at O, if $F_A = 750$ N and $\theta = 45°$.

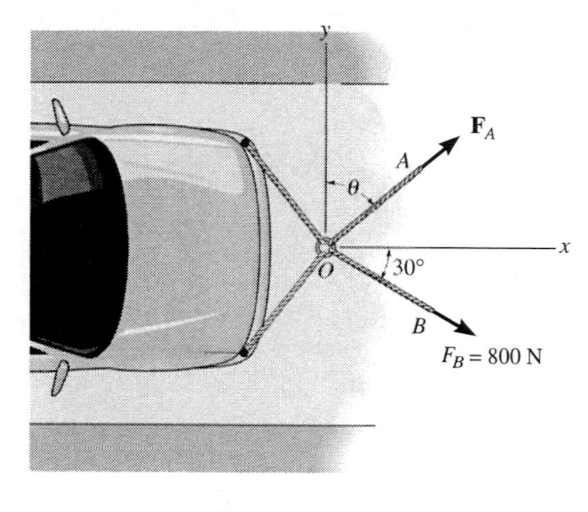

Probs. 2–33/34

2-35. Express each of the three forces acting on the column in Cartesian vector form and compute the magnitude of the resultant force.

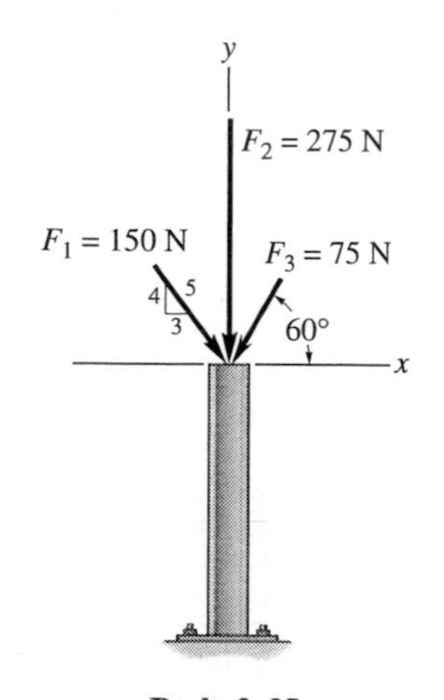

Prob. 2–35

*2-36. Three forces act on the bracket. Determine the magnitude and orientation θ of $\mathbf{F}_2$ so that the resultant force is directed along the positive u axis and has a magnitude of 50 kN.

2-37. If $F_2 = 150$ kN and $\theta = 55°$, determine the magnitude and orientation, measured clockwise from the positive x axis, of the resultant force of the three forces acting on the bracket.

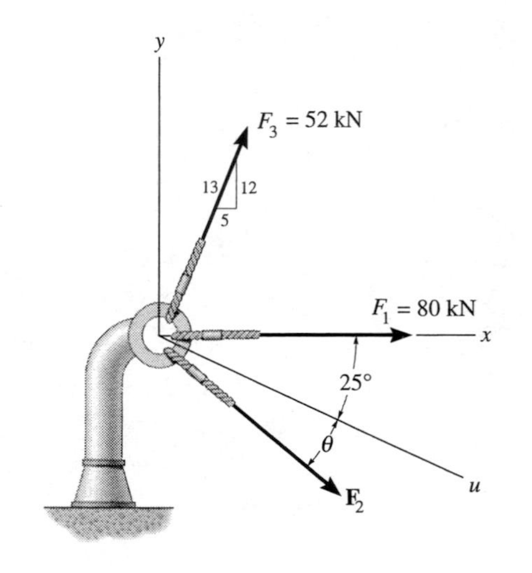

Probs. 2–36/37

2-38. Determine the magnitude of force **F** so that the resultant force of the three forces is as small as possible. What is the magnitude of the resultant force?

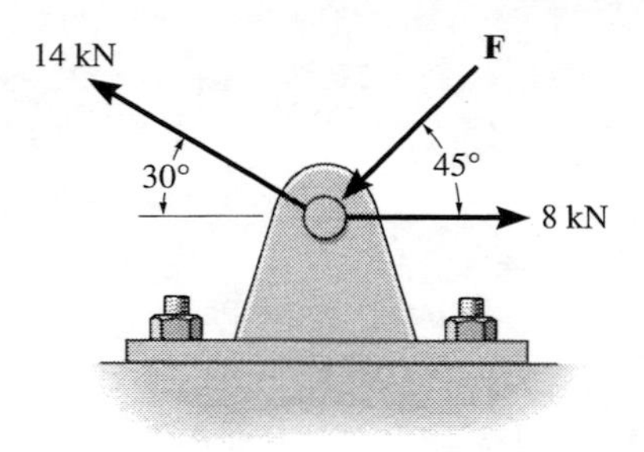

Prob. 2–38

CHAPTER 3

Force System Resultants

CHAPTER OBJECTIVES

- To discuss the concept of the moment of a force and show how to calculate it in two and three dimensions.
- To provide a method for finding the moment of a force about a specified axis.
- To define the moment of a couple.
- To present methods for determining the resultants of nonconcurrent force systems.
- To indicate how to reduce a simple distributed loading to a resultant force having a specified location.

3.1 Moment of a Force—Scalar Formulation

The *moment* of a force about a point or axis provides a measure of the tendency of the force to cause a body to rotate about the point or axis. For example, consider the horizontal force $\mathbf{F}_x$, which acts perpendicular to the handle of the wrench and is located a distance d_y from point O, Fig. 3–1*a*. It is seen that this force tends to cause the pipe to turn about the z axis. The larger the force or the distance d_y, the greater the turning effect. This tendency for rotation caused by $\mathbf{F}_x$ is sometimes called a *torque*, but most often it is called the *moment of a force* or simply the *moment* $(\mathbf{M}_O)_z$. Note that the *moment axis* (z) is perpendicular to the shaded plane (x–y) which contains both $\mathbf{F}_x$ and d_y and that this axis intersects the plane at point O.

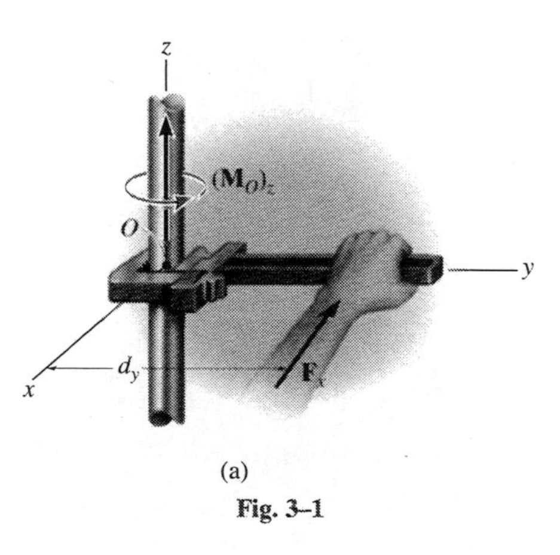

(a)

Fig. 3–1

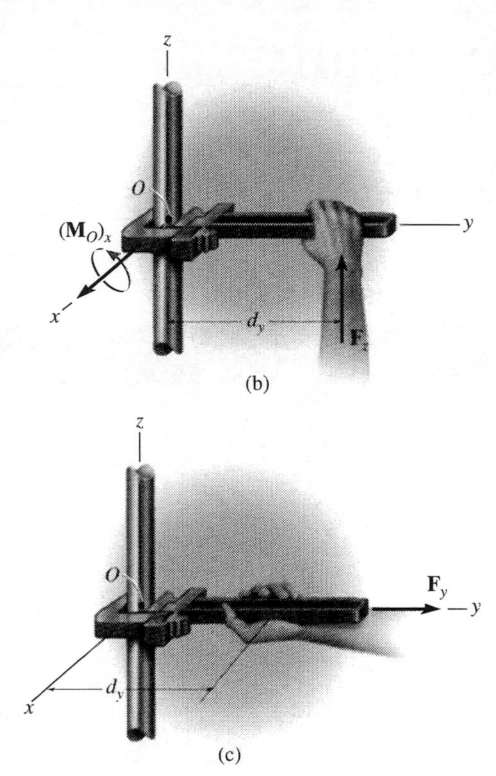

Fig. 3–1

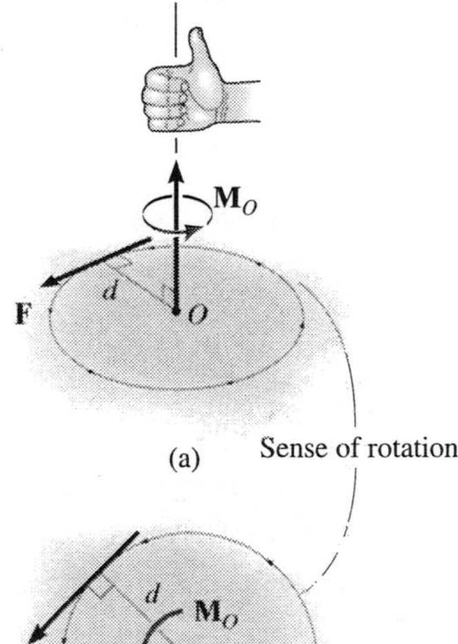

Fig. 3–2

Now consider applying the force $\mathbf{F}_z$ to the wrench, Fig. 3–1*b*. This force will *not* rotate the pipe about the z axis. Instead, it tends to rotate it about the x axis. Keep in mind that although it may not be possible to actually "rotate" or turn the pipe in this manner, $\mathbf{F}_z$ still creates the *tendency* for rotation and so the moment $(\mathbf{M}_O)_x$ is produced. As before, the force and distance d_y lie in the shaded plane (y–z) which is perpendicular to the moment axis (x). Lastly, if a force $\mathbf{F}_y$ is applied to the wrench, Fig. 3–1*c*, no moment is produced about point O. This results in a lack of turning since the line of action of the force passes through O and therefore no tendency for rotation is possible.

We will now generalize the above discussion and consider the force $\mathbf{F}$ and point O which lie in a shaded plane as shown in Fig. 3–2*a*. The moment $\mathbf{M}_O$ about point O, or about an axis passing through O and perpendicular to the plane, is a *vector quantity* since it has a specified magnitude and direction.

Magnitude. The magnitude of M_O is

$$\boxed{M_O = Fd} \tag{3–1}$$

where d is referred to as the *moment arm* or perpendicular distance from the axis at point O to the line of action of the force. Units of moment magnitude consist of force times distance, e.g., N · m.

Direction. The direction of $\mathbf{M}_O$ will be specified by using the "right-hand rule." To do this, the fingers of the right hand are curled such that they follow the sense of rotation, which would occur if the force could rotate about point O, Fig. 3–2*a*. The *thumb* then *points* along the *moment axis* so that it gives the direction and sense of the moment vector, which is *upward* and *perpendicular* to the shaded plane containing $\mathbf{F}$ and d.

In three dimensions, $\mathbf{M}_O$ is illustrated by a vector arrow with a curl on it to *distinguish* it from a force vector, Fig. 3–2*a*. Many problems in mechanics, however, involve coplanar force systems that may be conveniently viewed in two dimensions. For example, a two-dimensional view of Fig. 3–2*a* is given in Fig. 3–2*b*. Here $\mathbf{M}_O$ is simply represented by the (counterclockwise) curl, which indicates the action of $\mathbf{F}$. The arrowhead on this curl is used to show the *sense of rotation* caused by $\mathbf{F}$. Using the right-hand rule, however, realize that the direction and sense of the moment vector in Fig. 3–2*b* are specified by the thumb, which points *out* of the page since the fingers follow the curl. In particular, notice that *this curl or sense of rotation can always be determined by observing in which direction the force would "orbit" about point O* (counterclockwise in Fig. 3–2*b*). In two dimensions we will often refer to finding the moment of a force "about a point" (O). Keep in mind, however, that the moment *always acts about an axis* which is perpendicular to the plane containing $\mathbf{F}$ and d, and this axis intersects the plane at the point (O), Fig. 3–2*a*.

Resultant Moment of a System of Coplanar Forces. If a system of forces lies in an x–y plane, then the moment produced by each force about point O will be directed along the z axis, Fig. 3–3. Consequently, the resultant moment $\mathbf{M}_{R_O}$ of the system can be determined by simply adding the moments of all forces *algebraically* since all the moment vectors are collinear. We can write this vector sum symbolically as

$$\circlearrowleft + M_{R_O} = \Sigma F d \tag{3–2}$$

Here the counterclockwise curl written alongside the equation indicates that, by the scalar sign convention, the moment of any force will be positive if it is directed along the $+z$ axis, whereas a negative moment is directed along the $-z$ axis.

The following examples illustrate numerical application of Eqs. 3–1 and 3–2.

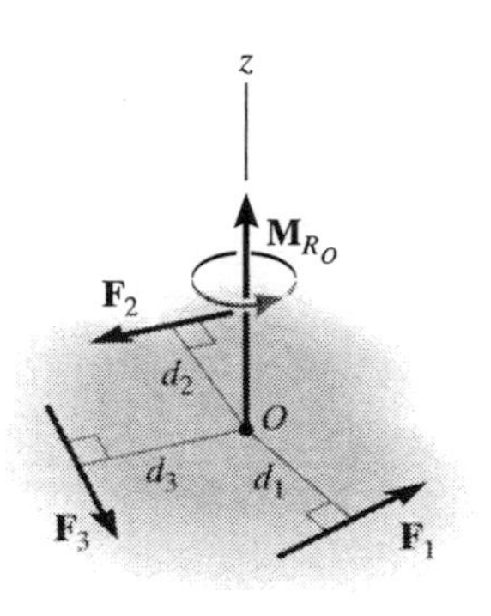

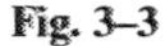
Fig. 3–3

By pushing down on the pry bar the load on the ground at A can be lifted. The turning effect, caused by the applied force, is due to the moment about A. To produce this moment with minimum effort we instinctively know that the force should be applied to the *end* of the bar; however, the *direction* in which this force is applied is also important. This is because moment is the product of the force and the moment arm. Notice that when the force is at an angle $\theta < 90°$, then the moment arm distance is *shorter* than when the force is applied perpendicular to the bar $\theta = 90°$, i.e., $d' < d$. Hence the greatest moment is produced when the force is farthest from point A and applied perpendicular to the axis of the bar so as to maximize the moment arm.

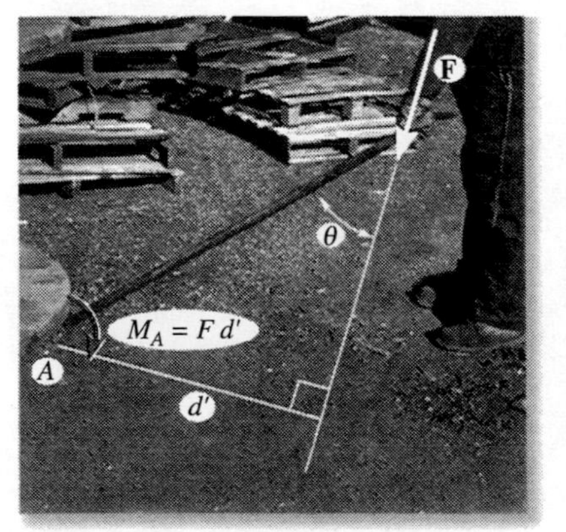

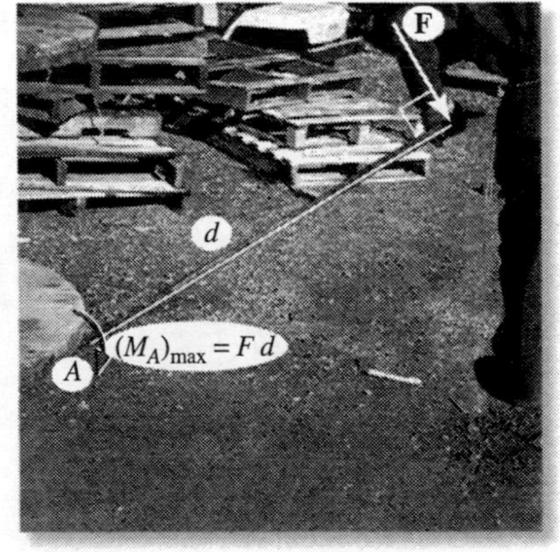

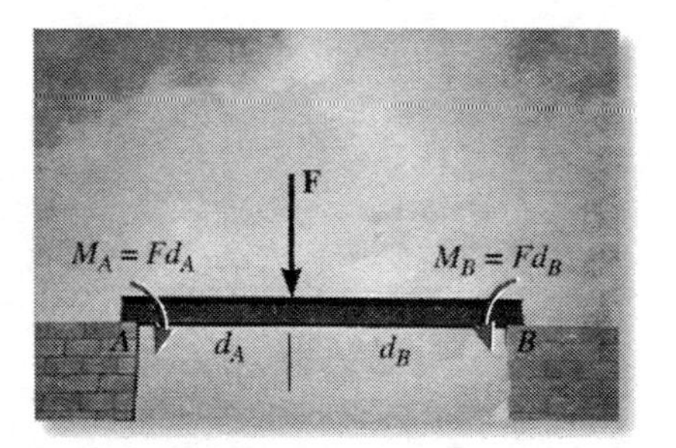

The moment of a force does not always cause a rotation. For example, the force $\mathbf{F}$ tends to rotate the beam clockwise about its support at A with a moment $M_A = Fd_A$. The actual rotation would occur if the support at B were removed. In the same manner. $\mathbf{F}$ creates a tendency to rotate the beam counterclockwise about B with a moment $M_B = Fd_B$. Here the support at A prevents the rotation.

EXAMPLE 3.1

For each case illustrated in Fig. 3–4, determine the moment of the force about point O.

100 N

O

2 m

(a)

Solution (Scalar Analysis)

The line of action of each force is extended as a dashed line in order to establish the moment arm d. Also illustrated is the tendency of rotation of the member as caused by the force. Furthermore, the orbit of the force is shown as a colored curl. Thus,

Fig. 3–4*a* $\quad M_O = (100\text{ N})(2\text{ m}) = 200\text{ N}\cdot\text{m}\ \circlearrowright$ *Ans.*

Fig. 3–4*b* $\quad M_O = (50\text{ N})(0.75\text{ m}) = 37.5\text{ N}\cdot\text{m}\ \circlearrowright$ *Ans.*

Fig. 3–4*c* $\quad M_O = (40\text{ N})(4\text{ m} + 2\cos 30^\circ\text{ m}) = 229\text{ N}\cdot\text{m}\ \circlearrowright$ *Ans.*

Fig. 3–4*d* $\quad M_O = (60\text{ N})(1\sin 45^\circ\text{ m}) = 42.4\text{ N}\cdot\text{m}\ \circlearrowleft$ *Ans.*

Fig. 3–4*e* $\quad M_O = (7\text{ kN})(4\text{ m} - 1\text{ m}) = 21.0\text{ kN}\cdot\text{m}\ \circlearrowleft$ *Ans.*

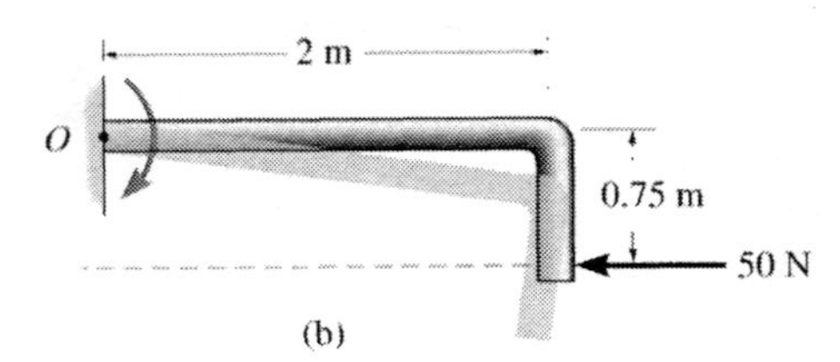

(b)

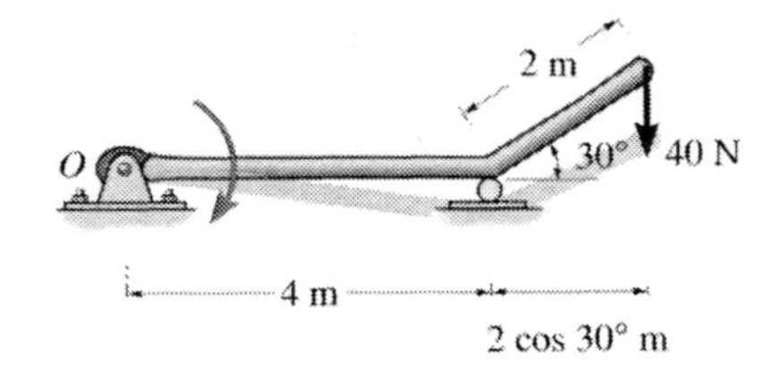

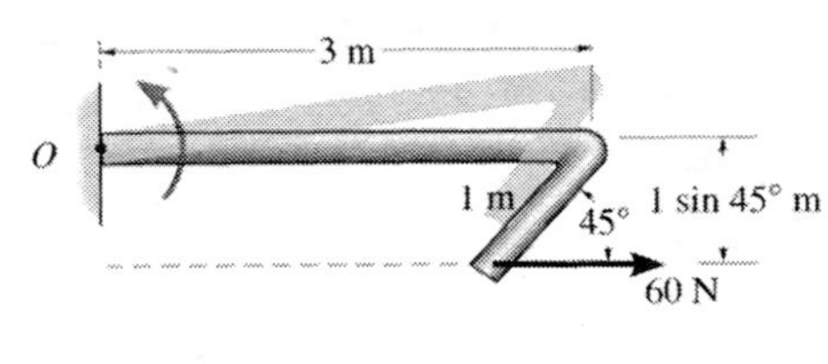

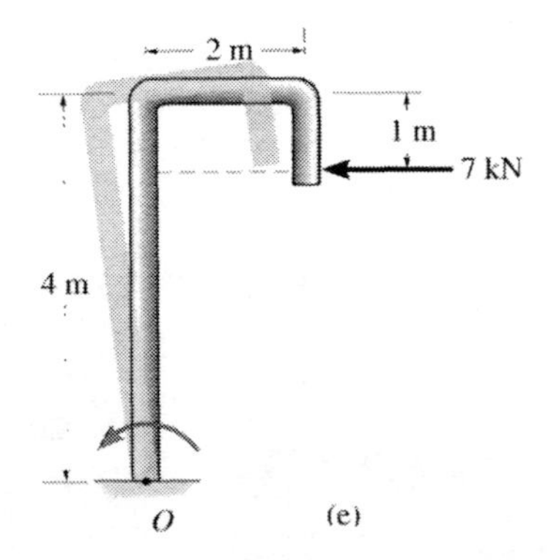

(e)

Fig. 3–4

EXAMPLE 3.2

Determine the moments of the 800-N force acting on the frame in Fig. 3–5 about points A, B, C, and D.

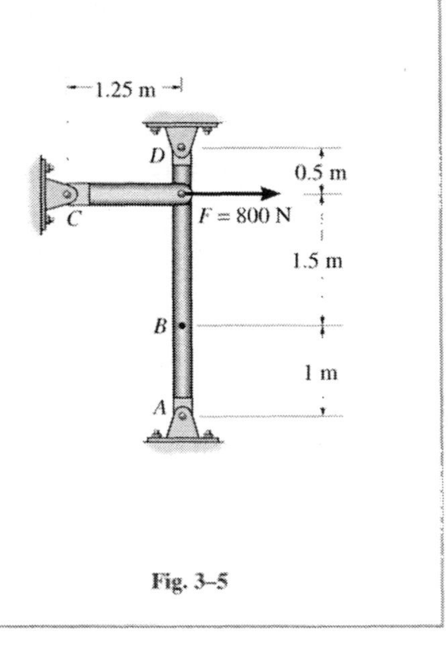

Fig. 3–5

Solution (Scalar Analysis)

In general, $M = Fd$, where d is the moment arm or *perpendicular distance* from the *point* on the moment axis to the *line of action* of the force. Hence,

$$M_A = 800\text{ N}(2.5\text{ m}) = 2000\text{ N}\cdot\text{m} \circlearrowright \qquad \textit{Ans.}$$

$$M_B = 800\text{ N}(1.5\text{ m}) = 1200\text{ N}\cdot\text{m} \circlearrowright \qquad \textit{Ans.}$$

$$M_C = 800\text{ N}(0) = 0 \quad (\text{line of action of } \mathbf{F} \text{ passes through } C) \qquad \textit{Ans.}$$

$$M_D = 800\text{ N}(0.5\text{ m}) = 400\text{ N}\cdot\text{m} \circlearrowleft \qquad \textit{Ans.}$$

The curls indicate the sense of rotation of the moment, which is defined by the direction the force orbits about each point.

EXAMPLE 3.3

Determine the resultant moment of the four forces acting on the rod shown in Fig. 3–6 about point O.

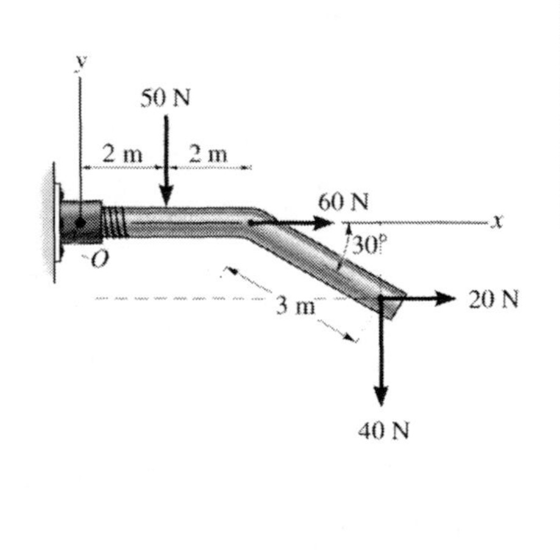

Fig. 3–6

Solution

Assuming that positive moments act in the $+\mathbf{k}$ direction, i.e., counterclockwise, we have

$$\circlearrowleft +M_{R_O} = \Sigma Fd;$$

$$M_{R_O} = -50\text{ N}(2\text{m}) + 60\text{ N}(0) + 20\text{ N}(3\sin 30^\circ\text{ m})$$
$$-40\text{ N}(4\text{ m} + 3\cos 30^\circ\text{ m})$$

$$M_{R_O} = -334\text{ N}\cdot\text{m} = 334\text{ N}\cdot\text{m} \circlearrowright \qquad \textit{Ans.}$$

For this calculation, note how the moment-arm distances for the 20-N and 40-N forces are established from the extended (dashed) lines of action of each of these forces.

3.4 Principle of Moments

A concept often used in mechanics is the *principle of moments*, which is sometimes referred to as *Varignon's theorem* since it was originally developed by the French mathematician Varignon (1654–1722). It states that *the moment of a force about a point is equal to the sum of the moments of the force's components about the point.* The proof follows directly from the distributive law of the vector cross product. To show this, consider the force **F** and two of its rectangular components, where $\mathbf{F} = \mathbf{F}_1 + \mathbf{F}_2$, Fig. 3–18. We have

$$\mathbf{M}_O = \mathbf{r} \times \mathbf{F}_1 + \mathbf{r} \times \mathbf{F}_2 = \mathbf{r} \times (\mathbf{F}_1 + \mathbf{F}_2) = \mathbf{r} \times \mathbf{F}$$

This concept has important applications to the solution of problems and proofs of theorems that follow, since it is often easier to determine the moments of a force's components rather than the moment of the force itself.

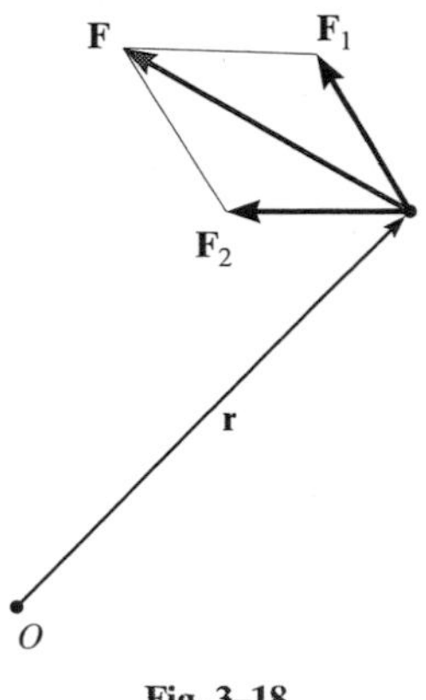

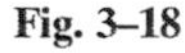
Fig. 3–18

The guy cable exerts a force **F** on the pole and this creates a moment about the base at A of $M_A = Fd$. If the force is replaced by its two components $\mathbf{F}_x$ and $\mathbf{F}_y$ at point B where the cable acts on the pole, then the sum of the moments of these two components about A will yield the *same* resultant moment. For the calculation $\mathbf{F}_y$ will create zero moment about A and so $M_A = F_x h$. This is an application of the *principle of moments*. In addition we can apply the *principle of transmissibility* and slide the force to where its line of action intersects the ground at C. In this case $\mathbf{F}_x$ will create zero moment about A, and so $M_A = F_y b$.

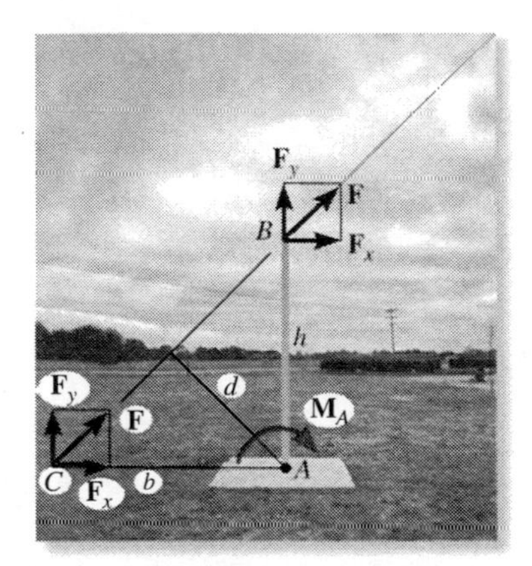

IMPORTANT POINTS

- The moment of a force indicates the tendency of a body to turn about an axis passing through a specific point O.
- Using the right-hand rule, the sense of rotation is indicated by the fingers, and the thumb is directed along the moment axis, or line of action of the moment.
- The magnitude of the moment is determined from $M_O = Fd$, where d is the perpendicular or shortest distance from point O to the line of action of the force **F**.
- In three dimensions use the vector cross product to determine the moment, i.e., $\mathbf{M}_O = \mathbf{r} \times \mathbf{F}$. Remember that **r** is directed *from* point O *to any point* on the line of action of **F**.
- The principle of moments states that the moment of a force about a point is equal to the sum of the moments of the force's components about the point. This is a very convenient method to use in two dimensions.

EXAMPLE 3.6

A 200-N force acts on the bracket shown in Fig. 3–19a. Determine the moment of the force about point A.

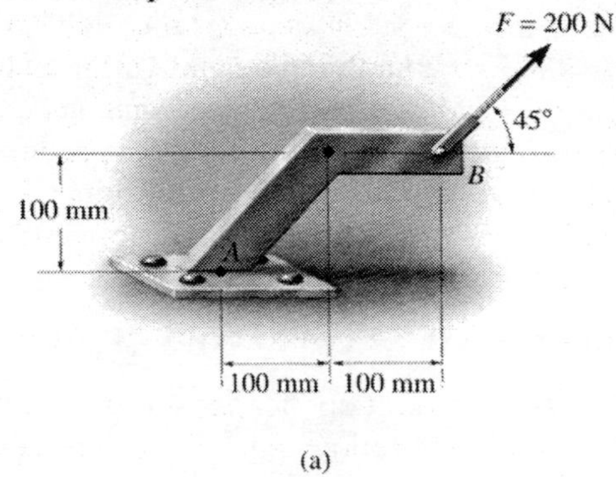

(a)

Fig. 3–19

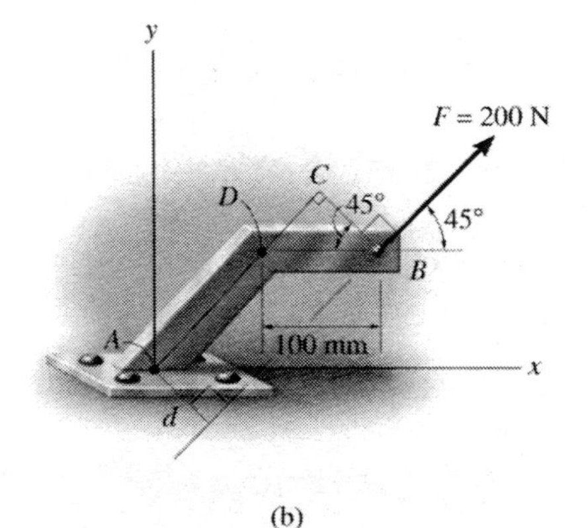

(b)

Solution I

The moment arm d can be found by trigonometry, using the construction shown in Fig. 3–19b. From the right triangle BCD,

$$CB = d = 100 \cos 45° = 70.71 \text{ mm} = 0.070\,71 \text{ m}$$

Thus,

$$M_A = Fd = 200 \text{ N}(0.070\,71 \text{ m}) = 14.1 \text{ N} \cdot \text{m} \circlearrowleft$$

According to the right-hand rule, $\mathbf{M}_A$ is directed in the $+\mathbf{k}$ direction since the force tends to rotate or orbit *counterclockwise* about point A. Hence, reporting the moment as a Cartesian vector, we have

$$\mathbf{M}_A = \{14.1\mathbf{k}\} \text{ N} \cdot \text{m} \qquad \textit{Ans.}$$

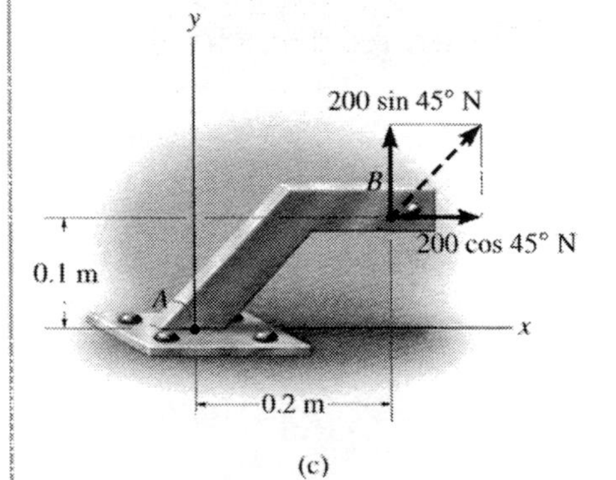

(c)

Solution II

The 200-N force may be resolved into x and y components, as shown in Fig. 3–19c. In accordance with the principle of moments, the moment of $\mathbf{F}$ computed about point A is equivalent to the sum of the moments produced by the two force components. Assuming counterclockwise rotation as positive, i.e., in the $+\mathbf{k}$ direction, we can apply Eq. 3–2 ($M_A = \Sigma Fd$), in which case

$$\circlearrowleft +M_A = (200 \sin 45° \text{ N})(0.20 \text{ m}) - (200 \cos 45° \text{ N})(0.10 \text{ m})$$
$$= 14.1 \text{ N} \cdot \text{m} \circlearrowleft$$

Thus

$$\mathbf{M}_A = \{14.1\mathbf{k}\} \text{ N} \cdot \text{m} \qquad \textit{Ans.}$$

By comparison, it is seen that Solution II provides a more *convenient method* for analysis than Solution I since the moment arm for each component force is easier to establish.

EXAMPLE 3.7

The force **F** acts at the end of the angle bracket shown in Fig. 3–20*a*. Determine the moment of the force about point *O*.

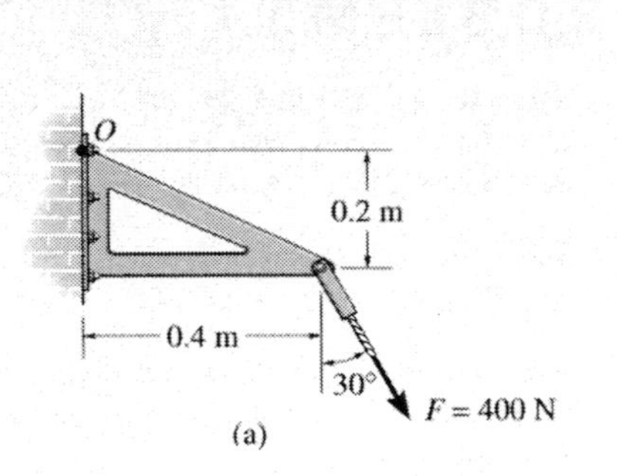

Solution I *(Scalar Analysis)*

The force is resolved into its *x* and *y* components as shown in Fig. 3–20*b*, and the moments of the components are computed about point *O*. Taking positive moments as counterclockwise, i.e., in the $+\mathbf{k}$ direction, we have

$$\circlearrowleft + M_O = 400 \sin 30^\circ \text{ N}(0.2 \text{ m}) - 400 \cos 30^\circ \text{ N}(0.4 \text{ m})$$
$$= -98.6 \text{ N}\cdot\text{m} = 98.6 \text{ N}\cdot\text{m} \circlearrowright$$

or

$$\mathbf{M}_O = \{-98.6\mathbf{k}\} \text{ N}\cdot\text{m} \qquad \textit{Ans.}$$

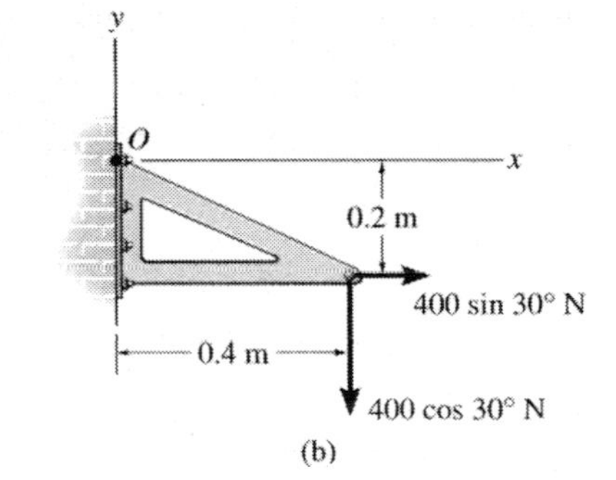

Solution II *(Vector Analysis)*

Using a Cartesian vector approach, the force and position vectors shown in Fig. 3–20*c* can be represented as

$$\mathbf{r} = \{0.4\mathbf{i} - 0.2\mathbf{j}\} \text{ m}$$
$$\mathbf{F} = \{400 \sin 30^\circ \mathbf{i} - 400 \cos 30^\circ \mathbf{j}\} \text{ N}$$
$$= \{200.0\mathbf{i} - 346.4\mathbf{j}\} \text{ N}$$

The moment is therefore

$$\mathbf{M}_O = \mathbf{r} \times \mathbf{F} = \begin{vmatrix} \mathbf{i} & \mathbf{j} & \mathbf{k} \\ 0.4 & -0.2 & 0 \\ 200.0 & -346.4 & 0 \end{vmatrix}$$
$$= 0\mathbf{i} - 0\mathbf{j} + [0.4(-346.4) - (-0.2)(200.0)]\mathbf{k}$$
$$= \{-98.6\mathbf{k}\} \text{ N}\cdot\text{m} \qquad \textit{Ans.}$$

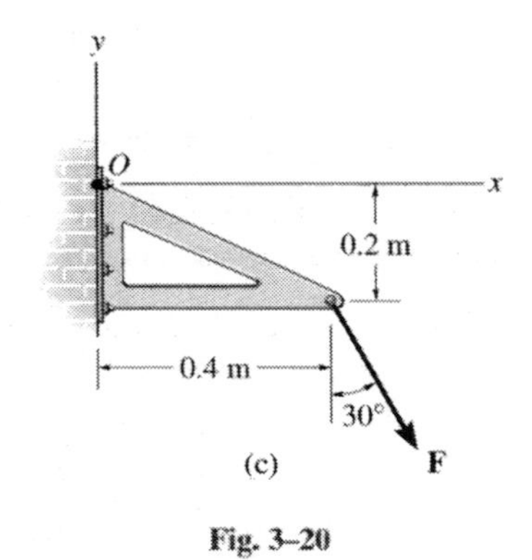

Fig. 3–20

By comparison, it is seen that the scalar analysis (Solution I) provides a more *convenient method* for analysis than Solution II since the direction of the moment and the moment arm for each component force are easy to establish. Hence, this method is generally recommended for solving problems displayed in two dimensions. On the other hand, Cartesian vector analysis is generally recommended only for solving three-dimensional problems, where the moment arms and force components are often more difficult to determine.

PROBLEMS

3-1. If **A**, **B**, and **D** are given vectors, prove the distributive law for the vector cross product, i.e., $\mathbf{A} \times (\mathbf{B} + \mathbf{D}) = (\mathbf{A} \times \mathbf{B}) + (\mathbf{A} \times \mathbf{D})$.

3-2. Prove the triple scalar product identity $\mathbf{A} \cdot (\mathbf{B} \times \mathbf{C}) = (\mathbf{A} \times \mathbf{B}) \cdot \mathbf{C}$.

3-3. Given the three nonzero vectors **A**, **B**, and **C**, show that if $\mathbf{A} \cdot (\mathbf{B} \times \mathbf{C}) = 0$, the three vectors *must* lie in the same plane.

***3-4.** Determine the magnitude and directional sense of the moment of the force at *A* about point *O*.

3-5. Determine the magnitude and directional sense of the moment of the force at *A* about point *P*.

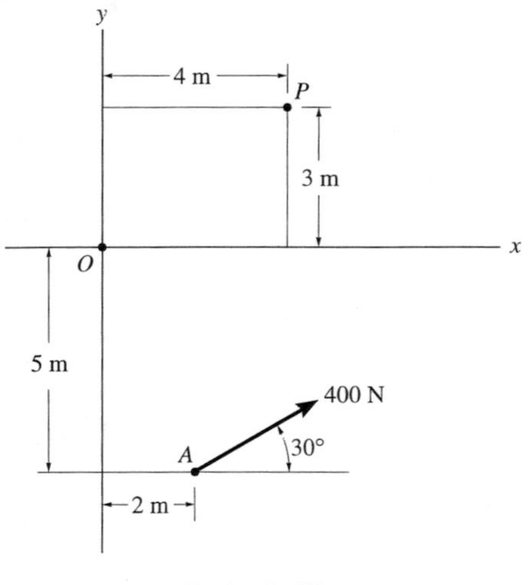

Probs. 3–4/5

3-6. Determine the magnitude and directional sense of the moment of the force at *A* about point *O*.

3-7. Determine the magnitude and directional sense of the moment of the force at *A* about point *P*.

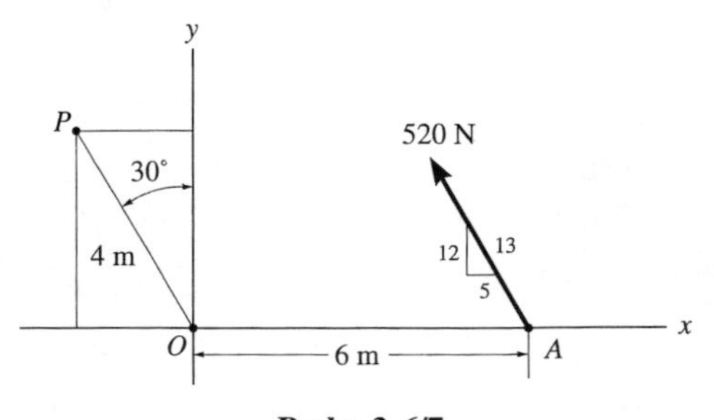

Probs. 3–6/7

***3-8.** Determine the magnitude and directional sense of the resultant moment of the forces about point *O*.

3-9. Determine the magnitude and directional sense of the resultant moment of the forces about point *P*.

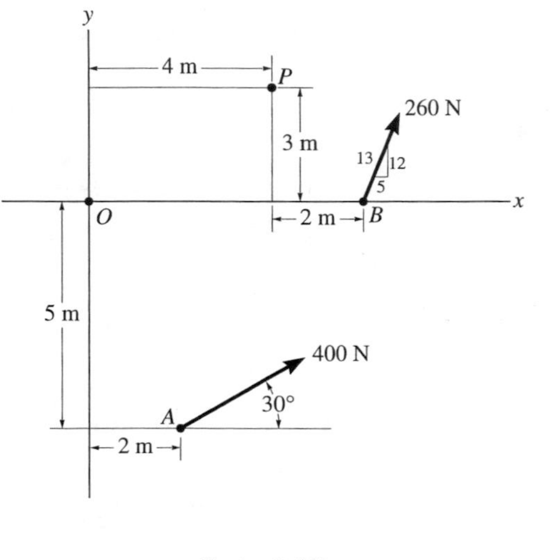

Probs. 3–8/9

3-10. The wrench is used to loosen the bolt. Determine the moment of each force about the bolt's axis passing through point *O*.

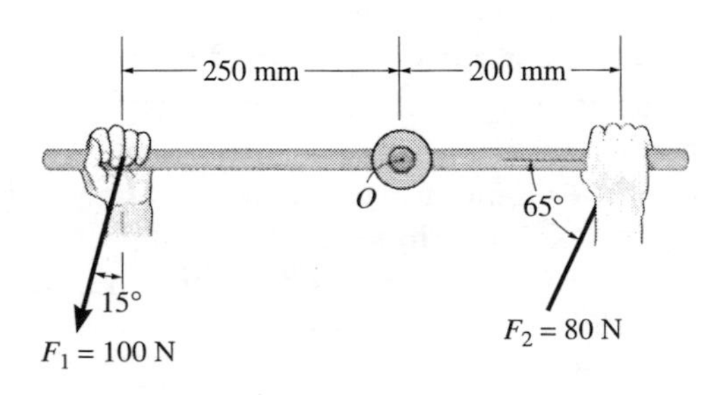

Prob. 3–10

3-11. Determine the magnitude and directional sense of the resultant moment of the forces about point O.

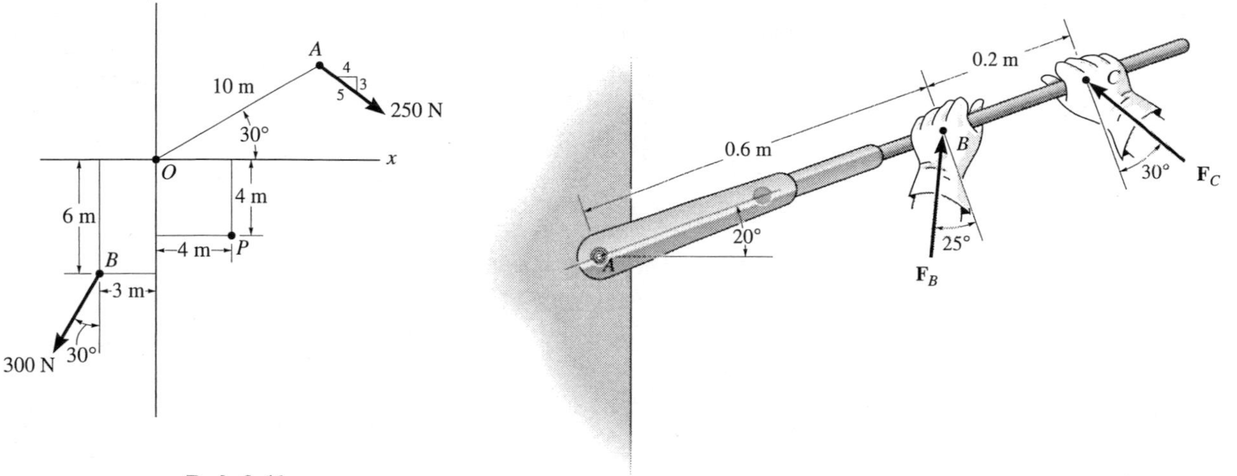

Prob. 3–11

*3-12. Determine the moment about point A of each of the three forces acting on the beam.

3-13. Determine the moment about point B of each of the three forces acting on the beam.

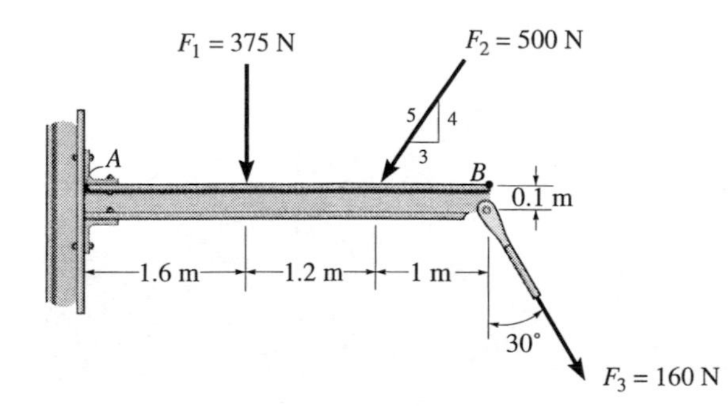

Probs. 3–12/13

3-14. Determine the moment of each force about the bolt located at A. Take $F_B = 200$ N, $F_C = 250$ N.

3-15. If $F_B = 150$ N and $F_C = 225$ N, determine the resultant moment about the bolt located at A.

Probs. 3–14/15

*3-16. The power pole supports the three lines, each line exerting a vertical force on the pole due to its weight as shown. Determine the resultant moment at the base D due to all of these forces. If it is possible for wind or ice to snap the lines, determine which line(s) when removed create(s) a condition for the greatest moment about the base. What is this resultant moment?

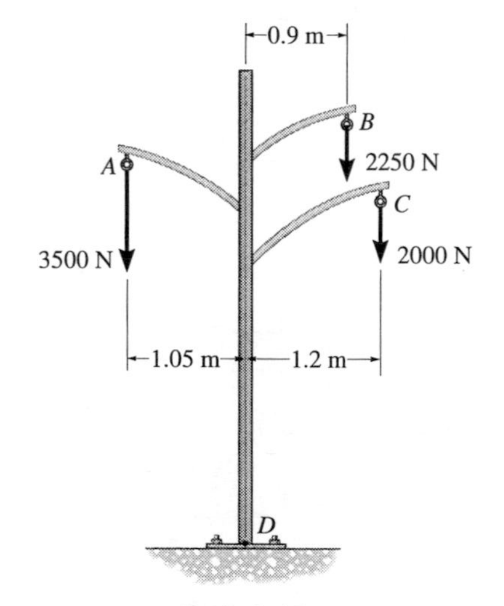

Prob. 3–16

3-17. A force of 80 N acts on the handle of the paper cutter at A. Determine the moment created by this force about the hinge at O, if $\theta = 60°$. At what angle θ should the force be applied so that the moment it creates about point O is a maximum (clockwise)? What is this maximum moment?

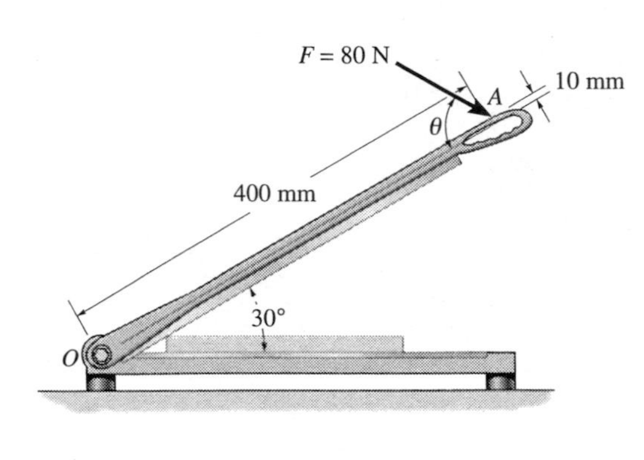

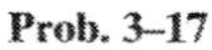

Prob. 3–17

3-19. The hub of the wheel can be attached to the axle either with negative offset (left) or with positive offset (right). If the tire is subjected to both a normal and radial load as shown, determine the resultant moment of these loads about the axle, point O for both cases.

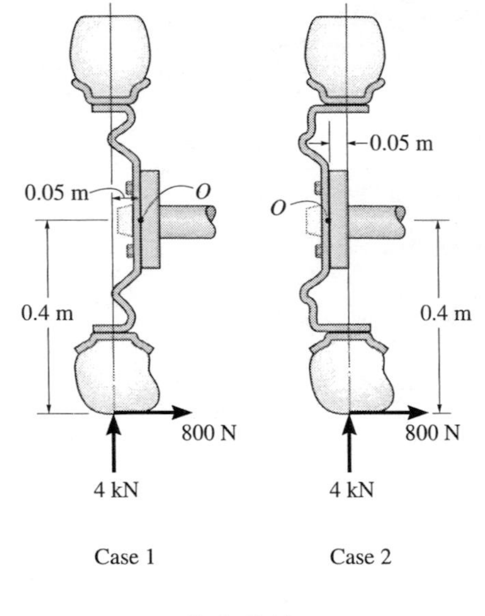

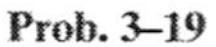

Prob. 3–19

3-18. Determine the direction $\theta (0° \leq \theta \leq 180°)$ of the force $F = 200$ N so that it produces (a) the maximum moment about point A and (b) the minimum moment about point A. Compute the moment in each case.

***3-20.** The boom has a length of 9 m, a weight of 4000 N, and mass center at G. If the maximum moment that can be developed by the motor at A is $M = 30(10^3)$ N · m, determine the maximum load W, having a mass center at G', that can be lifted. Take $\theta = 30°$.

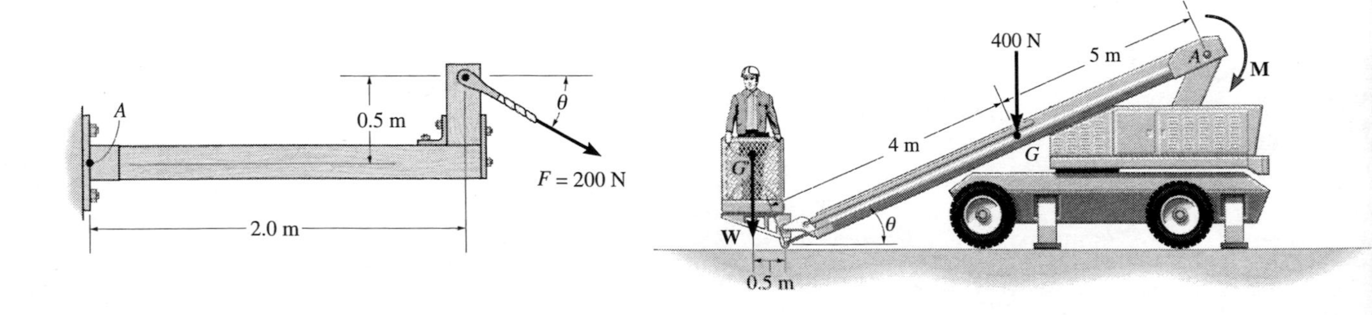

Prob. 3–18

Prob. 3–20

3-21. The tool at A is used to hold a power lawnmower blade stationary while the nut is being loosened with the wrench. If a force of 50 N is applied to the wrench at B in the direction shown, determine the moment it creates about the nut at C. What is the magnitude of force $\mathbf{F}$ at A so that it creates the opposite moment about C?

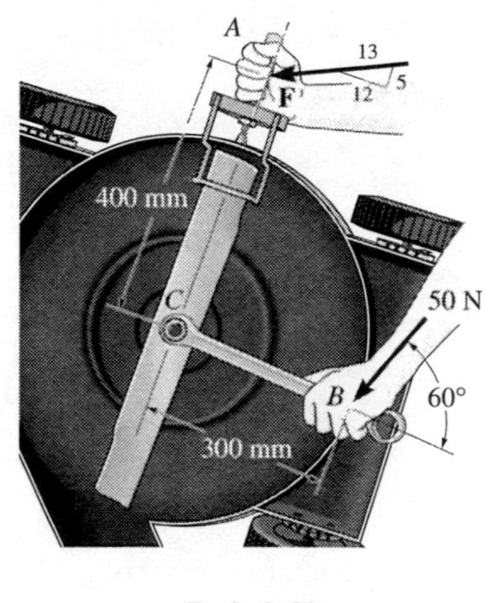

Prob. 3–21

3-22. Determine the moment of each of the three forces about point A. Solve the problem first by using each force as a whole, and then by using the principle of moments.

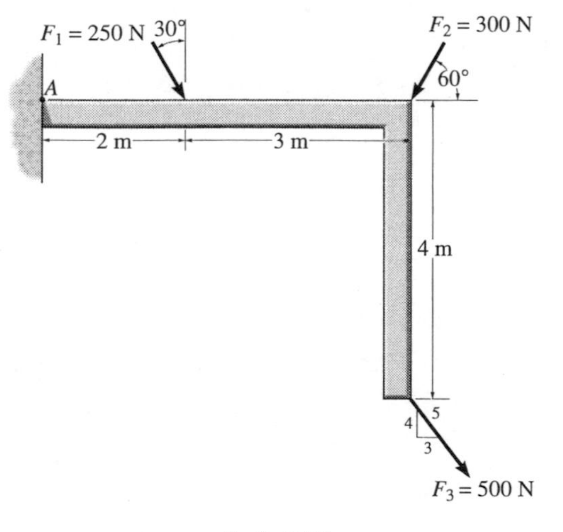

Prob. 3–22

3-23. As part of an acrobatic stunt, a man supports a girl who has a weight of 500 N ($\approx$ 50 kg) and is seated on a chair on top of the pole. If her center of gravity is at G, and if the maximum counterclockwise moment the man can exert on the pole at A is 350 N · m, determine the maximum angle of tilt, θ, which will not allow the girl to fall, i.e., so her clockwise moment about A does not exceed 350 N · m.

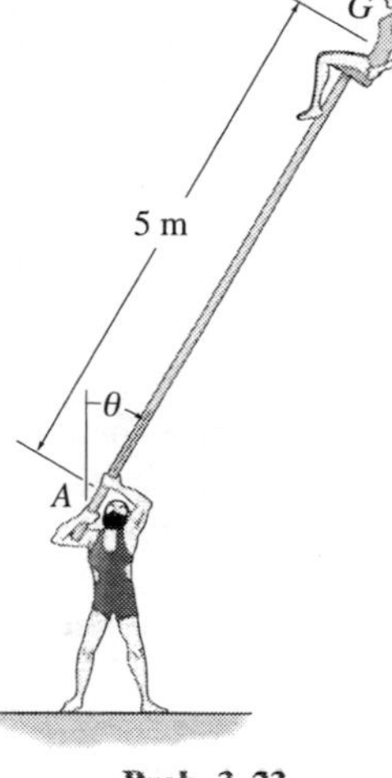

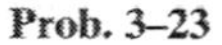

Prob. 3–23

***3-24.** The two boys push on the gate with forces of $F_A = 120$ N and $F_B = 200$ N as shown. Determine the moment of each force about C. Which way will the gate rotate, clockwise or counterclockwise? Neglect the thickness of the gate.

3-25. Two boys push on the gate as shown. If the boy at B exerts a force of $F_B = 120$ N, determine the magnitude of the force F_A the boy at A must exert in order to prevent the gate from turning. Neglect the thickness of the gate.

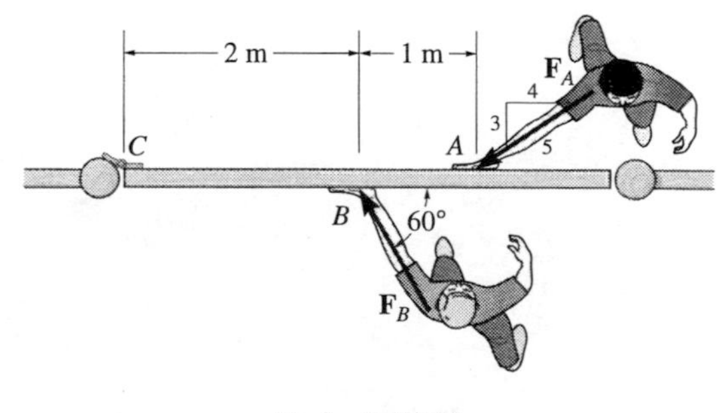

Probs. 3–24/25

*3-26. Determine the angle θ at which the 500-N force must act at A so that the moment of this force about point B is equal to zero.

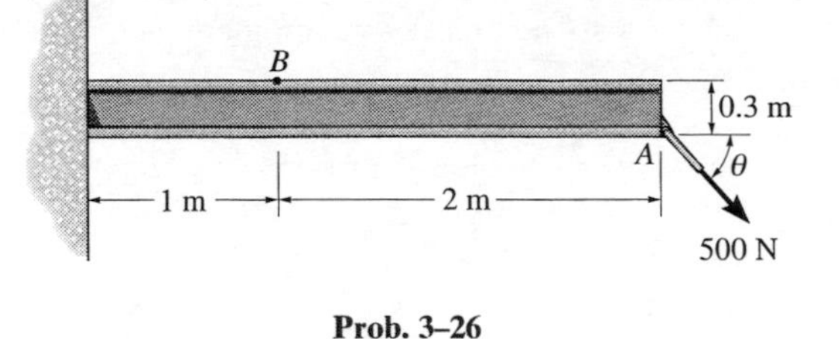

Prob. 3–26

3-27. Segments of drill pipe D for an oil well are tightened a prescribed amount by using a set of tongs T, which grip the pipe, and a hydraulic cylinder (not shown) to regulate the force **F** applied to the tongs. This force acts along the cable which passes around the small pulley P. If the cable is originally perpendicular to the tongs as shown, determine the magnitude of force **F** which must be applied so that the moment about the pipe is $M = 2000$ N · m. In order to maintain this same moment what magnitude of **F** is required when the tongs rotate 30° to the dashed position? *Note:* The angle DAP is not 90° in this position.

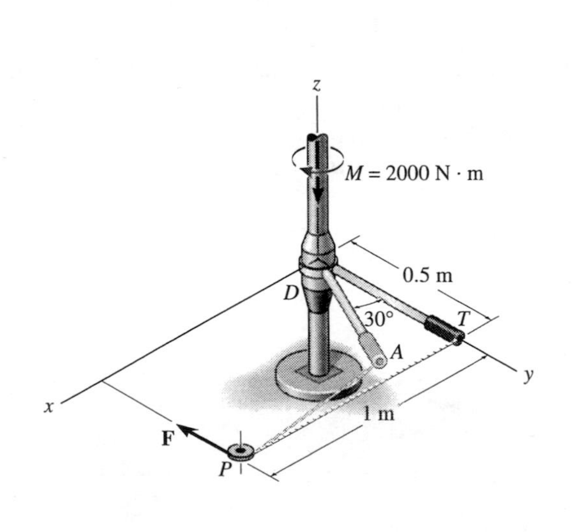

Prob. 3–37

3-28. Determine the moment of the force at A about point O. Express the result as a Cartesian vector.

3-29. Determine the moment of the force at A about point P. Express the result as a Cartesian vector.

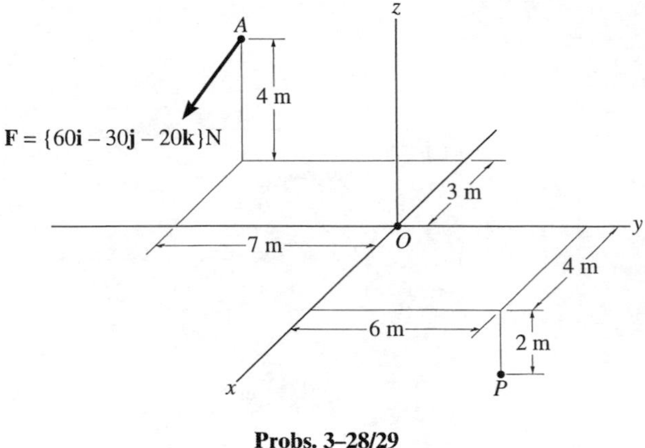

Probs. 3–28/29

*3-30. Determine the moment of the force **F** at A about point O. Express the result as a Cartesian vector.

3-31. Determine the moment of the force **F** at A about point P. Express the result as a Cartesian vector.

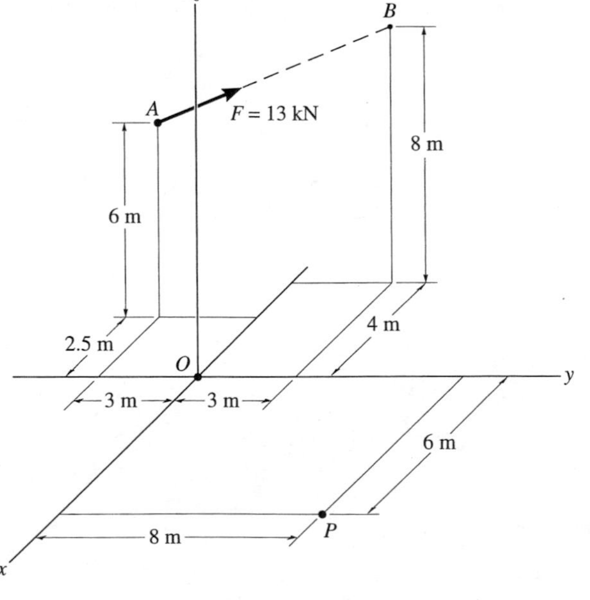

Probs. 3–30/31

3-32. The curved rod lies in the x-y plane and has a radius of 3 m. If a force of $F = 80$ N acts at its end as shown, determine the moment of this force about point O.

3-33. The curved rod lies in the x-y plane and has a radius of 3 m. If a force of $F = 80$ N acts at its end as shown, determine the moment of this force about point B.

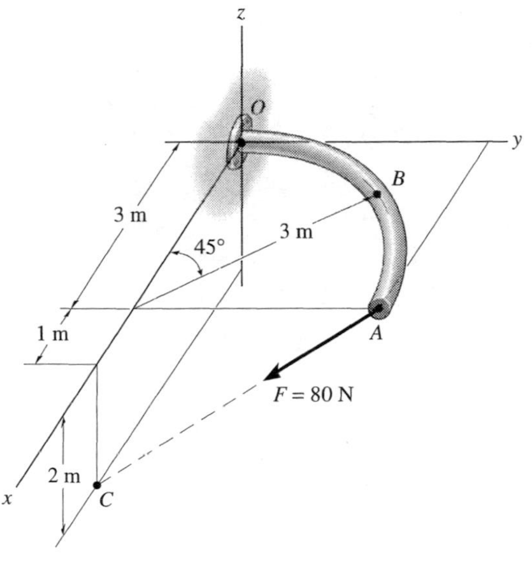

Probs. 3–32/33

3-35. The curved rod has a radius of 0.5 m. If a force of 60 N acts at its end as shown, determine the moment of this force about point C.

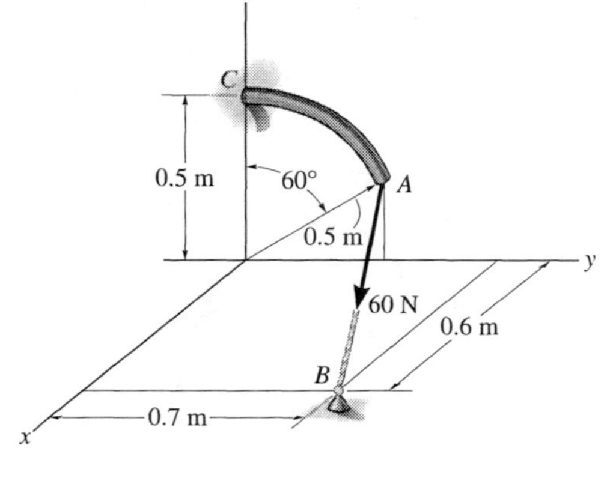

Prob. 3–35

***3-34.** The force $\mathbf{F} = \{600\mathbf{i} + 300\mathbf{j} - 600\mathbf{k}\}$ N acts at the end of the beam. Determine the moment of the force about point A.

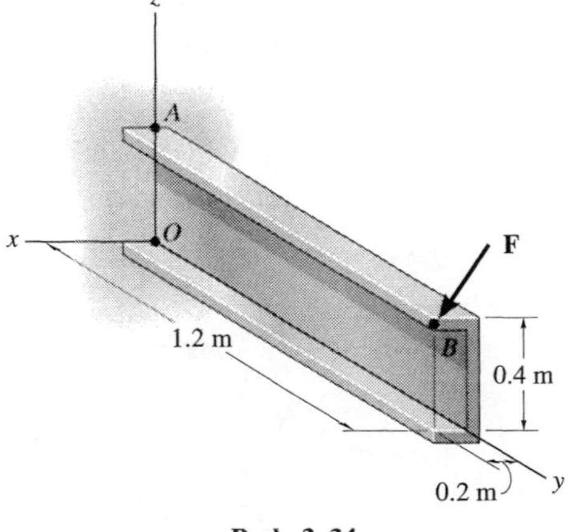

Prob. 3–34

3-36. A force $\mathbf{F}$ having a magnitude of $F = 100$ N acts along the diagonal of the parallelepiped. Determine the moment of $\mathbf{F}$ about point A, using $\mathbf{M}_A = \mathbf{r}_B \times \mathbf{F}$ and $\mathbf{M}_A = \mathbf{r}_C \times \mathbf{F}$.

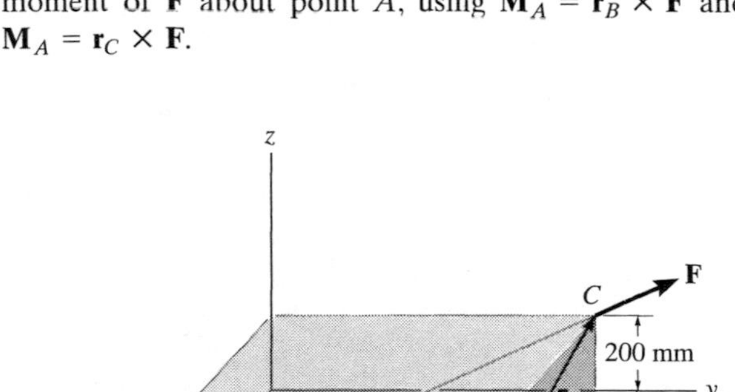

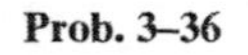

Prob. 3–36

3-37. Determine the smallest force F that must be applied along the rope in order to cause the curved rod, which has a radius of 0.5 m, to fail at the support C. This requires a moment of $M = 80 \text{ N} \cdot \text{m}$ to be developed at C.

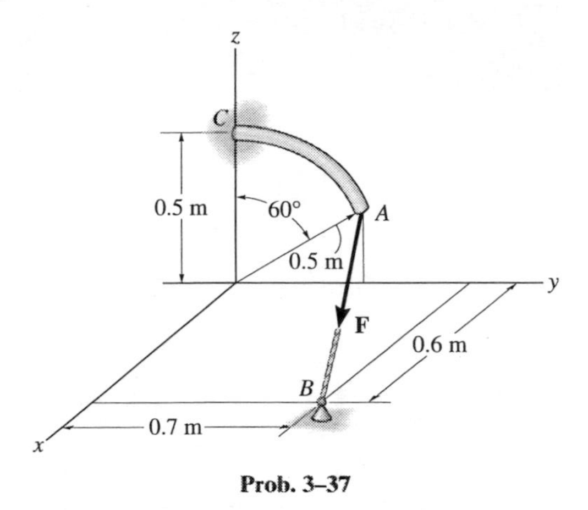

Prob. 3–37

***3-38.** The pipe assembly is subjected to the 80-N force. Determine the moment of this force about point A.

3-39. The pipe assembly is subjected to the 80-N force. Determine the moment of this force about point B.

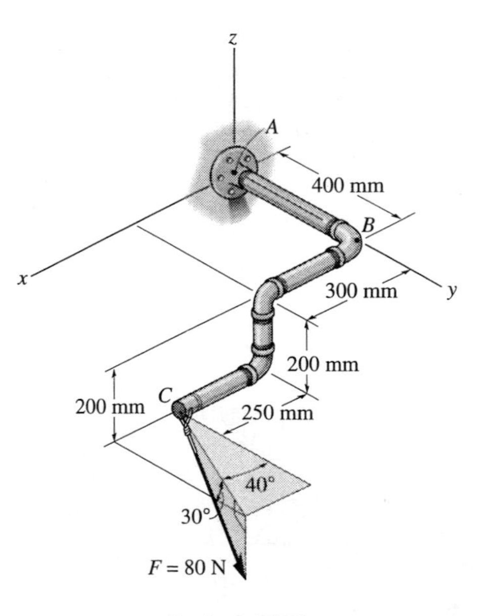

Probs. 3–38/39

3-40. Strut AB of the 1-m-diameter hatch door exerts a force of 450 N on point B. Determine the moment of this force about point O.

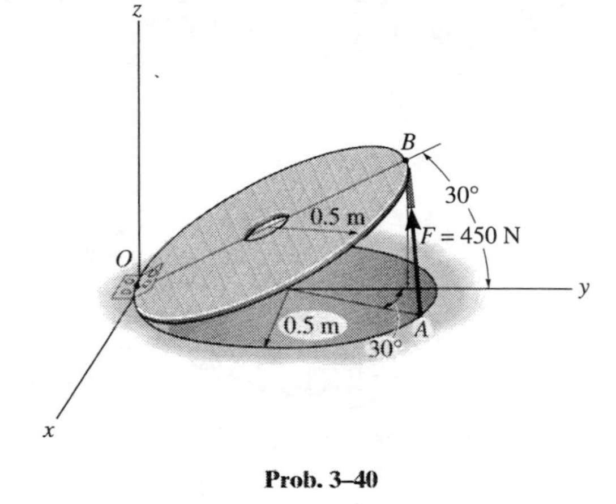

Prob. 3–40

3-41. Using Cartesian vector analysis, determine the resultant moment of the three forces about the base of the column at A. Take $\mathbf{F}_1 = \{400\mathbf{i} + 300\mathbf{j} + 120\mathbf{k}\}$ N.

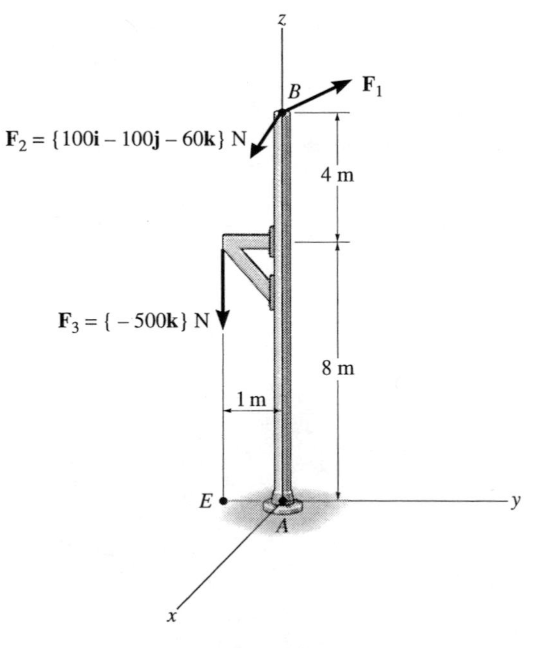

Prob. 3–41

3.5 Moment of a Force about a Specified Axis

Recall that when the moment of a force is computed about a point, the moment and its axis are *always* perpendicular to the plane containing the force and the moment arm. In some problems it is important to find the *component* of this moment along a *specified axis* that passes through the point. To solve this problem either a scalar or vector analysis can be used.

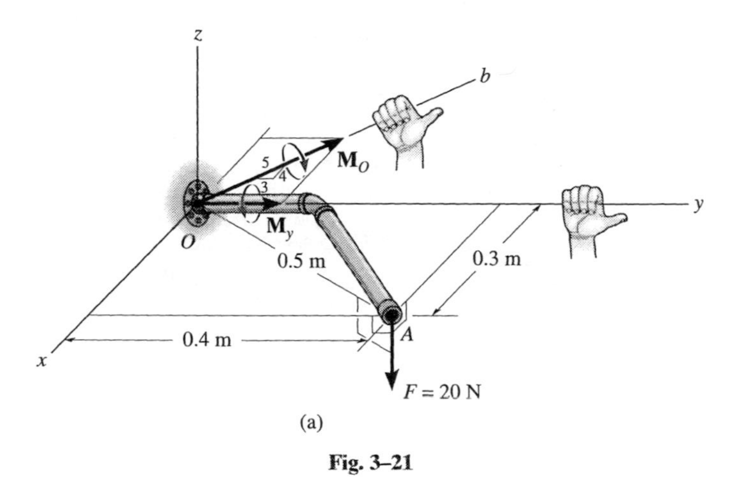

Fig. 3–21

Scalar Analysis. As a numerical example of this problem, consider the pipe assembly shown in Fig. 3–21*a*, which lies in the horizontal plane and is subjected to the vertical force of $F = 20$ N applied at point A. The moment of this force about point O has a *magnitude* of $M_O = (20\text{ N})(0.5\text{ m}) = 10\text{ N}\cdot\text{m}$, and a *direction* defined by the right-hand rule, as shown in Fig. 3–21*a*. This moment tends to turn the pipe about the Ob axis. For practical reasons, however, it may be necessary to determine the *component* of $\mathbf{M}_O$ about the y axis, $\mathbf{M}_y$, since this component tends to unscrew the pipe from the flange at O. From Fig. 3–21*a*, $\mathbf{M}_y$ has a magnitude of $M_y = \frac{3}{5}(10\text{ N}\cdot\text{m}) = 6\text{ N}\cdot\text{m}$ and a sense of direction shown by the vector resolution. Rather than performing this *two-step* process of first finding the moment of the force about point O and then resolving the moment along the y axis, it is also possible to solve this problem *directly*. To do so, it is necessary to determine the perpendicular or moment-arm distance from the line of action of $\mathbf{F}$ to the y axis. From Fig. 3–21*a* this distance is 0.3 m. Thus the *magnitude* of the moment of the force about the y axis is again $M_y = 0.3(20\text{ N}) = 6\text{ N}\cdot\text{m}$, and the *direction* is determined by the right-hand rule as shown.

In general, then, *if the line of action of a force* $\mathbf{F}$ *is perpendicular to any specified axis aa*, the magnitude of the moment of $\mathbf{F}$ about the axis can be determined from the equation

$$M_a = Fd_a \qquad (3\text{–}10)$$

Here d_a is the *perpendicular or shortest distance* from the force line of action to the axis. The direction is determined from the thumb of the right hand when the fingers are curled in accordance with the direction of rotation as produced by the force. In particular, realize that a *force will not contribute a moment about a specified axis if the force line of action is parallel to the axis or its line of action passes through the axis.*

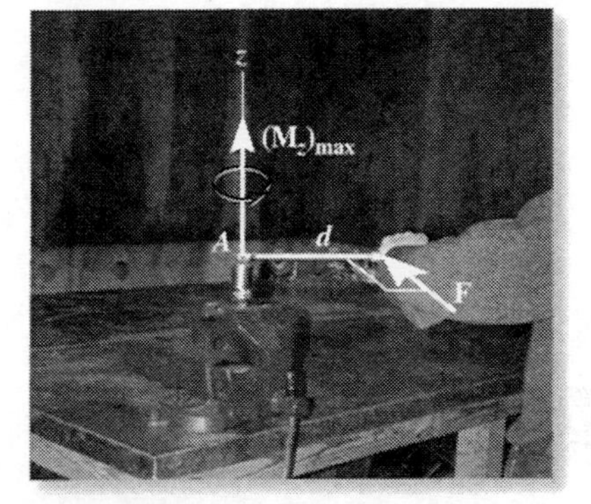

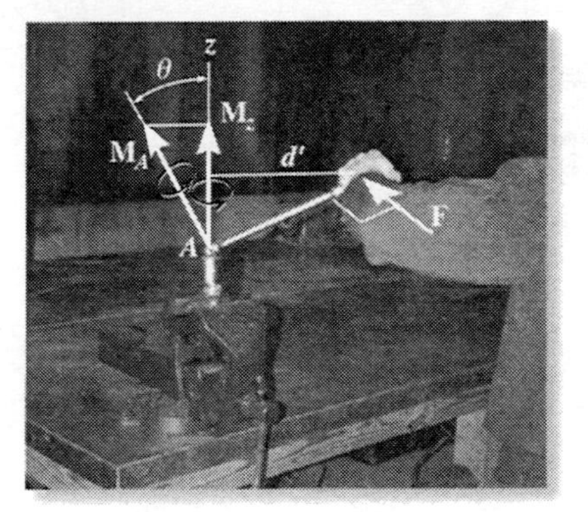

If a horizontal force **F** is applied to the handle of the flex-headed wrench, it tends to turn the socket at A about the z axis. This effect is caused by the moment of **F** about the z axis. The *maximum moment* is determined when the wrench is in the horizontal plane so that full leverage from the handle can be achieved, i.e., $(M_z)_{max} = Fd$. If the handle is not in the horizontal position, then the moment about the z axis is determined from $M_z = Fd'$, where d' is the perpendicular distance from the force line of action to the axis. We can also determine this moment by first finding the moment of **F** about A, $M_A = Fd$, then finding the projection or component of this moment along z, i.e., $M_z = M_A \cos\theta$.

Vector Analysis. The previous two-step solution of first finding the moment of the force about a point on the axis and then finding the projected component of the moment about the axis can also be performed using a vector analysis, Fig. 3–21*b*. Here the moment about point O is first determined from $\mathbf{M}_O = \mathbf{r}_A \times \mathbf{F} = (0.3\mathbf{i} + 0.4\mathbf{j}) \times (-20\mathbf{k}) = \{-8\mathbf{i} + 6\mathbf{j}\}\,\text{N}\cdot\text{m}$. The component or projection of this moment along the y axis is then determined from the dot product (Sec. 2.9). Since the unit vector for this axis (or line) is $\mathbf{u}_a = \mathbf{j}$, then $M_y = \mathbf{M}_O \cdot \mathbf{u}_a = (-8\mathbf{i} + 6\mathbf{j}) \cdot \mathbf{j} = 6\,\text{N}\cdot\text{m}$. This result, of course, is to be expected, since it represents the **j** component of $\mathbf{M}_O$.

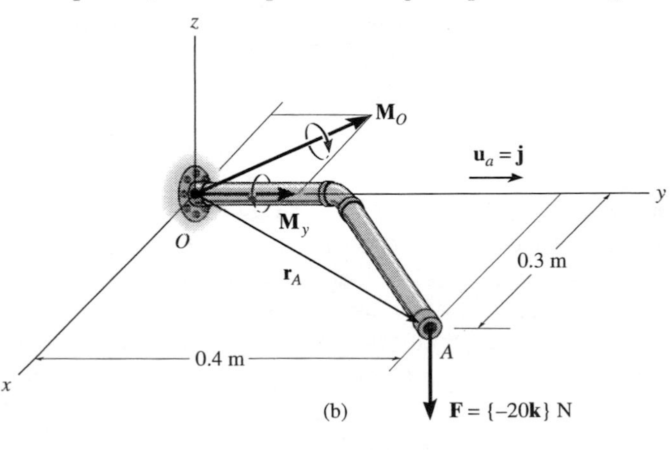

Fig. 3–21

A vector analysis such as this is particularly advantageous for finding the moment of a force about an axis when the force components or the appropriate moment arms are difficult to determine. For this reason, the above two-step process will now be generalized and applied to a body of arbitrary shape. To do so, consider the body in Fig. 3–22, which is subjected to the force **F** acting at point A. Here we wish to determine the effect of **F** in tending to rotate the body about the aa' axis. This tendency for rotation is measured by the moment component $\mathbf{M}_a$. To determine $\mathbf{M}_a$ we first compute the moment of **F** about any *arbitrary point* O that lies on the aa' axis. In this case, $\mathbf{M}_O$ is expressed by the cross product $\mathbf{M}_O = \mathbf{r} \times \mathbf{F}$, where **r** is directed from O to A. Here $\mathbf{M}_O$ acts along the moment axis bb', and so the component or projection of $\mathbf{M}_O$ onto the aa' axis is then $\mathbf{M}_a$. The *magnitude* of $\mathbf{M}_a$ is determined by the dot product, $M_a = M_O \cos\theta = \mathbf{M}_O \cdot \mathbf{u}_a$ where $\mathbf{u}_a$ is a unit vector that defines the direction of the aa' axis. Combining these two steps as a general expression, we have $M_a = (\mathbf{r} \times \mathbf{F}) \cdot \mathbf{u}_a$. Since the dot product is commutative, we can also write

$$M_a = \mathbf{u}_a \cdot (\mathbf{r} \times \mathbf{F})$$

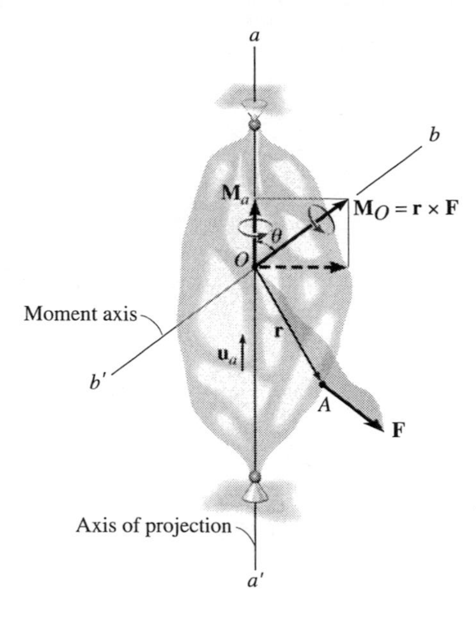

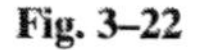
Fig. 3–22

In vector algebra, this combination of dot and cross product yielding the scalar M_a is called the *triple scalar product*. Provided x, y, z axes are established and the Cartesian components of each of the vectors can be determined, then the triple scalar product may be written in determinant form as

$$M_a = (u_{a_x}\mathbf{i} + u_{a_y}\mathbf{j} + u_{a_z}\mathbf{k}) \cdot \begin{vmatrix} \mathbf{i} & \mathbf{j} & \mathbf{k} \\ r_x & r_y & r_z \\ F_x & F_y & F_z \end{vmatrix}$$

or simply

$$M_a = \mathbf{u}_a \cdot (\mathbf{r} \times \mathbf{F}) = \begin{vmatrix} u_{a_x} & u_{a_y} & u_{a_z} \\ r_x & r_y & r_z \\ F_x & F_y & F_z \end{vmatrix} \qquad (3\text{–}11)$$

where

$u_{a_x}, u_{a_y}, u_{a_z}$ represent the x, y, z components of the unit vector defining the direction of the aa' axis

r_x, r_y, r_z represent the x, y, z components of the position vector drawn from *any point* O on the aa' axis to *any point* A on the line of action of the force

F_x, F_y, F_z represent the x, y, z components of the force vector.

When M_a is evaluated from Eq. 3–11, it will yield a positive or negative scalar. The sign of this scalar indicates the sense of direction of $\mathbf{M}_a$ along the aa' axis. If it is positive, then $\mathbf{M}_a$ will have the same sense as $\mathbf{u}_a$, whereas if it is negative, then $\mathbf{M}_a$ will act opposite to $\mathbf{u}_a$.

Once M_a is determined, we can then express $\mathbf{M}_a$ as a Cartesian vector, namely,

$$\mathbf{M}_a = M_a\mathbf{u}_a = [\mathbf{u}_a \cdot (\mathbf{r} \times \mathbf{F})]\mathbf{u}_a \tag{3–12}$$

Finally, if the resultant moment of a series of forces is to be computed about the aa' axis, then the moment components of each force are added together *algebraically*, since each component lies along the same axis. Thus the magnitude of $\mathbf{M}_a$ is

$$M_a = \Sigma[\mathbf{u}_a \cdot (\mathbf{r} \times \mathbf{F})] = \mathbf{u}_a \cdot \Sigma(\mathbf{r} \times \mathbf{F})$$

The examples which follow illustrate a numerical application of the above concepts.

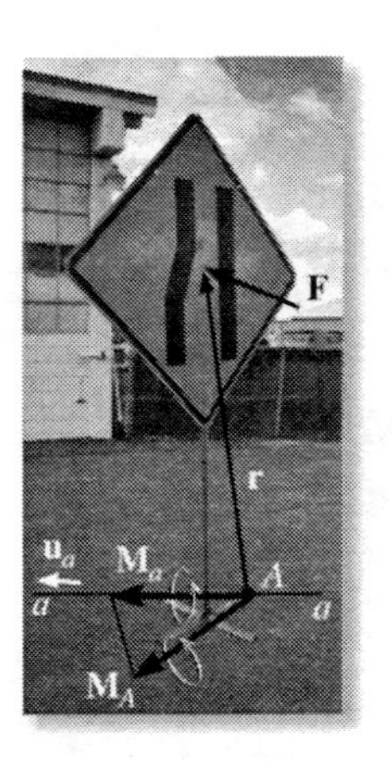

Wind blowing on the face of this traffic sign creates a resultant force $\mathbf{F}$ that tends to tip the sign over due to the moment $\mathbf{M}_A$ created about the a-a axis. The moment of $\mathbf{F}$ about a point A that lies on the axis is $\mathbf{M}_A = \mathbf{r} \times \mathbf{F}$. The projection of this moment along the axis, whose direction is defined by the unit vector $\mathbf{u}_a$, is $M_a = \mathbf{u}_a \cdot (\mathbf{r} \times \mathbf{F})$. Had this moment been calculated using scalar methods, then the perpendicular distance from the force line of action to the a-a axis would have to be determined, which in this case would be a more difficult task.

IMPORTANT POINTS

- The moment of a force about a specified axis can be determined provided the perpendicular distance d_a from *both* the force line of action and the axis can be determined. $M_a = Fd_a$.
- If vector analysis is used, $M_a = \mathbf{u}_a \cdot (\mathbf{r} \times \mathbf{F})$, where $\mathbf{u}_a$ defines the direction of the axis and $\mathbf{r}$ is directed from *any point* on the axis to *any point* on the line of action of the force.
- If M_a is calculated as a negative scalar, then the sense of direction of $\mathbf{M}_a$ is opposite to $\mathbf{u}_a$.
- The moment $\mathbf{M}_a$ expressed as a Cartesian vector is determined from $\mathbf{M}_a = M_a\mathbf{u}_a$.

EXAMPLE 3.8

The force $\mathbf{F} = \{-40\mathbf{i} + 20\mathbf{j} + 10\mathbf{k}\}$ N acts at point A shown in Fig. 3–23a. Determine the moments of this force about the x and a axes.

Solution I *(Vector Analysis)*

We can solve this problem by using the position vector $\mathbf{r}_A$. Why? Since $\mathbf{r}_A = \{-3\mathbf{i} + 4\mathbf{j} + 6\mathbf{k}\}$ m and $\mathbf{u}_x = \mathbf{i}$, then applying Eq. 3–11,

$$M_x = \mathbf{i}\cdot(\mathbf{r}_A \times \mathbf{F}) = \begin{vmatrix} 1 & 0 & 0 \\ -3 & 4 & 6 \\ -40 & 20 & 10 \end{vmatrix}$$

$$= 1[4(10)-6(20)]-0[(-3)(10)-6(-40)]+0[(-3)(20)-4(-40)]$$

$$= -80 \text{ N}\cdot\text{m} \qquad \textit{Ans.}$$

The negative sign indicates that the sense of $\mathbf{M}_x$ is opposite to $\mathbf{i}$.

We can compute M_a also using $\mathbf{r}_A$ because $\mathbf{r}_A$ extends from a point on the a axis to the force. Also, $\mathbf{u}_a = -\frac{3}{5}\mathbf{i} + \frac{4}{5}\mathbf{j}$. Thus,

$$M_a = \mathbf{u}_a\cdot(\mathbf{r}_A \times \mathbf{F}) = \begin{vmatrix} -\frac{3}{5} & \frac{4}{5} & 0 \\ -3 & 4 & 6 \\ -40 & 20 & 10 \end{vmatrix}$$

$$= -\tfrac{3}{5}[4(10)-6(20)]-\tfrac{4}{5}[(-3)(10)-6(-40)]+0[(-3)(20)-4(-40)]$$

$$= -120 \text{ N}\cdot\text{m} \qquad \textit{Ans.}$$

What does the negative sign indicate?

The moment components are shown in Fig. 3–23b.

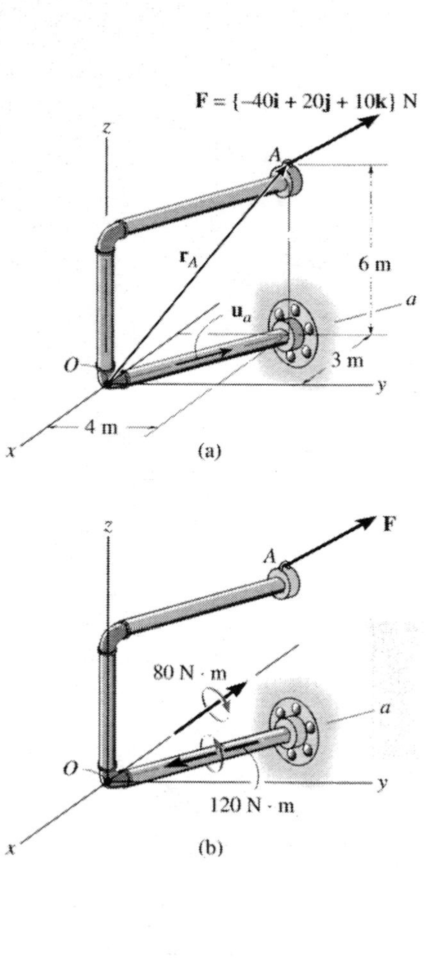

Solution II *(Scalar Analysis)*

Since the force components and moment arms are easy to determine for computing M_x, a scalar analysis can be used to solve this problem. Referring to Fig. 3–23c, only the 10-N and 20-N forces contribute moments about the x axis. (The line of action of the 40-N force is parallel to this axis and hence its moment about the x axis is zero.) Using the right-hand rule, the algebraic sum of the moment components about the x axis is therefore

$$M_x = (10 \text{ N})(4 \text{ m}) - (20 \text{ N})(6 \text{ m}) = -80 \text{ N}\cdot\text{m} \qquad \textit{Ans.}$$

Although not required here, note also that

$$M_y = (10 \text{ N})(3 \text{ m}) - (40 \text{ N})(6 \text{ m}) = -210 \text{ N}\cdot\text{m}$$
$$M_z = (40 \text{ N})(4 \text{ m}) - (20 \text{ N})(3 \text{ m}) = 100 \text{ N}\cdot\text{m}$$

If we were to determine M_a by this scalar method, it would require much more effort since the force components of 40 N and 20 N are *not perpendicular* to the direction of the a axis. The vector analysis yields a more direct solution.

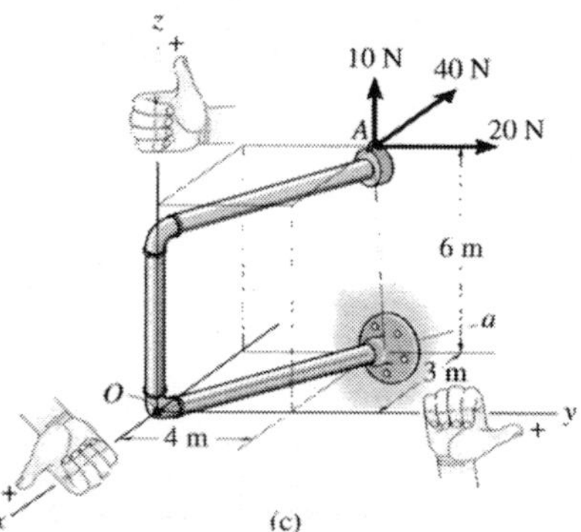

Fig. 3–23

EXAMPLE 3.9

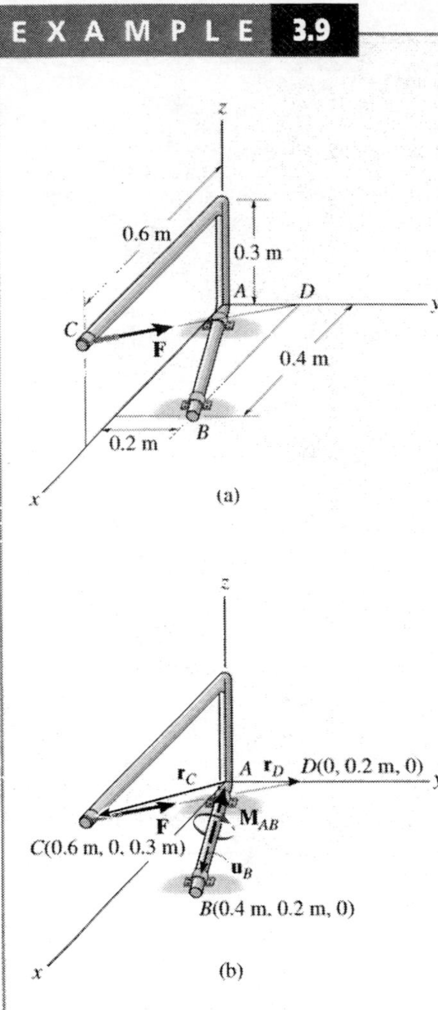

Fig. 3–24

The rod shown in Fig. 3–24*a* is supported by two brackets at *A* and *B*. Determine the moment $\mathbf{M}_{AB}$ produced by $\mathbf{F} = \{-600\mathbf{i}+200\mathbf{j}-300\mathbf{k}\}$ N, which tends to rotate the rod about the *AB* axis.

Solution

A vector analysis using $M_{AB} = \mathbf{u}_B \cdot (\mathbf{r} \times \mathbf{F})$ will be considered for the solution since the moment arm or perpendicular distance from the line of action of **F** to the *AB* axis is difficult to determine. Each of the terms in the equation will now be identified.

Unit vector $\mathbf{u}_B$ defines the direction of the *AB* axis of the rod, Fig. 3–24*b*, where

$$\mathbf{u}_B = \frac{\mathbf{r}_B}{r_B} = \frac{0.4\mathbf{i} + 0.2\mathbf{j}}{\sqrt{(0.4)^2 + (0.2)^2}} = 0.894\mathbf{i} + 0.447\mathbf{j}$$

Vector **r** is directed from *any point* on the *AB* axis to *any point* on the line of action of the force. For example, position vectors $\mathbf{r}_C$ and $\mathbf{r}_D$ are suitable, Fig. 3–24*b*. (Although not shown, $\mathbf{r}_{BC}$ or $\mathbf{r}_{BD}$ can also be used.) For simplicity, we choose $\mathbf{r}_D$, where

$$\mathbf{r}_D = \{0.2\mathbf{j}\} \text{ m}$$

The force is

$$\mathbf{F} = \{-600\mathbf{i} + 200\mathbf{j} - 300\mathbf{k}\} \text{ N}$$

Substituting these vectors into the determinant form and expanding, we have

$$M_{AB} = \mathbf{u}_B \cdot (\mathbf{r}_D \times \mathbf{F}) = \begin{vmatrix} 0.894 & 0.447 & 0 \\ 0 & 0.2 & 0 \\ -600 & 200 & -300 \end{vmatrix}$$

$$= 0.894[0.2(-300) - 0(200)] - 0.447[0(-300) - 0(-600)] + 0[0(200) - 0.2(-600)]$$

$$= -53.67 \text{ N}\cdot\text{m}$$

The negative sign indicates that the sense of $\mathbf{M}_{AB}$ is opposite to that of $\mathbf{u}_B$.

Expressing $\mathbf{M}_{AB}$ as a Cartesian vector yields

$$\mathbf{M}_{AB} = M_{AB}\mathbf{u}_B = (-53.67 \text{ N}\cdot\text{m})(0.894\mathbf{i} + 0.447\mathbf{j})$$

$$= \{-48.0\mathbf{i} - 24.0\mathbf{j}\} \text{ N}\cdot\text{m} \qquad \textit{Ans.}$$

The result is shown in Fig. 3–24*b*.

Note that if axis *AB* is defined using a unit vector directed from *B* toward *A*, then in the above formulation $-\mathbf{u}_B$ would have to be used. This would lead to $M_{AB} = +53.67 \text{ N}\cdot\text{m}$. Consequently, $\mathbf{M}_{AB} = M_{AB}(-\mathbf{u}_B)$, and the above result would again be determined.

PROBLEMS

3-42. Determine the moment of the force **F** about the Oa axis. Express the result as a Cartesian vector.

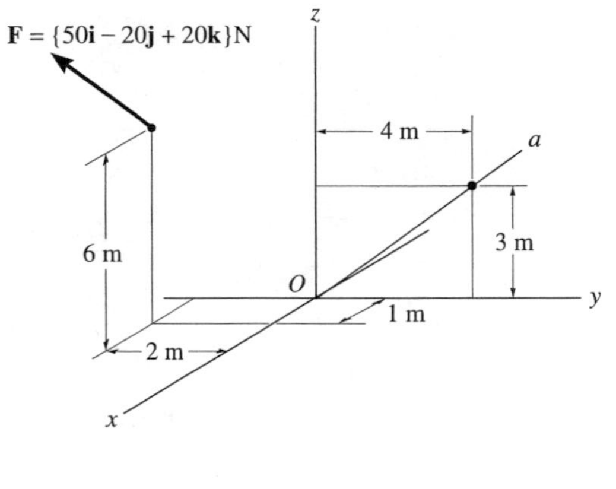

Prob. 3–42

***3-43.** Determine the moment of the force **F** about the aa axis. Express the result as a Cartesian vector.

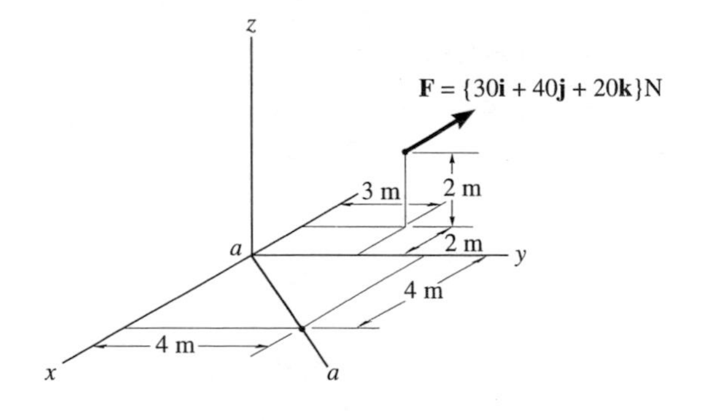

Prob. 3–43

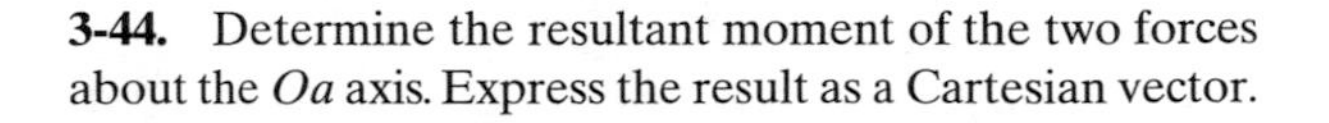
3-44. Determine the resultant moment of the two forces about the Oa axis. Express the result as a Cartesian vector.

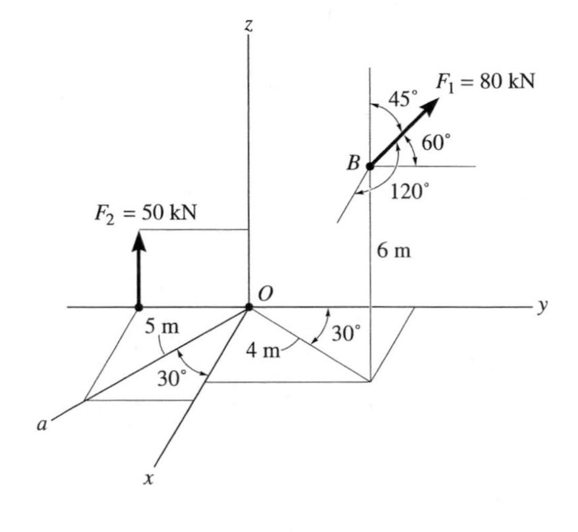

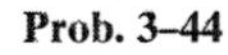
Prob. 3–44

3-45. Determine the magnitude of the moment of each of the three forces about the axis AB. Solve the problem (a) using a Cartesian vector approach and (b) using a scalar approach.

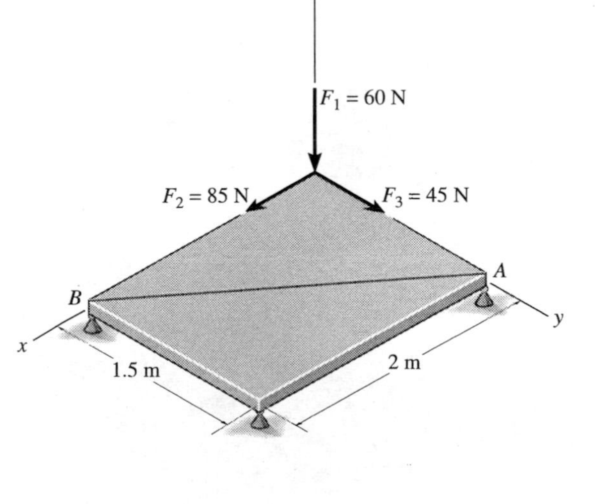

Prob. 3–45

3-46. The chain AB exerts a force of 100 N on the door at B. Determine the magnitude of the moment of this force along the hinged axis x of the door.

Prob. 3–46

***3-47.** The force of $F = 30$ N acts on the bracket as shown. Determine the moment of the force about the a–a axis of the pipe. Also, determine the coordinate direction angles of F in order to produce the maximum moment about the a–a axis. What is this moment?

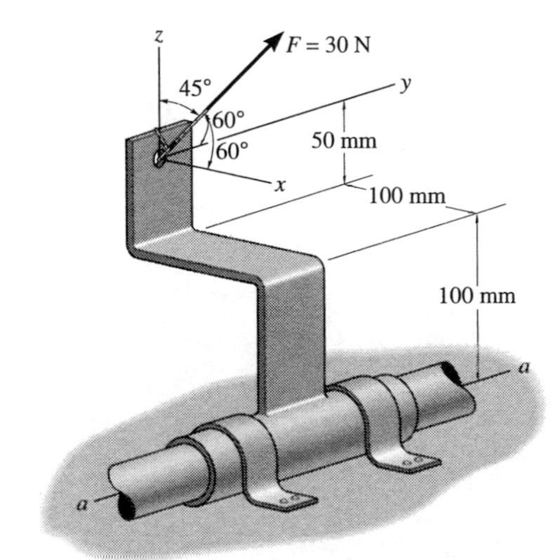

Prob. 3–47

3-48. The cutting tool on the lathe exerts a force **F** on the shaft in the direction shown. Determine the moment of this force about the y axis of the shaft.

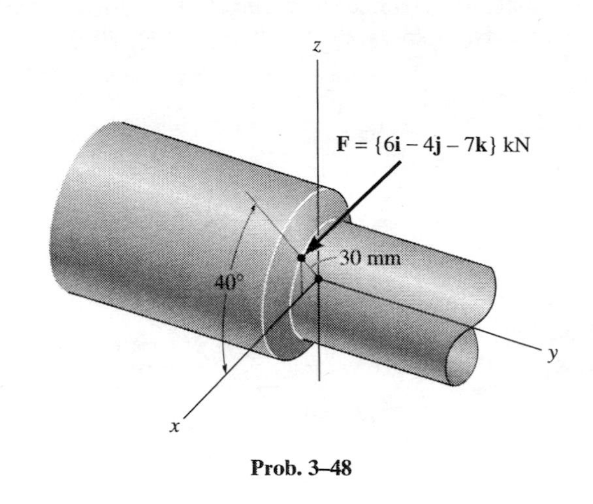

Prob. 3–48

3-49. The hood of the automobile is supported by the strut AB, which exerts a force of $F = 100$ N on the hood. Determine the moment of this force about the hinged axis y.

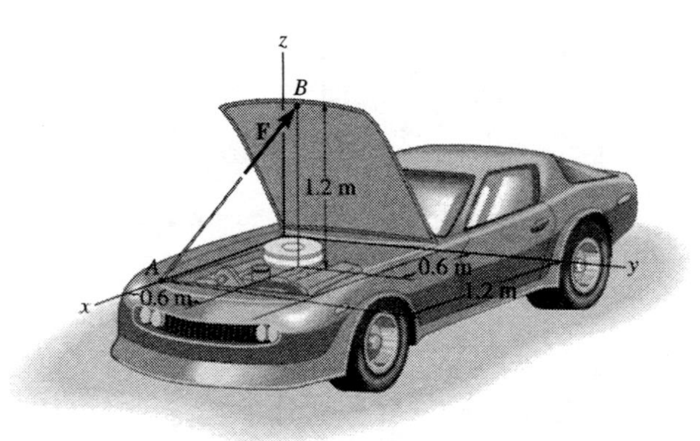

Prob. 3–49

3-50. Determine the magnitude of the moments of the force **F** about the *x*, *y*, and *z* axes. Solve the problem (a) using a Cartesian vector approach and (b) using a scalar approach.

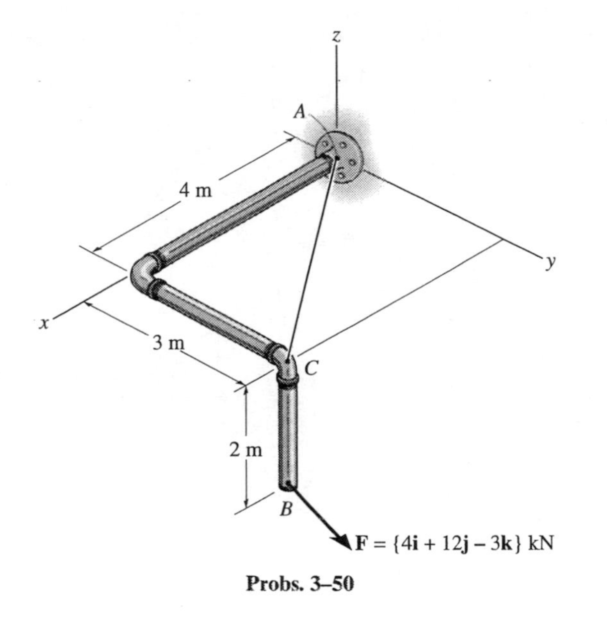

Probs. 3–50

***3-51.** Determine the moment of the force **F** about an axis extending between *A* and *C*. Express the result as a Cartesian vector.

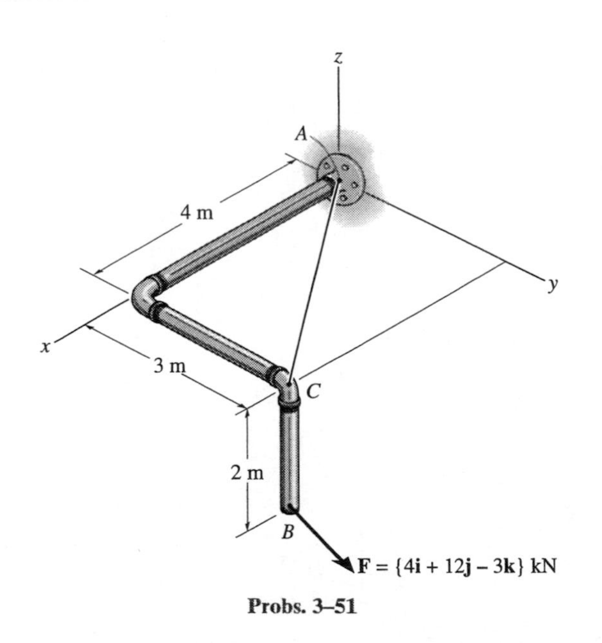

Probs. 3–51

3-52. The lug and box wrenches are used in combination to remove the lug nut from the wheel hub. If the applied force on the end of the box wrench is $\mathbf{F} = \{4\mathbf{i} - 12\mathbf{j} + 2\mathbf{k}\}$ N, determine the magnitude of the moment of this force about the *x* axis which is effective in unscrewing the lug nut.

Prob. 3–52

3-53. A 70-N (≈ 7-kg) force acts vertically on the "Z" bracket. Determine the magnitude of the moment of this force about the bolt axis (z axis).

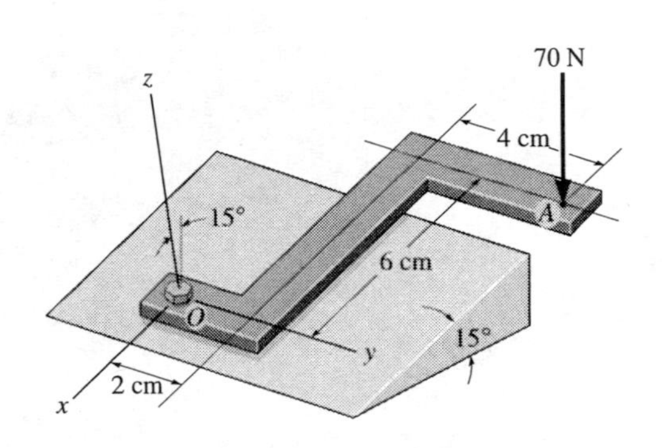

Prob. 3–53

3-54. Determine the magnitude of the moment of the force $\mathbf{F} = \{50\mathbf{i} - 20\mathbf{j} - 80\mathbf{k}\}$ N about the base line CA of the tripod.

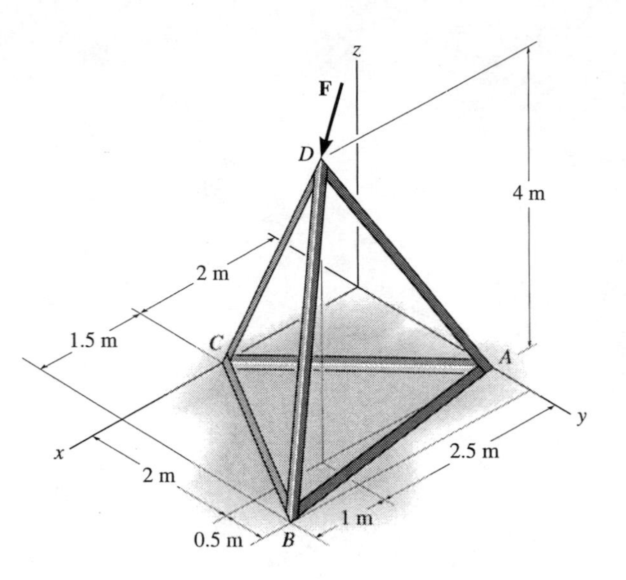

Prob. 3–54

3.6 Moment of a Couple

A *couple* is defined as two parallel forces that have the same magnitude, have opposite directions, and are separated by a perpendicular distance d, Fig. 3–25. Since the resultant force is zero, the only effect of a couple is to produce a rotation or tendency of rotation in a specified direction.

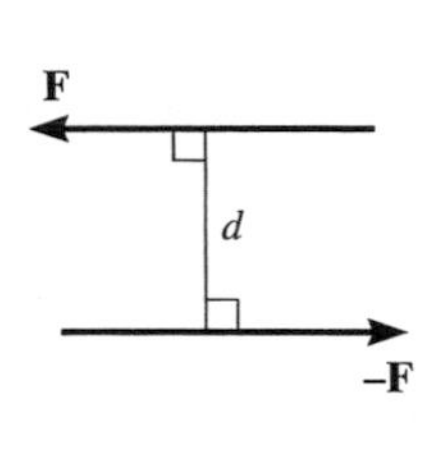

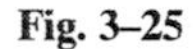
Fig. 3–25

The moment produced by a couple is called a *couple moment*. We can determine its value by finding the sum of the moments of both couple forces about *any* arbitrary point. For example, in Fig. 3–26, position vectors $\mathbf{r}_A$ and $\mathbf{r}_B$ are directed from point O to points A and B lying on the line of action of $-\mathbf{F}$ and $\mathbf{F}$. The couple moment computed about O is therefore

$$\mathbf{M} = \mathbf{r}_A \times (-\mathbf{F}) + \mathbf{r}_B \times \mathbf{F}$$

Rather than sum the moments of both forces to determine the couple moment, it is simpler to take moments about a point lying on the line of action of one of the forces. If point A is chosen, then the moment of $-\mathbf{F}$ about A is zero, and we have

$$\mathbf{M} = \mathbf{r} \times \mathbf{F} \tag{3–13}$$

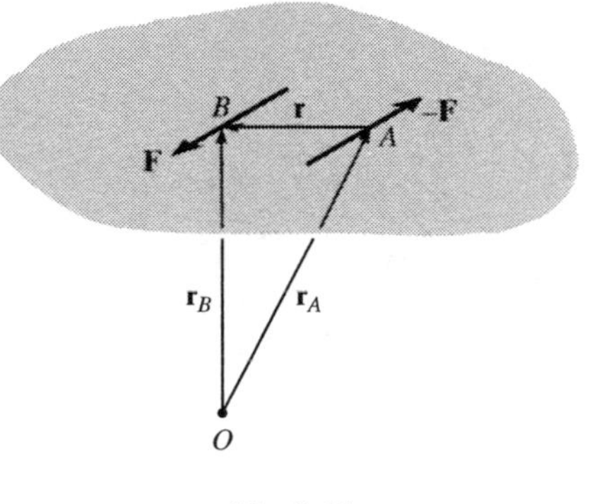

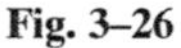
Fig. 3–26

The fact that we obtain the *same result* in both cases can be demonstrated by noting that in the first case we can write $\mathbf{M} = (\mathbf{r}_B - \mathbf{r}_A) \times \mathbf{F}$; and by the triangle rule of vector addition, $\mathbf{r}_A + \mathbf{r} = \mathbf{r}_B$ or $\mathbf{r} = \mathbf{r}_B - \mathbf{r}_A$, so that upon substitution we obtain Eq. 3–13. This result indicates that a couple moment is a *free vector*, i.e., it can act at *any point* since $\mathbf{M}$ depends *only* upon the position vector $\mathbf{r}$ directed *between* the forces and *not* the position vectors $\mathbf{r}_A$ and $\mathbf{r}_B$, directed from the arbitrary point O to the forces. This concept is therefore unlike the moment of a force, which requires a definite point (or axis) about which moments are determined.

Scalar Formulation. The moment of a couple, $\mathbf{M}$, Fig. 3–27, is defined as having a *magnitude* of

$$M = Fd \tag{3–14}$$

where F is the magnitude of one of the forces and d is the perpendicular distance or moment arm between the forces. The *direction* and sense of the couple moment are determined by the right-hand rule, where the thumb indicates the direction when the fingers are curled with the sense of rotation caused by the two forces. In all cases, $\mathbf{M}$ acts perpendicular to the plane containing these forces.

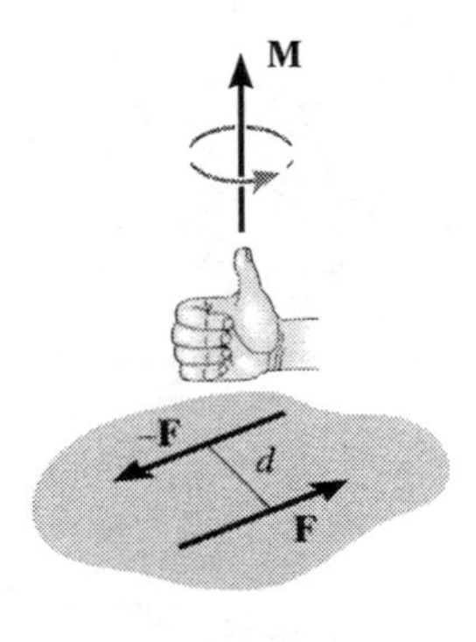

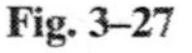
Fig. 3–27

Vector Formulation. The moment of a couple can also be expressed by the vector cross product using Eq. 3–13, i.e.,

$$\mathbf{M} = \mathbf{r} \times \mathbf{F} \tag{3–15}$$

Application of this equation is easily remembered if one thinks of taking the moments of both forces about a point lying on the line of action of one of the forces. For example, if moments are taken about point A in Fig. 3–26, the moment of $-\mathbf{F}$ is *zero* about this point, and the moment or **F** is defined from Eq. 3–15. Therefore, in the formulation **r** is crossed with the force **F** to which it is directed.

Equivalent Couples. Two couples are said to be equivalent if they produce the same moment. Since the moment produced by a couple is always perpendicular to the plane containing the couple forces, it is therefore necessary that the forces of equal couples lie either in the same plane or in planes that are *parallel* to one another. In this way, the direction of each couple moment will be the same, that is, perpendicular to the parallel planes.

Resultant Couple Moment. Since couple moments are free vectors, they may be applied at any point P on a body and added vectorially. For example, the two couples acting on different planes of the body in Fig. 3–28*a* may be replaced by their corresponding couple moments $\mathbf{M}_1$ and $\mathbf{M}_2$, Fig. 3–28*b*, and then these free vectors may be moved to the *arbitrary point P* and added to obtain the resultant couple moment $\mathbf{M}_R = \mathbf{M}_1 + \mathbf{M}_2$, shown in Fig. 3–28*c*.

If more than two couple moments act on the body, we may generalize this concept and write the vector resultant as

$$\mathbf{M}_R = \Sigma(\mathbf{r} \times \mathbf{F}) \qquad (3\text{–}16)$$

These concepts are illustrated numerically in the examples which follow. In general, problems projected in two dimensions should be solved using a scalar analysis since the moment arms and force components are easy to compute.

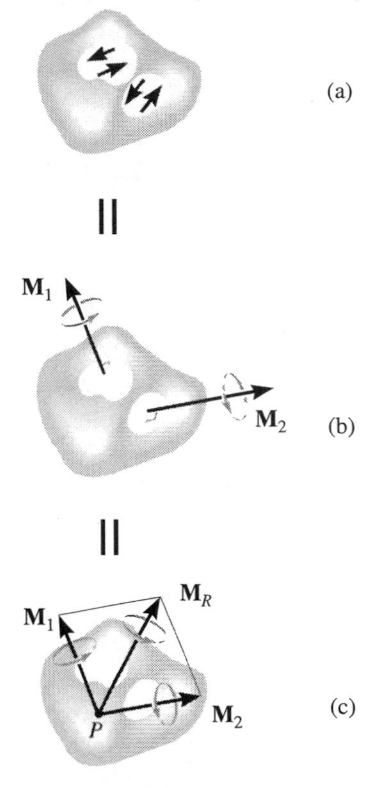

Fig. 3–28

The frictional forces of the floor on the blades of the concrete finishing machine create a couple moment $\mathbf{M}_c$ on the machine that tends to turn it. An equal but opposite couple moment must be applied by the hands of the operator to prevent the turning. Here the couple moment, $M_c = Fd$, is applied on the handle, although it could be applied at any other point on the machine.

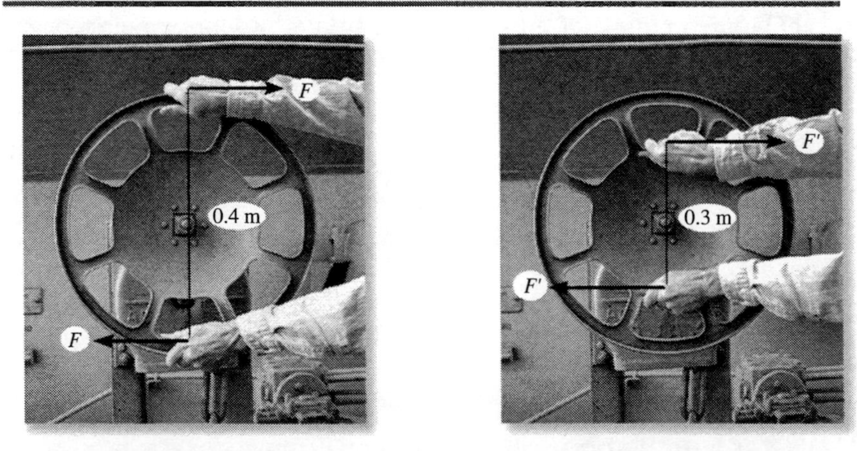

A moment of 12 N · m is needed to turn the shaft connected to the center of the wheel. To do this it is efficient to apply a couple since this effect produces a pure rotation. The couple forces can be made as small as possible by placing the hands on the *rim* of the wheel, where the spacing is 0.4 m. In this case $12\ \text{N}\cdot\text{m} = F(0.4\ \text{m})$, $F = 30$ N. An equivalent couple moment of 12 N · m can be produced if one grips the wheel within the inner hub, although here much larger forces are needed. If the distance between the hands becomes 0.3 m, then $12\ \text{N}\cdot\text{m} = F'(0.3)$, $F' = 40$ N. Also, realize that if the wheel was connected to the shaft at a point other than at its center, the wheel would still turn when the forces are applied since the 12-N · m couple moment is a *free vector*.

IMPORTANT POINTS

- A couple moment is produced by two noncollinear forces that are equal but opposite. Its effect is to produce pure rotation, or tendency for rotation in a specified direction.
- A couple moment is a free vector, and as a result it causes the same effect of rotation on a body regardless of where the couple moment is applied to the body.
- The moment of the two couple forces can be computed about *any point*. For convenience, this point is often chosen on the line of action of one of the forces in order to eliminate the moment of this force about the point.
- In three dimensions the couple moment is often determined using the vector formulation, $\mathbf{M} = \mathbf{r} \times \mathbf{F}$, where $\mathbf{r}$ is directed from *any point* on the line of action of one of the forces to *any point* on the line of action of the other force $\mathbf{F}$.
- A resultant couple moment is simply the vector sum of all the couple moments of the system.

EXAMPLE 3.10

A couple acts on the gear teeth as shown in Fig. 3–29*a*. Replace it by an equivalent couple having a pair of forces that act through points *A* and *B*.

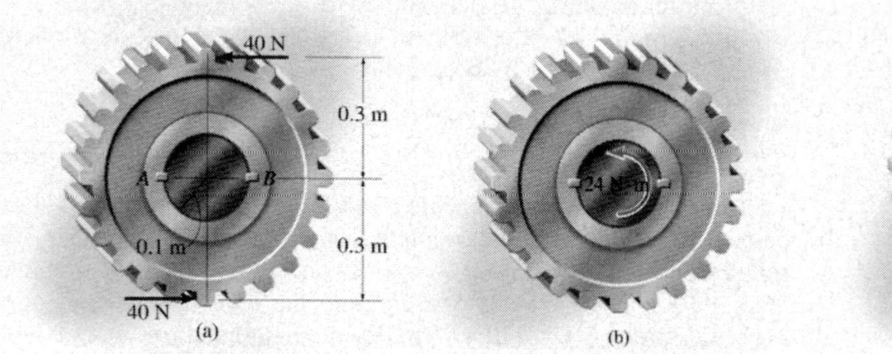

Fig. 3–29

Solution *(Scalar Analysis)*

The couple has a magnitude of $M = Fd = 40(0.6) = 24\ \text{N}\cdot\text{m}$ and a direction that is out of the page since the forces tend to rotate counterclockwise. **M** is a free vector, and so it can be placed at any point on the gear, Fig. 3–29*b*. To preserve the counterclockwise rotation of **M**, *vertical* forces acting through points *A* and *B* must be directed as shown in Fig. 3–29*c*. The magnitude of each force is

$$M = Fd \qquad 24\ \text{N}\cdot\text{m} = F(0.2\ \text{m})$$

$$F = 120\ \text{N} \qquad\qquad \textit{Ans.}$$

EXAMPLE 3.11

Determine the moment of the couple acting on the member shown in Fig. 3–30*a*.

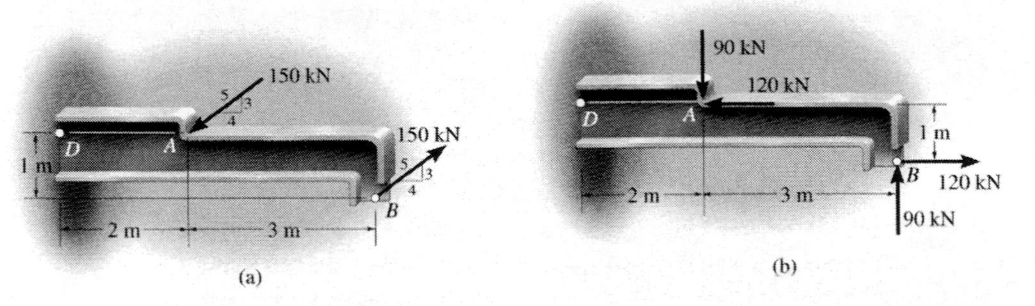

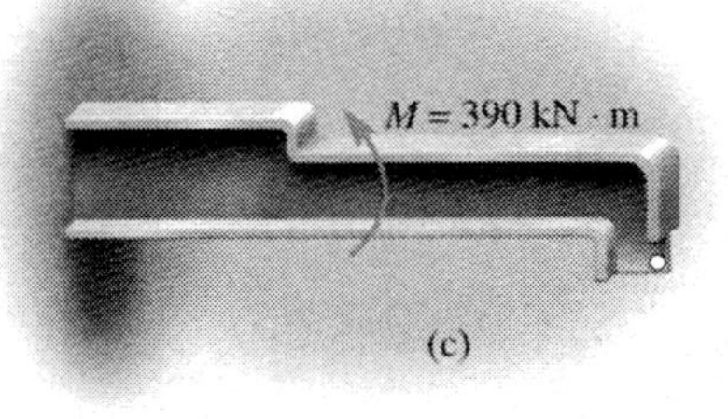

Fig. 3–30

Solution (*Scalar Analysis*)

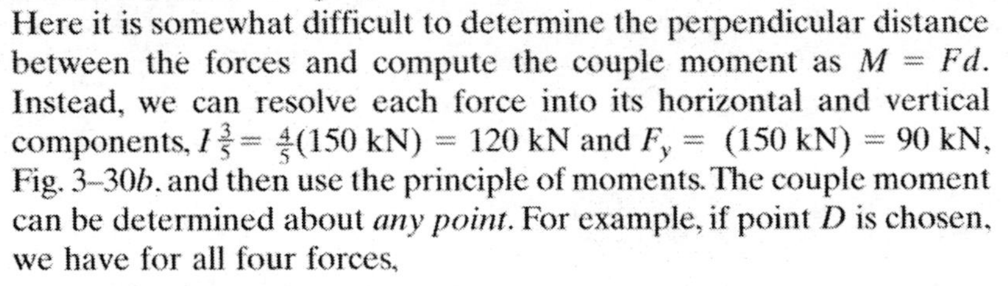

Here it is somewhat difficult to determine the perpendicular distance between the forces and compute the couple moment as $M = Fd$. Instead, we can resolve each force into its horizontal and vertical components, $I\frac{3}{5} = \frac{4}{5}(150\text{ kN}) = 120\text{ kN}$ and $F_y = (150\text{ kN}) = 90\text{ kN}$, Fig. 3–30*b*, and then use the principle of moments. The couple moment can be determined about *any point*. For example, if point D is chosen, we have for all four forces,

$$\circlearrowleft + M = 120\text{ kN }(0\text{ m}) - 90\text{ kN }(2\text{ m}) + 90\text{ kN }(5\text{ m}) + 120\text{ kN }(1\text{ m})$$

$$= 390\text{ kN}\cdot\text{m} \circlearrowleft \qquad \textit{Ans.}$$

It is easier, however, to determine the moments about point A or B in order to *eliminate* the moment of the forces acting at the moment point. For point A, Fig. 3-30*b*, we have

$$\circlearrowleft + M = 90\text{ kN }(3\text{ m}) + 120\text{ kN }(1\text{ m})$$

$$= 390\text{ kN}\cdot\text{m} \circlearrowleft \qquad \textit{Ans.}$$

Show that one obtains this same result if moments are summed about point B. Notice also that the couple in Fig. 3–30*a* can be replaced by *two* couples in Fig. 3–30*b*. Using $M = Fd$, one couple has a moment of $M_1 = 90\text{ kN }(3\text{ m}) = 270\text{ kN}\cdot\text{m}$ and the other has a moment of $M_2 = 120\text{ kN }(1\text{ m}) = 120\text{ kN}\cdot\text{m}$. By the right-hand rule, both couple moments are counterclockwise and are therefore directed out of the page. Since these couples are free vectors, they can be moved to any point and added, which yields $M = 270\text{ kN}\cdot\text{m} + 120\text{ kN}\cdot\text{m} = 390\text{ kN}\cdot\text{m} \circlearrowleft$, the same result determined above. **M** is a free vector and can therefore act at any point on the member, Fig. 3–30*c*. Also, realize that the external effect, such as the support reactions on the member, will be the *same* if the member supports the couple, Fig. 3–30*a*, or the couple moment, Fig. 3–30*c*.

EXAMPLE 3.12

Determine the couple moment acting on the pipe shown in Fig. 3–31*a*. Segment *AB* is directed 30° below the *x-y* plane.

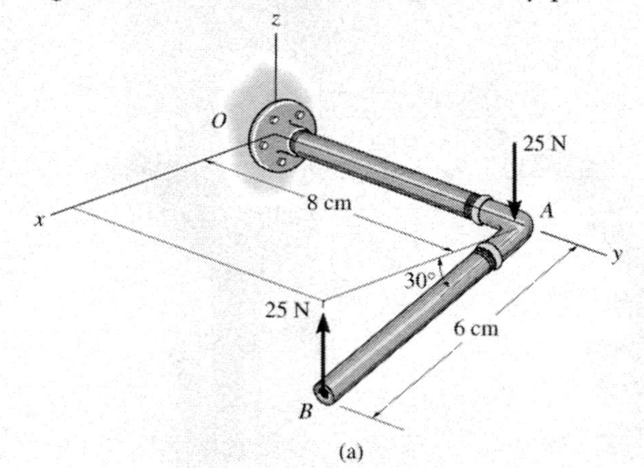

(a)

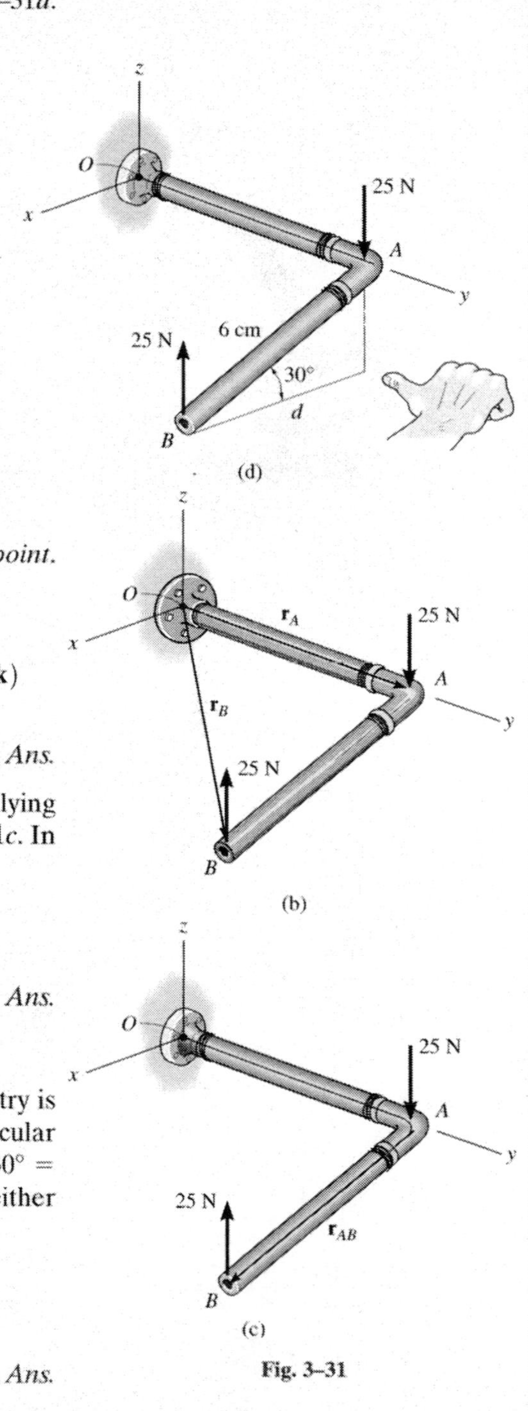

Fig. 3–31

Solution I *(Vector Analysis)*

The moment of the two couple forces can be found about *any point*. If point *O* is considered, Fig. 3–31*b*, we have

$$\begin{aligned}\mathbf{M} &= \mathbf{r}_A \times (-25\mathbf{k}) + \mathbf{r}_B \times (25\mathbf{k})\\ &= (8\mathbf{j}) \times (-25\mathbf{k}) + (6\cos 30°\mathbf{i} + 8\mathbf{j} - 6\sin 30°\mathbf{k}) \times (25\mathbf{k})\\ &= -200\mathbf{i} - 129.9\mathbf{j} + 200\mathbf{i}\\ &= \{-130\mathbf{j}\}\ \text{N}\cdot\text{cm}\end{aligned}$$ *Ans.*

It is *easier* to take moments of the couple forces about a point lying on the line of action of one of the forces, e.g., point *A*, Fig. 3–31*c*. In this case the moment of the force *A* is zero, so that

$$\begin{aligned}\mathbf{M} &= \mathbf{r}_{AB} \times (25\mathbf{k})\\ &= (6\cos 30°\mathbf{i} - 6\sin 30°\mathbf{k}) \times (25\mathbf{k})\\ &= \{-130\mathbf{j}\}\ \text{N}\cdot\text{cm}\end{aligned}$$ *Ans.*

Solution II *(Scalar Analysis)*

Although this problem is shown in three dimensions, the geometry is simple enough to use the scalar equation $M = Fd$. The perpendicular distance between the lines of action of the forces is $d = 6\cos 30° = 5.20$ cm, Fig. 3–31*d*. Hence, taking moments of the forces about either point *A* or *B* yields

$$M = Fd = 25\ \text{N}\ (5.20\ \text{cm}) = 129.9\ \text{N}\cdot\text{cm}$$

Applying the right-hand rule, **M** acts in the $-\mathbf{j}$ direction. Thus,

$$\mathbf{M} = \{-130\mathbf{j}\}\ \text{N}\cdot\text{cm}$$ *Ans.*

EXAMPLE 3.13

Replace the two couples acting on the pipe column in Fig. 3–32*a* by a resultant couple moment.

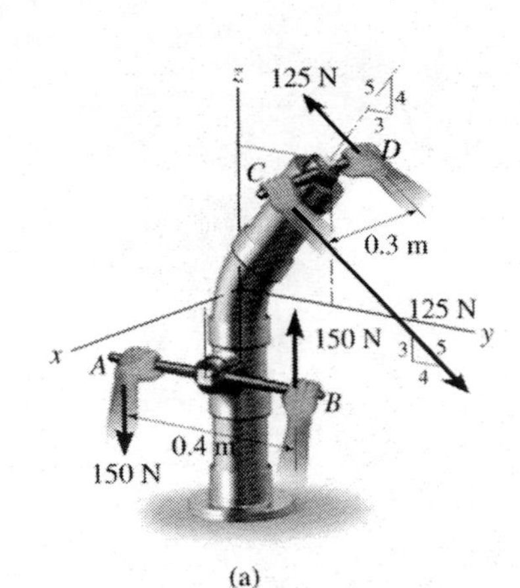

(a)

(b)

(c)

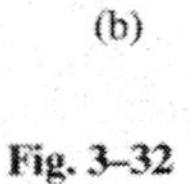

Fig. 3–32

Solution *(Vector Analysis)*

The couple moment $\mathbf{M}_1$, developed by the forces at A and B, can easily be determined from a scalar formulation.

$$M_1 = Fd = 150\text{ N}(0.4\text{ m}) = 60\text{ N}\cdot\text{m}$$

By the right-hand rule, $\mathbf{M}_1$ acts in the $+\mathbf{i}$ direction, Fig. 3–32*b*. Hence,

$$\mathbf{M}_1 = \{60\mathbf{i}\}\text{ N}\cdot\text{m}$$

Vector analysis will be used to determine $\mathbf{M}_2$, caused by forces at C and D. If moments are computed about point D, Fig. 3–32*a*, $\mathbf{M}_2 = \mathbf{r}_{DC} \times \mathbf{F}_C$, then

$$\begin{aligned}\mathbf{M}_2 &= \mathbf{r}_{DC} \times \mathbf{F}_C = (0.3\mathbf{i}) \times [125(\tfrac{4}{5})\mathbf{j} - 125(\tfrac{3}{5})\mathbf{k}] \\ &= (0.3\mathbf{i}) \times [100\mathbf{j} - 75\mathbf{k}] = 30(\mathbf{i} \times \mathbf{j}) - 22.5(\mathbf{i} \times \mathbf{k}) \\ &= \{22.5\mathbf{j} + 30\mathbf{k}\}\text{ N}\cdot\text{m}\end{aligned}$$

Try to establish $\mathbf{M}_2$ by using a scalar formulation, Fig. 3–32*b*.

Since $\mathbf{M}_1$ and $\mathbf{M}_2$ are free vectors, they may be moved to some arbitrary point P and added vectorially, Fig. 3–32*c*. The resultant couple moment becomes

$$\mathbf{M}_R = \mathbf{M}_1 + \mathbf{M}_2 = \{60\mathbf{i} + 22.5\mathbf{j} + 30\mathbf{k}\}\text{ N}\cdot\text{m} \qquad \textit{Ans.}$$

PROBLEMS

3-55. Determine the magnitude and sense of the couple moment.

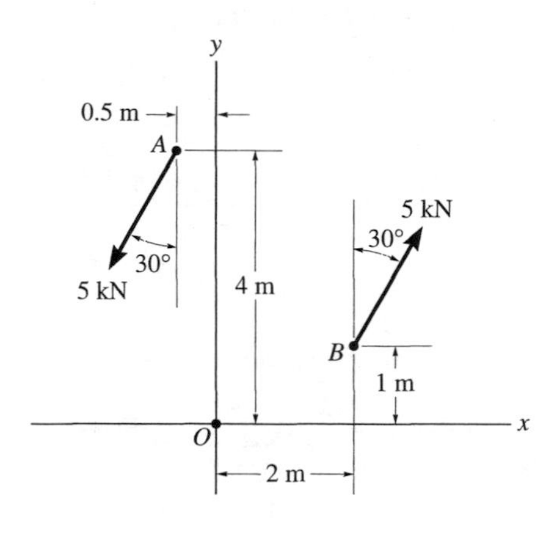

Prob. 3–55

3-57. Determine the magnitude and sense of the couple moment. Each force has a magnitude of $F = 8$ kN.

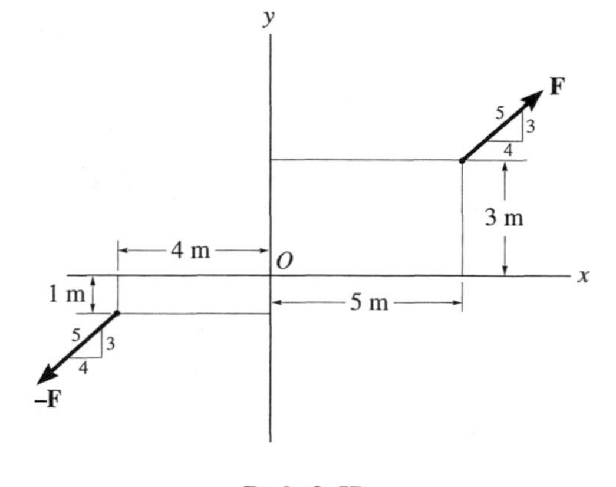

Prob. 3–57

3-56. If the couple moment has a magnitude of 220 N · m, determine the magnitude F of the couple forces.

***3-58.** If the couple moment has a magnitude of 300 N · m, determine the magnitude F of the couple forces.

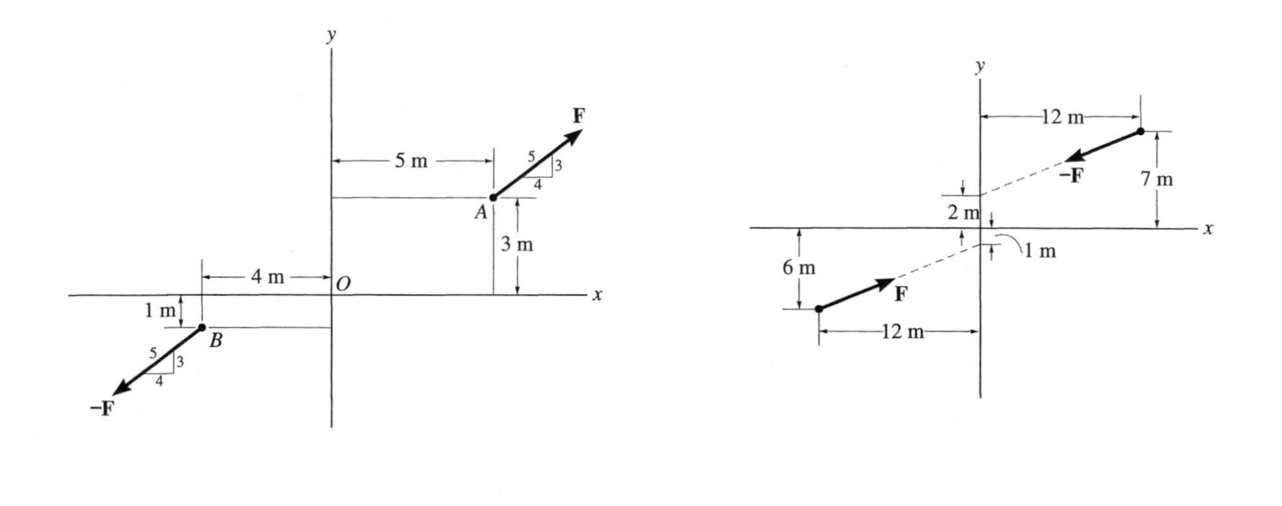

Prob. 3–56

Prob. 3–58

3-59. A twist of 4 N·m is applied to the handle of the screwdriver. Resolve this couple moment into a pair of couple forces **F** exerted on the handle and **P** exerted on the blade.

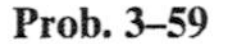

Prob. 3–59

3-60. The resultant couple moment created by the two couples acting on the disk is $\mathbf{M_R} = \{10\mathbf{k}\}$ kN · cm. Determine the magnitude of force **T**.

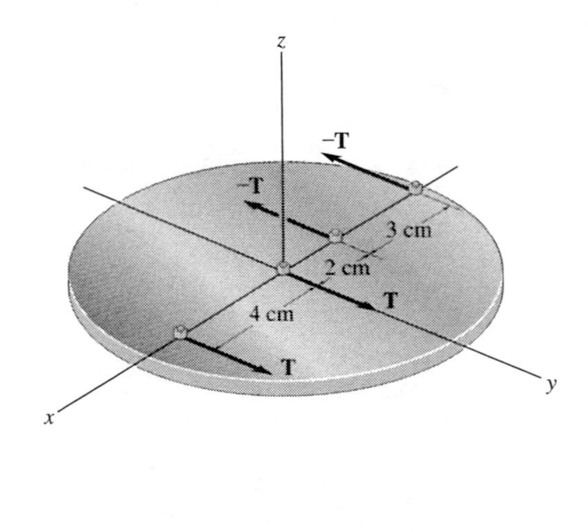

Prob. 3–60

3-61. A device called a rolamite is used in various ways to replace slipping motion with rolling motion. If the belt, which wraps between the rollers, is subjected to a tension of 15 N, determine the reactive forces N of the top and bottom plates on the rollers so that the resultant couple acting on the rollers is equal to zero.

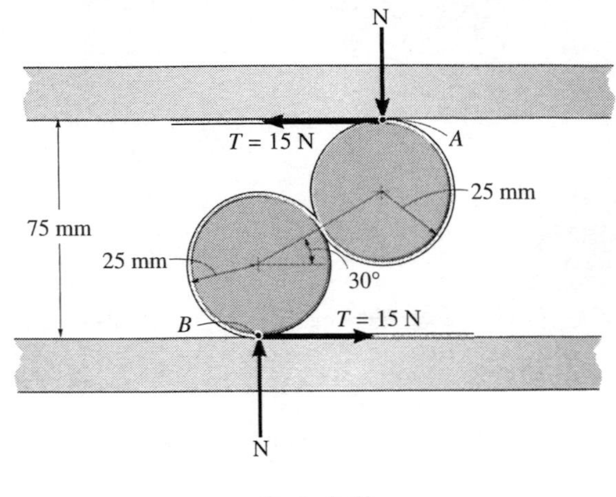

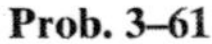

Prob. 3–61

***3-62.** The caster wheel is subjected to the two couples. Determine the forces **F** that the bearings create on the shaft so that the resultant couple moment on the caster is zero.

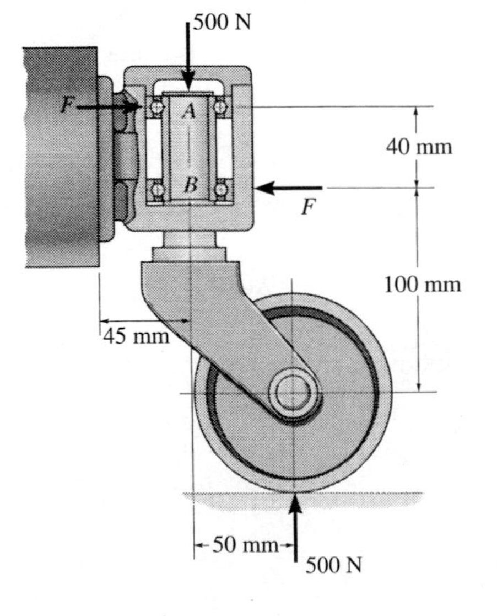

Prob. 3–62

3-63. Two couples act on the beam as shown. Determine the magnitude of **F** so that the resultant couple moment is 100 N · m counterclockwise. Where on the beam does the resultant couple act?

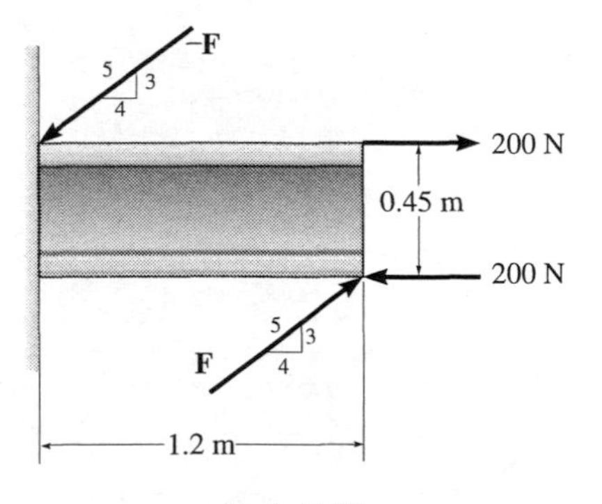

Prob. 3–63

3-64. Two couples act on the frame. If the resultant couple moment is to be zero, determine the distance d between the 80-N couple forces.

***3-65.** Two couples act on the frame. If $d = 0.4$ m, determine the resultant couple moment. Compute the result by resolving each force into x and y components and (a) finding the moment of each couple (Eq. 3–13) and (b) summing the moments of all the force components about point A.

3-66. Two couples act on the frame. If $d = 0.4$ m, determine the resultant couple moment. Compute the result by resolving each force into x and y components and (a) finding the moment of each couple (Eq. 3–13) and (b) summing the moments of all the force components about point B.

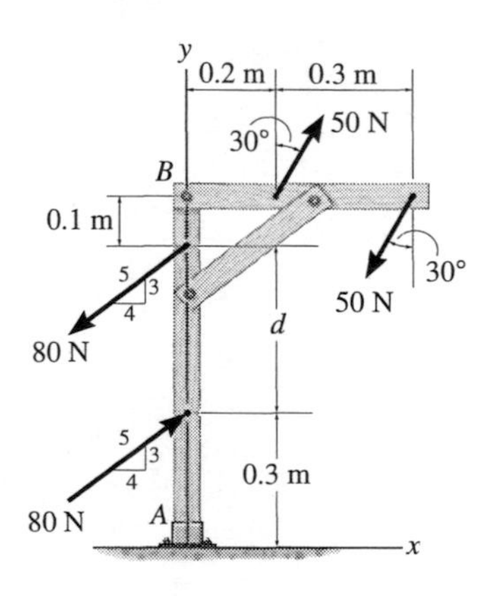

Probs. 3–64/65/66

3-67. Determine the couple moment. Express the result as a Cartesian vector.

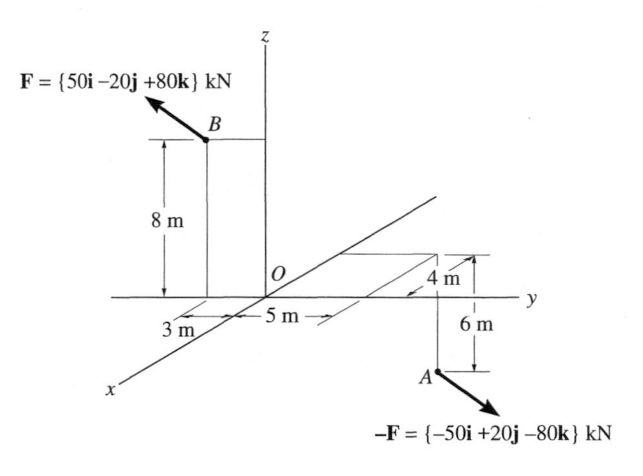

Prob. 3–67

3-68. Determine the couple moment. Express the result as a Cartesian vector. Each force has a magnitude of $F = 120$ kN.

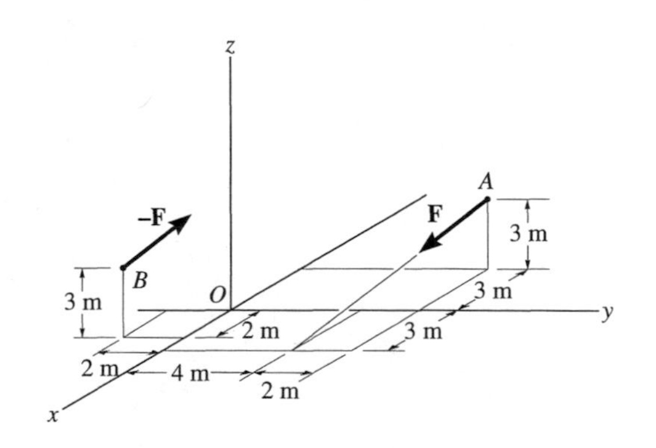

Prob. 3–68

3-69. The gear reducer is subject to the couple moments shown. Determine the resultant couple moment and specify its magnitude and coordinate direction angles.

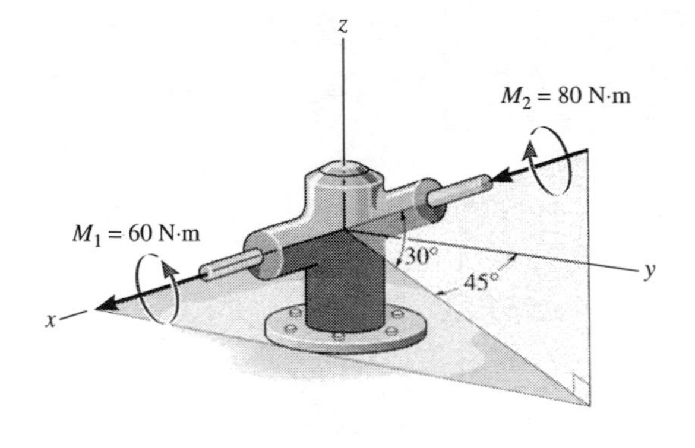

Prob. 3–69

3-70. The meshed gears are subjected to the couple moments shown. Determine the magnitude of the resultant couple moment and specify its coordinate direction angles.

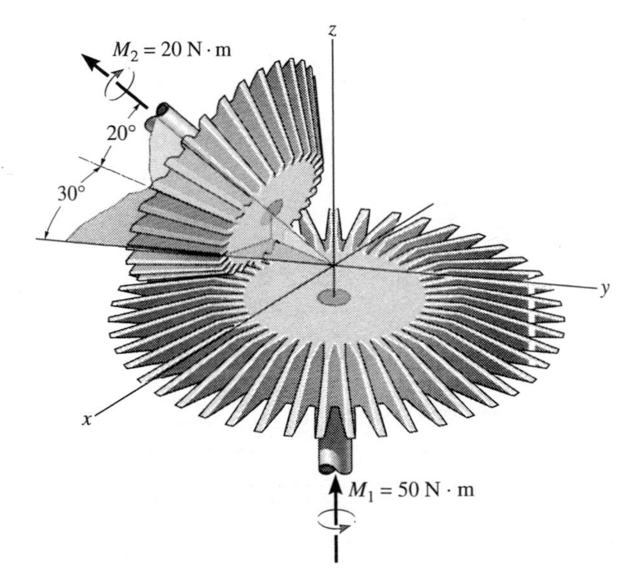

Prob. 3–70

3-71. A couple acts on each of the handles of the minidual valve. Determine the magnitude and coordinate direction angles of the resultant couple moment.

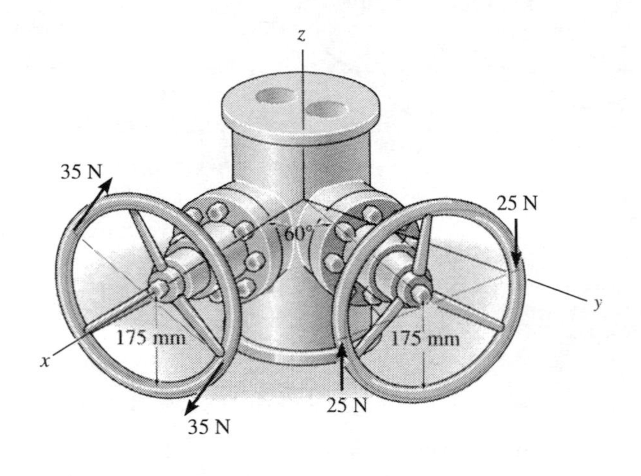

Prob. 3–71

***3-72.** Determine the resultant couple moment of the two couples that act on the pipe assembly. The distance from A to B is $d = 400$ mm. Express the result as a Cartesian vector.

3-73. Determine the distance d between A and B so that the resultant couple moment has a magnitude of $M_R = 20$ N · m.

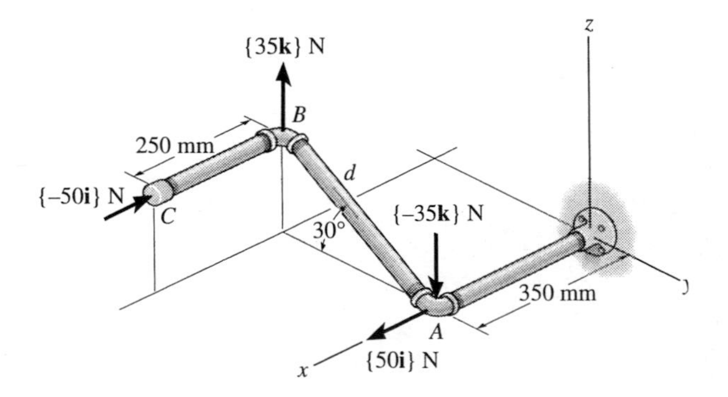

Probs. 3–72/73

CHAPTER

4 Equilibrium of a Rigid Body

CHAPTER OBJECTIVES

- To develop the equations of equilibrium for a rigid body.
- To introduce the concept of the free-body diagram for a rigid body.
- To show how to solve rigid body equilibrium problems using the equations of equilibrium.
- To develop the concepts of static and kinetic friction with applications to equilibrium problems

4.1 Conditions for Rigid-Body Equilibrium

In this section we will develop both the necessary and sufficient conditions required for equilibrium of a rigid body. To do this, consider the rigid body in Fig. 4–1*a*, which is fixed in the *x, y, z* reference and is either at rest or moves with the reference at constant velocity. A free-body diagram of the arbitrary *i*th particle of the body is shown in Fig. 4–1*b*. There are two types of forces which act on it. The resultant *internal force*, $\mathbf{f}_i$, is caused by interactions with adjacent particles. The resultant *external force* $\mathbf{F}_i$ represents, for example, the effects of gravitational, electrical, magnetic, or contact forces between the *i*th particle and adjacent bodies or particles *not* included within the body. If the particle is in equilibrium, then applying Newton's first law we have

$$\mathbf{F}_i + \mathbf{f}_i = 0$$

When the equation of equilibrium is applied to each of the other particles of the body, similar equations will result. If all these equations are added together *vectorially*, we obtain

$$\Sigma\mathbf{F}_i + \Sigma\mathbf{f}_i = 0$$

The summation of the internal forces will equal zero since the internal forces between particles within the body will occur in equal

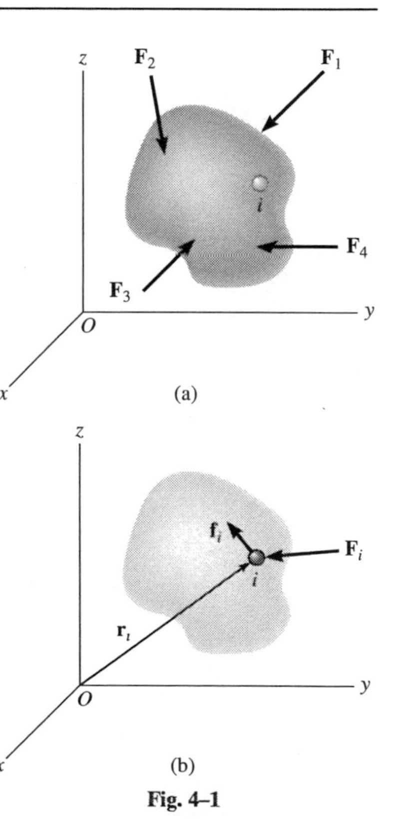

Fig. 4–1

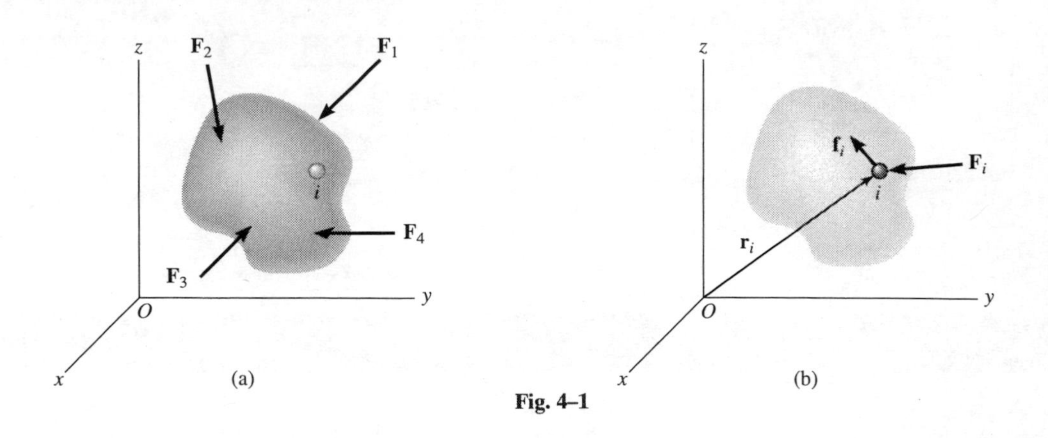

Fig. 4–1

but opposite collinear pairs, Newton's third law. Consequently, only the sum of the *external forces* will remain; and therefore, letting $\Sigma \mathbf{F}_i = \Sigma \mathbf{F}$, the above equation can be written as

$$\Sigma \mathbf{F} = \mathbf{0}$$

Let us now consider the moments of the forces acting on the ith particle about the arbitrary point O, Fig. 4–1*b*. Using the above particle equilibrium equation and the distributive law of the vector cross product we have

$$\mathbf{r}_i \times (\mathbf{F}_i + \mathbf{f}_i) = \mathbf{r}_i \times \mathbf{F}_i + \mathbf{r}_i \times \mathbf{f}_i = \mathbf{0}$$

Similar equations can be written for the other particles of the body, and adding them together vectorially, we obtain

$$\Sigma \mathbf{r}_i \times \mathbf{F}_i + \Sigma \mathbf{r}_i \times \mathbf{f}_i = \mathbf{0}$$

The second term is zero since, as stated above, the internal forces occur in equal but opposite collinear pairs, and therefore the resultant moment of each pair of forces about point O is zero. Hence, using the notation $\Sigma \mathbf{M}_O = \Sigma \mathbf{r}_i = \mathbf{F}_i$, we have

$$\Sigma \mathbf{M}_O = \mathbf{0}$$

Hence the two *equations of equilibrium* for a rigid body can be summarized as follows:

$$\Sigma \mathbf{F} = \mathbf{0}$$
$$\Sigma \mathbf{M}_O = \mathbf{0} \qquad (4\text{–}1)$$

These equations require that a rigid body will remain in equilibrium provided the sum of all the *external forces* acting on the body is equal to zero and the sum of the moments of the external forces about a point is equal to zero. The fact that these conditions are *necessary* for equilibrium has now been proven. They are also *sufficient* for maintaining equilibrium. To show this, let us assume that the body is in equilibrium and the force system acting on the body satisfies Eqs. 4–1. Suppose that an *additional force* $\mathbf{F}'$ is applied to the body. As a result, the equilibrium equations become

$$\Sigma\mathbf{F} + \mathbf{F}' = \mathbf{0}$$
$$\Sigma\mathbf{M}_O + \mathbf{M}'_O = \mathbf{0}$$

where $\mathbf{M}'_O$ is the moment of F' about O. Since $\Sigma\mathbf{F} = 0$ and $\Sigma\mathbf{M}_O = 0$, then we require $\mathbf{F}' = 0$ (also $\mathbf{M}'_O = \mathbf{0}$). Consequently, the additional force $\mathbf{F}'$ is not required, and indeed Eqs. 4–1 are also sufficient conditions for maintaining equilibrium.

Many types of engineering problems involve symmetric loadings and can be solved by projecting all the forces acting on a body onto a single plane. Hence, in the next section, the equilibrium of a body subjected to a *coplanar* or *two-dimensional force system* will be considered. Ordinarily the geometry of such problems is not very complex, so a scalar solution is suitable for analysis. The more general discussion of rigid bodies subjected to *three-dimensional force systems* is given in the latter part of this chapter. It will be seen that many of these types of problems can best be solved by using vector analysis.

Equilibrium in Two Dimensions

4.2 Free-Body Diagrams

Successful application of the equations of equilibrium requires a complete specification of *all* the known and unknown external forces that act *on* the body. The best way to account for these forces is to draw the body's free-body diagram. This diagram is a sketch of the outlined shape of the body, which represents it as being *isolated* or "free" from its surroundings, i.e., a "free body." On this sketch it is necessary to show *all* the forces and couple moments that the surroundings exert *on the body* so that these effects can be accounted for when the equations of equilibrium are applied. For this reason, *a thorough understanding of how to draw a free-body diagram is of primary importance for solving problems in mechanics.*

TABLE 4–1 • Supports for Rigid Bodies Subjected to Two-Dimensional Force Systems

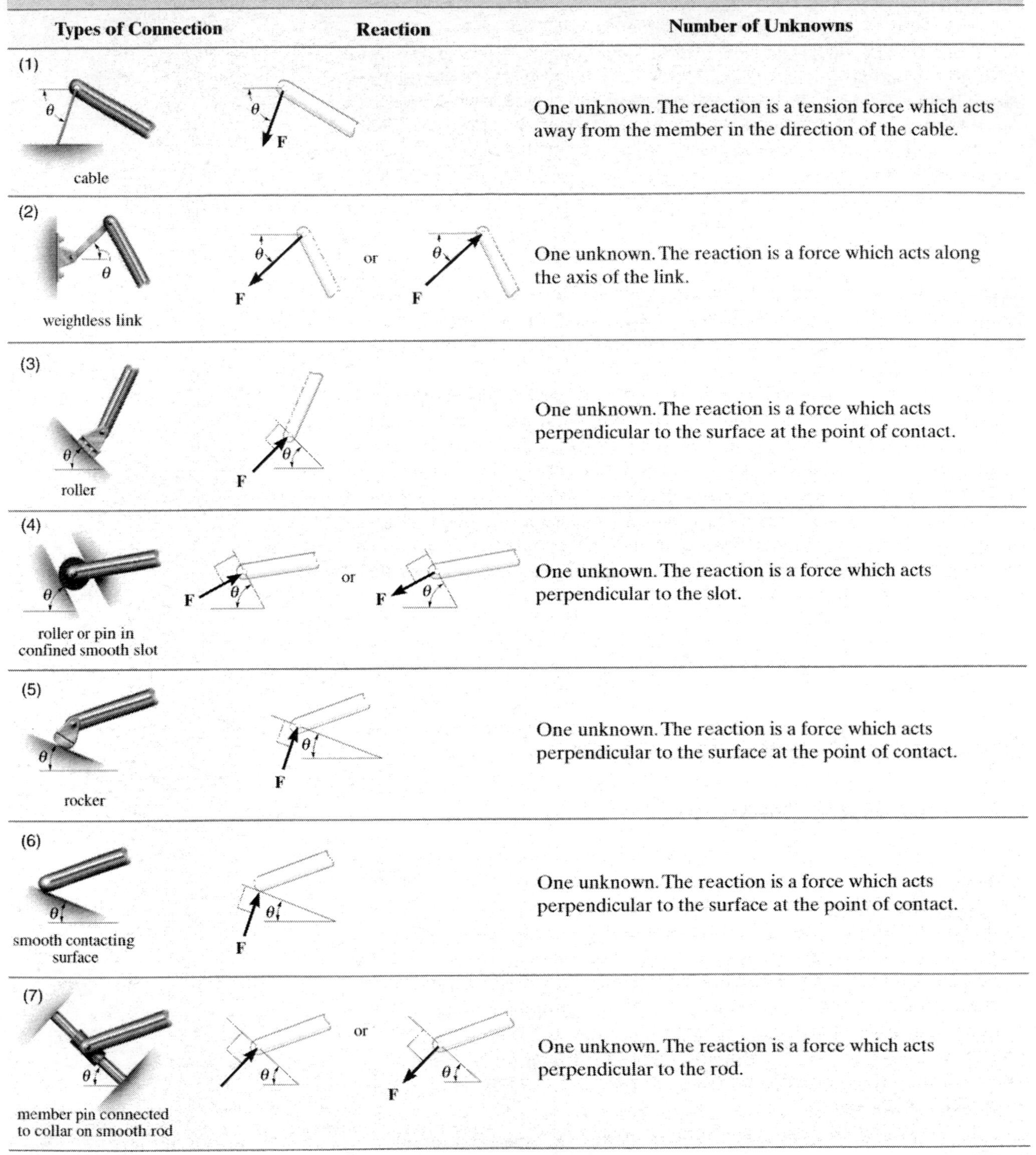

Types of Connection	Reaction	Number of Unknowns
(1) cable	θ, **F**	One unknown. The reaction is a tension force which acts away from the member in the direction of the cable.
(2) weightless link	θ, **F** or θ, **F**	One unknown. The reaction is a force which acts along the axis of the link.
(3) roller	θ, **F**	One unknown. The reaction is a force which acts perpendicular to the surface at the point of contact.
(4) roller or pin in confined smooth slot	**F**, θ or **F**, θ	One unknown. The reaction is a force which acts perpendicular to the slot.
(5) rocker	θ, **F**	One unknown. The reaction is a force which acts perpendicular to the surface at the point of contact.
(6) smooth contacting surface	θ, **F**	One unknown. The reaction is a force which acts perpendicular to the surface at the point of contact.
(7) member pin connected to collar on smooth rod	θ or θ, **F**	One unknown. The reaction is a force which acts perpendicular to the rod.

continued

TABLE 4–1 • Continued

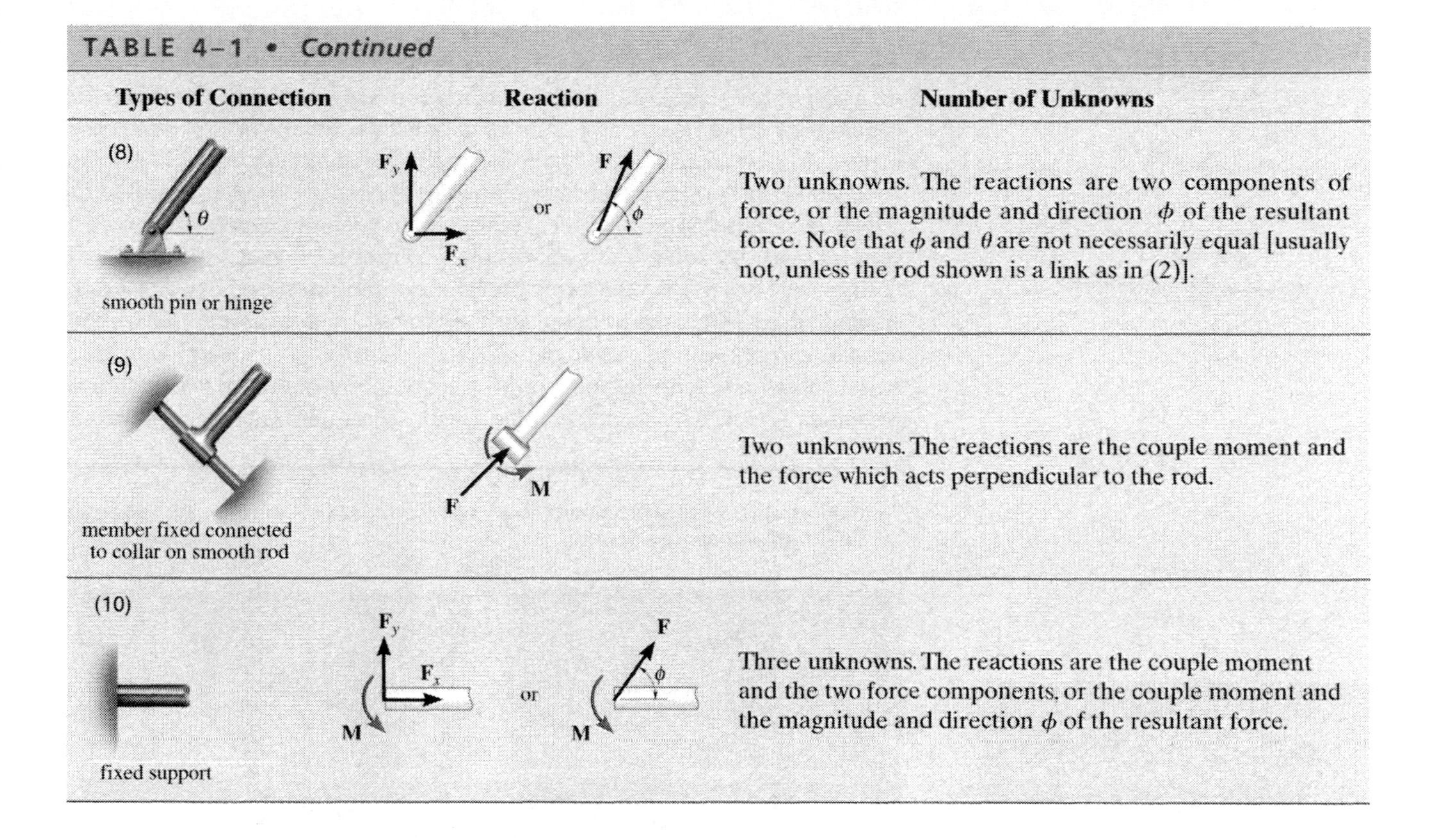

Types of Connection	Reaction	Number of Unknowns
(8) smooth pin or hinge	F_y, F_x or F, ϕ	Two unknowns. The reactions are two components of force, or the magnitude and direction ϕ of the resultant force. Note that ϕ and θ are not necessarily equal [usually not, unless the rod shown is a link as in (2)].
(9) member fixed connected to collar on smooth rod	F, M	Two unknowns. The reactions are the couple moment and the force which acts perpendicular to the rod.
(10) fixed support	F_y, F_x, M or F, ϕ, M	Three unknowns. The reactions are the couple moment and the two force components, or the couple moment and the magnitude and direction ϕ of the resultant force.

Support Reactions. Before presenting a formal procedure as to how to draw a free-body diagram, we will first consider the various types of reactions that occur at supports and points of support between bodies subjected to coplanar force systems. *As a general rule, if a support prevents the translation of a body in a given direction, then a force is developed on the body in that direction. Likewise, if rotation is prevented, a couple moment is exerted on the body.*

For example, let us consider three ways in which a horizontal member, such as a beam, is supported at its end. One method consists of a *roller* or cylinder, Fig. 4–2*a*. Since this support only prevents the beam from *translating* in the vertical direction, the roller can only exert a *force* on the beam in this direction, Fig. 4–2*b*.

The beam can be supported in a more restrictive manner by using a *pin* as shown in Fig. 4–3*a*. The pin passes through a hole in the beam and two leaves which are fixed to the ground. Here the pin can prevent *translation* of the beam in *any direction* ϕ, Fig. 4–3*b*, and so the pin must exert a *force* **F** on the beam in this direction. For purposes of analysis, it is generally easier to represent this resultant force **F** by its two components $\mathbf{F}_x$ and $\mathbf{F}_y$, Fig. 4–3*c*. If F_x and F_y are known, then F and ϕ can be calculated.

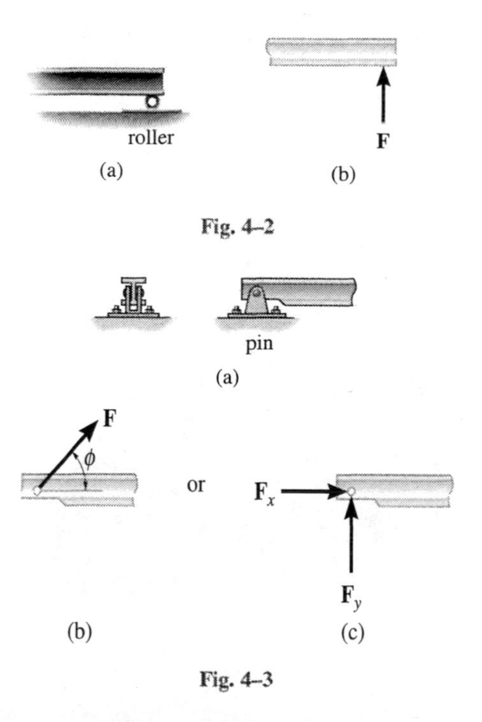

Fig. 4–2

Fig. 4–3

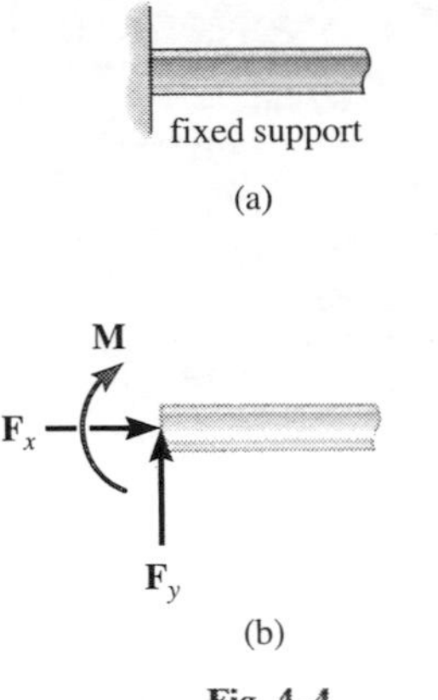

Fig. 4–4

The most restrictive way to support the beam would be to use a *fixed support* as shown in Fig. 4–4*a*. This support will prevent both *translation and rotation* of the beam, and so to do this a *force and couple moment* must be developed on the beam at its point of connection, Fig. 4–4*b*. As in the case of the pin, the force is usually represented by its components $\mathbf{F}_x$ and $\mathbf{F}_y$.

Table 4–1 lists other common types of supports for bodies subjected to coplanar force systems. (In all cases the angle θ is assumed to be known.) Carefully study each of the symbols used to represent these supports and the types of reactions they exert on their contacting members. Although concentrated forces and couple moments are shown in this table, they actually represent the *resultants* of small *distributed surface loads* that exist between each support and its contacting member. It is these *resultants* which will be determined from the equations of equilibrium.

Typical examples of actual supports that are referenced to Table 4–1 are shown in the following sequence of photos.

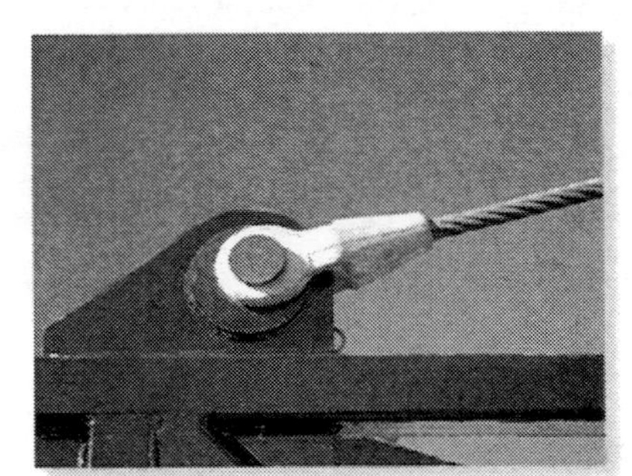

The cable exerts a force on the bracket in the direction of the cable. (1)

The rocker support for this bridge girder allows horizontal movement so the bridge is free to expand and contract due to temperature. (5)

This concrete girder rests on the ledge that is assumed to act as a smooth contacting surface. (6)

This utility building is pin supported at the top of the column. (8)

The floor beams of this building are welded together and thus form fixed connections. (10)

Springs. If a *linear elastic spring* is used for support, the length of the spring will change in direct proportion to the force acting on it. A characteristic that defines the "elasticity" of a spring is the *spring constant* or *stiffness* k. The magnitude of force exerted on a linear elastic spring which has a stiffness k and is deformed (elongated or compressed) a distance s, measured from its *unloaded* position, is

$$F = ks \tag{4–2}$$

Here s is determined from the difference in the spring's deformed length l and its undeformed length l_0, i.e., $s = l - l_0$. If s is positive, **F** "pulls" on the spring; whereas if s is negative, **F** must "push" on it. For example, the spring shown in Fig. 4–5 has an undeformed length $l_0 = 0.4$ m and stiffness $k = 500$ N/m. To stretch it so that $l = 0.6$ m, a force $F = ks = (500 \text{ N/m})(0.6 \text{ m} - 0.4 \text{ m}) = 100$ N is needed. Likewise, to compress it to a length $l = 0.2$ m, a force $F = ks = (500 \text{ N/m})(0.2 \text{ m} - 0.4 \text{ m}) = -100$ N is required, Fig. 4–5.

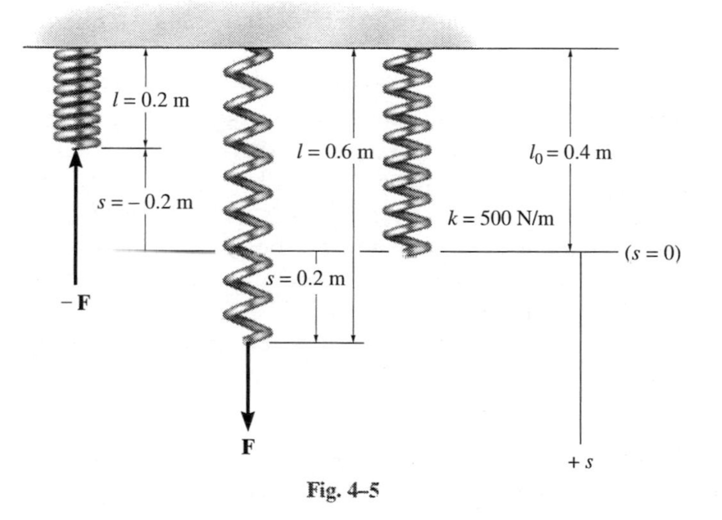

Fig. 4–5

External and Internal Forces. Since a rigid body is a composition of particles, both *external* and *internal* loadings may act on it. It is important to realize, however, that if the free-body diagram for the body is drawn, the forces that are *internal* to the body are *not represented* on the free-body diagram. As discussed in Sec. 4.1, these forces always occur in equal but opposite collinear pairs, and therefore their *net effect* on the body is zero.

In some problems, a free-body diagram for a "system" of connected bodies may be used for an analysis. An example would be the free-body diagram of an entire automobile (system) composed of its many parts. Obviously, the connecting forces between its parts would represent *internal forces* which would *not* be included on the free-body diagram of the automobile. To summarize, internal forces act between particles which are contained within the boundary of the free-body diagram. Particles or bodies outside this boundary exert external forces on the system, and these alone must be shown on the free-body diagram.

Weight and the Center of Gravity. When a body is subjected to a gravitational field, then each of its particles has a specified weight. For the entire body it is appropriate to consider these gravitational forces to be represented as a *system of parallel forces* acting on all the particles contained within the boundary of the body. It was shown in Sec. 3.9 that such a system can be reduced to a single resultant force acting through a specified point. We refer to this force resultant as the *weight* **W** of the body and to the location of its point of application as the *center of gravity*. The methods used for its calculation will be developed in Chapter 6.

In the examples and problems that follow, if the weight of the body is important for the analysis, this force will then be reported in the problem statement. Also, when the body is *uniform* or made of homogeneous material, the center of gravity will be located at the body's *geometric center* or *centroid*; however, if the body is nonhomogeneous or has an unusual shape, then the location of its center of gravity will be given.

Idealized Models. In order to perform a correct force analysis of any object, it is important to consider a corresponding analytical or idealized model that gives results that approximate as closely as possible the actual situation. To do this, careful choices have to be made so that selection of the type of supports, the material behavior, and the object's dimensions can be justified. This way the engineer can feel confident that any design or analysis will yield results which can be trusted. In complex cases this process may require developing several different models of the object that must be analyzed, but in any case, this selection process requires both skill and experience.

To illustrate what is required to develop a proper model, we will now consider a few cases. As shown in Fig. 4–6*a*, the steel beam is to be used to support the roof joists of a building. For a force analysis it is reasonable to assume the material is rigid since only very small deflections will occur when the beam is loaded. A bolted connection at A will allow for any slight rotation that occurs when the load is applied, and so a *pin* can be considered for this support. At B a *roller* can be considered since the support offers no resistance to horizontal movement here. Building code requirements are used to specify the roof loading which results in a calculation of the joist loads **F**. These forces will be larger than any actual loading on the beam since they account for extreme loading cases and for dynamic or vibrational effects. The weight of the beam is generally neglected when it is small compared to the load the beam supports. The idealized model of the beam is shown with average dimensions a, b, c, and d in Fig. 4–6*b*.

As a second case, consider the lift boom in Fig. 4–7*a*. By inspection, it is supported by a pin at A and by the hydraulic cylinder BC, which can be approximated as a weightless link. The material can be assumed rigid, and with its density known, the weight of the boom and the location of its center of gravity G are determined. When a design loading **P** is specified, the idealized model shown in Fig. 4–7*b* can be used for a force analysis. Average dimensions (not shown) are used to specify the location of the loads and the supports.

Idealized models of specific objects will be given in some of the examples throughout the text. It should be realized, however, that each case represents the reduction of a practical situation using simplifying assumptions like the ones illustrated here.

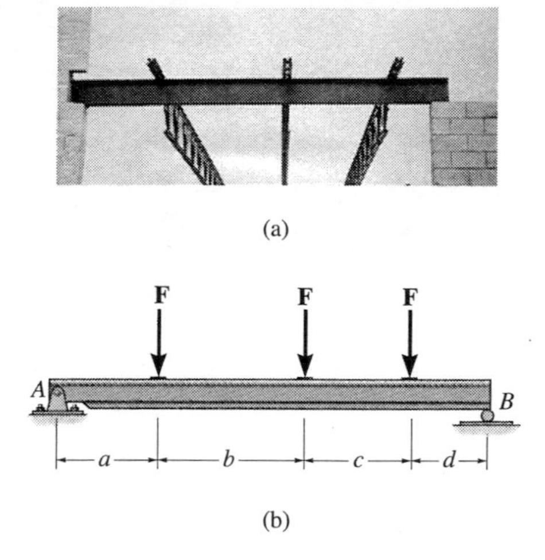

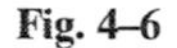
Fig. 4–6

(a)

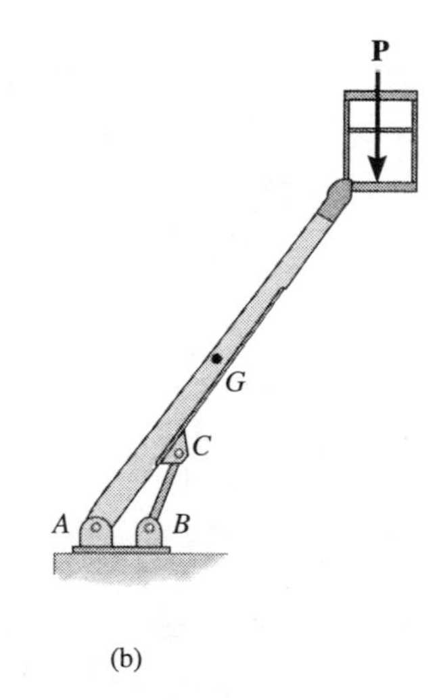

(b)

Fig. 4–7

PROCEDURE FOR DRAWING A FREE-BODY DIAGRAM

To construct a free-body diagram for a rigid body or group of bodies considered as a single system, the following steps should be performed:

Draw Outlined Shape. Imagine the body to be *isolated* or cut "free" from its constraints and connections and draw (sketch) its outlined shape.

Show All Forces and Couple Moments. Identify all the external forces and couple moments that act on the body. Those generally encountered are due to (1) applied loadings, (2) reactions occurring at the supports or at points of contact with other bodies (see Table 4–1), and (3) the weight of the body. To account for all these effects, it may help to trace over the boundary, carefully noting each force or couple moment acting on it.

Identify Each Loading and Give Dimensions. The forces and couple moments that are known should be labeled with their proper magnitudes and directions. Letters are used to represent the magnitudes and direction angles of forces and couple moments that are *unknown*. Establish an x, y coordinate system so that these unknowns, A_x, B_y, etc., can be identified. Indicate the dimensions of the body necessary for calculating the moments of forces.

IMPORTANT POINTS

- No equilibrium problem should be solved without *first* drawing the free-body diagram, so as to account for all the forces and couple moments that act on the body.
- If a support *prevents translation* of a body in a particular direction, then the support exerts a *force* on the body in that direction.
- If *rotation is prevented*, then the support exerts a *couple moment* on the body.
- Study Table 4–1.
- Internal forces are never shown on the free-body diagram since they occur in equal but opposite collinear pairs and therefore cancel out.
- The weight of a body is an external force, and its effect is shown as a single resultant force acting through the body's center of gravity G.
- *Couple moments* can be placed anywhere on the free-body diagram since they are *free vectors*. *Forces* can act at any point along their lines of action since they are *sliding vectors*.

EXAMPLE 4.1

Draw the free-body diagram of the uniform beam shown in Fig. 4–8*a*. The beam has a mass of 100 kg.

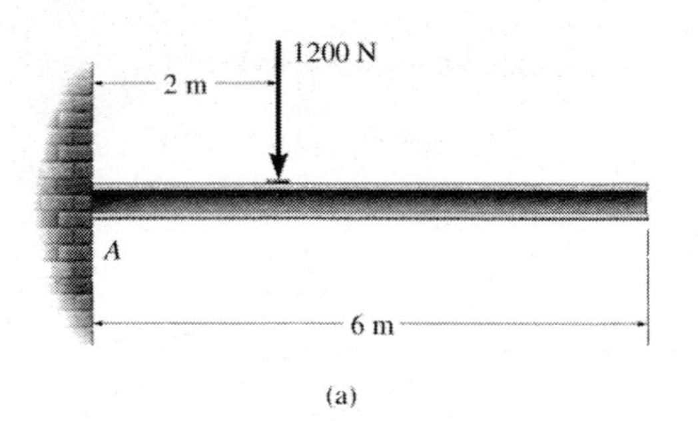

(a)

Solution

The free-body diagram of the beam is shown in Fig. 4–8*b*. Since the support at A is a fixed wall, there are three reactions acting *on the beam* at A, denoted as $\mathbf{A}_x$, $\mathbf{A}_y$, and $\mathbf{M}_A$ drawn in an arbitrary direction. The magnitudes of these vectors are *unknown*, and their sense has been *assumed*. The weight of the beam, $W = 100(9.81) = 981$ N, acts through the beam's center of gravity G, which is 3 m from A since the beam is uniform.

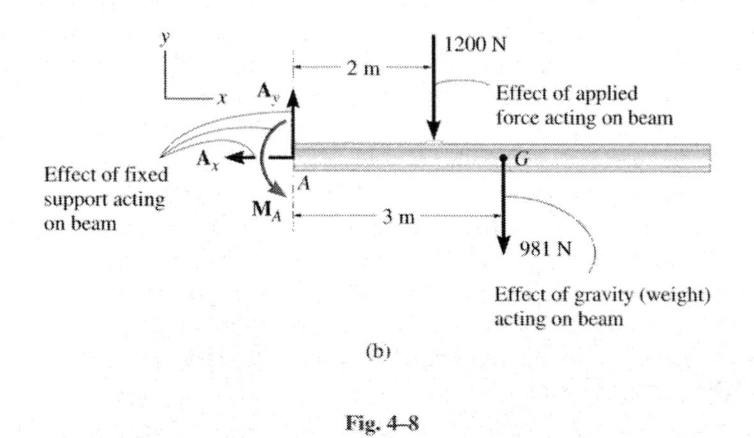

(b)

Fig. 4–8

EXAMPLE 4.2

Draw the free-body diagram of the foot lever shown in Fig. 4–9*a*. The operator applies a vertical force to the pedal so that the spring is stretched 40 mm and the force in the short link at B is 100 N.

(a)

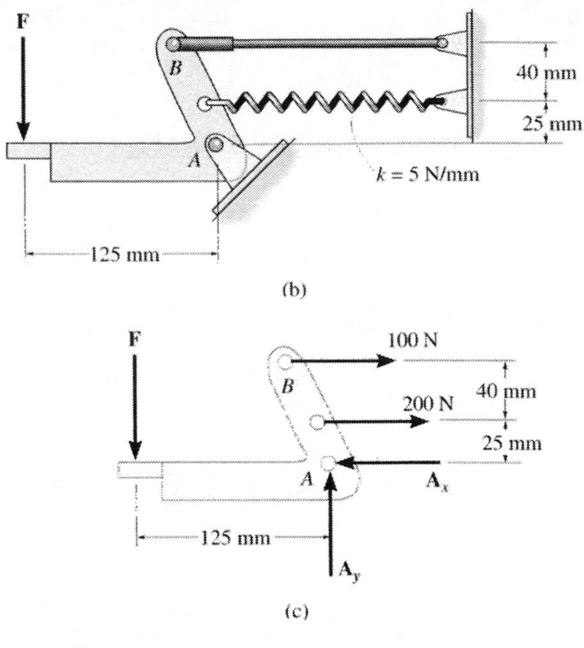

Fig. 4–9

Solution

By inspection, the lever is loosely bolted to the frame at A. The rod at B is pinned at its ends and acts as a "short link." After making the proper measurements, the idealized model of the lever is shown in Fig. 4–9*b*. From this the free-body diagram must be drawn. As shown in Fig. 4–9*c*, the pin support at A exerts force components $\mathbf{A}_x$ and $\mathbf{A}_y$ on the lever, each force has a known line of action but unknown magnitude. The link at B exerts a force of 100 N, acting in the direction of the link. In addition the spring also exerts a horizontal force on the lever. If the stiffness is measured and found to be $k = 5$ N/mm, then since the stretch $s = 40$ mm, using Eq. 4–2, $F_s = ks = 5$ N/mm (40 mm) $= 200$ N. Finally, the operator's shoe applies a vertical force of $\mathbf{F}$ on the pedal. The dimensions of the lever are also shown on the free-body diagram, since this information will be useful when computing the moments of the forces. As usual, the senses of the unknown forces at A have been assumed. The correct senses will become apparent after solving the equilibrium equations.

EXAMPLE 4.3

Two smooth pipes, each having a mass of 300 kg, are supported by the forks of the tractor in Fig. 4–10*a*. Draw the free-body diagrams for each pipe and both pipes together.

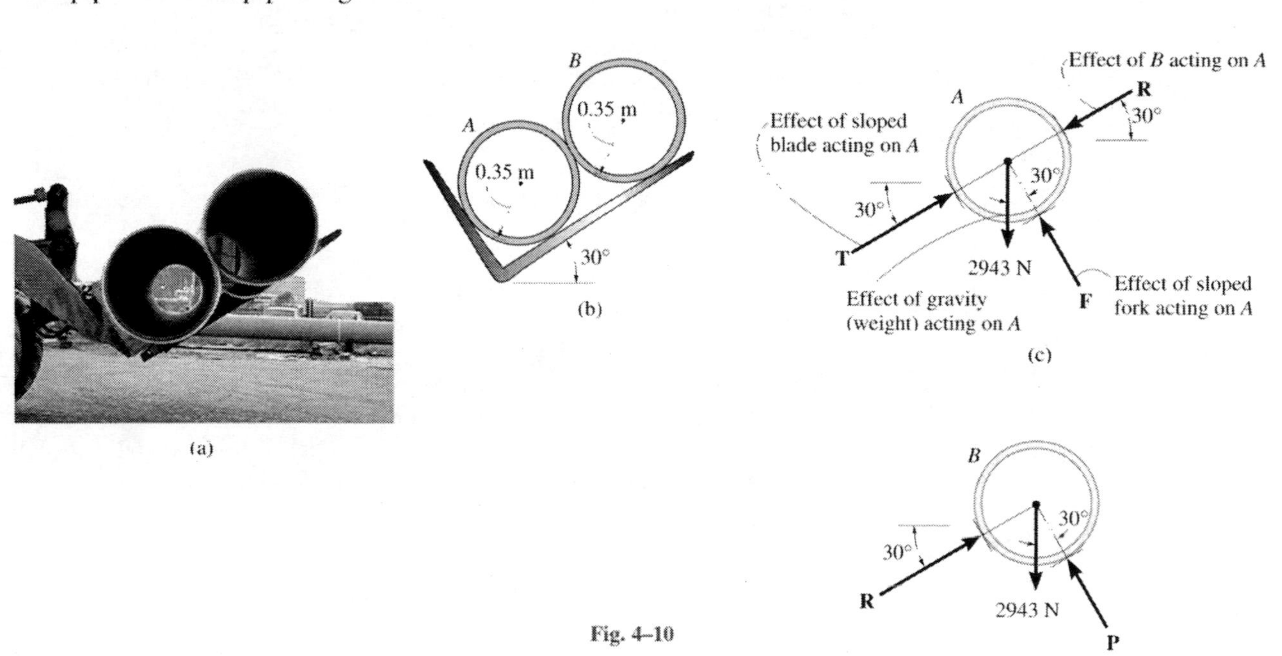

Fig. 4–10

Solution

The idealized model from which we must draw the free-body diagrams is shown in Fig. 4–10*b*. Here the pipes are identified, the dimensions have been added, and the physical situation reduced to its simplest form.

The free-body diagram for pipe A is shown in Fig. 4–10*c*. Its weight is $W = 300(9.81) = 2943$ N. Assuming all contacting surfaces are *smooth*, the reactive forces **T**, **F**, **R** act in a direction *normal* to the tangent at their surfaces of contact.

The free-body diagram of pipe B is shown in Fig. 4–10*d*. Can you identify each of the three forces acting *on this pipe*? In particular, note that **R**, representing the force of A on B, Fig. 4–10*d*, is equal and opposite to **R** representing the force of B on A, Fig. 4–10*c*. This is a consequence of Newton's third law of motion.

The free-body diagram of both pipes combined ("system") is shown in Fig. 4–10*e*. Here the contact force **R**, which acts between A and B, is considered as an *internal* force and hence is not shown on the free-body diagram. That is, it represents a pair of equal but opposite collinear forces which cancel each other.

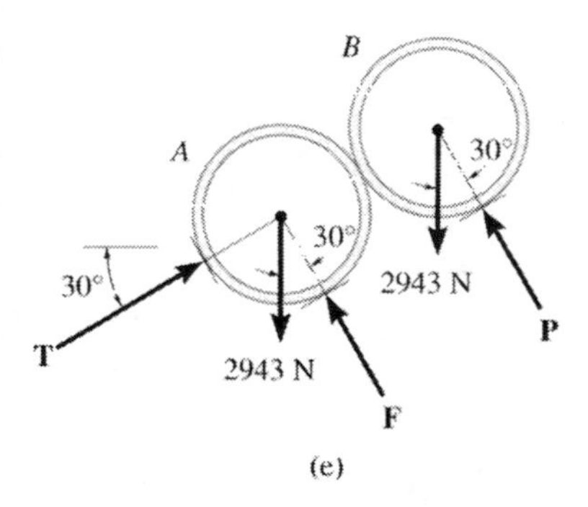

(e)

4.3 Equations of Equilibrium

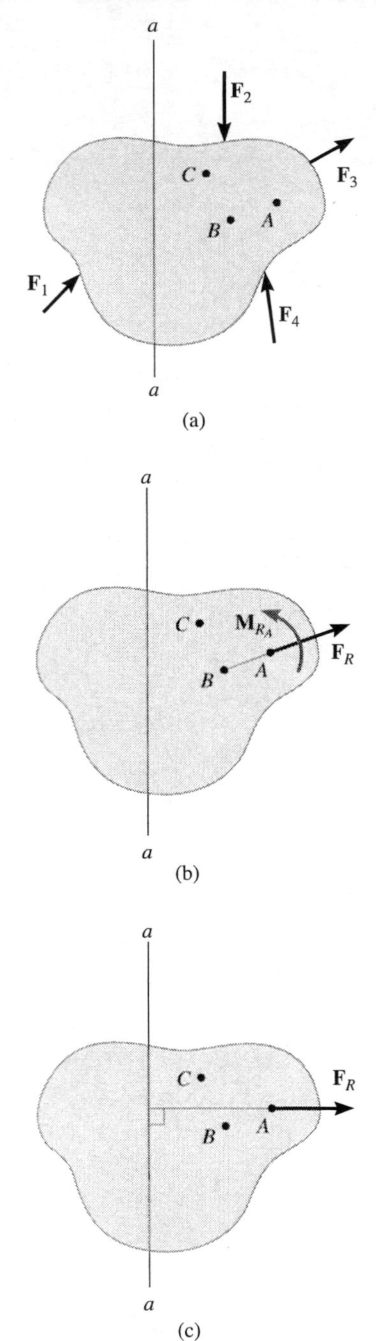

Fig. 4–11

In Sec. 4.1 we developed the two equations which are both necessary and sufficient for the equilibrium of a rigid body, namely, $\Sigma \mathbf{F} = \mathbf{0}$ and $\Sigma \mathbf{M}_O = \mathbf{0}$. When the body is subjected to a system of forces, which all lie in the x–y plane, then the forces can be resolved into their x and y components. Consequently, the conditions for equilibrium in two dimensions are

$$\Sigma F_x = 0 \quad \Sigma F_y = 0 \quad \Sigma M_O = 0 \tag{4–3}$$

Here ΣF_x and ΣF_y represent, respectively, the algebraic sums of the x and y components of all the forces acting on the body, and ΣM_O represents the algebraic sum of the couple moments and the moments of all the force components about an axis perpendicular to the x–y plane and passing through the arbitrary point O, which may lie either on or off the body.

Alternative Sets of Equilibrium Equations. Although Eqs. 4–3 are *most often* used for solving coplanar equilibrium problems, two *alternative* sets of three independent equilibrium equations may also be used. One such set is

$$\Sigma F_a = 0 \quad \Sigma M_A = 0 \quad \Sigma M_B = 0 \tag{4–4}$$

When using these equations it is required that a line passing through points A and B is *not perpendicular* to the a axis. To prove that Eqs. 4–4 provide the *conditions* for equilibrium, consider the free-body diagram of an arbitrarily shaped body shown in Fig. 4–11*a*. Using the methods of Sec. 3.8, all the forces on the free-body diagram may be replaced by an equivalent resultant force $\mathbf{F}_R = \Sigma \mathbf{F}$, acting at point A, and a resultant couple moment $\mathbf{M}_{R_A} = \Sigma \mathbf{M}_A$, Fig. 4–11*b*. If $\Sigma M_A = 0$ is satisfied, it is necessary that $\mathbf{M}_{R_A} = \mathbf{0}$. Furthermore, in order that F_R satisfy $\Sigma F_a = 0$, it must have *no component* along the a axis, and therefore its line of action must be perpendicular to the a axis, Fig. 4–11*c*. Finally, if it is required that $\Sigma M_B = 0$, where B does not lie on the line of action of $\mathbf{F}_R$, then $\mathbf{F}_R = 0$. Since $\Sigma \mathbf{F} = \mathbf{0}$ and $\Sigma \mathbf{M}_A = \mathbf{0}$ indeed the body in Fig. 4–11*a* must be in equilibrium.

A second alternative set of equilibrium equations is

$$\Sigma M_A = 0$$
$$\Sigma M_B = 0 \qquad (4\text{–}5)$$
$$\Sigma M_C = 0$$

Here it is necessary that points A, B, and C do not lie on the same line. To prove that these equations, when satisfied, ensure equilibrium, consider the free-body diagram in Fig. 4–12. If $\Sigma M_A = 0$ is to be satisfied, then $\mathbf{M}_{R_A} = \mathbf{0}$. $\Sigma M_B = 0$ is satisfied if the line of action of $\mathbf{F}_R$ passes through point B as shown. Finally, if we require $\Sigma M_C = 0$, where C does not lie on line AB, it is necessary that $\mathbf{F}_R = \mathbf{0}$, and the body in Fig. 4–11*a* must then be in equilibrium.

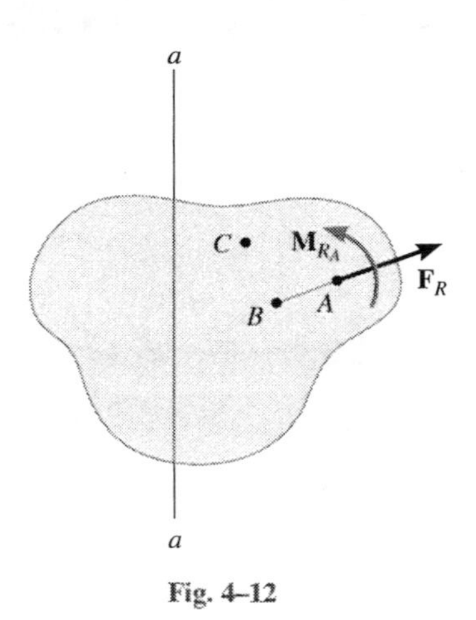

Fig. 4–12

PROCEDURE FOR ANALYSIS

Coplanar force equilibrium problems for a rigid body can be solved using the following procedure.

Free-Body Diagram.

- Establish the x, y coordinate axes in any suitable orientation.
- Draw an outlined shape of the body.
- Show all the forces and couple moments acting on the body.
- Label all the loadings and specify their directions relative to the x, y axes. The sense of a force or couple moment having an *unknown* magnitude but known line of action can be *assumed*.
- Indicate the dimensions of the body necessary for computing the moments of forces.

Equations of Equilibrium.

- Apply the moment equation of equilibrium, $\Sigma M_O = 0$, about a point (O) that lies at the intersection of the lines of action of two unknown forces. In this way, the moments of these unknowns are zero about O, and a *direct solution* for the third unknown can be determined.
- When applying the force equilibrium equations, $\Sigma F_x = 0$ and $\Sigma F_y = 0$, orient the x and y axes along lines that will provide the simplest resolution of the forces into their x and y components.
- If the solution of the equilibrium equations yields a negative scalar for a force or couple moment magnitude, this indicates that the sense is opposite to that which was assumed on the free-body diagram.

EXAMPLE 4.4

Determine the horizontal and vertical components of reaction for the beam loaded as shown in Fig. 4–13*a*. Neglect the weight of the beam in the calculations.

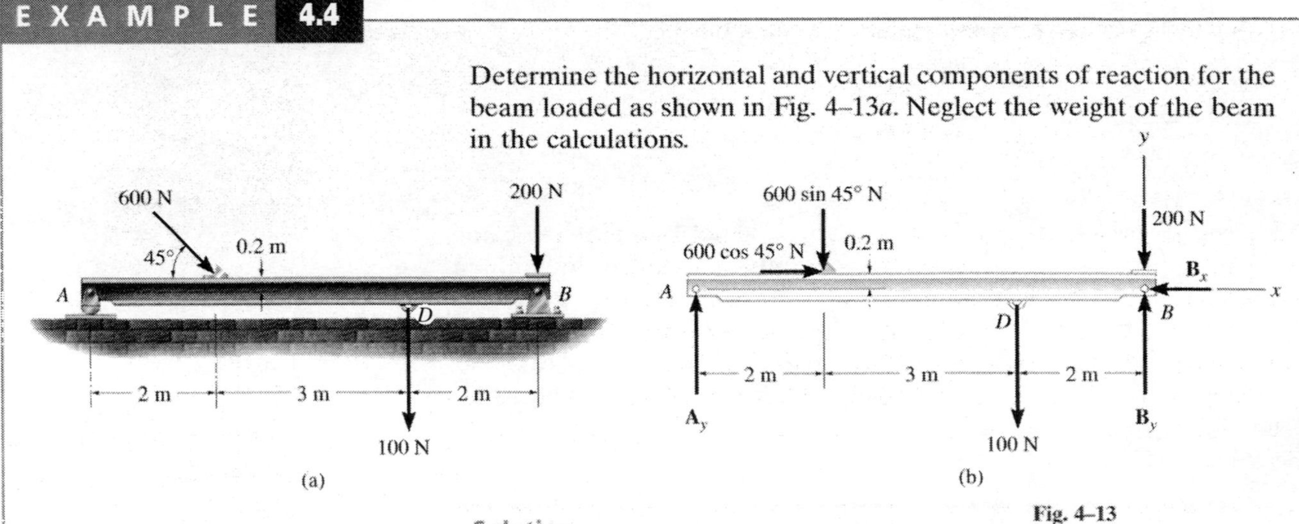

Fig. 4–13

Solution

Free-Body Diagram. Can you identify each of the forces shown on the free-body diagram of the beam, Fig. 4–13*b*? For simplicity, the 600-N force is represented by its x and y components as shown. Also, note that a 200-N force acts on the beam at B and is independent of the force components $\mathbf{B}_x$ and $\mathbf{B}_y$, which represent the effect of the pin on the beam.

Equations of Equilibrium. Summing forces in the x direction yields

$$\xrightarrow{+} \Sigma F_x = 0; \qquad 600 \cos 45^\circ \text{ N} - B_x = 0$$

$$B_x = 424 \text{ N} \qquad \textit{Ans.}$$

A direct solution for $\mathbf{A}_y$ can be obtained by applying the moment equation $\Sigma M_B = 0$ about point B. For the calculation, it should be apparent that forces 200 N, $\mathbf{B}_x$, and $\mathbf{B}_y$ all create zero moment about B. Assuming counterclockwise rotation about B to be positive (in the $+\mathbf{k}$ direction), Fig. 4–14*b*, we have

$$\circlearrowleft + \Sigma M_B = 0; \qquad 100 \text{ N}(2 \text{ m}) + (600 \sin 45^\circ \text{ N})(5 \text{ m})$$

$$- (600 \cos 45^\circ \text{ N})(0.2 \text{ m}) - A_y(7 \text{ m}) = 0$$

$$A_y = 319 \text{ N} \qquad \textit{Ans.}$$

Summing forces in the y direction, using this result, gives

$$+\uparrow \Sigma F_y = 0; \qquad 319 \text{ N} - 600 \sin 45^\circ \text{ N} - 100 \text{ N} - 200 \text{ N} + B_y = 0$$

$$B_y = 405 \text{ N} \qquad \textit{Ans.}$$

We can check this result by summing moments about point A.

$$\circlearrowleft + \Sigma M_A = 0; \qquad -(600 \sin 45^\circ \text{ N})(2 \text{ m}) - (600 \cos 45^\circ \text{ N})(0.2 \text{ m})$$

$$-(100 \text{ N})(5 \text{ m}) - (200 \text{ N})(7 \text{ m}) + B_y(7 \text{ m}) = 0$$

$$B_y = 405 \text{ N} \qquad \textit{Ans.}$$

EXAMPLE 4.5

The cord shown in Fig. 4–14*a* supports a force of 500 N and wraps over the frictionless pulley. Determine the tension in the cord at *C* and the horizontal and vertical components of reaction at pin *A*.

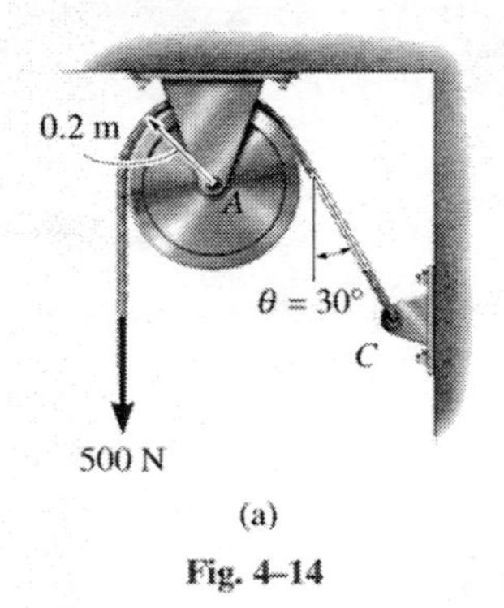

(a)

Fig. 4–14

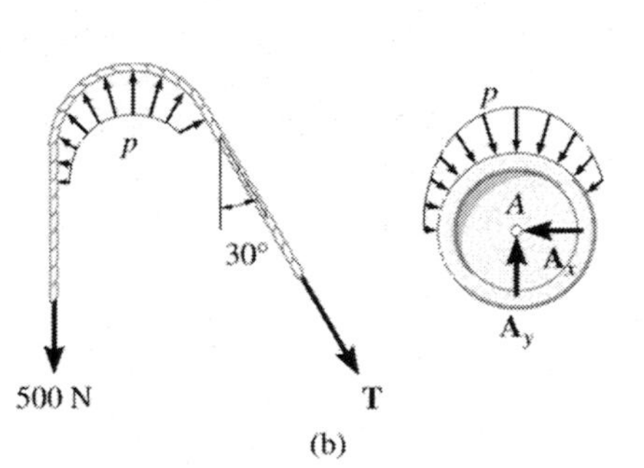

(b)

Solution

Free-Body Diagrams. The free-body diagrams of the cord and pulley are shown in Fig. 4–14*b*. Note that the principle of action, equal but opposite reaction must be carefully observed when drawing each of these diagrams: the cord exerts an unknown load distribution p along part of the pulley's surface, whereas the pulley exerts an equal but opposite effect on the cord. For the solution, however, it is simpler to *combine* the free-body diagrams of the pulley and the contacting portion of the cord, so that the distributed load becomes *internal* to the system and is therefore eliminated from the analysis, Fig. 4–14*c*.

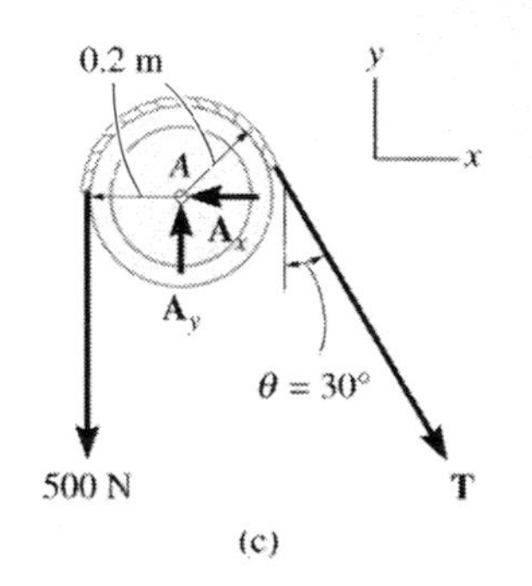

(c)

Equations of Equilibrium. Summing moments about point A to eliminate $\mathbf{A}_x$ and $\mathbf{A}_y$, Fig. 4–15*c*, we have

$$\circlearrowleft + \Sigma M_A = 0; \qquad 500\text{ N}(0.2\text{ m}) - T(0.2\text{ m}) = 0$$

$$T = 500\text{ N} \qquad \textit{Ans.}$$

It is seen that the tension remains *constant* as the cord passes over the pulley. (This of course is true for *any angle* θ at which the cord is directed and for *any radius* r of the pulley.) Using the result for T, a force summation is applied to determine the components of reaction at pin A.

$$\overset{+}{\rightarrow} \Sigma F_x = 0; \qquad -A_x + 500 \sin 30^\circ \text{ N} = 0$$

$$A_x = 250\text{ N} \qquad \textit{Ans.}$$

$$+\uparrow \Sigma F_y = 0; \qquad A_y - 500\text{ N} - 500 \cos 30^\circ \text{ N} = 0$$

$$A_y = 933\text{ N} \qquad \textit{Ans.}$$

EXAMPLE 4.6

The link shown in Fig. 4–15*a* is pin-connected at A and rests against a smooth support at B. Compute the horizontal and vertical components of reaction at the pin A.

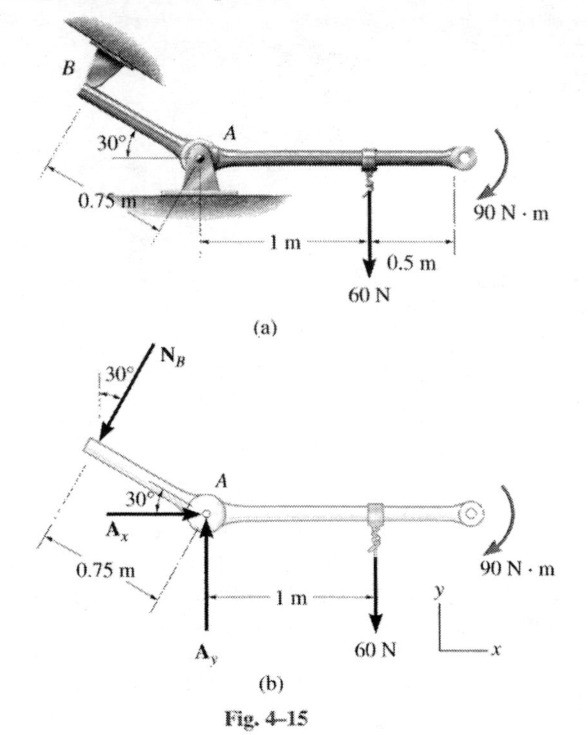

Fig. 4–15

Solution

Free-Body Diagram. As shown in Fig. 4–15*b*, the reaction $\mathbf{N}_B$ is perpendicular to the link at B. Also, horizontal and vertical components of reaction are represented at A.

Equations of Equilibrium. Summing moments about A, we obtain a direct solution for N_B,

$$\circlearrowright + \Sigma M_A = 0; \qquad -90\ \text{N}\cdot\text{m} - 60\ \text{N}(1\ \text{m}) + N_B(0.75\ \text{m}) = 0$$

$$N_B = 200\ \text{N}$$

Using this result,

$$\overset{+}{\rightarrow} \Sigma F_x = 0; \qquad A_x - 200 \sin 30°\ \text{N} = 0$$

$$A_x = 100\ \text{N} \qquad \textit{Ans.}$$

$$+\uparrow \Sigma F_y = 0; \qquad A_y - 200 \cos 30°\ \text{N} - 60\ \text{N} = 0$$

$$A_y = 233\ \text{N} \qquad \textit{Ans.}$$

EXAMPLE 4.7

The box wrench in Fig. 4–16*a* is used to tighten the bolt at A. If the wrench does not turn when the load is applied to the handle, determine the torque or moment applied to the bolt and the force of the wrench on the bolt.

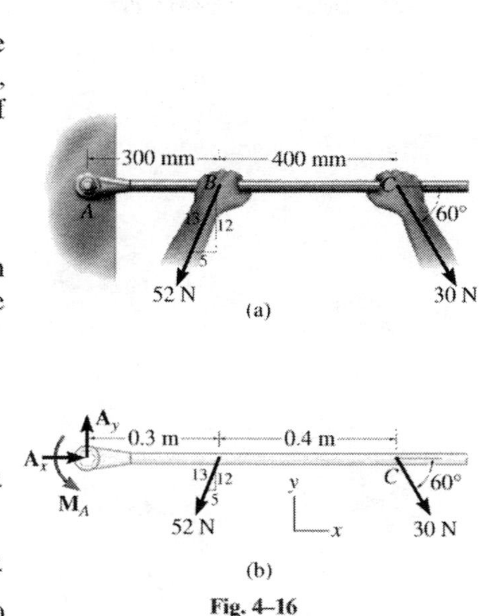

Fig. 4–16

Solution

Free-Body Diagram. The free-body diagram for the wrench is shown in Fig. 4–16*b*. Since the bolt acts as a "fixed support," it exerts force components $\mathbf{A}_x$ and $\mathbf{A}_y$ and a torque $\mathbf{M}_A$ on the wrench at A.

Equations of Equilibrium.

$$\xrightarrow{+} \Sigma F_x = 0; \qquad A_x - 52\left(\tfrac{5}{13}\right)\text{N} + 30 \cos 60^\circ\,\text{N} = 0$$

$$A_x = 5.00\ \text{N} \qquad \textit{Ans.}$$

$$+\uparrow \Sigma F_y = 0; \qquad A_y - 52\left(\tfrac{12}{13}\right)\text{N} - 30 \sin 60^\circ\,\text{N} = 0$$

$$A_y = 74.0\ \text{N} \qquad \textit{Ans.}$$

$$\circlearrowleft + \Sigma M_A = 0; \qquad M_A - 52\left(\tfrac{12}{13}\right)\text{N}\,(0.3\ \text{m}) - (30 \sin 60^\circ\,\text{N})(0.7\ \text{m}) = 0$$

$$M_A = 32.6\ \text{N}\cdot\text{m} \qquad \textit{Ans.}$$

Point A was chosen for summing moments because the lines of action of the *unknown* forces $\mathbf{A}_x$ and $\mathbf{A}_y$ pass through this point, and therefore these forces were not included in the moment summation. Realize, however, that $\mathbf{M}_A$ must be *included* in this moment summation. This couple moment is a free vector and represents the twisting resistance of the bolt on the wrench. By Newton's third law, the wrench exerts an equal but opposite moment or torque on the bolt. Furthermore, the resultant force on the wrench is

$$F_A = \sqrt{(5.00)^2 + (74.0)^2} = 74.1\ \text{N} \qquad \textit{Ans.}$$

Because the force components A_x and A_y were calculated as positive quantities, their directional sense is shown correctly on the free-body diagram in Fig. 4–16*b*. Hence

$$\theta = \tan^{-1}\frac{74.0\ \text{N}}{5.00\ \text{N}} = 86.1^\circ \measuredangle$$

Realize that $\mathbf{F}_A$ acts in the opposite direction on the bolt. Why?

Although only *three* independent equilibrium equations can be written for a rigid body, it is a good practice to *check* the calculations using a fourth equilibrium equation. For example, the above computations may be verified in part by summing moments about point C:

$$\circlearrowleft + \Sigma M_C = 0;\ 52\left(\tfrac{12}{13}\right)\text{N}\,(0.4\ \text{m}) + 32.6\ \text{N}\cdot\text{m} - 74.0\ \text{N}(0.7\ \text{m}) = 0$$

$$19.2\ \text{N}\cdot\text{m} + 32.6\ \text{N}\cdot\text{m} - 51.8\ \text{N}\cdot\text{m} = 0$$

EXAMPLE 4.8

(a)

Placement of concrete from the truck is accomplished using the chute shown in the photos, Fig. 4–17*a*. Determine the force that the hydraulic cylinder and the truck frame exert on the chute to hold it in the position shown. The chute and wet concrete contained along its length have a uniform weight of 560 N/m.

Solution

The idealized model of the chute is shown in Fig. 4–17*b*. Here the dimensions are given, and it is assumed the chute is pin connected to the frame at A and the hydraulic cylinder BC acts as a short link.

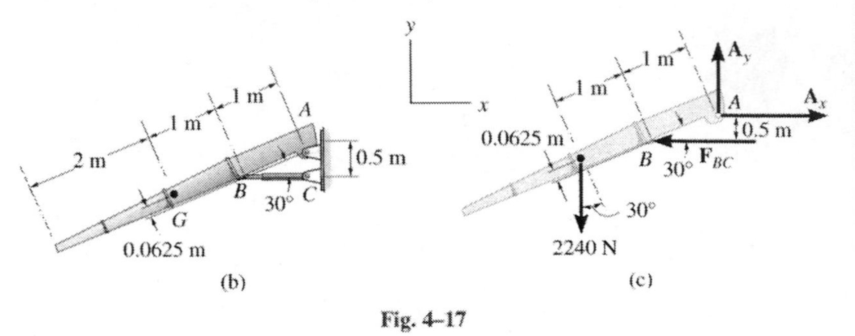

Fig. 4–17

Free-Body Diagram. Since the chute has a length of 4 m, the total supported weight is (560 N/m)(4 m) = 2240 N, which is assumed to act at its midpoint, G. The hydraulic cylinder exerts a horizontal force $\mathbf{F}_{BC}$ on the chute, Fig. 4–17*c*.

Equations of Equilibrium. A direct solution for $\mathbf{F}_{BC}$ is possible by summing moments about the pin at A. To do this we will use the principle of moments and resolve the weight into components parallel and perpendicular to the chute. We have,

$$\circlearrowleft + \Sigma M_A = 0;$$

$$-F_{BC}(0.5 \text{ m}) + 2240 \cos 30^\circ \text{ N } (2 \text{ m}) + 2240 \sin 30^\circ \text{ N } (0.0625 \text{ m}) = 0$$

$$F_{BC} = 7900 \text{ N} \qquad \textit{Ans.}$$

Summing forces to obtain A_x and A_y, we obtain

$$\overset{+}{\rightarrow} \Sigma F_x = 0; \qquad -A_x + 7900 \text{ N} = 0$$

$$A_x = 7900 \text{ N} \qquad \textit{Ans.}$$

$$+\uparrow \Sigma F_y = 0; \qquad A_y - 2240 \text{ N} = 0$$

$$A_y = 2240 \text{ N} \qquad \textit{Ans.}$$

To verify this solution we can sum moments about point B.

$$\circlearrowleft + \Sigma M_B = 0; \qquad -7900 \text{ N } (0.5 \text{ m}) + 2240 \text{ N } (1 \cos 30^\circ \text{ m}) +$$

$$2240 \cos 30^\circ \text{ N } (1 \text{ m}) + 2240 \text{ N} \sin 30^\circ \, (0.0625 \text{ m}) = 0$$

4.4 Two- and Three-Force Members

The solution to some equilibrium problems can be simplified if one is able to recognize members that are subjected to only two or three forces.

Two-Force Members. When a member is subject to *no couple moments* and forces are applied at only two points on a member, the member is called a *two-force member*. An example is shown in Fig. 4–18*a*. The forces at A and B are summed to obtain their respective *resultants* $\mathbf{F}_A$ and $\mathbf{F}_B$, Fig. 4–18*b*. These two forces will maintain *translational or force equilibrium* ($\Sigma\mathbf{F} = \mathbf{0}$) provided $\mathbf{F}_A$ is of equal magnitude and opposite direction to $\mathbf{F}_B$. Furthermore, *rotational or moment equilibrium* ($\Sigma\mathbf{M}_O = \mathbf{0}$) is satisfied if $\mathbf{F}_A$ is *collinear* with $\mathbf{F}_B$. As a result, the line of action of both forces is known since it always passes through A and B. Hence, only the force magnitude must be determined or stated. Other examples of two-force members held in equilibrium are shown in Fig. 4–19.

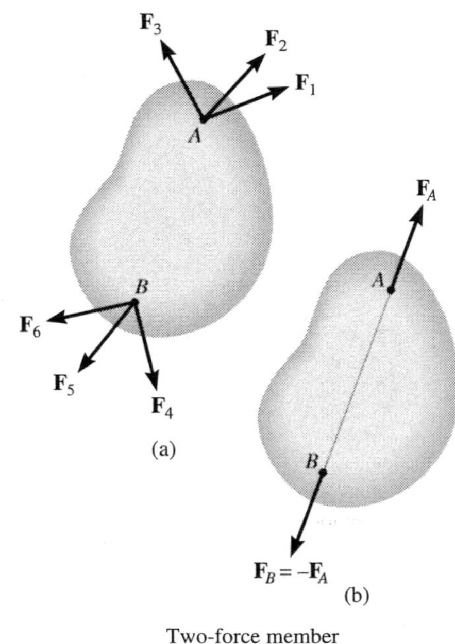

Two-force member

Fig. 4–18

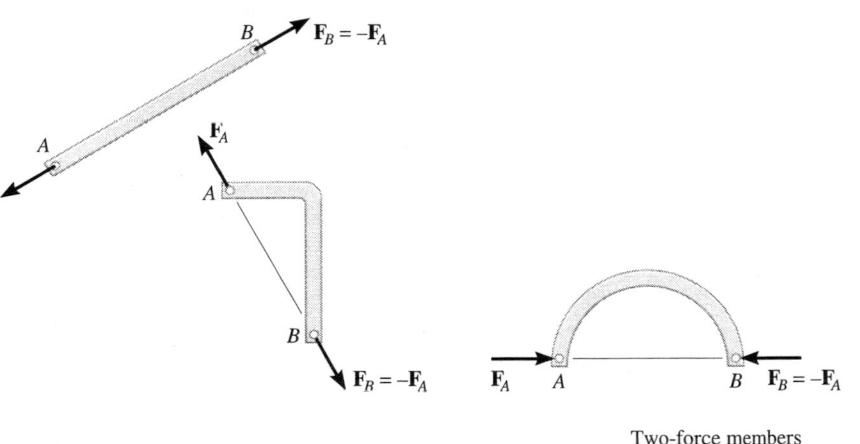

Two-force members

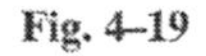
Fig. 4–19

Three-Force Members. If a member is subjected to only three forces, then it is necessary that the forces be either *concurrent* or *parallel* for the member to be in equilibrium. To show the concurrency requirement, consider the body in Fig. 4–20*a* and suppose that any two of the three forces acting on the body have lines of action that intersect at point O. To satisfy moment equilibrium about O, i.e., $\Sigma M_O = 0$, the third force must also pass through O, which then makes the force system *concurrent*. If two of the three forces are parallel, Fig. 4–20*b*, the point of concurrency, O, is considered to be at "infinity," and the third force must be parallel to the other two forces to intersect at this "point."

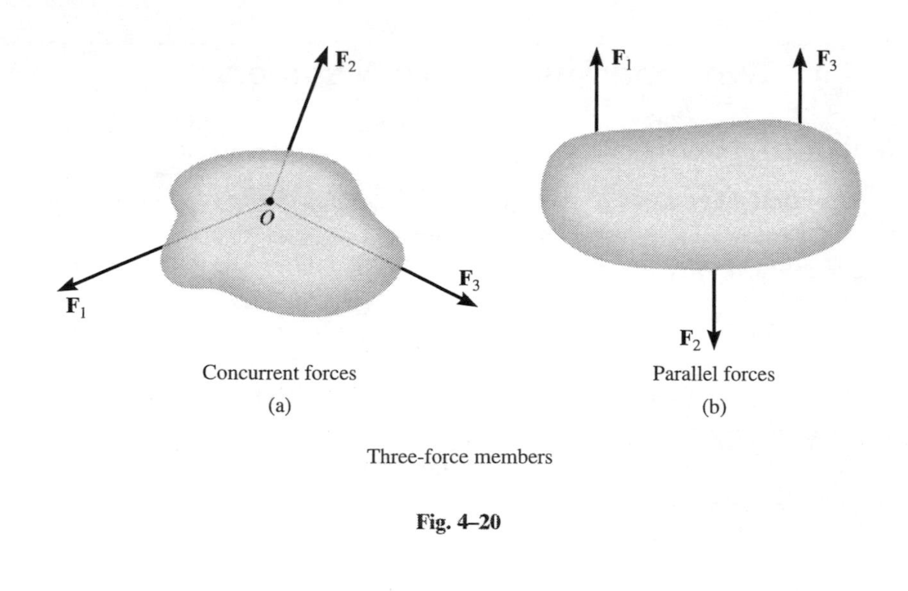

Concurrent forces
(a)

Parallel forces
(b)

Three-force members

Fig. 4–20

Many mechanical elements act as two- or three-force members, and the ability to recognize them in a problem will considerably simplify an equilibrium analysis.

- The bucket link AB on the back-hoe is a typical example of a two-force member since it is pin connected at its ends and, provided its weight is neglected, no other force acts on this member.
- The hydraulic cylinder BC is pin connected at its ends. It is a two-force member. The boom ABD is subjected to the weight of the suspended motor at D, the force of the hydraulic cylinder at B, and the force of the pin at A. If the boom's weight is neglected, it is a three-force member.
- The dump bed of the truck operates by extending the telescopic hydraulic cylinder AB. If the weight of AB is neglected, we can classify it as a two-force member since it is pin connected at its end points.

EXAMPLE 4.9

The lever ABC is pin-supported at A and connected to a short link BD as shown in Fig. 4–21a. If the weight of the members is negligible, determine the force of the pin on the lever at A.

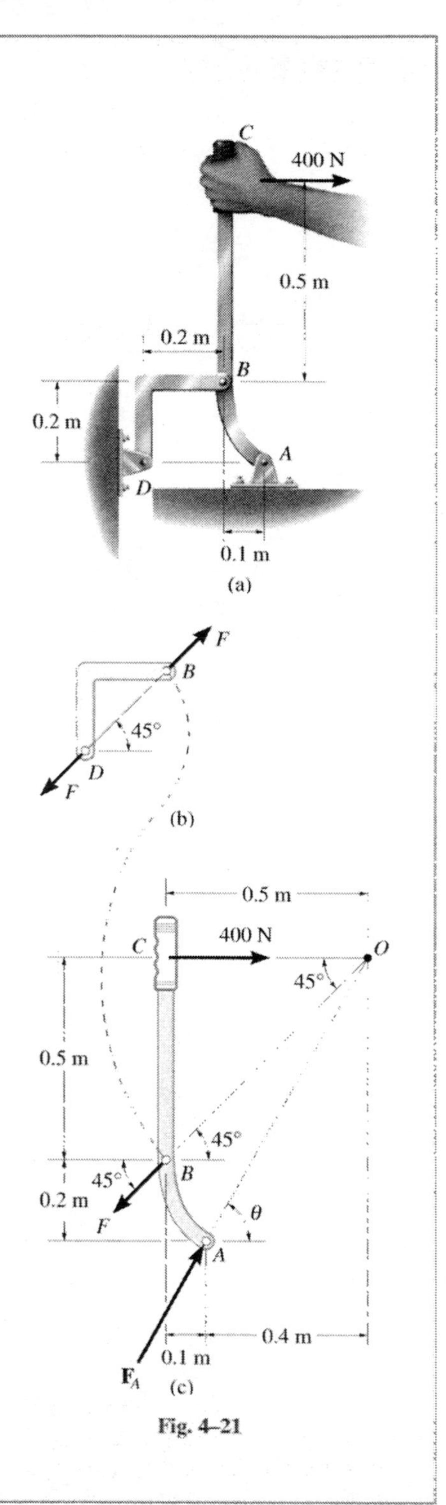

Fig. 4–21

Solution

Free-Body Diagrams. As shown by the free-body diagram, Fig. 4–21b, the short link BD is a *two-force member*, so the *resultant forces* at pins D and B must be equal, opposite, and collinear. Although the magnitude of the force is unknown, the line of action is known since it passes through B and D.

Lever ABC is a *three-force member*, and therefore, in order to satisfy moment equilibrium, the three nonparallel forces acting on it must be concurrent at O, Fig. 4–21c. In particular, note that the force F on the lever at B is equal but opposite to the force F acting at B on the link. Why? The distance CO must be 0.5 m since the lines of action of $\mathbf{F}$ and the 400-N force are known.

Equations of Equilibrium. By requiring the force system to be concurrent at O, since $\Sigma M_O = 0$, the angle θ which defines the line of action of $\mathbf{F}_A$ can be determined from trigonometry,

$$\theta = \tan^{-1}\left(\frac{0.7}{0.4}\right) = 60.3^\circ \quad \measuredangle\theta \qquad \textit{Ans.}$$

Using the x, y axes and applying the force equilibrium equations, we can obtain F_A and F.

$$\overset{+}{\rightarrow}\Sigma F_x = 0; \qquad F_A \cos 60.3^\circ - F\cos 45^\circ + 400\text{ N} = 0$$

$$+\uparrow\Sigma F_y = 0; \qquad F_A \sin 60.3^\circ - F\sin 45^\circ = 0$$

Solving, we get

$$F_A = 1.07\text{ kN} \qquad \textit{Ans.}$$

$$F = 1.32\text{ kN}$$

Note: We can also solve this problem by representing the force at A by its two components $\mathbf{A}_x$ and $\mathbf{A}_y$ and applying $\Sigma M_A = 0$, $\Sigma F_x = 0$, $\Sigma F_y = 0$ to the lever. Once A_x and A_y are determined, how would you find F_A and θ?

PROBLEMS

4-1. Determine the magnitude of the reactions on the beam at A and B. Neglect the thickness of the beam.

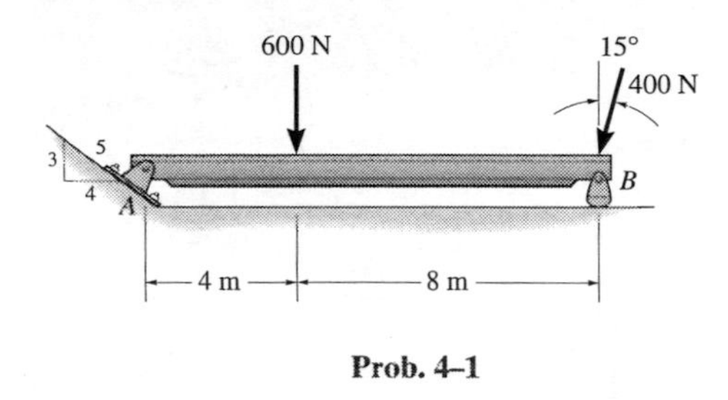

Prob. 4–1

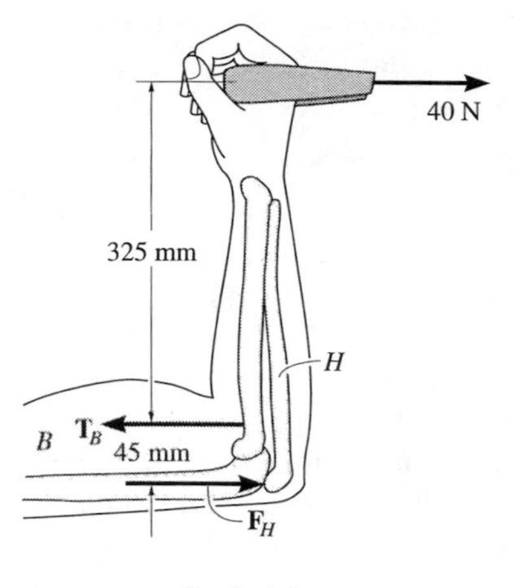

Prob. 4–3

4-2. When holding the 20-N (≈ 2-kg) stone in equilibrium, the humerus H, assumed to be smooth, exerts normal forces $\mathbf{F}_C$ and $\mathbf{F}_A$ on the radius C and ulna A as shown. Determine these forces and the force $\mathbf{F}_B$ that the biceps B exerts on the radius for equilibrium. The stone has a center of mass at G. Neglect the weight of the arm.

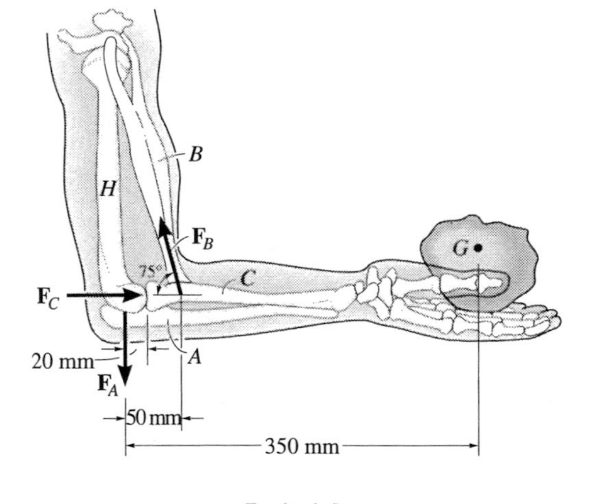

Prob. 4–2

4-3. The man is pulling a load of 40 N with one arm held as shown. Determine the force $\mathbf{F}_H$ this exerts on the humerus bone H, and the tension developed in the biceps muscle B. Neglect the weight of the man's arm.

4-4. The ramp of a ship has a weight of 1000 N (≈ 100 kg) and a center of gravity at G. Determine the cable force in CD needed to just start lifting the ramp, (i.e., so the reaction at B becomes zero). Also, determine the horizontal and vertical components of force at the hinge (pin) at A.

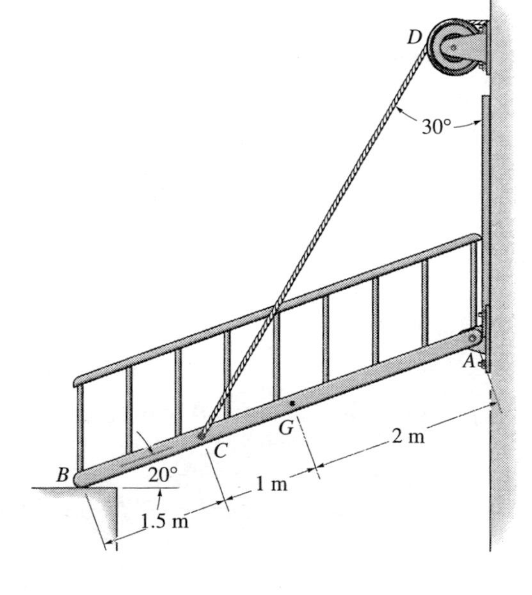

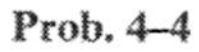
Prob. 4–4

*4-5. Determine the magnitude of force at the pin A and in the cable BC needed to support the 2000-N load. Neglect the weight of the boom AB.

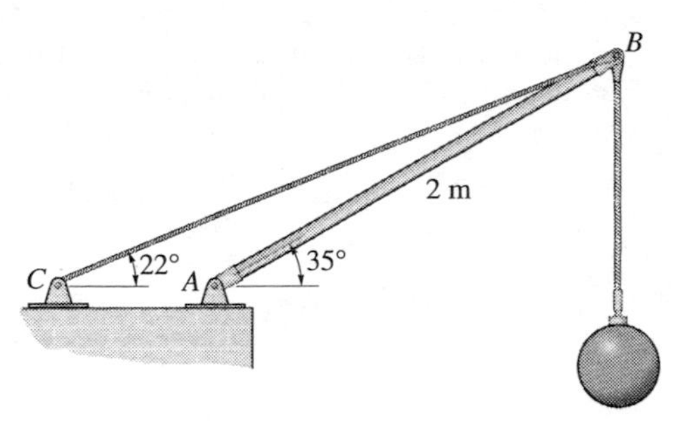

Prob. 4–5

4-6. Compare the force exerted on the toe and heel of a 480-N ($\approx$ 48-kg) woman when she is wearing regular shoes and stiletto heels. Assume all her weight is placed on one foot and the reactions occur at points A and B as shown.

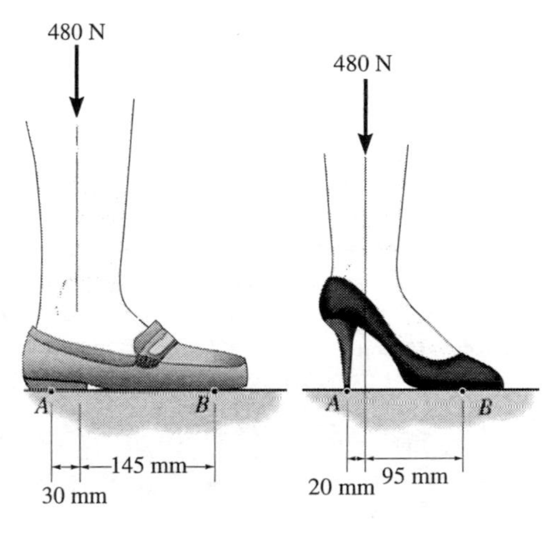

Prob. 4–6

4-7. Determine the reactions at the pins A and B. The spring has an unstretched length of 80 mm.

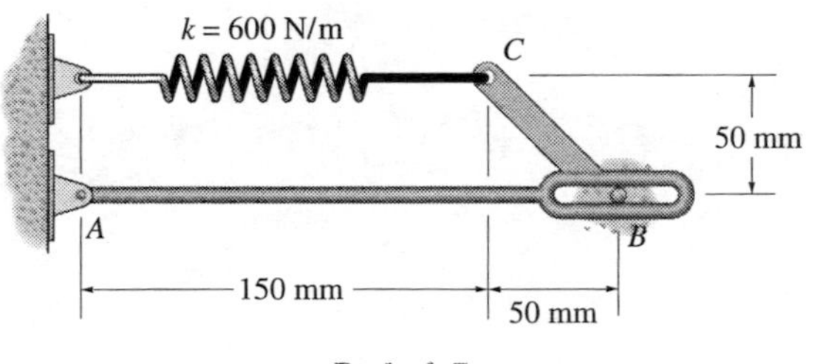

Prob. 4–7

4-8. The platform assembly has a weight of 1000 N ($\approx$ 100 kg) and center of gravity at G_1. If it is intended to support a maximum load of 1600 N placed at point G_2, determine the smallest counterweight W that should be placed at B in order to prevent the platform from tipping over.

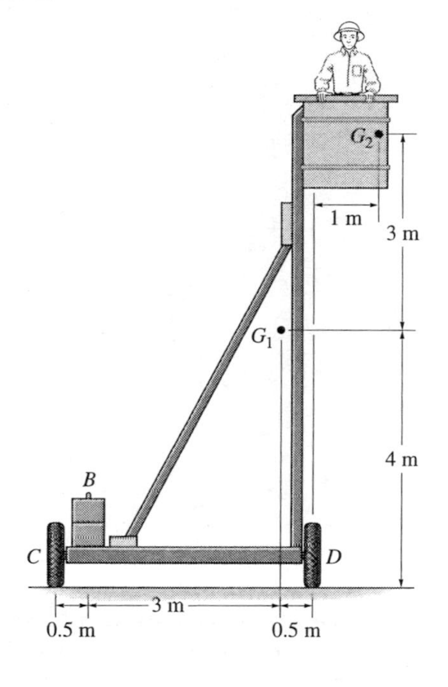

Prob. 4–8

*4-9. Determine the tension in the cable and the horizontal and vertical components of reaction of the pin A. The pulley at D is frictionless and the cylinder weighs 80 N ($\approx$ 8 kg).

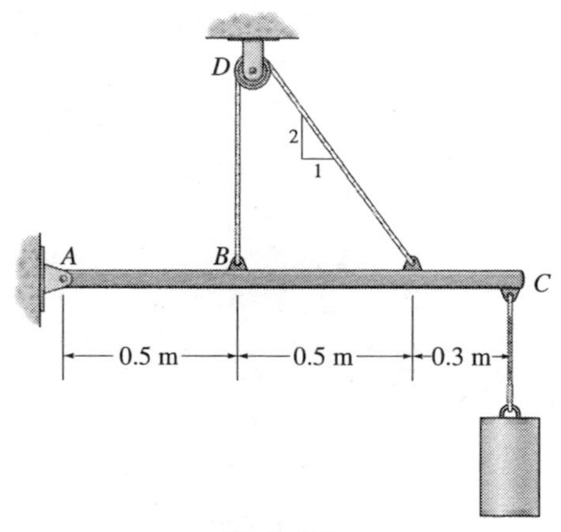

Prob. 4–9

4-10. The device is used to hold an elevator door open. If the spring has a stiffness of $k = 40$ N/m and it is compressed 0.2 m, determine the horizontal and vertical components of reaction at the pin A and the resultant force at the wheel bearing B.

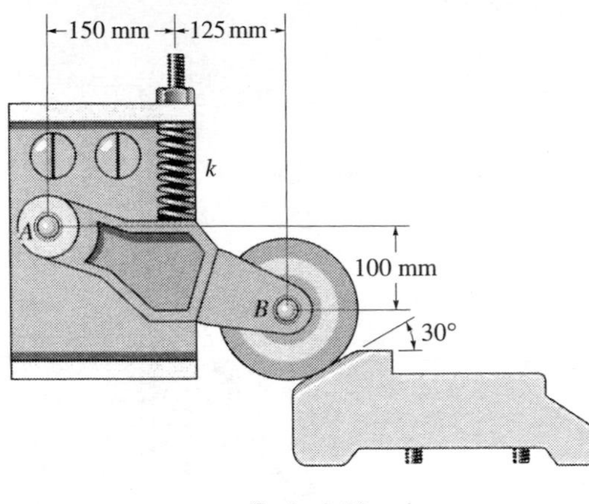

Prob. 4–10

4-11. The cutter is subjected to a horizontal force of 580 N and a normal force of 350 N. Determine the horizontal and vertical components of force acting on the pin A and the force along the hydraulic cylinder BC (a two-force member).

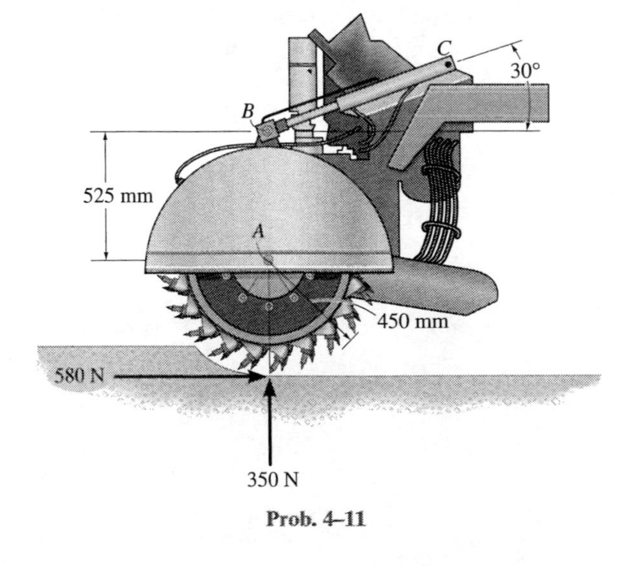

Prob. 4–11

4-12. The cantilevered jib crane is used to support the load of 780 N. If the trolley T can be placed anywhere between 0.45 m $\leq x \leq$ 2.25 m, determine the maximum magnitude of reaction at the supports A and B. Note that the supports are collars that allow the crane to rotate freely about the vertical axis. The collar at B supports a force in the vertical direction, whereas the one at A does not.

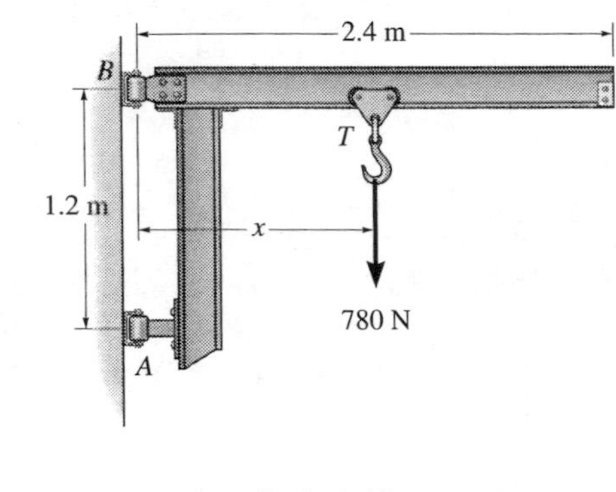

Prob. 4–12

***4-13.** The sports car has a mass of 1.5 Mg and mass center at G. If the front two springs each have a stiffness of $k_A = 58$ kN/m and the rear two springs each have a stiffness of $k_B = 65$ kN/m, determine their compression when the car is parked on the 30° incline. Also, what friction force $\mathbf{F}_B$ must be applied to each of the rear wheels to hold the car in equilibrium? *Hint:* First determine the normal force at A and B, then determine the compression in the springs.

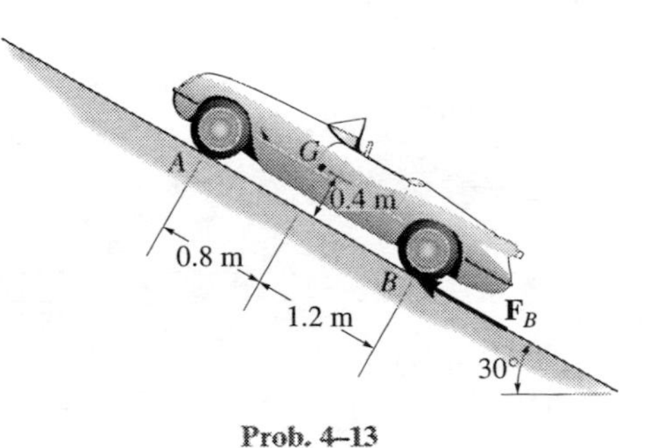

Prob. 4–13

4-14. The power pole supports the three lines, each line exerting a vertical force on the pole due to its weight as shown. Determine the reactions at the fixed support D. If it is possible for wind or ice to snap the lines, determine which line(s) when removed create(s) a condition for the greatest moment reaction at D.

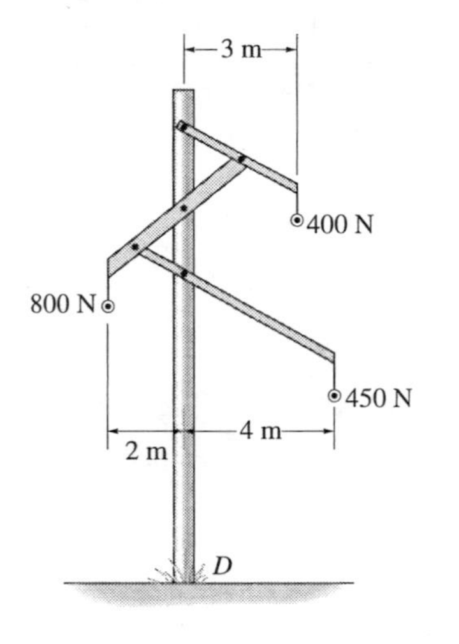

Prob. 4–14

4-15. The jib crane is pin-connected at A and supported by a smooth collar at B. Determine the roller placement x of the 5000-N load so that it gives the maximum and minimum reactions at the supports. Calculate these reactions in each case. Neglect the weight of the crane. Require $1\text{ m} \leq x \leq 2.5\text{ m}$.

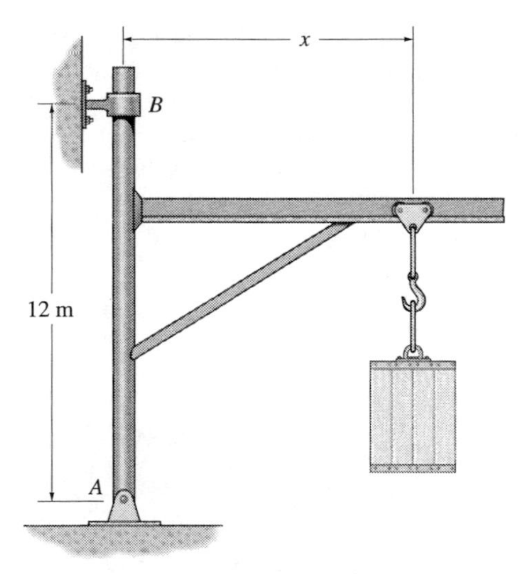

Prob. 4–15

4-16. If the wheelbarrow and its contents have a mass of 60 kg and center of mass at G, determine the magnitude of the resultant force which the man must exert on *each* of the two handles in order to hold the wheelbarrow in equilibrium.

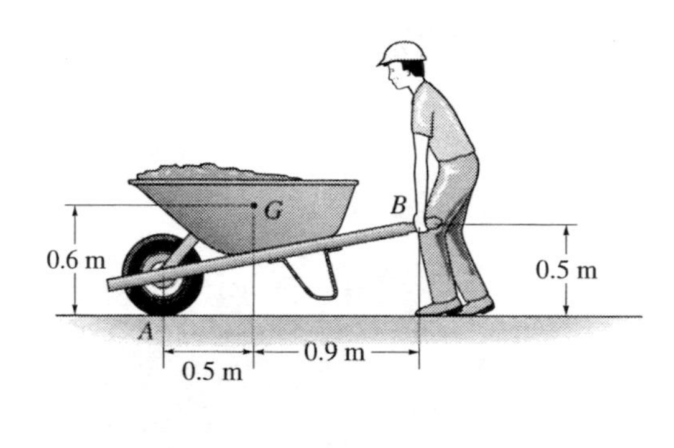

Prob. 4–16

4-17. The telephone pole of negligible thickness is subjected to the force of 400 N directed as shown. It is supported by the cable BCD and can be assumed pinned at its base A. In order to provide clearance for a sidewalk right of way, where D is located, the strut CE is attached at C, as shown by the dashed lines (cable segment CD is removed). If the tension in CD' is to be twice the tension in BCD, determine the height h for placement of the strut CE.

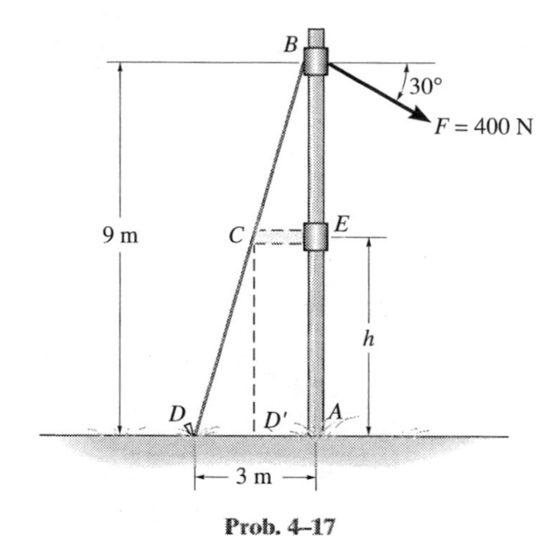

Prob. 4–17

4-18. The worker uses the hand truck to move material down the ramp. If the truck and its contents are held in the position shown and have a weight of 500 N ($\approx$ 50 kg) with center of gravity at G, determine the resultant normal force of both wheels on the ground A and the magnitude of the force required at the grip B.

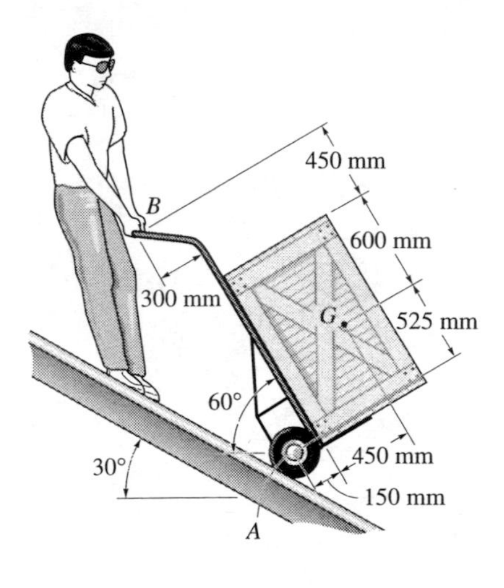

Prob. 4–18

4-19. The shelf supports the electric motor which has a mass of 15 kg and mass center at G_m. The platform upon which it rests has a mass of 4 kg and mass center at G_p. Assuming that a single bolt B holds the shelf up and the bracket bears against the smooth wall at A, determine this normal force at A and the horizontal and vertical components of reaction of the bolt on the bracket.

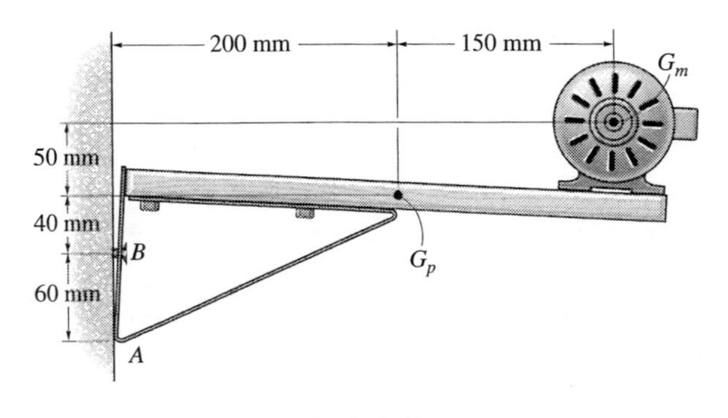

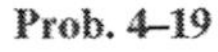
Prob. 4–19

4-20. The upper portion of the crane boom consists of the jib AB, which is supported by the pin at A, the guy line BC, and the backstay CD, each cable being separately attached to the mast at C. If the 5-kN load is supported by the hoist line, which passes over the pulley at B, determine the magnitude of the resultant force the pin exerts on the jib at A for equilibrium, the tension in the guy line BC, and the tension T in the hoist line. Neglect the weight of the jib. The pulley at B has a radius of 0.1 m.

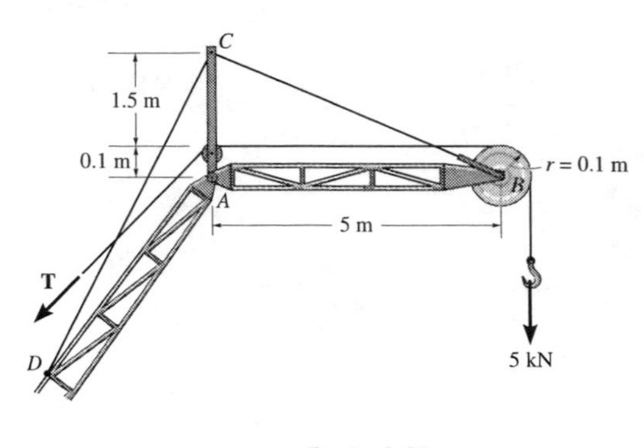

Prob. 4–20

***4-21.** The mobile crane has a weight of 600 000 N ($\approx$ 60 tonne) and center of gravity at G_1; the boom has a weight of 150 000 N ($\approx$ 15 tonne) and center of gravity at G_2. Determine the smallest angle of tilt θ of the boom, without causing the crane to overturn if the suspended load is $W = 200\,000$ N. Neglect the thickness of the tracks at A and B.

4-22. The mobile crane has a weight of 600 000 N ($\approx$ 60 tonne) and center of gravity at G_1; the boom has a weight of 150 000 N ($\approx$ 15 tonne) and center of gravity at G_2. If the suspended load has a weight of $W = 80\,000$ N ($\approx$ 8 tonne), determine the normal reactions at the tracks A and B. For the calculation, neglect the thickness of the tracks and take $\theta = 30°$.

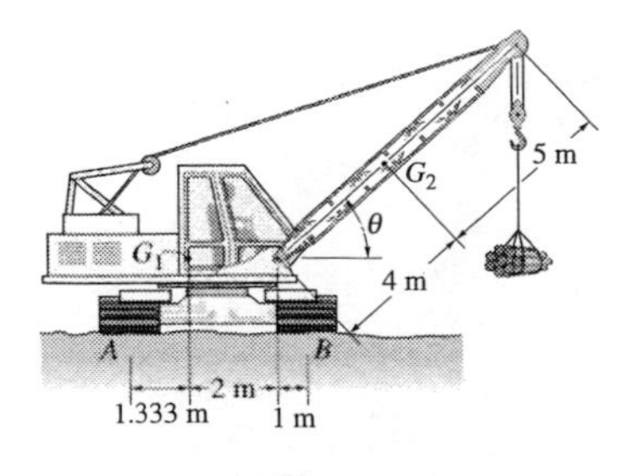

Probs. 4–21/22

4-23. The winch consists of a drum of radius 100 mm, which is pin-connected at its center C. At its outer rim is a ratchet gear having a mean radius of 150 mm. The pawl AB serves as a two-force member (short link) and holds the drum from rotating. If the suspended load is 2000 N, determine the horizontal and vertical components of reaction at the pin C.

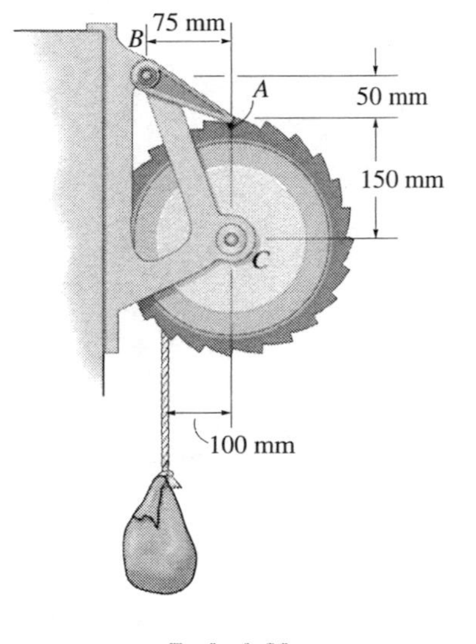

Prob. 4–23

4-24. The crane consists of three parts, which have weights of $W_1 = 14\,000$ N ($\approx$ 1400 kg), $W_2 = 3600$ N ($\approx$ 360 kg), $W_3 = 6000$ N ($\approx$ 600 kg) and centers of gravity at G_1, G_2, and G_3, respectively. Neglecting the weight of the boom, determine (a) the reactions on each of the four tires if the load is hoisted at constant velocity and has a weight of 3200 N ($\approx$ 320 kg), and (b), with the boom held in the position shown, the maximum load the crane can lift without tipping over.

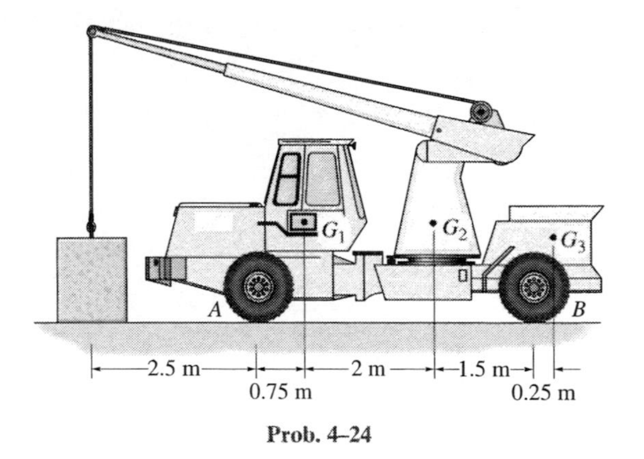

Prob. 4–24

***4-25.** The boom supports the two vertical loads. Neglect the size of the collars at D and B and the thickness of the boom, and compute the horizontal and vertical components of force at the pin A and the force in cable CB. Set $F_1 = 800$ N and $F_2 = 350$ N.

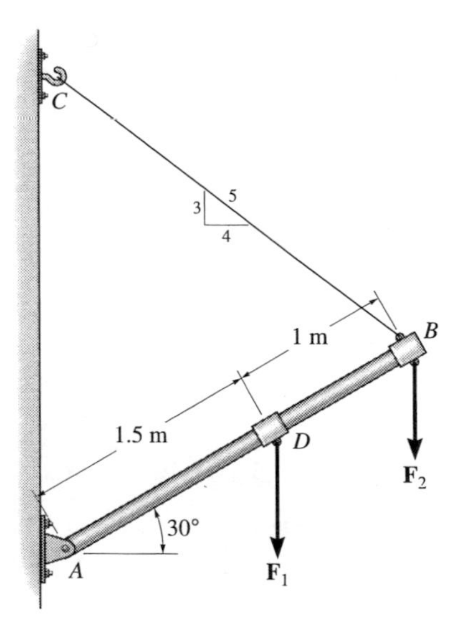

Probs. 4–25

4-26. The boom is intended to support two vertical loads, $\mathbf{F}_1$ and $\mathbf{F}_2$. If the cable CB can sustain a maximum load of 1500 N before it fails, determine the critical loads if $F_1 = 2F_2$. Also, what is the magnitude of the maximum reaction at pin A?

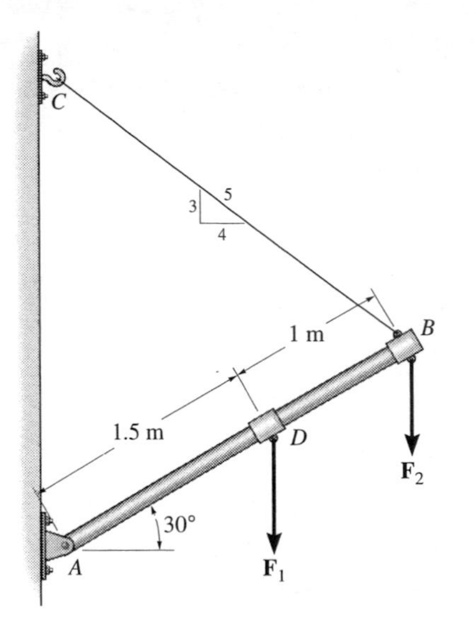

Probs. 4–26

4-27. Three uniform books, each having a weight W and length a, are stacked as shown. Determine the maximum distance d that the top book can extend out from the bottom one so the stack does not topple over.

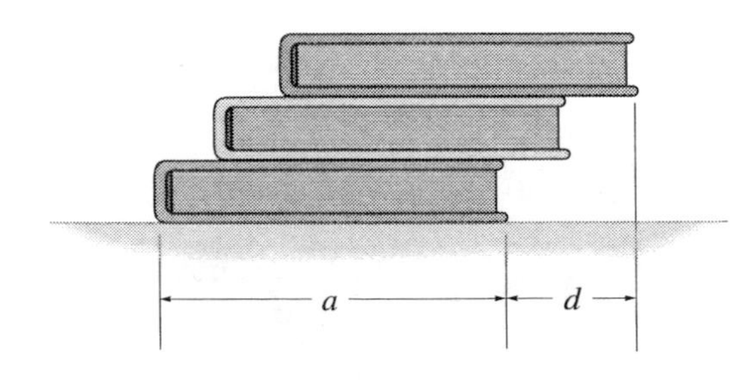

Prob. 4–27

4-28. The toggle switch consists of a cocking lever that is pinned to a fixed frame at A and held in place by the spring which has an unstretched length of 200 mm. Determine the magnitude of the resultant force at A and the normal force on the peg at B when the lever is in the position shown.

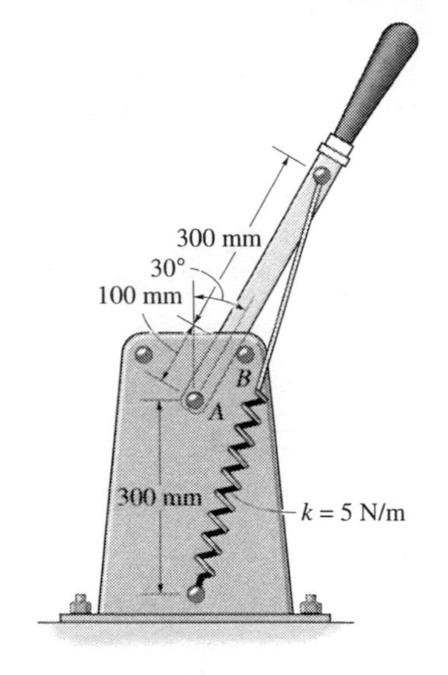

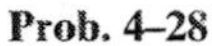
Prob. 4–28

4-29. The rigid beam of negligible weight is supported horizontally by two springs and a pin. If the springs are uncompressed when the load $\mathbf{P}$ is removed, determine the force in each spring when the load $\mathbf{P}$ is applied. Also, compute the vertical deflection of end C. Assume the spring stiffness k is large enough so that only small deflections occur. *Hint:* The beam rotates about A so the deflections in the springs can be related.

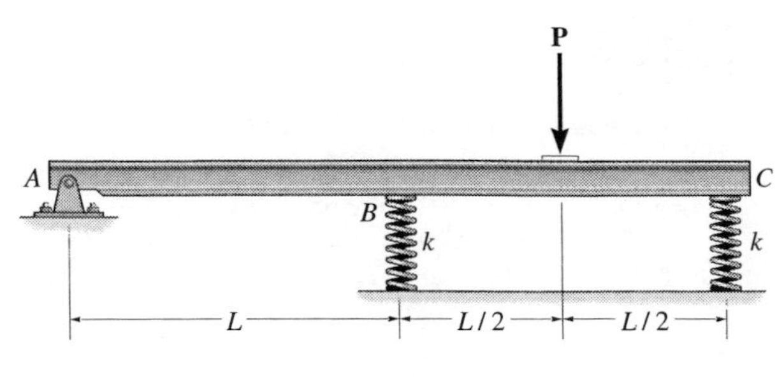

Prob. 4–29

4-30. The uniform rod AB has a weight of 150 N ($\approx$ 15 kg) and the spring is unstretched when $\theta = 0°$. If $\theta = 30°$, determine the stiffness k of the spring so that the rod is in equilibrium.

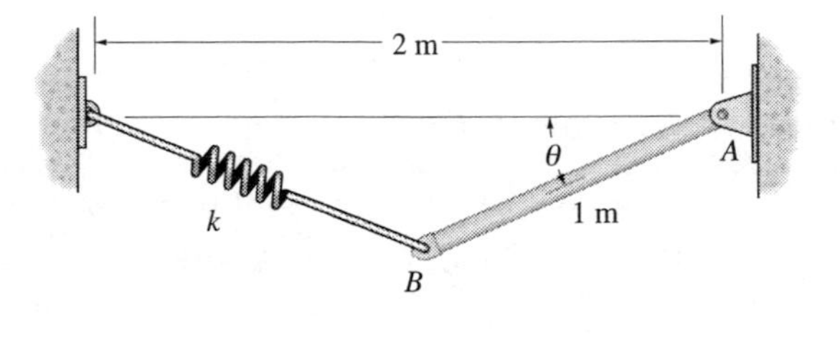

Prob. 4–30

4-31. The smooth pipe rests against the wall at the points of contact A, B, and C. Determine the reactions at these points needed to support the vertical force of 180 N. Neglect the pipe's thickness in the calculation.

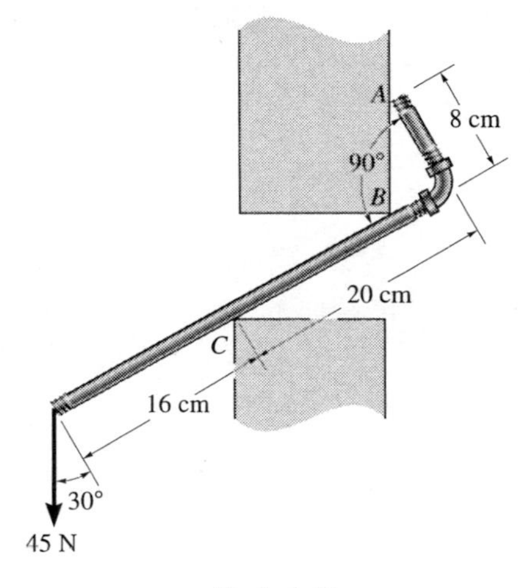

Prob. 4–31

Equilibrium in Three Dimensions

4.5 Free-Body Diagrams

The first step in solving three-dimensional equilibrium problems, as in the case of two dimensions, is to draw a free-body diagram of the body (or group of bodies considered as a system). Before we show this, however, it is necessary to discuss the types of reactions that can occur at the supports.

Support Reactions. The reactive forces and couple moments acting at various types of supports and connections, when the members are viewed in three dimensions, are listed in Table 4–2. It is important to recognize the symbols used to represent each of these supports and to understand clearly how the forces and couple moments are developed by each support. As in the two-dimensional case, *a force is developed by a support that restricts the translation of the attached member, whereas a couple moment is developed when rotation of the attached member is prevented.* For example, in Table 4–2, the ball-and-socket joint (4) prevents any translation of the connecting member; therefore, a force must act on the member at the point of connection. This force has three components having unknown magnitudes, F_x, F_y, F_z. Provided these components are known, one can obtain the magnitude of force. $F = \sqrt{F_x^2 + F_y^2 + F_z^2}$, and the force's orientation defined by the coordinate direction angles α, β, γ, Eqs. 2–7.* Since the connecting member is allowed to rotate freely about *any* axis, no couple moment is resisted by a ball-and-socket joint.

It should be noted that the *single* bearing supports (5) and (7), the *single* pin (8), and the *single* hinge (9) are shown to support both force and couple-moment components. If, however, these supports are used in conjunction with *other* bearings, pins, or hinges to hold a rigid body in equilibrium and the supports are *properly aligned* when connected to the body, then the *force reactions* at these supports *alone* may be adequate for supporting the body. In other words, the couple moments become redundant and are not shown on the free-body diagram. The reason for this should become clear after studying the examples which follow.

*The three unknowns may also be represented as an unknown force magnitude F and two unknown coordinate direction angles. The third direction angle is obtained using the identity $\cos^2 \alpha + \cos^2 \beta + \cos^2 \gamma = 1$, Eq. 2–10.

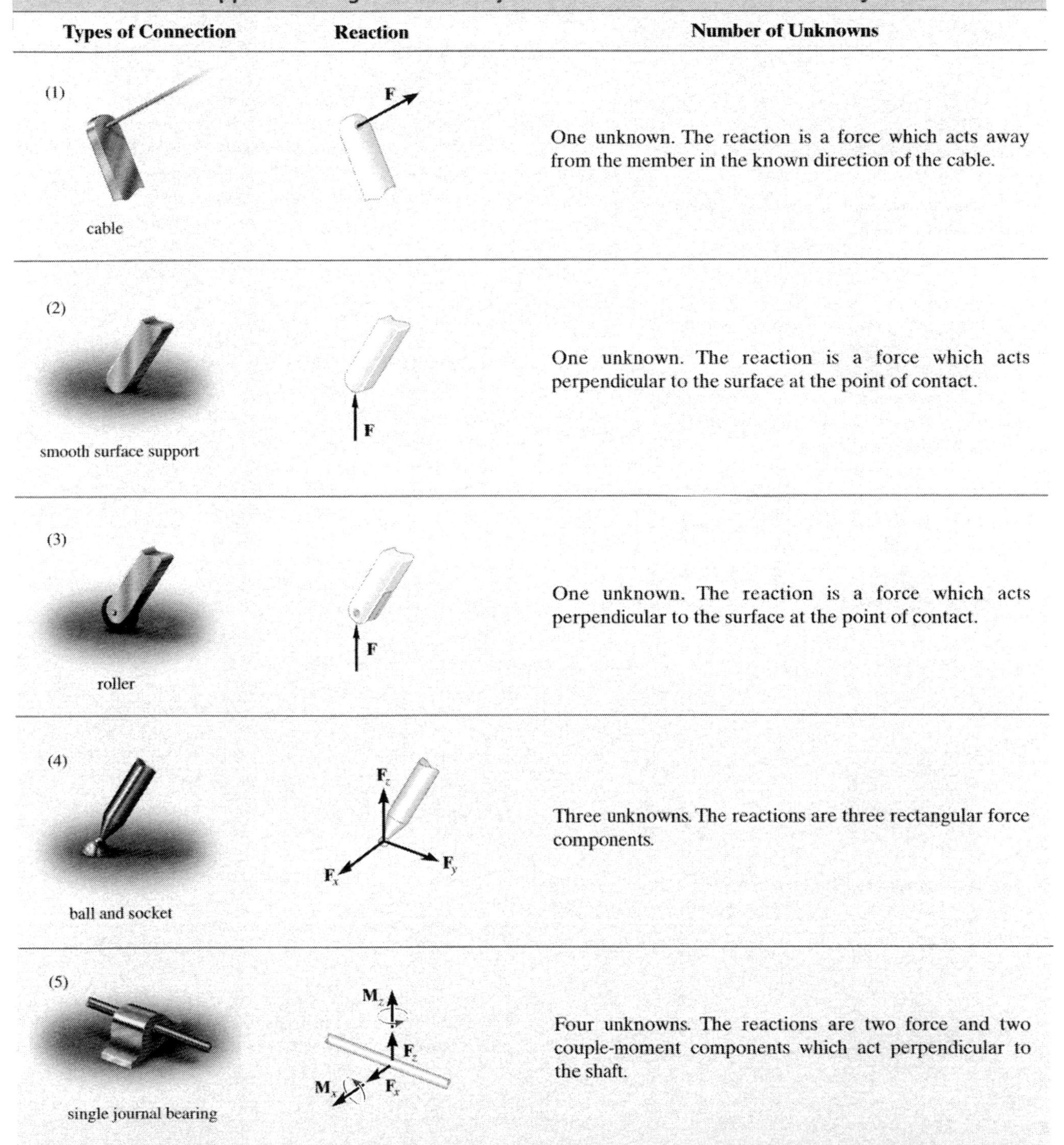

TABLE 4–2 • Supports for Rigid Bodies Subjected to Three-Dimensional Force Systems

Types of Connection	Reaction	Number of Unknowns
(1) cable	$\mathbf{F}$	One unknown. The reaction is a force which acts away from the member in the known direction of the cable.
(2) smooth surface support	$\mathbf{F}$	One unknown. The reaction is a force which acts perpendicular to the surface at the point of contact.
(3) roller	$\mathbf{F}$	One unknown. The reaction is a force which acts perpendicular to the surface at the point of contact.
(4) ball and socket	$\mathbf{F}_z$, $\mathbf{F}_x$, $\mathbf{F}_y$	Three unknowns. The reactions are three rectangular force components.
(5) single journal bearing	$\mathbf{M}_z$, $\mathbf{F}_z$, $\mathbf{M}_x$, $\mathbf{F}_x$	Four unknowns. The reactions are two force and two couple-moment components which act perpendicular to the shaft.

continued

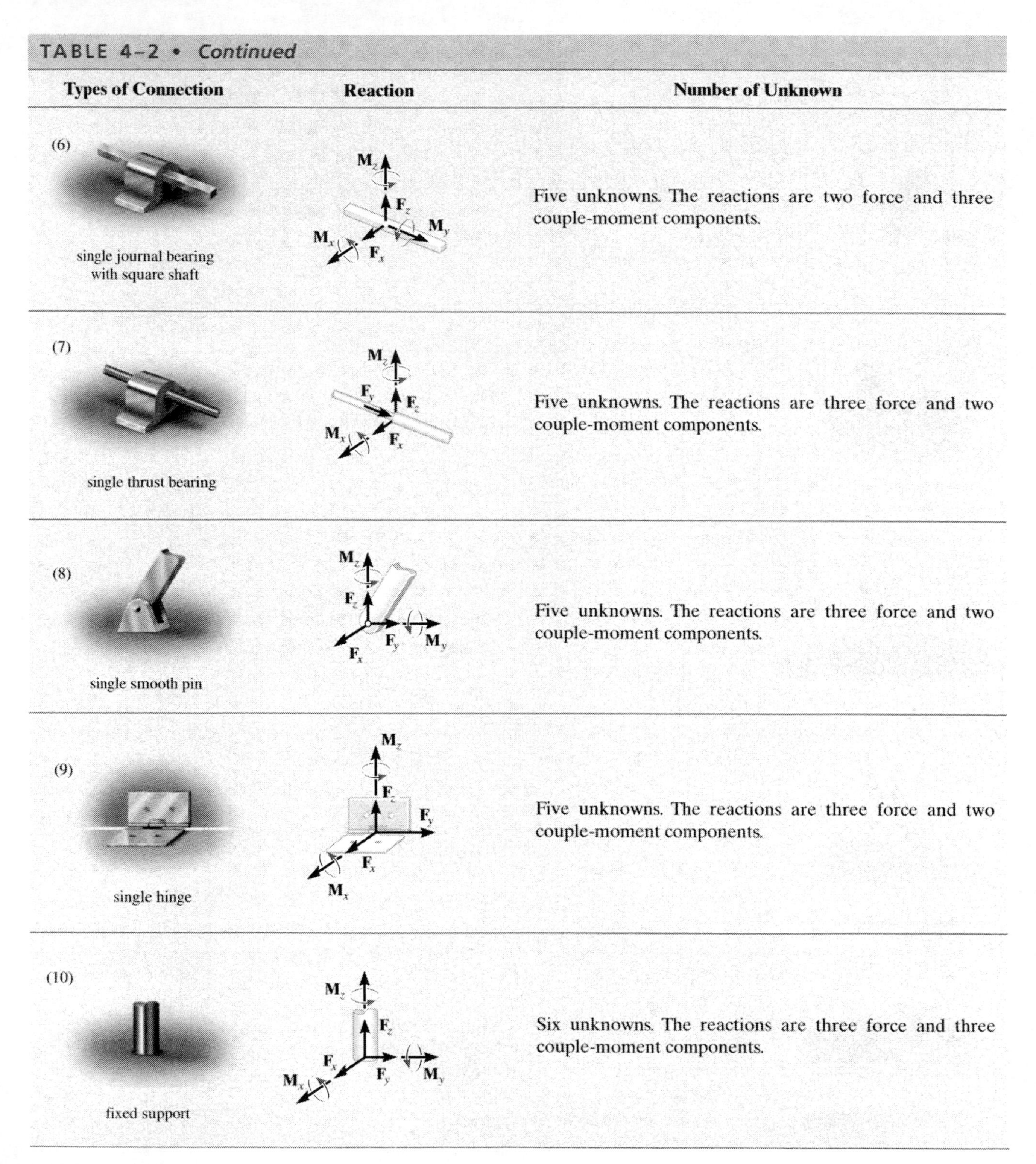

TABLE 4–2 • *Continued*

Types of Connection	Reaction	Number of Unknown
(6) single journal bearing with square shaft	$\mathbf{M}_z$, $\mathbf{F}_z$, $\mathbf{M}_y$, $\mathbf{M}_x$, $\mathbf{F}_x$	Five unknowns. The reactions are two force and three couple-moment components.
(7) single thrust bearing	$\mathbf{M}_z$, $\mathbf{F}_y$, $\mathbf{F}_z$, $\mathbf{M}_x$, $\mathbf{F}_x$	Five unknowns. The reactions are three force and two couple-moment components.
(8) single smooth pin	$\mathbf{M}_z$, $\mathbf{F}_z$, $\mathbf{F}_y$, $\mathbf{M}_y$, $\mathbf{F}_x$	Five unknowns. The reactions are three force and two couple-moment components.
(9) single hinge	$\mathbf{M}_z$, $\mathbf{F}_z$, $\mathbf{F}_y$, $\mathbf{F}_x$, $\mathbf{M}_x$	Five unknowns. The reactions are three force and two couple-moment components.
(10) fixed support	$\mathbf{M}_z$, $\mathbf{F}_z$, $\mathbf{F}_x$, $\mathbf{M}_x$, $\mathbf{F}_y$, $\mathbf{M}_y$	Six unknowns. The reactions are three force and three couple-moment components.

Typical examples of actual supports that are referenced to Table 4–2 are shown in the following sequence of photos.

This ball-and-socket joint provides a connection for the housing of an earth grader to its frame. (4)

This journal bearing supports the end of the shaft. (5)

This thrust bearing is used to support the drive shaft on a machine. (7)

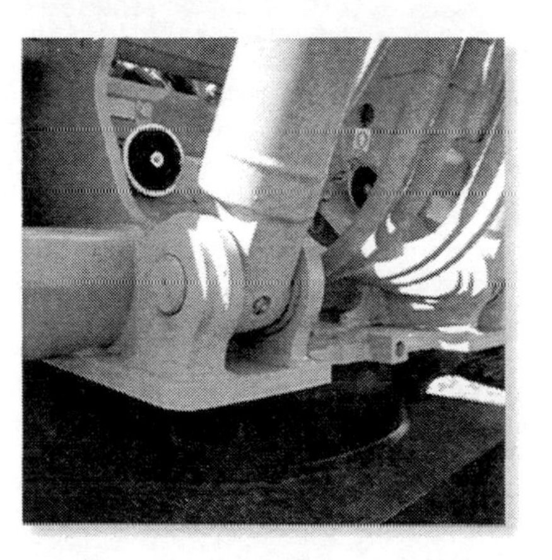

This pin is used to support the end of the strut used on a tractor. (8)

Free-Body Diagrams. The general procedure for establishing the free-body diagram of a rigid body has been outlined in Sec. 4.2. Essentially it requires first "isolating" the body by drawing its outlined shape. This is followed by a careful *labeling* of *all* the forces and couple moments in reference to an established x, y, z coordinate system. As a general rule, *components of reaction* having an *unknown magnitude* are shown acting on the free-body diagram in the *positive sense*. In this way, if any negative values are obtained, they will indicate that the components act in the negative coordinate directions.

It is a mistake to support a door using a single hinge since the hinge must develop a force C_y to support the weight **W** of the door and a couple moment **M** to support the moment of **W**, i.e., $M = Wd$. If instead two properly aligned hinges are used, then the weight is carried by both hinges, $A_y + B_y = W$, and the moment of the door is resisted by the two hinge forces $\mathbf{F}_x$ and $-\mathbf{F}_x$. These forces form a couple, such that $F_x d' = Wd$. In other words, no couple moments are produced by the hinges on the door provided they are in *proper alignment*. Instead, the forces $\mathbf{F}_x$ and $-\mathbf{F}_x$. resist the rotation caused by **W**.

EXAMPLE 4.10

Several examples of objects along with their associated free-body diagrams are shown in Fig. 4–22. In all cases, the *x, y, z* axes are established and the unknown reaction components are indicated in the positive sense. The weight of the objects is neglected.

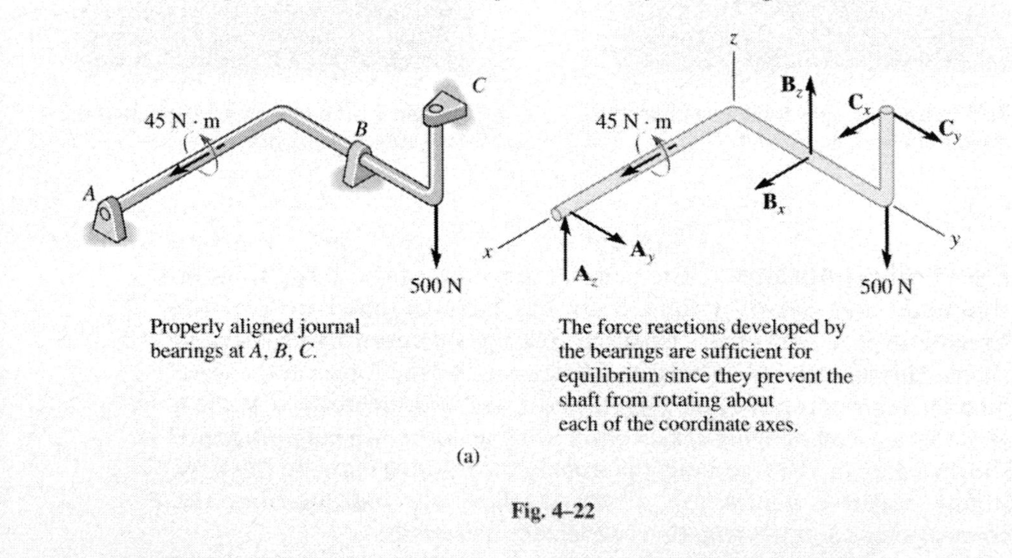

Properly aligned journal bearings at *A*, *B*, *C*.

The force reactions developed by the bearings are sufficient for equilibrium since they prevent the shaft from rotating about each of the coordinate axes.

(a)

Fig. 4–22

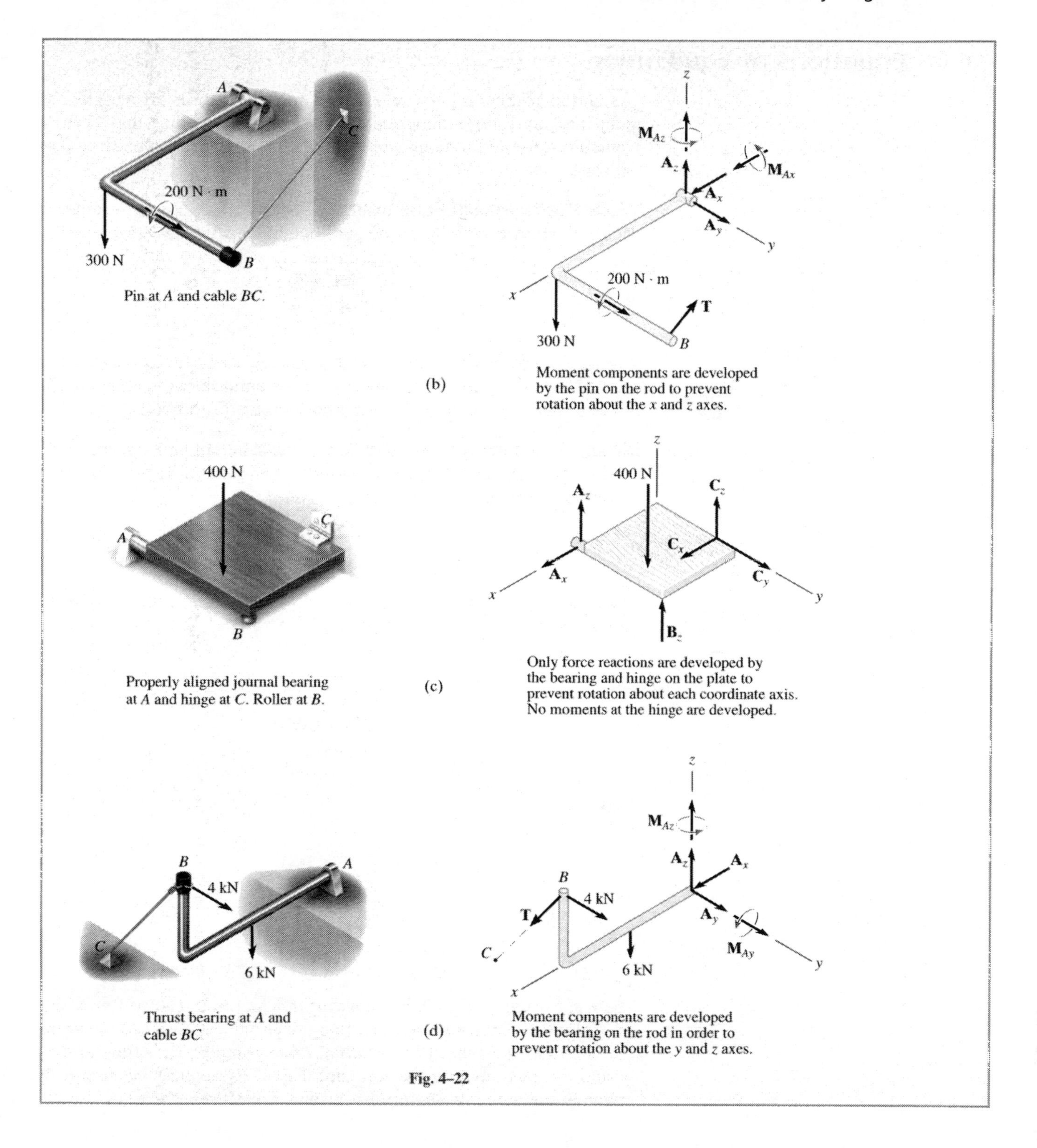

Pin at A and cable BC.

(b)

Moment components are developed by the pin on the rod to prevent rotation about the x and z axes.

Properly aligned journal bearing at A and hinge at C. Roller at B.

(c)

Only force reactions are developed by the bearing and hinge on the plate to prevent rotation about each coordinate axis. No moments at the hinge are developed.

Thrust bearing at A and cable BC

(d)

Moment components are developed by the bearing on the rod in order to prevent rotation about the y and z axes.

Fig. 4–22

4.6 Equations of Equilibrium

As stated in Sec. 4.1, the conditions for equilibrium of a rigid body subjected to a three-dimensional force system require that both the *resultant* force and *resultant* couple moment acting on the body be equal to *zero*.

Vector Equations of Equilibrium. The two conditions for equilibrium of a rigid body may be expressed mathematically in vector form as

$$\begin{aligned} \Sigma \mathbf{F} &= \mathbf{0} \\ \Sigma \mathbf{M}_O &= \mathbf{0} \end{aligned} \qquad (4\text{–}6)$$

where $\Sigma \mathbf{F}$ is the vector sum of all the external forces acting on the body and $\Sigma \mathbf{M}_O$ is the sum of the couple moments and the moments of all the forces about any point O located either on or off the body.

Scalar Equations of Equilibrium. If all the applied external forces and couple moments are expressed in Cartesian vector form and substituted into Eqs. 4–6, we have

$$\Sigma \mathbf{F} = \Sigma F_x \mathbf{i} + \Sigma F_y \mathbf{j} + \Sigma F_z \mathbf{k} = 0$$

$$\Sigma \mathbf{M}_O = \Sigma M_x \mathbf{i} + \Sigma M_y \mathbf{j} + \Sigma M_z \mathbf{k} = 0$$

Since the **i**, **j**, and **k** components are independent from one another, the above equations are satisfied provided

$$\begin{aligned} \Sigma F_x &= 0 \\ \Sigma F_y &= 0 \\ \Sigma F_z &= 0 \end{aligned} \qquad (4\text{–}7a)$$

and

$$\begin{aligned} \Sigma M_x &= 0 \\ \Sigma M_y &= 0 \\ \Sigma M_z &= 0 \end{aligned} \qquad (4\text{–}7b)$$

These *six scalar equilibrium equations* may be used to solve for at most six unknowns shown on the free-body diagram. Equations 4–7*a* express the fact that the sum of the external force components acting in the x, y, and z directions must be zero, and Eqs. 4–7*b* require the sum of the moment components about the x, y, and z axes to be zero.

PROCEDURE FOR ANALYSIS

Three-dimensional equilibrium problems for a rigid body can be solved using the following procedure.

Free-Body Diagram

- Draw an outlined shape of the body.
- Show all the forces and couple moments acting on the body.
- Establish the origin of the x, y, z axes at a convenient point and orient the axes so that they are parallel to as many of the external forces and moments as possible.
- Label all the loadings and specify their directions relative to the x, y, z axes. In general, show all the unknown components having a positive sense along the x, y, z axes if the sense cannot be determined.
- Indicate the dimensions of the body necessary for computing the moments of forces.

Equations of Equilibrium

- If the x, y, z force and moment components seem easy to determine, then apply the six scalar equations of equilibrium; otherwise use the vector equations.
- It is not necessary that the set of axes chosen for force summation coincide with the set of axes chosen for moment summation. Also, any set of nonorthogonal axes may be chosen for this purpose.
- Choose the direction of an axis for moment summation such that it intersects the lines of action of as many unknown forces as possible. In this way, the moments of forces passing through points on this axis and forces which are parallel to the axis will then be zero.
- If the solution of the equilibrium equations yields a negative scalar for a force or couple moment magnitude, it indicates that the sense is opposite to that which was assumed on the free-body diagram.

The homogeneous plate shown in Fig. 4–23*a* has a mass of 100 kg and is subjected to a force and couple moment along its edges. If it is supported in the horizontal plane by means of a roller at *A*, a ball-and-socket joint at *B*, and a cord at *C*, determine the components of reaction at the supports.

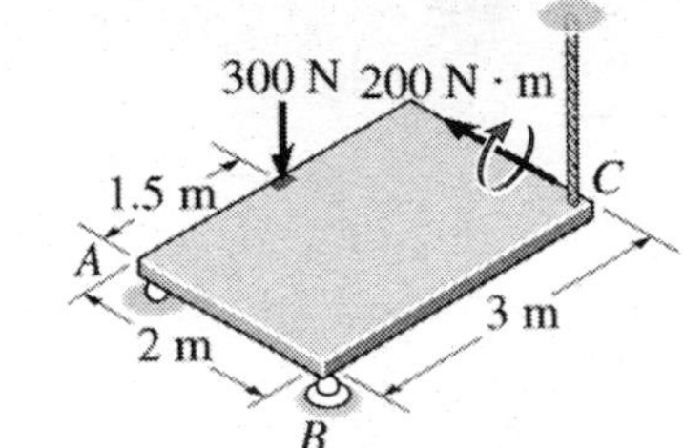

(a)

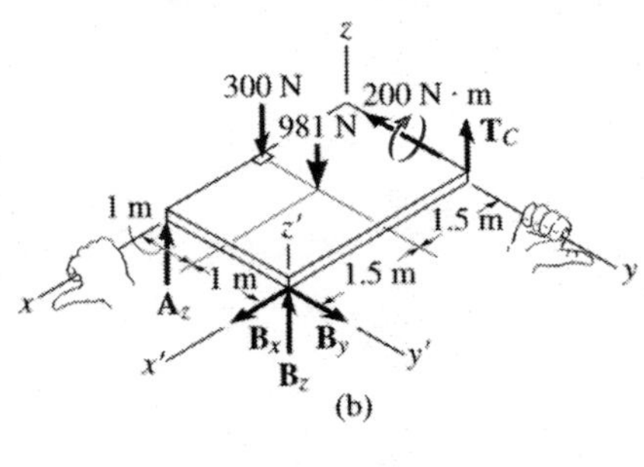

(b)

Fig. 4–23

Solution (*Scalar Analysis*)

Free-Body Diagram. There are five unknown reactions acting on the plate, as shown in Fig. 4–23*b*. Each of these reactions is assumed to act in a positive coordinate direction.

Equations of Equilibrium. Since the three-dimensional geometry is rather simple, a *scalar analysis* provides a *direct solution* to this problem. A force summation along each axis yields

$$\Sigma F_x = 0; \qquad B_x = 0 \qquad \textit{Ans.}$$

$$\Sigma F_y = 0; \qquad B_y = 0 \qquad \textit{Ans.}$$

$$\Sigma F_z = 0; \qquad A_z + B_z + T_C - 300\text{ N} - 981\text{ N} = 0 \qquad (1)$$

Recall that the moment of a force about an axis is equal to the product of the force magnitude and the perpendicular distance (moment arm) from the line of action of the force to the axis. The sense of the moment is determined by the right-hand rule. Also, forces that are parallel to an axis or pass through it create no moment about the axis. Hence, summing moments of the forces on the free-body diagram, with positive moments acting along the positive *x* or *y* axis, we have

$$\Sigma M_x = 0; \qquad T_C(2\text{ m}) - 981\text{ N}(1\text{ m}) + B_z(2\text{ m}) = 0 \qquad (2)$$

$$\Sigma M_y = 0;$$

$$300\text{ N}(1.5\text{ m}) + 981\text{ N}(1.5\text{ m}) - B_z(3\text{ m}) - A_z(3\text{ m}) - 200\text{ N}\cdot\text{m} = 0 \quad (3)$$

The components of force at *B* can be eliminated if the x', y', z' axes are used. We obtain

$$\Sigma M_{x'} = 0; \qquad 981\text{ N}(1\text{ m}) + 300\text{ N}(2\text{ m}) - A_z(2\text{ m}) = 0 \qquad (4)$$

$$\Sigma M_{y'} = 0;$$

$$-300\text{ N}(1.5\text{ m}) - 981\text{ N}(1.5\text{ m}) - 200\text{ N}\cdot\text{m} + T_C(3\text{ m}) = 0 \qquad (5)$$

Solving Eqs. 1 through 3 or the more convenient Eqs. 1, 4, and 5 yields

$$A_z = 790\text{ N} \qquad B_z = -217\text{ N} \qquad T_C = 707\text{ N} \qquad \textit{Ans.}$$

The negative sign indicates that $\mathbf{B}_z$ acts downward.

Note that the solution of this problem does not require the use of a summation of moments about the *z* axis. The plate is partially constrained since the supports cannot prevent it from turning about the *z* axis if a force is applied to it in the *x*–*y* plane.

EXAMPLE 4.12

The windlass shown in Fig. 4–24*a* is supported by a thrust bearing at A and a smooth journal bearing at B, which are properly aligned on the shaft. Determine the magnitude of the vertical force **P** that must be applied to the handle to maintain equilibrium of the 100-kg bucket. Also calculate the reactions at the bearings.

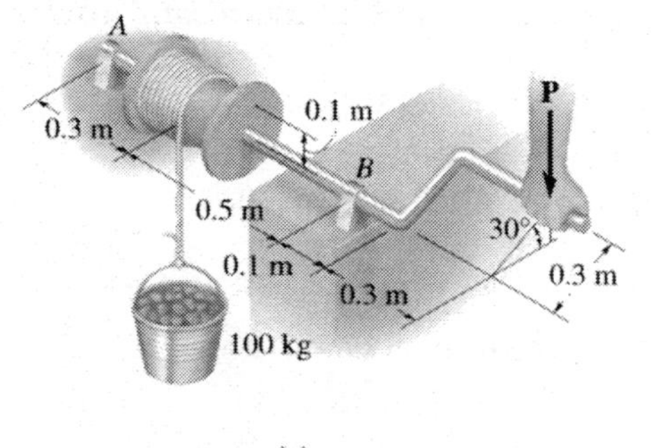

(a)

(b)

Fig. 4–24

Solution (Scalar Analysis)

Free-Body Diagram. Since the bearings at A and B are aligned correctly, *only* force reactions occur at these supports, Fig. 4–24*b*. Why are there no moment reactions?

Equations of Equilibrium. Summing moments about the x axis yields a direct solution for **P**. Why? For a scalar moment summation, it is necessary to determine the moment of each force as the product of the force magnitude and the *perpendicular distance* from the x axis to the line of action of the force. Using the right-hand rule and assuming positive moments act in the $+\mathbf{i}$ direction, we have

$$\Sigma M_x = 0; \qquad 981\text{ N}(0.1\text{ m}) - P(0.3\cos 30°\text{m}) = 0$$

$$P = 377.6\text{ N} \qquad \textit{Ans.}$$

Using this result and summing moments about the y and z axes yields

$$\Sigma M_y = 0;$$

$$-981\text{ N}(0.5\text{ m}) + A_z(0.8\text{ m}) + (377.6\text{ N})(0.4\text{ m}) = 0$$

$$A_z = 424.3\text{ N} \qquad \textit{Ans.}$$

$$\Sigma M_z = 0; \qquad -A_y(0.8\text{ m}) = 0 \qquad A_y = 0$$

The reactions at B are determined by a force summation using these results.

$$\Sigma F_x = 0; \qquad A_x = 0$$

$$\Sigma F_y = 0; \qquad 0 + B_y = 0 \qquad B_y = 0$$

$$\Sigma F_z = 0; \qquad 424.3 - 981 + B_z - 377.6 = 0 \qquad B_z = 934\text{ N} \qquad \textit{Ans.}$$

EXAMPLE 4.13

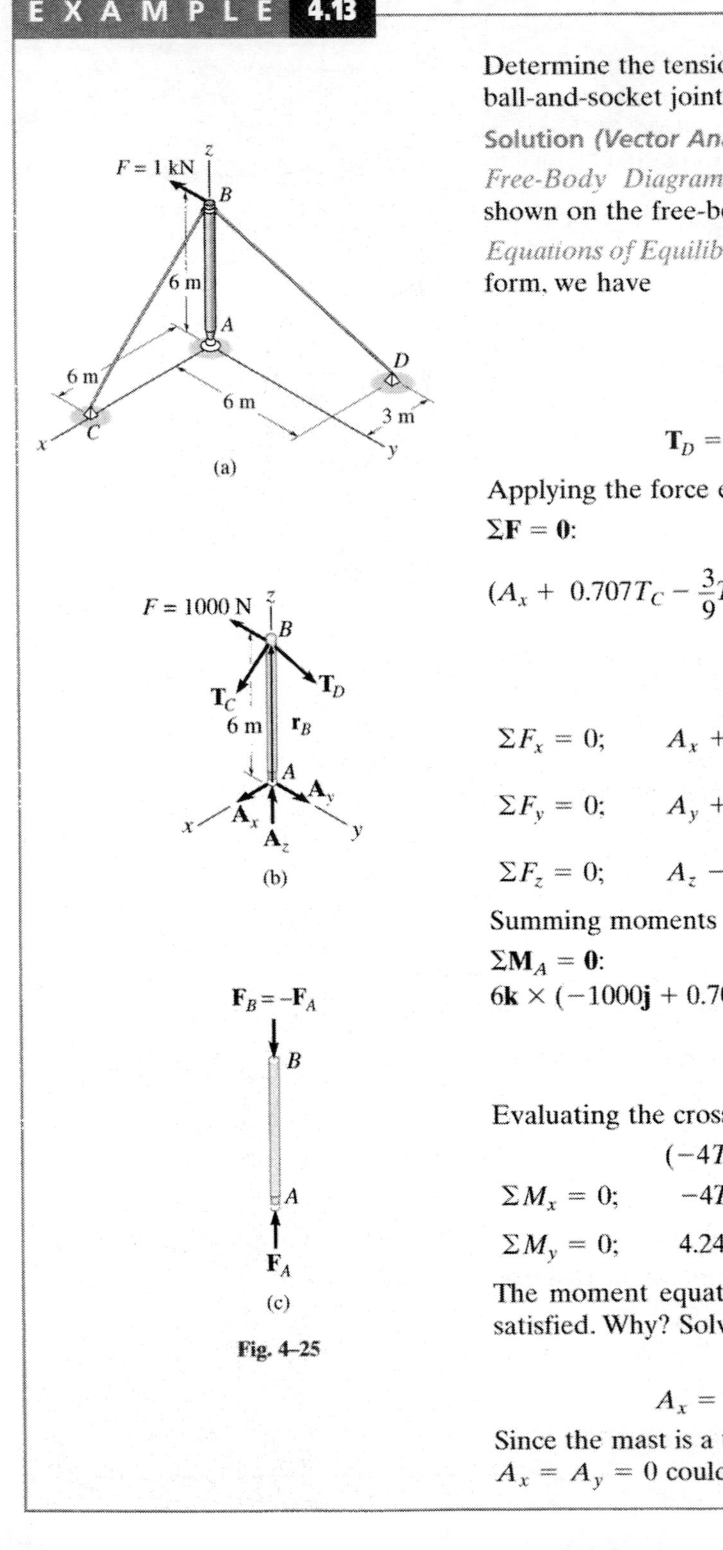

Fig. 4–25

Determine the tension in cables BC and BD and the reactions at the ball-and-socket joint A for the mast shown in Fig. 4–25a.

Solution (Vector Analysis)

Free-Body Diagram. There are five unknown force magnitudes shown on the free-body diagram, Fig. 4–25b.

Equations of Equilibrium. Expressing each force in Cartesian vector form, we have

$$\mathbf{F} = \{-1000\mathbf{j}\}\ \text{N}$$

$$\mathbf{F}_A = A_x\mathbf{i} + A_y\mathbf{j} + A_z\mathbf{k}$$

$$\mathbf{T}_C = 0.707T_C\mathbf{i} - 0.707T_C\mathbf{k}$$

$$\mathbf{T}_D = T_D\left(\frac{\mathbf{r}_{BD}}{r_{BD}}\right) = -\frac{3}{9}T_D\mathbf{i} + \frac{6}{9}T_D\mathbf{j} - \frac{6}{9}T_D\mathbf{k}$$

Applying the force equation of equilibrium gives

$\Sigma\mathbf{F} = \mathbf{0}$: $\quad \mathbf{F} + \mathbf{F}_A + \mathbf{T}_C + \mathbf{T}_D = \mathbf{0}$

$$\left(A_x + 0.707T_C - \frac{3}{9}T_D\right)\mathbf{i} + \left(-1000 + A_y + \frac{6}{9}T_D\right)\mathbf{j} + \left(A_z - 0.707T_C - \frac{6}{9}T_D\right)\mathbf{k} = \mathbf{0}$$

$\Sigma F_x = 0;\quad A_x + 0.707T_C - \frac{3}{9}T_D = 0 \qquad (1)$

$\Sigma F_y = 0;\quad A_y + \frac{6}{9}T_D - 1000 = 0 \qquad (2)$

$\Sigma F_z = 0;\quad A_z - 0.707T_C - \frac{6}{9}T_D = 0 \qquad (3)$

Summing moments about point A, we have

$\Sigma\mathbf{M}_A = \mathbf{0}$: $\quad \mathbf{r}_B \times (\mathbf{F} + \mathbf{T}_C + \mathbf{T}_D) = \mathbf{0}$

$$6\mathbf{k} \times \left(-1000\mathbf{j} + 0.707T_C\mathbf{i} - 0.707T_C\mathbf{k} - \frac{3}{9}T_D\mathbf{i} + \frac{6}{9}T_D\mathbf{j} - \frac{6}{9}T_D\mathbf{k}\right) = \mathbf{0}$$

Evaluating the cross product and combining terms yields

$$(-4T_D + 6000)\mathbf{i} + (4.24T_C - 2T_D)\mathbf{j} = \mathbf{0}$$

$\Sigma M_x = 0;\quad -4T_D + 6000 = 0 \qquad (4)$

$\Sigma M_y = 0;\quad 4.24T_C - 2T_D = 0 \qquad (5)$

The moment equation about the z axis, $\Sigma M_z = 0$, is automatically satisfied. Why? Solving Eqs. 1 through 5 we have

$T_C = 707\ \text{N} \qquad T_D = 1500\ \text{N}$ *Ans.*

$A_x = 0\ \text{N} \qquad A_y = 0\ \text{N} \qquad A_z = 1500\ \text{N}$ *Ans.*

Since the mast is a two-force member, Fig. 4–25c, note that the value $A_x = A_y = 0$ could have been determined *by inspection*.

PROBLEMS

***4-32.** Determine the x, y, z components of reaction at the fixed wall A.

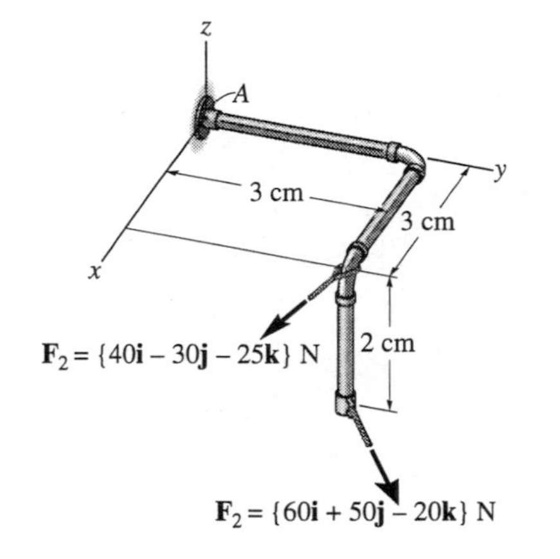

Prob. 4–32

4-33. The nonhomogeneous door of a large pressure vessel has a weight of 15 kN ($\approx$ 1500 kg) and a center of gravity at G. Determine the magnitudes of the resultant force and resultant couple moment, developed at the hinge A, needed to support the door in any open position.

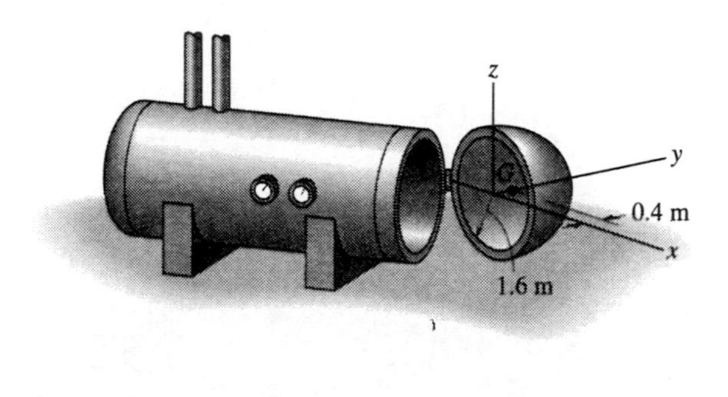

Prob. 4–33

4-34. The power drill is subjected to the forces shown acting on the grips. Determine the x, y, z components of force and the y and z components of moment reaction acting on the drill bit at A.

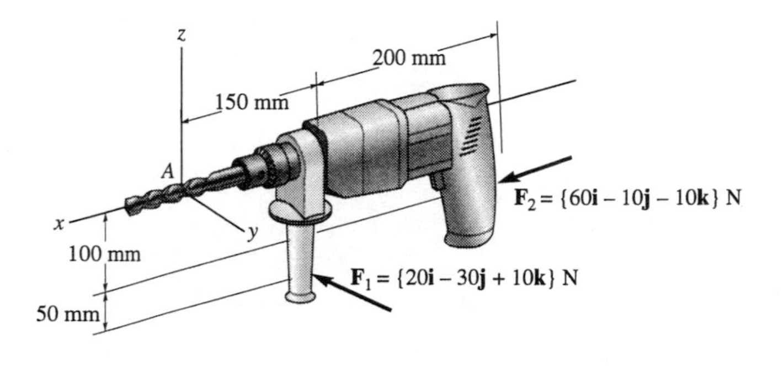

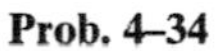

Prob. 4–34

4-35. Determine the floor reaction on each wheel of the engine stand. The engine weighs 750 N ($\approx$ 75 kg) and has a center of gravity at G.

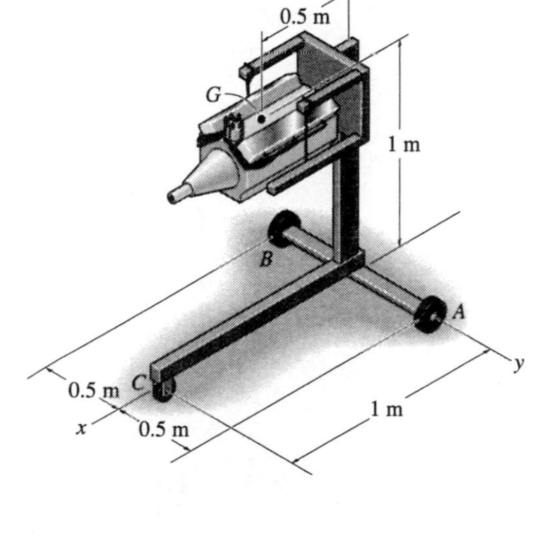

Prob. 4–35

*4-36. The shaft is supported by a thrust bearing at A and a journal bearing at B. Determine the x, y, z components of reaction at these supports and the magnitude of force acting on the gear at C necessary to hold the shaft in equilibrium. The bearings are in proper alignment and exert only force reactions on the shaft.

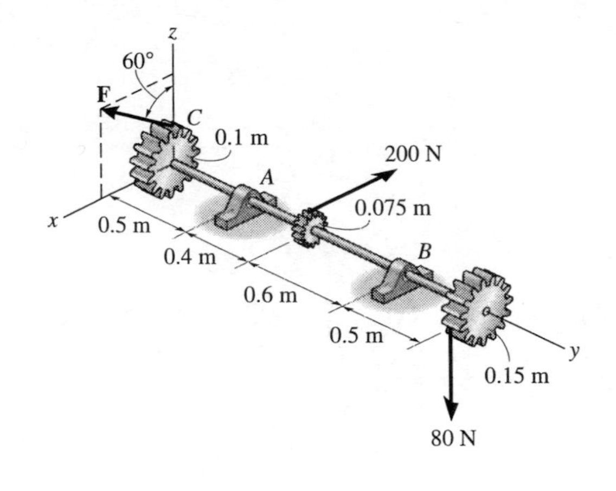

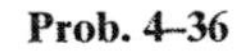
Prob. 4–36

4-37. The windlass supports the 50-kg mass. Determine the horizontal force **P** needed to hold the handle in the position shown, and the components of reaction at the ball-and-socket joint A and the smooth journal bearing B. The bearing at B is in proper alignment and exerts only force reactions on the windlass.

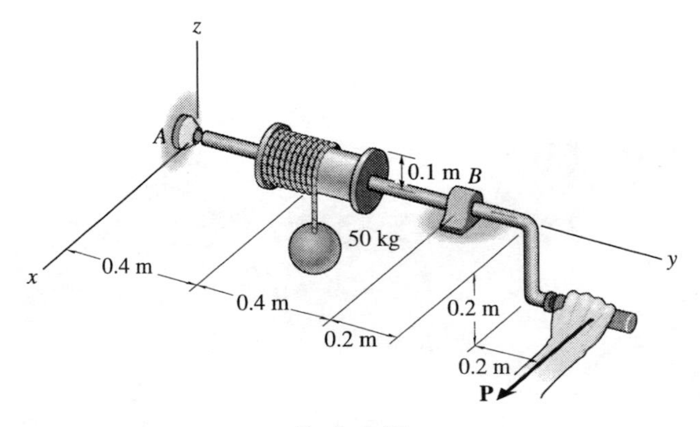

Prob. 4–37

4-38. The shaft is supported by journal bearings at A and B. A key is inserted into the bearing at B in order to prevent the shaft from rotating about and translating along its axis. Determine the x, y, z components of reaction at the bearings when the 600-N force is applied to the arm. The bearings are in proper alignment and exert only force reactions on the shaft.

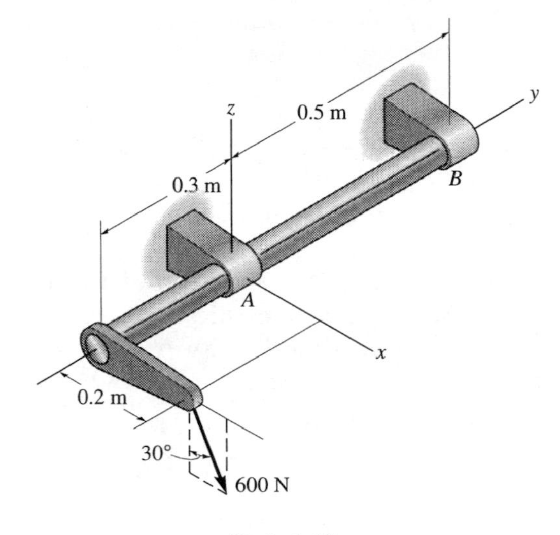

Prob. 4–38

4-39. The bent rod is supported at A, B, and C by journal bearings. Determine the x, y, z reaction components at the bearings if the rod is subjected to a 200-N vertical force and a 30-N · m couple moment as shown. The bearings are in proper alignment and exert only force reactions on the rod.

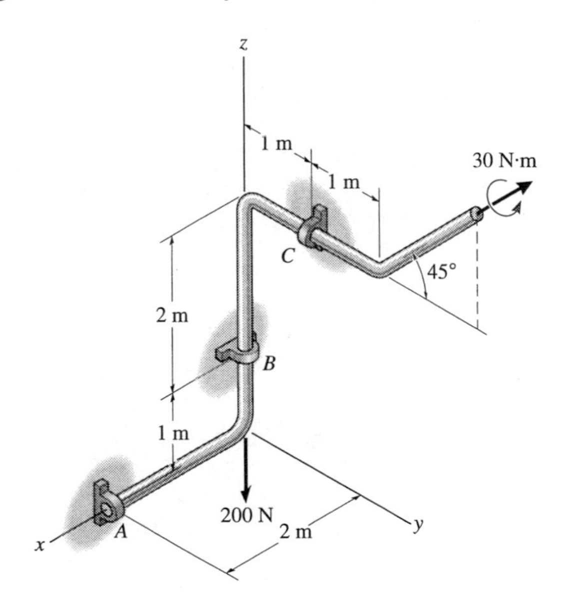

Prob. 4–39

4.7 Friction

Friction may be defined as a force of resistance acting on a body which prevents or retards slipping of the body relative to a second body or surface with which it is in contact. This force always acts *tangent* to the surface at points of contact with other bodies and is directed so as to oppose the possible or existing motion of the body relative to these points.

In general, two types of friction can occur between surfaces. *Fluid friction* exists when the contacting surfaces are separated by a film of fluid (gas or liquid). The nature of fluid friction is studied in fluid mechanics since it depends upon knowledge of the velocity of the fluid and the fluid's ability to resist shear force. In this book only the effects of *dry friction* will be presented. This type of friction is often called *Coulomb friction* since its characteristics were studied extensively by C. A. Coulomb in 1781. Specifically, dry friction occurs between the contacting surfaces of bodies in the absence of a lubricating fluid.

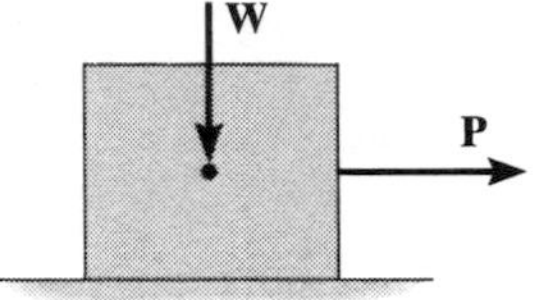

(a)

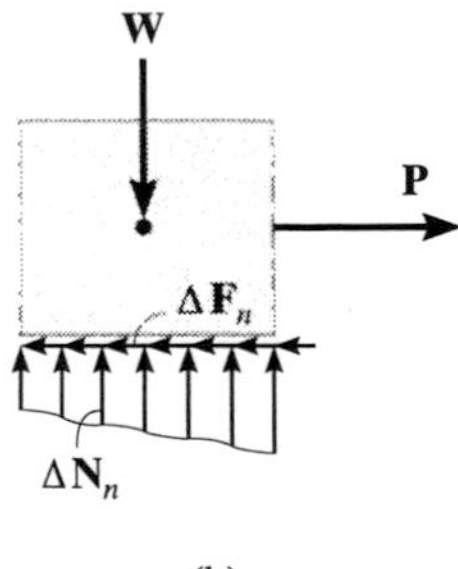

(b)

Fig. 4–26

Theory of Dry Friction. The theory of dry friction can best be explained by considering what effects are caused by pulling horizontally on a block of uniform weight **W** which is resting on a rough horizontal surface, Fig. 4–26*a*. To properly develop a full understanding of the nature of friction, it is necessary to consider the surfaces of contact to be *nonrigid or deformable*. The other portion of the block, however, will be considered rigid. As shown on the free-body diagram of the block, Fig. 4–26*b*, the floor exerts a *distribution* of both *normal force* $\Delta\mathbf{N}_n$ and *frictional force* $\Delta\mathbf{F}_n$ along the contacting surface. For equilibrium, the normal forces must act *upward* to balance the block's weight **W**, and the frictional forces act to the left to prevent the applied force **P** from moving the block to the right. Close examination of the contacting surfaces between the floor and block reveals how these frictional and normal forces develop, Fig. 4–26*c*. It can be seen that many microscopic irregularities exist between the two surfaces and, as a result, reactive forces $\Delta\mathbf{R}_n$ are developed at each of the protuberances.* These forces act at all points of contact, and, as shown, each reactive force contributes both a frictional component $\Delta\mathbf{F}_n$ and a normal component $\Delta\mathbf{N}_n$.

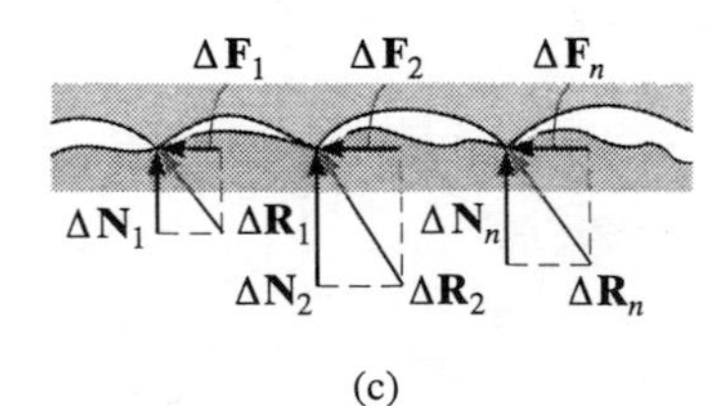

(c)

Equilibrium. For simplicity in the following analysis, the effect of the *distributed* normal and frictional loadings will be indicated by their *resultants* **N** and **F**, which are represented on the free-body diagram as shown in Fig. 4–26*d*. Clearly, the distribution of $\Delta\mathbf{F}_n$ in Fig. 4–26*b* indicates that **F** always acts *tangent to the contacting surface, opposite* to the direction of **P**. On the other hand, the normal force **N** is determined from the distribution of $\Delta\mathbf{N}_n$ in Fig. 4–26*b* and is directed upward to balance the block's weight **W**. Notice that **N** acts a distance x to the right of the line of action of **W**, Fig. 4–26*d*. This location, which coincides with the centroid or geometric center of the loading diagram in Fig. 4–26*b*, is necessary in order to balance the "tipping effect" caused by **P**. For example, if **P** is applied at a height h from the surface, Fig. 4–26*d*, then moment equilibrium about point O is satisfied if $Wx = Ph$ or $x = Ph/W$. In particular, the block will be on the verge of *tipping* if N acts at the right corner of the block, $x = a/2$.

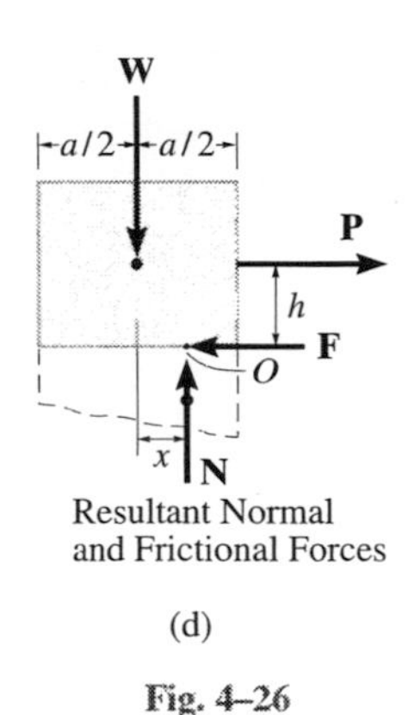

Resultant Normal and Frictional Forces

(d)

Fig. 4–26

The heat generated by the abrasive action of friction can be noticed when using this grinder to sharpen a metal blade.

*Besides mechanical interactions as explained here, which is referred to as a classical approach, a detailed treatment of the nature of frictional forces must also include the effects of temperature, density, cleanliness, and atomic or molecular attraction between the contacting surfaces. See J. Krim, *Scientific American*, October, 1996.

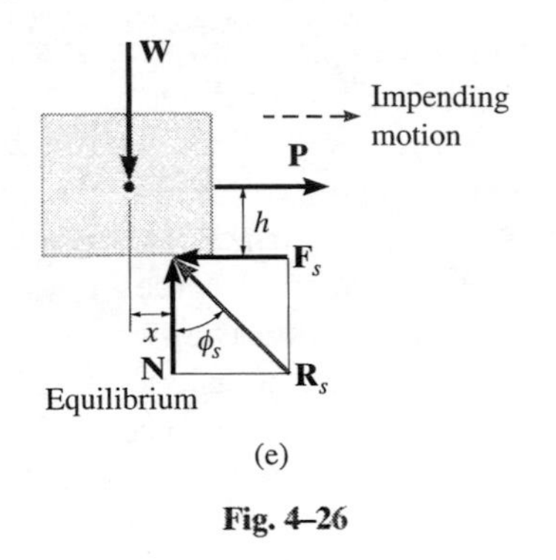

(e)

Fig. 4–26

Impending Motion. In cases where h is small or the surfaces of contact are rather "slippery," the frictional force **F** may *not* be great enough to balance **P**, and consequently the block will tend to slip *before* it can tip. In other words, as P is slowly increased, F correspondingly increases until it attains a certain *maximum value* F_s, called the *limiting static frictional force*, Fig. 4–26*e*. When this value is reached, the block is in *unstable equilibrium* since any further increase in P will cause deformations and fractures at the points of surface contact, and consequently the block will begin to move. Experimentally, it has been determined that the limiting static frictional force F_s is *directly proportional* to the resultant normal force N. This may be expressed mathematically as

$$F_s = \mu_s N \tag{4–8}$$

where the constant of proportionality, μ_s (mu "sub" s), is called the *coefficient of static friction*.

Thus, when the block is on the *verge of sliding*, the normal force **N** and frictional force $\mathbf{F}_s$ combine to create a resultant $\mathbf{R}_s$, Fig. 4–26*e*. The angle ϕ_s that $\mathbf{R}_s$ makes with **N** is called the *angle of static friction*. From the figure,

$$\phi_s = \tan^{-1}\left(\frac{F_s}{N}\right) = \tan^{-1}\left(\frac{\mu_s N}{N}\right) = \tan^{-1} \mu_s$$

Tabular Values of μ_s. Typical values for μ_s, found in many engineering handbooks, are given in Table 4–3. Although this coefficient is generally less than 1, be aware that in some cases it is possible, as in the case of aluminum on aluminum, for μ_s to be greater than 1. Physically this means, of course, that in this case the frictional force is greater than the corresponding normal force. Furthermore, it should be noted that μ_s is dimensionless and depends only on the characteristics of the two surfaces in contact. A wide range of values is given for each value of μ_s since experimental testing was done under variable conditions of roughness and cleanliness of the contacting surfaces. For applications, therefore, it is important that both caution and judgment be exercised when selecting a coefficient of friction for a given set of conditions. When a more accurate calculation of F_s is required, the coefficient of friction should be determined directly by an experiment that involves the two materials to be used.

TABLE 4–3
Typical Values for μ_s

Contact Materials	Coefficient of Static Friction (μ_s)
Metal on ice	0.03–0.05
Wood on wood	0.30–0.70
Leather on wood	0.20–0.50
Leather on metal	0.30–0.60
Aluminum on aluminum	1.10–1.70

Motion. If the magnitude of **P** acting on the block is increased so that it becomes greater than F_s, the frictional force at the contacting surfaces drops slightly to a smaller value F_k, called the *kinetic frictional force*. The block will *not* be held in equilibrium ($P > F_k$); instead, it will begin to slide with increasing speed, Fig. 4–27*a*. The drop made in the frictional force magnitude, from F_s (static) to F_k (kinetic), can be explained by again examining the surfaces of contact, Fig. 4–27*b*. Here it is seen that when $P > F_s$, then P has the capacity to shear off the peaks at the contact surfaces and cause the block to "lift" somewhat out of its settled position and "ride" on top of these peaks. Once the block begins to slide, high local temperatures at the points of contact cause momentary adhesion (welding) of these points. The continued shearing of these welds is the dominant mechanism creating friction. Since the resultant contact forces $\Delta\mathbf{R}_n$ are aligned slightly more in the vertical direction than before, they thereby contribute *smaller* frictional components, $\Delta\mathbf{F}_n$, than when the irregularities are meshed.

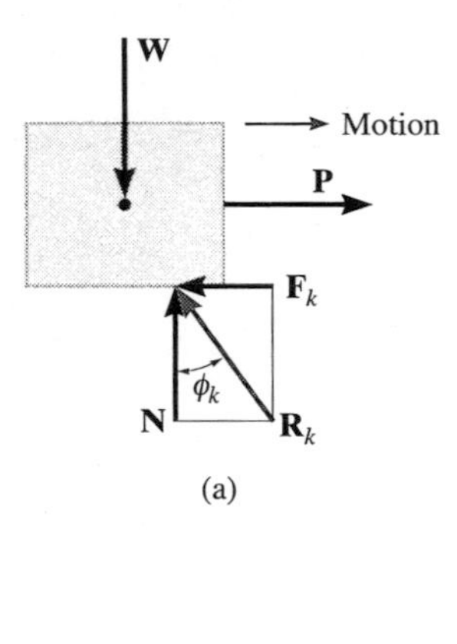

(a)

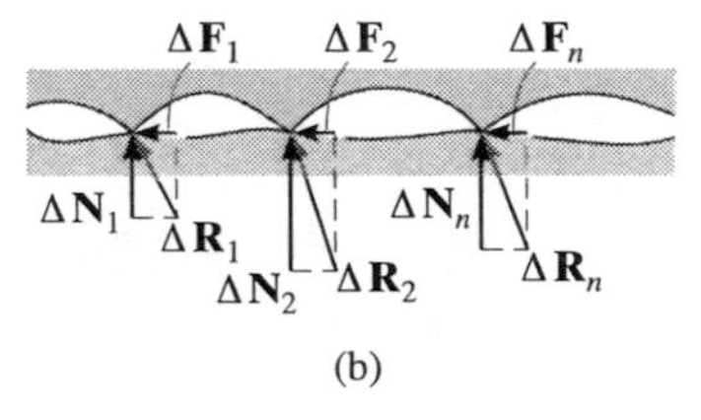

(b)

Fig. 4–27

Experiments with sliding blocks indicate that the magnitude of the resultant frictional force $\mathbf{F}_k$ is directly proportional to the magnitude of the resultant normal force **N**. This may be expressed mathematically as

$$F_k = \mu_k N \qquad (4\text{–}9)$$

Here the constant of proportionality, μ_k, is called the *coefficient of kinetic friction*. Typical values for μ_k are approximately 25 percent *smaller* than those listed in Table 4–3 for μ_s.

As shown in Fig. 4–27*a*, in this case, the resultant $\mathbf{R}_k$ has a line of action defined by ϕ_k. This angle is referred to as the *angle of kinetic friction*, where

$$\phi_k = \tan^{-1}\left(\frac{F_k}{N}\right) = \tan^{-1}\left(\frac{\mu_k N}{N}\right) = \tan^{-1}\mu_k$$

By comparison, $\phi_s \geq \phi_k$.

The above effects regarding friction can be summarized by reference to the graph in Fig. 4–28, which shows the variation of the frictional force F versus the applied load P. Here the frictional force is categorized in three different ways: namely, F is a *static-frictional force* if equilibrium is maintained; F is a *limiting static-frictional force* F_s when it reaches a maximum value needed to maintain equilibrium; and finally, F is termed a *kinetic-frictional force* F_k when sliding occurs at the contacting surface. Notice also from the graph that for very large values of P or for high speeds, because of aerodynamic effects, F_k and likewise μ_k begin to decrease.

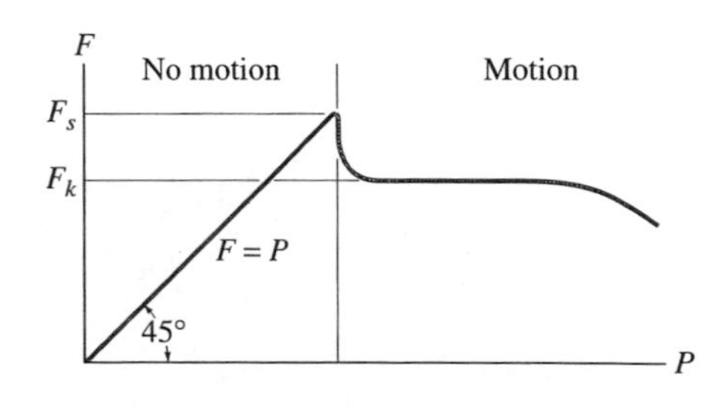

Fig. 4–28

Characteristics of Dry Friction. As a result of *experiments* that pertain to the foregoing discussion, the following rules which apply to bodies subjected to dry friction may be stated.

- The frictional force acts *tangent* to the contacting surfaces in a direction *opposed* to the *relative motion* or tendency for motion of one surface against another.
- The maximum static frictional force $\mathbf{F}_s$ that can be developed is independent of the area of contact, provided the normal pressure is not very low nor great enough to severely deform or crush the contacting surfaces of the bodies.
- The maximum static frictional force is generally greater than the kinetic frictional force for any two surfaces of contact. However, if one of the bodies is moving with a *very low velocity* over the surface of another, F_k becomes approximately equal to F_s, i.e., $\mu_s \approx \mu_k$.
- When *slipping* at the surface of contact is *about to occur*, the maximum static frictional force is proportional to the normal force, such that $F_s = \mu_s N$.
- When *slipping* at the surface of contact is *occurring*, the kinetic frictional force is proportional to the normal force, such that $F_k = \mu_k N$.

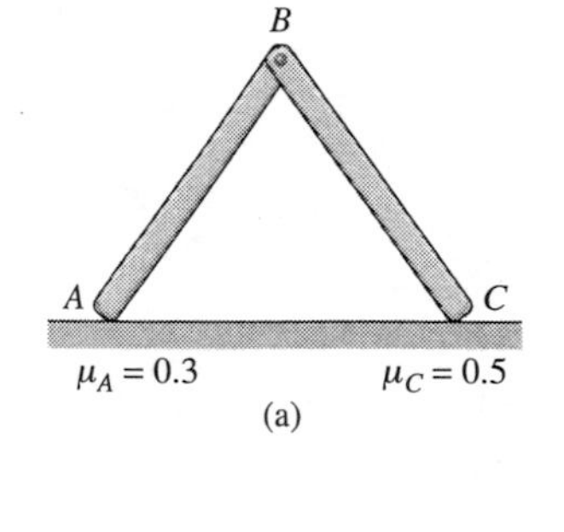

(a)

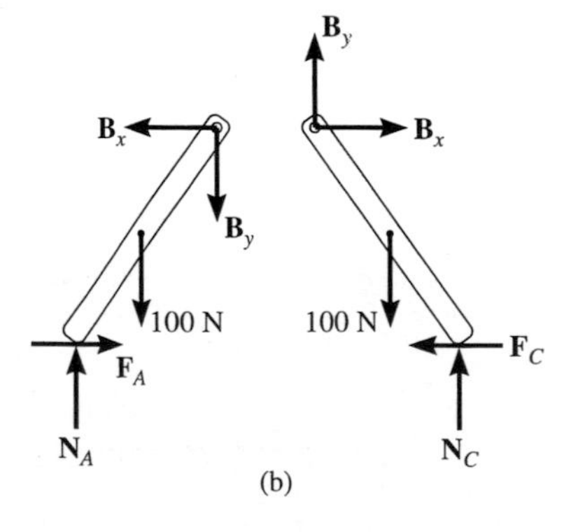

(b)

Fig. 4–29

Types of Friction Problems. In general, there are three types of mechanics problems involving dry friction. They can easily be classified once the free-body diagrams are drawn and the total number of unknowns are identified and compared with the total number of available equilibrium equations. Each type of problem will now be explained and illustrated graphically by examples. In all these cases the geometry and dimensions for the problem are assumed to be known.

Equilibrium. Problems in this category are strictly equilibrium problems which require *the total number of unknowns to be equal to the total number of available equilibrium equations*. Once the frictional forces are determined from the solution, however, their numerical values must be checked to be sure they satisfy the inequality $F \leq \mu_s N$; otherwise, slipping will occur and the body will not remain in equilibrium. A problem of this type is shown in Fig. 4–29*a*. Here we must determine the frictional forces at A and C to check if the equilibrium position of the two-member frame can be maintained. If the bars are uniform and have known weights of 100 N each, then the free-body diagrams are as shown in Fig. 4–29*b*. There are six unknown force components which can be determined *strictly* from the six equilibrium equations (three for each member). Once $\mathbf{F}_A$, $\mathbf{N}_A$, $\mathbf{F}_C$, and $\mathbf{N}_C$ are determined, then the bars will remain in equilibrium provided $F_A \leq 0.3N_A$ and $F_C \leq 0.5N_C$ are satisfied.

Impending Motion at All Points. In this case *the total number of unknowns will equal the total number of available equilibrium equations plus the total number of available frictional equations, $F = \mu N$.* In particular, if *motion is impending* at the points of contact, then $F_s = \mu_s N$; whereas if the body is *slipping*, then $F_k = \mu_k N$. For example, consider the problem of finding the smallest angle θ at which the 100-N bar in Fig. 4–30*a* can be placed against the wall without slipping. The free-body diagram is shown in Fig. 4–30*b*. Here there are *five* unknowns: F_A, N_A, F_B, N_B, θ. For the solution there are *three* equilibrium equations and *two* static frictional equations which apply at *both* points of contact, so that $F_A = 0.3N_A$ and $F_B = 0.4N_B$.

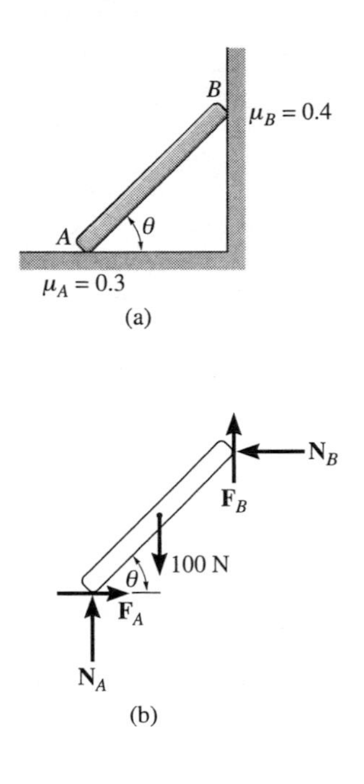

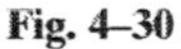

Fig. 4–30

Impending Motion at Some Points. Here *the total number of unknowns will be less than the number of available equilibrium equations plus the total number of frictional equations or conditional equations for tipping.* As a result, several possibilities for motion or impending motion will exist and the problem will involve a determination of the kind of motion which actually occurs. For example, consider the two-member frame shown in Fig. 4–31*a*. In this problem we wish to determine the horizontal force P needed to cause movement. If each member has a weight of 100 N, then the free-body diagrams are as shown in Fig. 4–31*b*. There are *seven* unknowns: N_A, F_A, N_C, F_C, B_x, B_y, P. For a unique solution we must satisfy the *six* equilibrium equations (three for each member) and only *one* of two possible static frictional equations. This means that as P increases it will either cause slipping at A and no slipping at C, so that $F_A = 0.3N_A$ and $F_C \leq 0.5N_C$; or slipping occurs at C and no slipping at A, in which case $F_C = 0.5N_C$ and $F_A \leq 0.3N_A$. The actual situation can be determined by calculating P for each case and then choosing the case for which P is *smaller*. If in both cases the *same value* for P is calculated, which in practice would be highly improbable, then slipping at both points occurs simultaneously; i.e., the *seven unknowns* will satisfy *eight equations*.

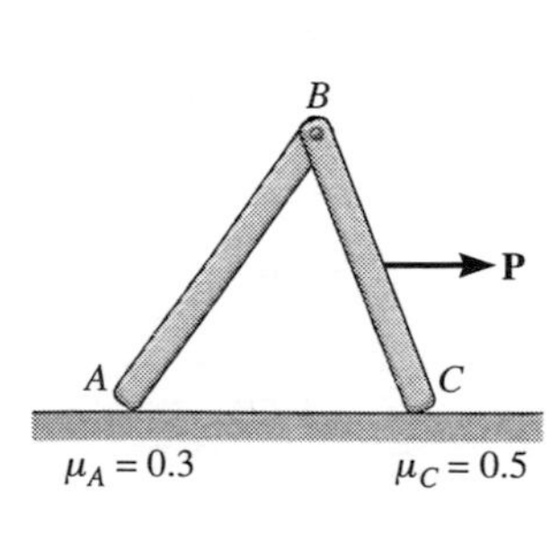

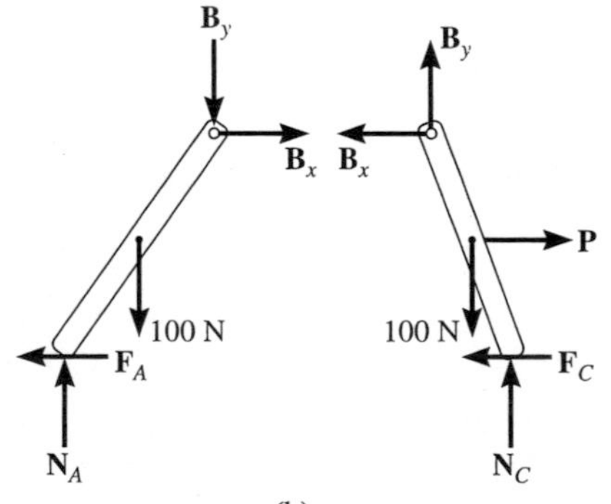

Fig. 4–31

As a second example, consider a block having a width b, height h, and weight W which is resting on a rough surface, Fig. 4–32*a*. The force **P** needed to cause motion is to be determined. Inspection of the free-body diagram, Fig. 4–32*b*, indicates that there are *four unknowns*, namely, P, F, N, and x. For a unique solution, however, we must satisfy the *three* equilibrium equations and either *one* static friction equation or *one* conditional equation which requires the block not to tip. Hence two possibilities of motion exist. Either the block will *slip*, Fig. 4–32*b*, in which case $F = \mu_s N$ and the value obtained for x must satisfy $0 \leq x \leq b/2$; or the block will *tip*, Fig. 4–32*c*, in which case $x = b/2$ and the frictional force will satisfy the inequality $F \leq \mu_s N$. The solution yielding the *smallest* value of P will define the type of motion the block undergoes. If it happens that the same value of P is calculated for both cases, although this would be very improbable, then slipping and tipping will occur simultaneously; i.e., the *four unknowns* will satisfy *five equations*.

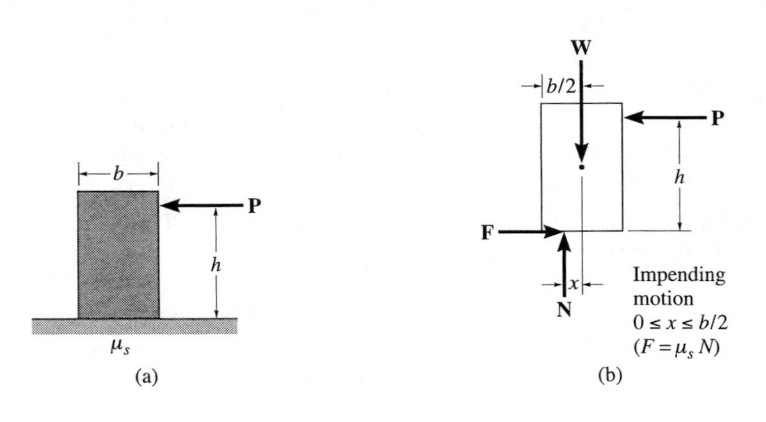

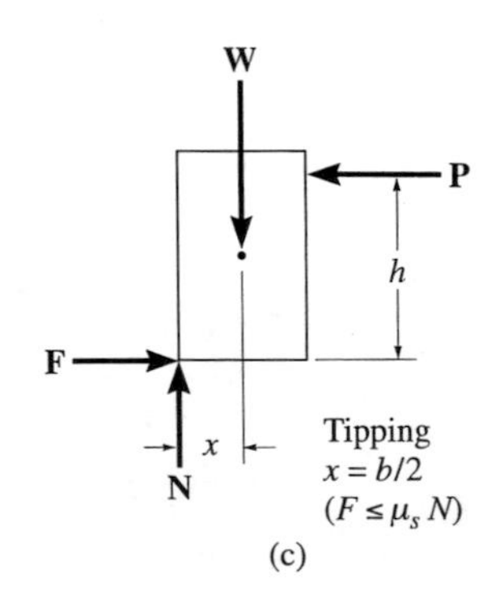

Fig. 4–32

Equilibrium Versus Frictional Equations. It was stated earlier that the frictional force *always* acts so as to either oppose the relative motion or impede the motion of a body over its contacting surface. Realize, however, that we can *assume* the sense of the frictional force in problems which require F to be an "equilibrium force" and satisfy the inequality $F < \mu_s N$. The correct sense is made known *after* solving the equations of equilibrium for F. For example, if F is a negative scalar the sense of $\mathbf{F}$ is the reverse of that which was assumed. This convenience of *assuming* the sense of $\mathbf{F}$ is possible because the equilibrium equations equate to zero the *components of vectors* acting in the *same direction*. In cases where the frictional equation $F = \mu N$ is used in the solution of a problem, however, the convenience of *assuming* the sense of $\mathbf{F}$ is *lost*, since the frictional equation relates only the *magnitudes* of two perpendicular vectors. Consequently, $\mathbf{F}$ *must always* be shown acting with its *correct sense* on the free-body diagram whenever the frictional equation is used for the solution of a problem.

PROCEDURE FOR ANALYSIS

The following procedure provides a method for solving equilibrium problems involving dry friction.

Free-Body Diagrams. Draw the necessary free-body diagrams and determine the number of unknowns or equations required for a complete solution. Unless stated in the problem, *always* show the frictional forces as *unknowns; i.e., do not assume that* $F = \mu N$. Recall that only three equations of coplanar equilibrium can be written for each body. Consequently, if there are more unknowns than equations of equilibrium, it will be necessary to apply the frictional equation at some, if not all, points of contact to obtain the extra equations needed for a complete solution.

Equations of Friction and Equilibrium. Apply the equations of equilibrium and the necessary frictional equations (or conditional equations if tipping is involved) and solve for the unknowns. If the problem involves a three-dimensional force system such that it becomes difficult to obtain the force components or the necessary moment arms, apply the equations of equilibrium using Cartesian vectors.

EXAMPLE 4.14

The uniform crate shown in Fig. 4–33*a* has a mass of 20 kg. If a force $P = 80\text{ N}$ is applied to the crate, determine if it remains in equilibrium. The coefficient of static friction is $\mu = 0.3$.

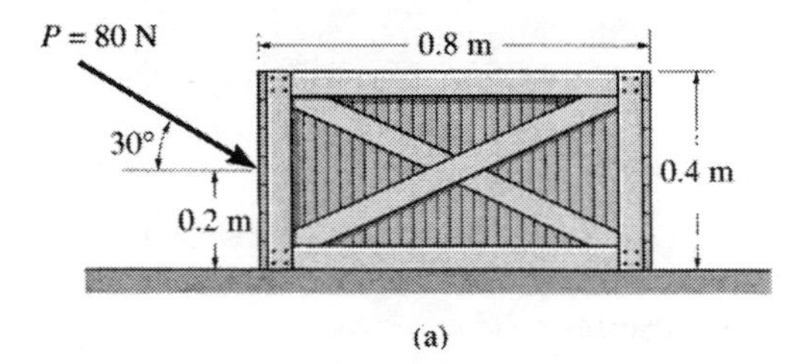

(a)

Fig. 4–33

Solution

Free-Body Diagram. As shown in Fig. 4–33*b*, the *resultant* normal force $\mathbf{N}_C$ must act a distance x from the crate's center line in order to counteract the tipping effect caused by **P**. There are *three unknowns*, F, N_C, and x, which can be determined strictly from the *three* equations of equilibrium.

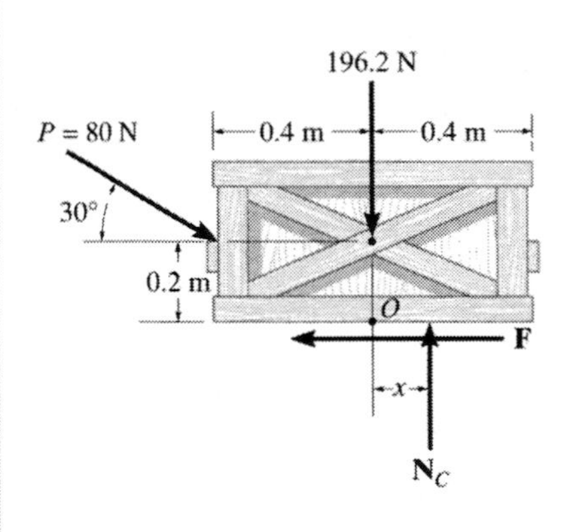

(b)

Equations of Equilibrium.

$$\xrightarrow{+} \Sigma F_x = 0; \qquad 80 \cos 30^\circ \text{ N} - F = 0$$

$$+\uparrow \Sigma F_y = 0; \qquad -80 \sin 30^\circ \text{ N} + N_C - 196.2 \text{ N} = 0$$

$$\circlearrowleft + \Sigma M_O = 0; \quad 80 \sin 30^\circ \text{ N}(0.4 \text{ m}) - 80 \cos 30^\circ \text{ N}(0.2 \text{ m}) + N_C(x) = 0$$

Solving,

$$F = 69.3 \text{ N}$$

$$N_C = 236 \text{ N}$$

$$x = -0.00908 \text{ m} = -9.08 \text{ mm}$$

Since x is negative it indicates the *resultant* normal force acts (slightly) to the *left* of the crate's center line. No tipping will occur since $x \le 0.4$ m. Also, the *maximum* frictional force which can be developed at the surface of contact is $F_{max} = \mu_s N_C = 0.3(236 \text{ N}) = 70.8$ N. Since $F = 69.3 \text{ N} < 70.8$ N, the crate will *not slip*, although it is very close to doing so.

EXAMPLE 4.15

It is observed that when the bed of the dump truck is raised to an angle of $\theta = 25^\circ$ the vending machines begin to slide off the bed, Fig. 4–34a. Determine the static coefficient of friction between them and the surface of the truck.

(a)

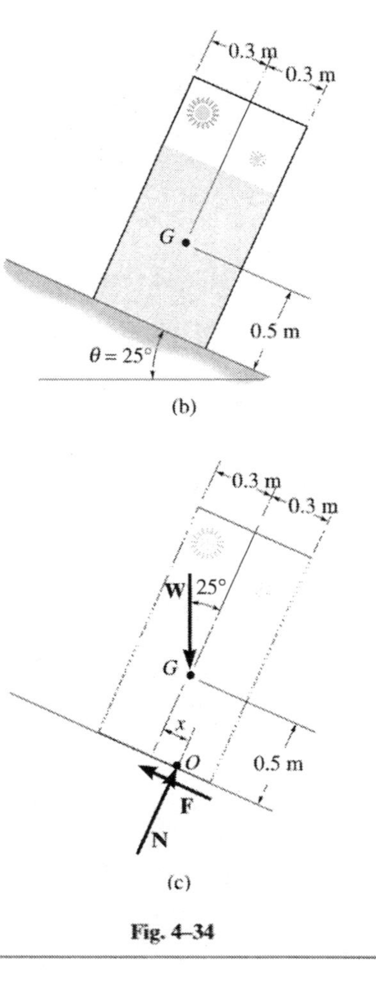

(b)

(c)

Fig. 4–34

Solution

An idealized model of a vending machine resting on the bed of the truck is shown in Fig. 4–34b. The dimensions have been measured and the center of gravity has been located. We will assume that the machine weighs W.

Free-Body Diagram. As shown in Fig. 4–34c, the dimension x is used to locate the position of the resultant normal force $\mathbf{N}$. There are four unknowns, N, F, μ_s, and x.

Equations of Equilibrium.

$$+\searrow\Sigma F_x = 0; \qquad W \sin 25^\circ - F = 0 \qquad (1)$$

$$+\nearrow\Sigma F_y = 0; \qquad N - W \cos 25^\circ = 0 \qquad (2)$$

$$\circlearrowleft + \Sigma M_O = 0; \qquad -W \sin \theta\,(0.5\text{ m}) + W \cos \theta\,(x) = 0 \qquad (3)$$

Since slipping impends at $\theta = 25^\circ$, using the first two equations, we have

$$F_s = \mu_s N; \qquad W \sin 25^\circ = \mu_s\,(W \cos 25^\circ)$$

$$\mu_s = \tan 25^\circ = 0.466 \qquad \textit{Ans.}$$

The angle of $\theta = 25^\circ$ is referred to as the *angle of repose*, and by comparison, it is equal to the angle of static friction $\theta = \phi_s$. Notice from the calculation that θ is independent of the weight of the vending machine, and so knowing θ provides a convenient method for determining the coefficient of static friction.

From Eq. 3, with $\theta = 25^\circ$, we find $x = 0.233$ m. Since $0.233\text{ m} < 0.5\text{ m}$, indeed the vending machine will slip before it can tip as observed in Fig. 4–34a.

EXAMPLE 4.16

The uniform rod having a weight W and length l is supported at its ends against the surface at A and B in Fig. 4–35*a*. If the rod is on the verge of slipping when $\theta = 30^\circ$, determine the coefficient of static friction μ_s at A and B. Neglect the thickness of the rod for the calculation.

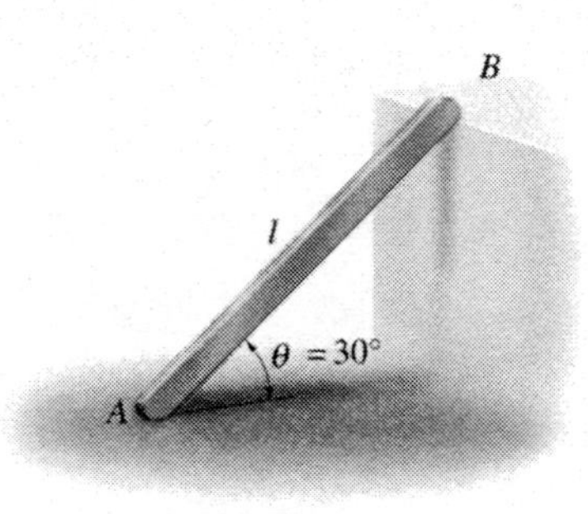

(a)

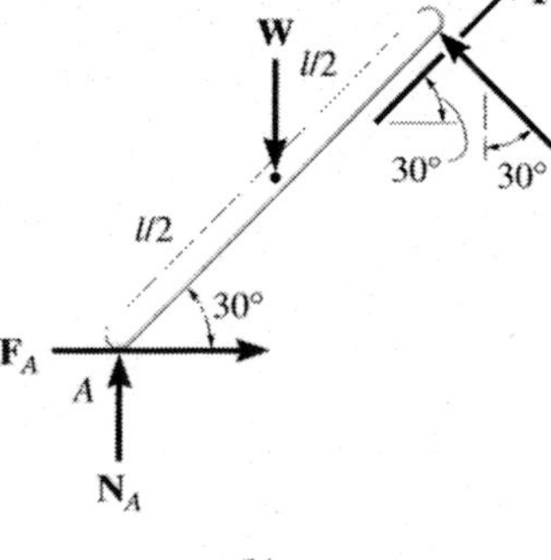

(b)

Fig. 4–35

Solution

Free-Body Diagram. As shown in Fig. 4–35*b*, there are *five* unknowns: F_A, N_A, F_B, N_B, and μ_s. These can be determined from the *three* equilibrium equations and *two* frictional equations applied at points A and B. The frictional forces must be drawn with their correct sense so that they oppose the tendency for motion of the rod. Why?

Equations of Friction and Equilibrium. Writing the frictional equations,

$$F = \mu_s N; \qquad F_A = \mu_s N_A$$

$$F_B = \mu_s N_B$$

Using these results and applying the equations of equilibrium yields

$$\overset{+}{\rightarrow} \Sigma F_x = 0; \quad \mu_s N_A + \mu_s N_B \cos 30^\circ - N_B \sin 30^\circ = 0 \tag{1}$$

$$+\uparrow \Sigma F_y = 0; \quad N_A - W + N_B \cos 30^\circ + \mu_s N_B \sin 30^\circ = 0 \tag{2}$$

$$\circlearrowleft + \Sigma M_A = 0; \quad N_B l - W\left(\frac{l}{2}\right)\cos 30^\circ = 0 \tag{3}$$

$$N_B = 0.4330\, W$$

From Eqs. 1 and 2,

$$\mu_s N_A = 0.2165\, W - (0.3750\, W)\mu_s$$

$$N_A = 0.6250\, W - (0.2165\, W)\mu_s$$

By division,

$$0.6250\mu_s - 0.2165\mu_s^2 = 0.2165 - 0.375\mu_s$$

or,

$$\mu_s^2 - 4.619\, \mu_s + 1 = 0$$

Solving for the smallest root,

$$\mu_s = 0.228 \qquad \textit{Ans.}$$

EXAMPLE 4.17

The concrete pipes are stacked in the yard as shown in Fig. 4–36*a*. Determine the minimum coefficient of static friction at each point of contact so that the pile does not collapse.

(a)

Solution

Free-body Diagrams. Recognize that the coefficient of static friction between two pipes, at A and B, and between a pipe and the ground, at C, will be different since the contacting surfaces are different. We will assume each pipe has an outer radius r and weight W. The free-body diagrams for two of the pipes are shown in Fig. 4–36*b*. There are six unknowns, N_A, F_A, N_B, F_B, N_C, F_C. (Note that when collapse is about to occur the normal force at D is zero.) Since only the six equations of equilibrium are necessary to obtain the unknowns, the sense of direction of the frictional forces can be verified from the solution.

Equations of Equilibrium. For the top pipe we have

$\circlearrowleft + \Sigma M_O = 0; \quad -F_A(r) + F_B(r) = 0; \; F_A = F_B = F$

$\xrightarrow{+} \Sigma F_x = 0; \quad N_A \sin 30° - F \cos 30° - N_B \sin 30° + F \cos 30° = 0$

$$N_A = N_B = N$$

$+\uparrow \Sigma F_y = 0; \quad 2N \cos 30° + 2F \sin 30° - W = 0 \qquad (1)$

For the bottom pipe, using $F_A = F$ and $N_A = N$, we have,

$\circlearrowleft + \Sigma M_{O'} = 0; \qquad F_C(r) - F(r) = 0; \qquad F_C = F$

$\xrightarrow{+} \Sigma F_x = 0; \qquad -N \sin 30° + F \cos 30° + F = 0 \qquad (2)$

$+\uparrow \Sigma F_y = 0; \quad N_C - W - N \cos 30° - F \sin 30° = 0 \qquad (3)$

From Eq. 2, $F = 0.2679\, N$, so that between the pipes

$$(\mu_s)_{\min} = \frac{F}{N} = 0.268 \qquad Ans$$

Using this result in Eq. 1.

$$N = 0.5\, W$$

From Eq. 3,

$$N_C - W - (0.5\, W) \cos 30° - 0.2679\,(0.5\, W) \sin 30° = 0$$

$$N_C = 1.5\, W$$

At the ground, the smallest required coefficient of static friction would be

$$(\mu_s')_{\min} = \frac{F}{N_C} = \frac{0.2679(0.5\, W)}{1.5\, W} = 0.0893 \qquad Ans.$$

Hence a greater coefficient of static friction is required between the pipes than that required at the ground; and so it is likely that if slipping would occur between the pipes the bottom two pipes would roll away from one another without slipping as the top pipe falls downward.

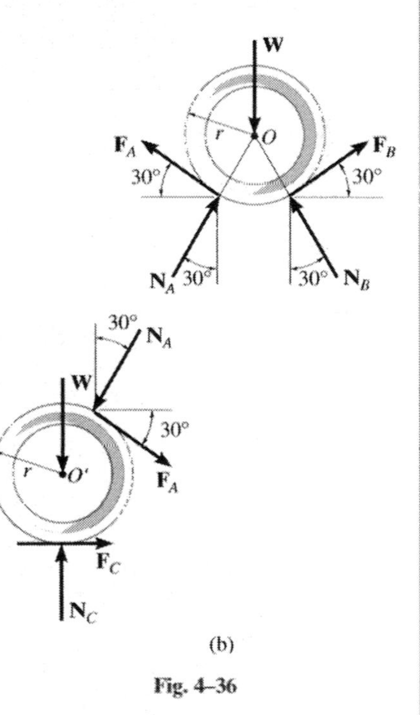

(b)

Fig. 4–36

EXAMPLE 4.18

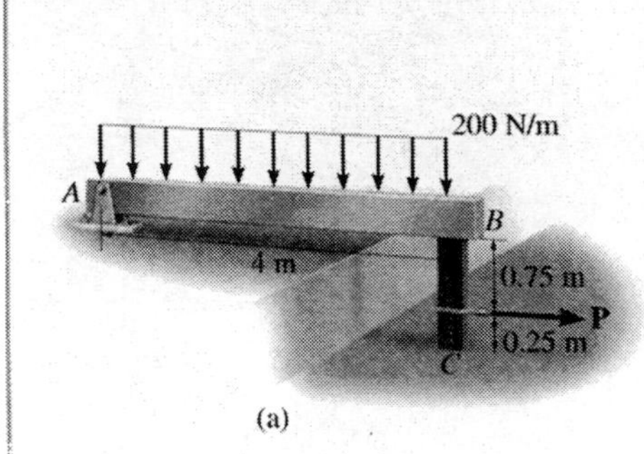

(a)

Beam AB is subjected to a uniform load of 200 N/m and is supported at B by post BC, Fig. 4–37*a*. If the coefficients of static friction at B and C are $\mu_B = 0.2$ and $\mu_C = 0.5$, determine the force **P** needed to pull the post out from under the beam. Neglect the weight of the members and the thickness of the post.

Solution

Free-Body Diagrams. The free-body diagram of beam AB is shown in Fig. 4–37*b*. Applying $\Sigma M_A = 0$, we obtain $N_B = 400$ N. This result is shown on the free-body diagram of the post, Fig. 4–37*c*. Referring to this member, the *four* unknowns F_B, P, F_C, and N_C are determined from the *three* equations of equilibrium and *one* frictional equation applied either at B or C.

(b)

Equations of Equilibrium and Friction.

$$\overset{+}{\rightarrow} \Sigma F_x = 0; \qquad P - F_B - F_C = 0 \qquad (1)$$

$$+\uparrow \Sigma F_y = 0; \qquad N_C - 400 \text{ N} = 0 \qquad (2)$$

$$\circlearrowright + \Sigma M_C = 0; \qquad -P(0.25 \text{ m}) + F_B(1 \text{ m}) = 0 \qquad (3)$$

(Post Slips Only at B) This requires $F_C \leq \mu_C N_C$ and

$$F_B = \mu_B N_B; \qquad F_B = 0.2(400 \text{ N}) = 80 \text{ N}$$

Using this result and solving Eqs. 1 through 3, we obtain

$$P = 320 \text{ N}$$
$$F_C = 240 \text{ N}$$
$$N_C = 400 \text{ N}$$

Since $F_C = 240 \text{ N} > \mu_C N_C = 0.5(400 \text{ N}) = 200$ N, the other case of movement must be investigated.

(Post Slips Only at C.) Here $F_B \leq \mu_B N_B$ and

$$F_C = \mu_C N_C; \qquad F_C = 0.5\, N_C \qquad (4)$$

Solving Eqs. 1 through 4 yields

$$P = 267 \text{ N} \qquad \textit{Ans.}$$
$$N_C = 400 \text{ N}$$
$$F_C = 200 \text{ N}$$
$$F_B = 66.7 \text{ N}$$

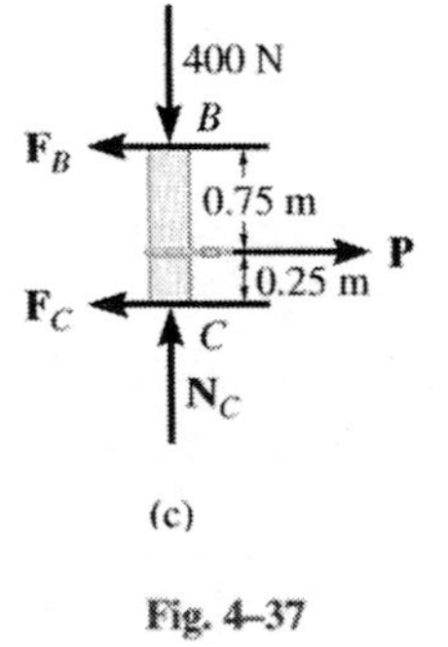

(c)

Fig. 4–37

Obviously, this case occurs first since it requires a *smaller* value for P.

EXAMPLE 4.19

Determine the normal force P that must be exerted on the rack to begin pushing the 100-kg pipe shown in Fig. 4–38*a* up the 20° incline. The coefficients of static friction at the points of contact are $(\mu_s)_A = 0.15$, and $(\mu_s)_B = 0.4$.

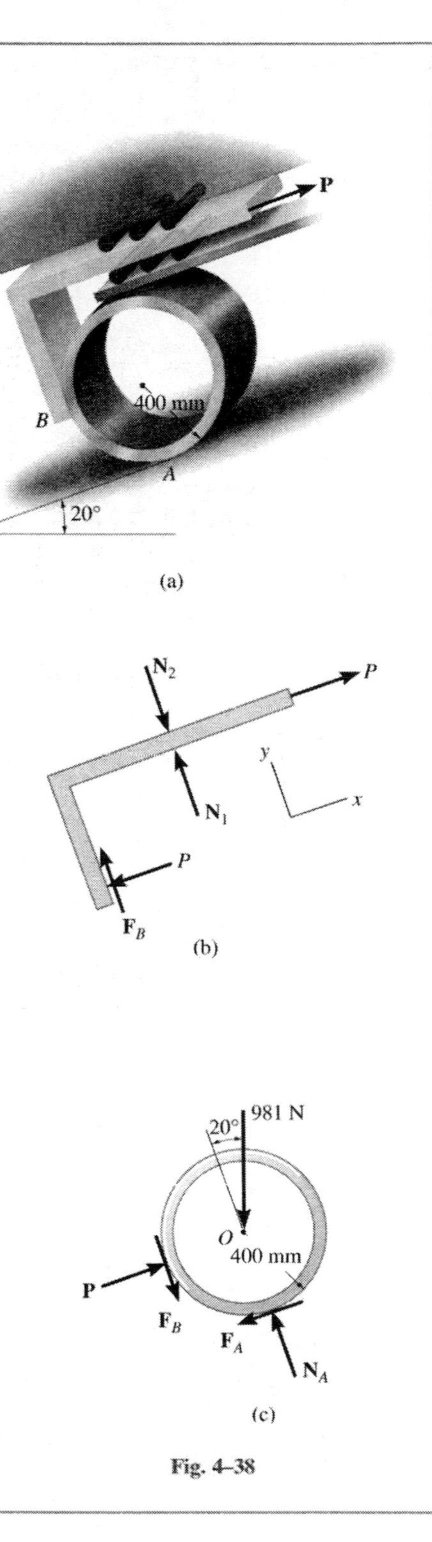

Fig. 4–38

Solution

Free-Body Diagram. As shown in Fig. 4–38*b*, the rack must exert a force P on the pipe due to force equilibrium in the x direction. There are four unknowns P, F_A, N_A, and F_B acting on the pipe Fig. 4–38*c*. These can be determined from the *three* equations of equilibrium and *one* frictional equation, which apply either at A or B. If slipping begins to occur only at B, the pipe will begin to roll up the incline; whereas if slipping occurs only at A, the pipe will begin to *slide* up the incline. Here we must find N_B.

Equations of Equilibrium and Friction (for Fig. 8–12c)

$$+\nearrow\Sigma F_x = 0; \qquad -F_A + P - 981 \sin 20^\circ \text{ N} = 0 \qquad (1)$$

$$+\nwarrow\Sigma F_y = 0; \qquad N_A - F_B - 981 \cos 20^\circ \text{ N} = 0 \qquad (2)$$

$$\circlearrowleft + \Sigma M_O = 0; \qquad F_B(400 \text{ mm}) - F_A(400 \text{ mm}) = 0 \qquad (3)$$

(Pipe Rolls up Incline.) In this case $F_A \leq 0.15N_A$ and

$$(F_s)_B = (\mu_s)_B N_B; \qquad F_B = 0.4P \qquad (4)$$

The direction of the frictional force at B must be specified correctly. Why? Since the spool is being forced up the incline $\mathbf{F}_B$ acts downward to prevent any clockwise rolling motion of the pipe, Fig. 4–38*c*. Solving Eqs. 1 through 4, we have

$$N_A = 1146 \text{ N} \quad F_A = 224 \text{ N} \quad F_B = 224 \text{ N} \quad P = 559 \text{ N}$$

The assumption regarding no slipping at A should be checked.

$$F_A \leq (\mu_s)_A N_A; \quad 224 \text{ N} \overset{?}{\leq} 0.15(1146 \text{ N}) = 172 \text{ N}$$

The inequality does *not apply*, and therefore slipping occurs at A and not at B. Hence, the other case of motion will occur.

(Pipe Slides up Incline.) In this case, $P \leq 0.4N_B$ and

$$(F_s)_A = (\mu_s)_A N_A; \qquad F_A = 0.15N_A \qquad (5)$$

Solving Eqs. 1 through 3 and 5 yields

$$N_A = 1085 \text{ N} \quad F_A = 163 \text{ N} \quad F_B = 163 \text{ N} \quad P = 498 \text{ N} \qquad \textit{Ans.}$$

The validity of the solution ($P = 498$ N) can be checked by testing the assumption that indeed no slipping occurs at B.

$$F_B \leq (\mu_s)_B P; \quad 163 \text{ N} < 0.4(498 \text{ N}) = 199 \text{ N} \qquad \text{(check)}$$

PROBLEMS

4-40. The mine car and its contents have a total mass of 6 Mg and a center of gravity at G. If the coefficient of static friction between the wheels and the tracks is $\mu_s = 0.4$ when the wheels are locked, find the normal force acting on the front wheels at B and the rear wheels at A when the brakes at both A and B are locked. Does the car move?

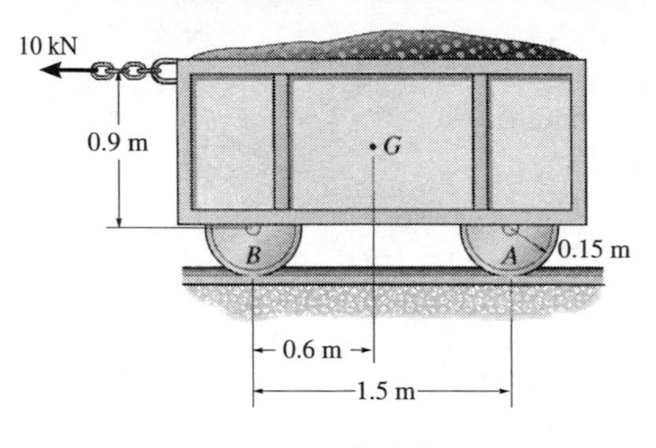

Prob. 4–40

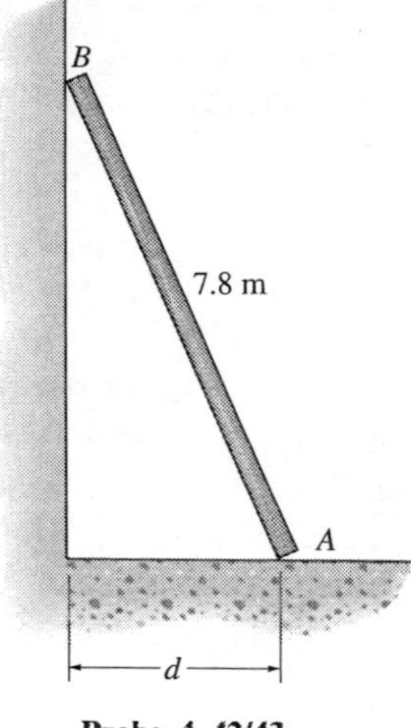

Probs. 4–42/43

4-41. If the horizontal force $P = 80$ N, determine the normal and frictional forces acting on the 300-N (≈ 30-kg) crate. Take $\mu_s = 0.3$, $\mu_k = 0.2$.

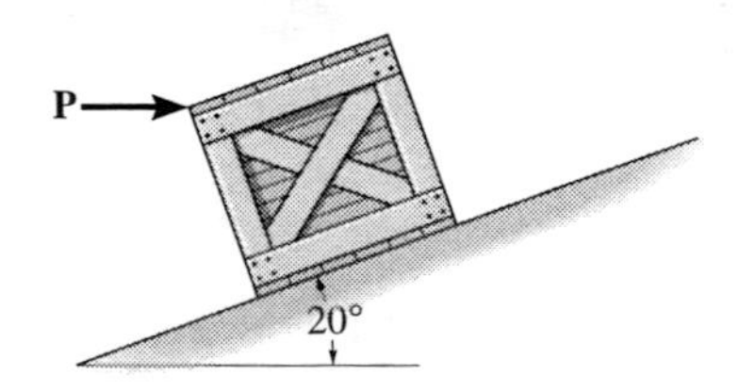

Prob. 4–41

4-42. The uniform pole has a weight of 150 N (≈ 15 kg) and a length of 7.8 m. If it is placed against the smooth wall and on the rough floor in the position $d = 3$ m, will it remain in this position when it is released? The coefficient of static friction is $\mu_s = 0.3$.

***4-43.** The uniform pole has a weight of 150 N (≈ 15 kg) and a length of 7.8 m. Determine the maximum distance d it can be placed from the smooth wall and not slip. The coefficient of static friction between the floor and the pole is $\mu_s = 0.3$.

4-44. The uniform 100-N (≈ 10-kg) ladder rests on the rough floor for which the coefficient of static friction is $\mu_s = 0.8$ and against the smooth wall at B. Determine the horizontal force P the man must exert on the ladder in order to cause it to move.

4-45. The uniform 100-N (≈ 10-kg) ladder rests on the rough floor for which the coefficient of static friction is $\mu_s = 0.4$ and against the smooth wall at B. Determine the horizontal force P the man must exert on the ladder in order to cause it to move.

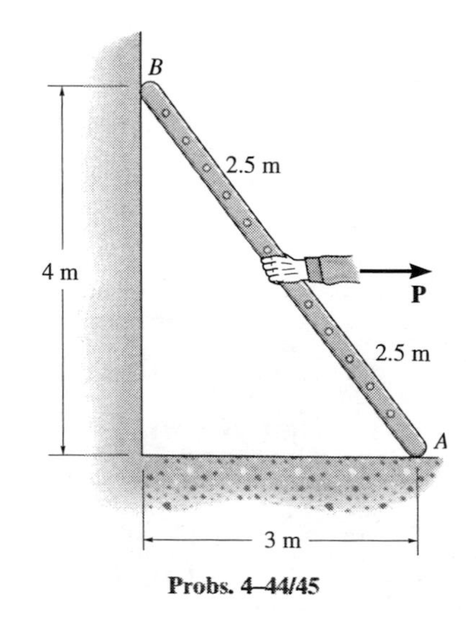

Probs. 4–44/45

4-46. An axial force of $T = 4000$ N is applied to the bar. If the coefficient of static friction at the jaws C and D is $\mu_s = 0.5$, determine the smallest normal force that the screw at A must exert on the smooth surface of the links at B and C in order to hold the bar stationary. The links are pin-connected at F and G.

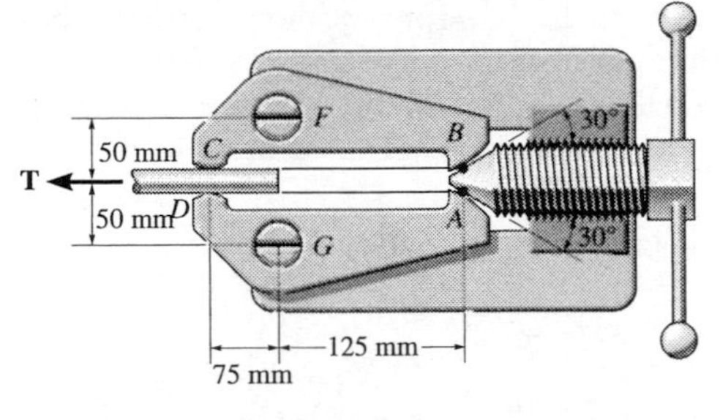

Prob. 4–46

***4-47.** The winch on the truck is used to hoist the garbage bin onto the bed of the truck. If the loaded bin has a weight of 40 000 N ($\approx$ 4 tonne) and center of gravity at G, determine the force in the cable needed to begin the lift. The coefficients of static friction at A and B are $\mu_A = 0.3$ and $\mu_B = 0.2$, respectively. Neglect the height of the support at A.

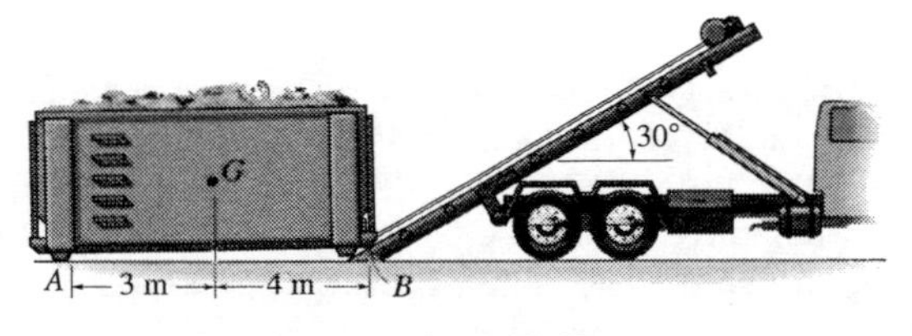

Prob. 4–47

4-48. The 5-m ladder has a uniform weight of 400 N ($\approx$ 40 kg) and rests against the smooth wall at B. If the coefficient of static friction at A is $\mu_s = 0.4$, determine if the ladder will slip. Take $\theta = 60°$.

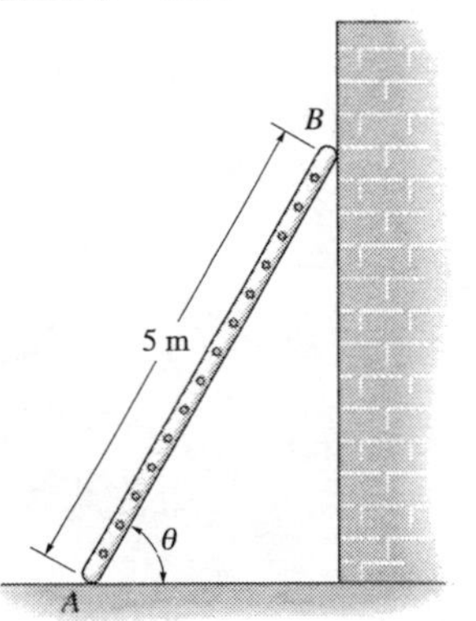

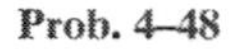

Prob. 4–48

4-49. The block brake is used to stop the wheel from rotating when the wheel is subjected to a couple moment $\mathbf{M}_0$. If the coefficient of static friction between the wheel and the block is μ_s, determine the smallest force P that should be applied.

4-50. Show that the brake in Prob. 4–49 is self locking, i.e., $P \leq 0$, provided $b/c \leq \mu_s$.

***4-51.** Solve Prob. 4–49 if the couple moment $\mathbf{M}_0$ is applied counterclockwise.

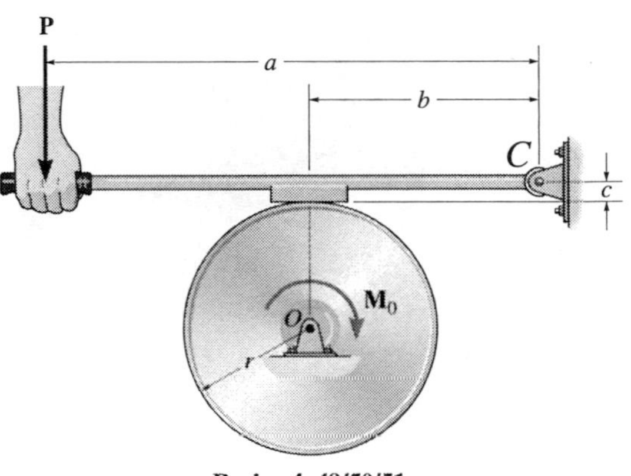

Probs. 4–49/50/51

4-52. The block brake consists of a pin-connected lever and friction block at B. The coefficient of static friction between the wheel and the lever is $\mu_s = 0.3$, and a torque of 5 N · m is applied to the wheel. Determine if the brake can hold the wheel stationary when the force applied to the lever is (a) $P = 30$ N, (b) $P = 70$ N.

4-53. Solve Prob. 4–52 if the 5-N · m torque is applied counter-clockwise.

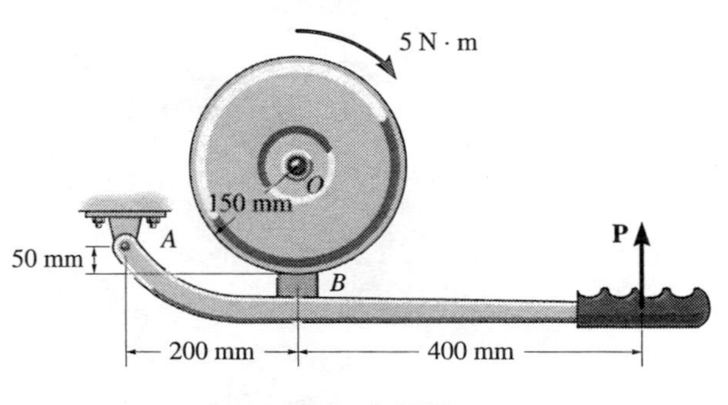

Probs. 4–52/53

4-54. The tractor has a weight of 22 500 N ($\approx$ 2250 kg) with center of gravity at G. The driving traction is developed at the rear wheels B, while the front wheels at A are free to roll. If the coefficient of static friction between the wheels at B and the ground is $\mu_s = 0.5$, determine if it is possible to pull at $P = 6000$ N without causing the wheels at B to slip or the front wheels at A to lift off the ground.

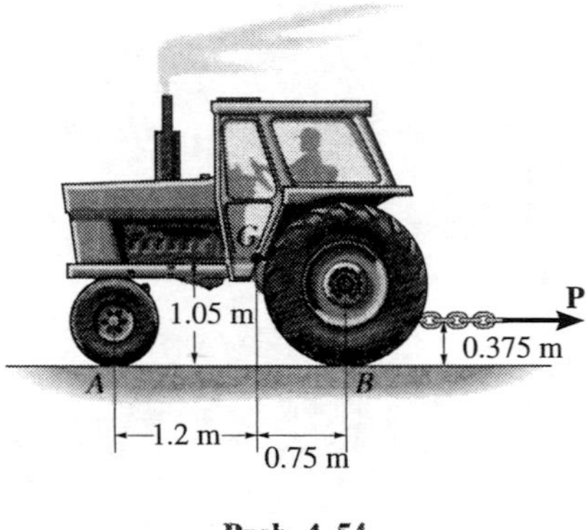

Prob. 4–54

***4-55.** The car has a mass of 1.6 Mg and center of mass at G. If the coefficient of static friction between the shoulder of the road and the tires is $\mu_s = 0.4$, determine the greatest slope θ the shoulder can have without causing the car to slip or tip over if the car travels along the shoulder at constant velocity.

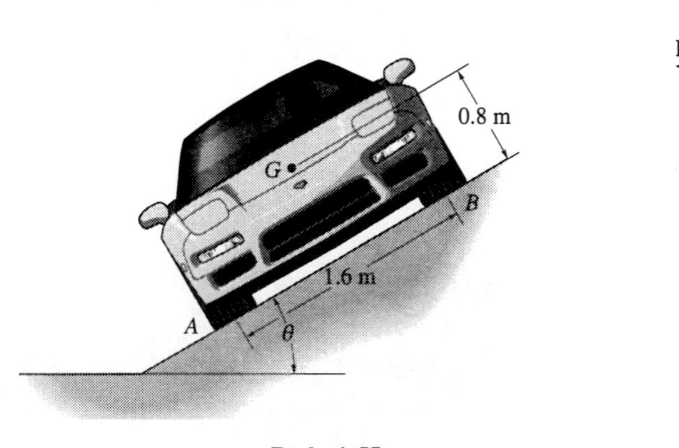

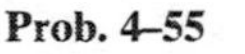

Prob. 4–55

4-56. The drum has a weight of 500 N ($\approx$ 50 kg) and rests on the floor for which the coefficient of static friction is $\mu_s = 0.6$. If $a = 0.6$ m and $b = 0.9$ m, determine the smallest magnitude of the force **P** that will cause impending motion of the drum.

4-57. The drum has a weight of 500 N ($\approx$ 50 kg) and rests on the floor for which the coefficient of static friction is $\mu_s = 0.5$. If $a = 0.9$ m and $a = 1.2$ m, determine the smallest magnitude of the force **P** that will cause impending motion of the drum.

Probs. 4–56/57

4-58. The coefficient of static friction between the shoes at A and B of the tongs and the pallet is $\mu_s' = 0.5$, and between the pallet and the floor $\mu_s = 0.4$. If a horizontal towing force of $P = 300$ N is applied to the tongs, determine the largest mass that can be towed.

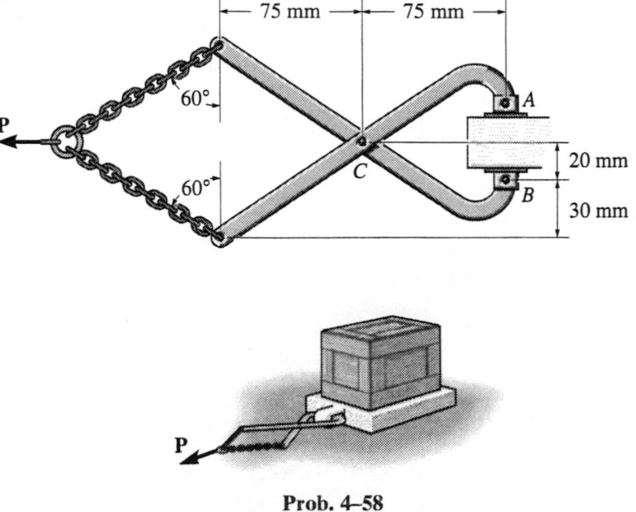

Prob. 4–58

***4-59.** The pipe is hoisted using the tongs. If the coefficient of static friction at A and B is μ_s, determine the smallest dimension b so that any pipe of inner diameter d can be lifted.

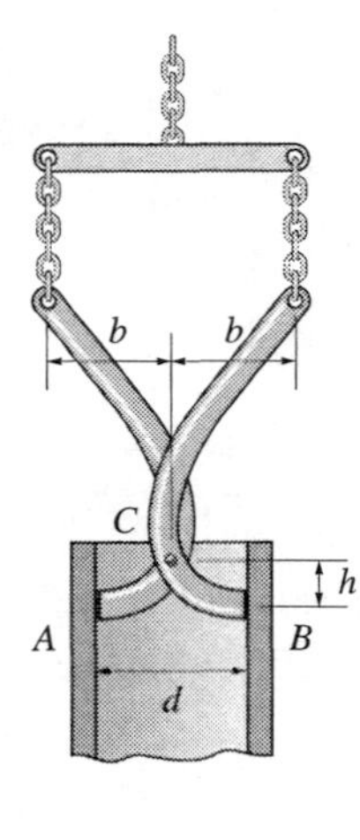

Prob. 4–59

4-60. Determine the maximum weight W the man can lift with constant velocity using the pulley system, without and then with the "leading block" or pulley at A. The man has a weight of 800 N ($\approx$ 80 kg) and the coefficient of static friction between his feet and the ground is $\mu_s = 0.6$.

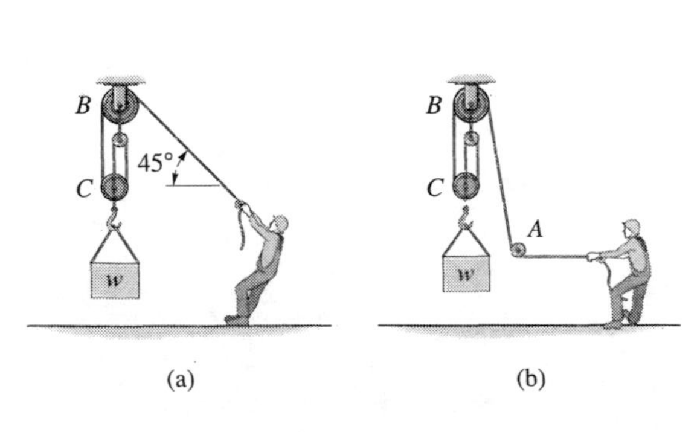

Prob. 4–60

4-61. The uniform dresser has a weight of 360 N ($\approx$ 36 kg) and rests on a tile floor for which $\mu_s = 0.25$. If the man pushes on it in the horizontal direction $\theta = 0°$, determine the smallest magnitude of force **F** needed to move the dresser. Also, if the man has a weight of 600 N ($\approx$ 60 kg), determine the smallest coefficient of static friction between his shoes and the floor so that he does not slip.

4-62. The uniform dresser has a weight of 360 N ($\approx$ 36 kg) and rests on a tile floor for which $\mu_s = 0.25$. If the man pushes on it in the direction $\theta = 30°$, determine the smallest magnitude of force **F** needed to move the dresser. Also, if the man has a weight of 600 N ($\approx$ 60 kg), determine the smallest coefficient of static friction between his shoes and the floor so that he does not slip.

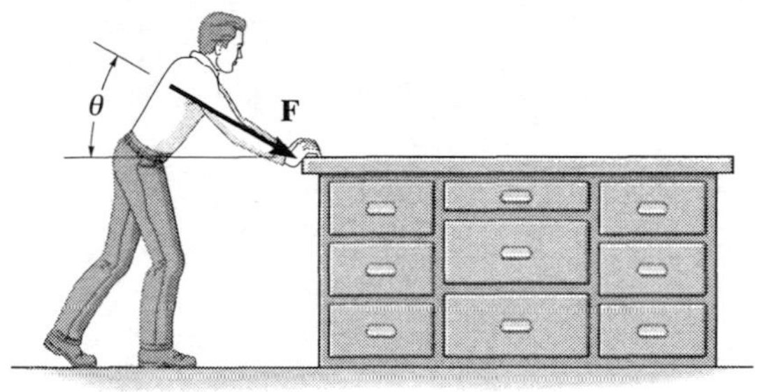

Probs. 4–61/62

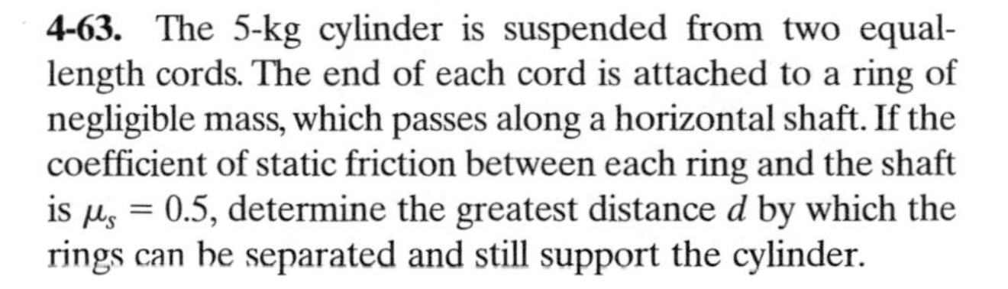

4-63. The 5-kg cylinder is suspended from two equal-length cords. The end of each cord is attached to a ring of negligible mass, which passes along a horizontal shaft. If the coefficient of static friction between each ring and the shaft is $\mu_s = 0.5$, determine the greatest distance d by which the rings can be separated and still support the cylinder.

d
600 mm
600 mm

Prob. 4–63

***4.64.** The board can be adjusted vertically by tilting it up and sliding the smooth pin A along the vertical guide G. When placed horizontally, the bottom C then bears along the edge of the guide, where $\mu_s = 0.4$. Determine the largest dimension d which will support any applied force $\mathbf{F}$ without causing the board to slip downward.

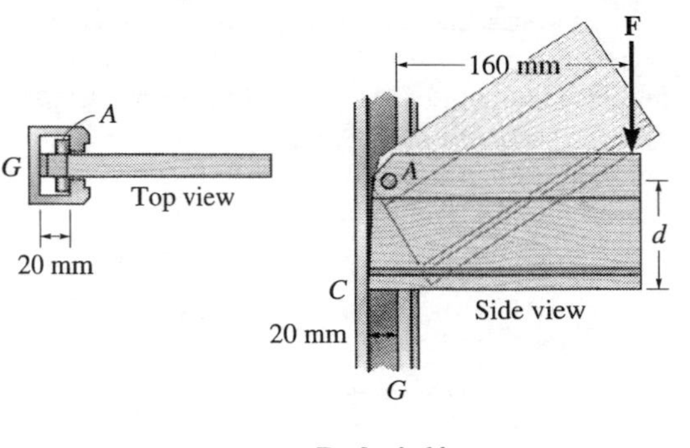

Prob. 4–64

4-65. The homogeneous semicylinder has a mass m and mass center at G. Determine the largest angle θ of the inclined plane upon which it rests so that it does not slip down the plane. The coefficient of static friction between the plane and the cylinder is $\mu_s = 0.3$. Also, what is the angle ϕ for this case?

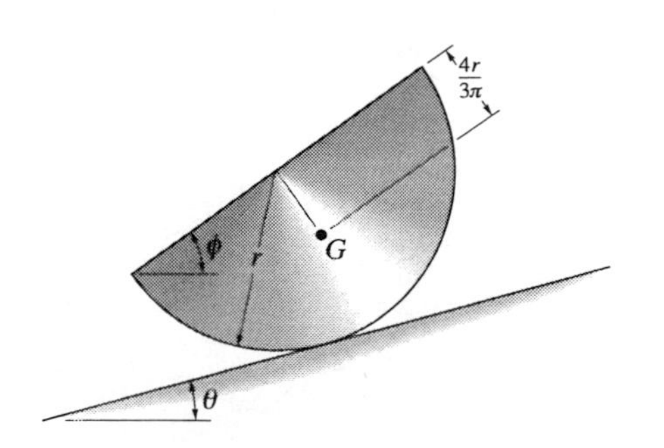

Prob. 4–65

4-66. Car A has a mass of 1.4 Mg and mass center at G. If car B exerts a horizontal force on A of 2 kN, determine if this force is great enough to move car A. The coefficients of static and kinetic friction between the tires and the road are $\mu_s = 0.5$ and $\mu_k = 0.35$. Assume B's bumper is smooth.

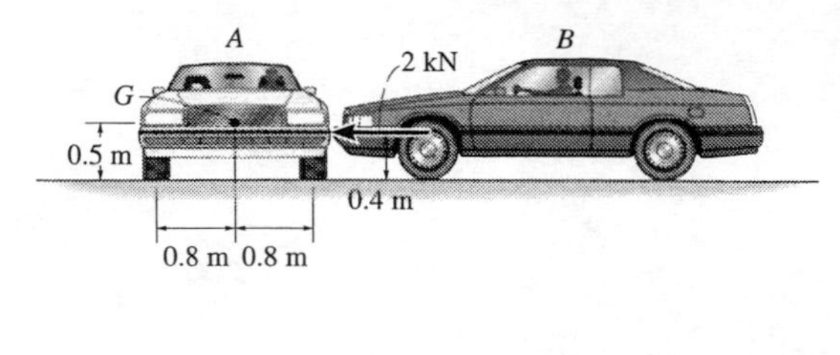

Prob. 4–66

4-67. A 35-kg disk rests on an inclined surface for which $\mu_s = 0.2$. Determine the maximum vertical force $\mathbf{P}$ that may be applied to link AB without causing the disk to slip at C.

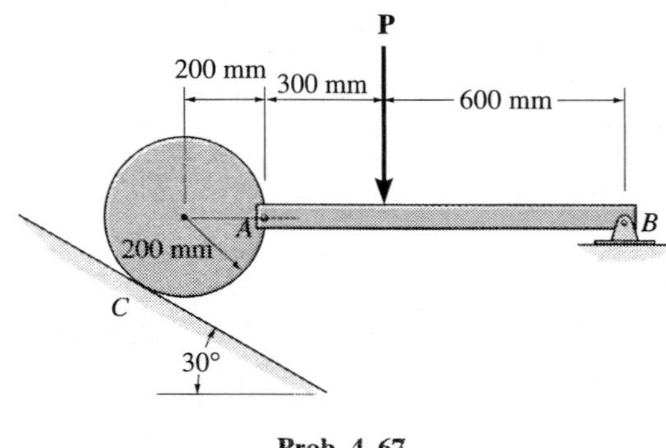

Prob. 4–67

***4-68.** The crate has a weight W and the coefficient of static friction at the surface is $\mu_s = 0.3$. Determine the orientation of the cord and the smallest possible force $\mathbf{P}$ that has to be applied to the cord so that the crate is on the verge of moving.

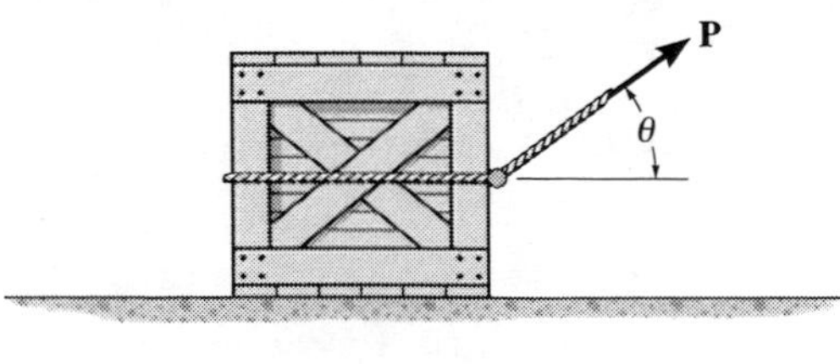

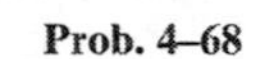
Prob. 4–68

4-69. The 4000-N ($\approx$ 400-kg) concrete pipe is being lowered from the truck bed when it is in the position shown. If the coefficient of static friction at the points of support A and B is $\mu_s = 0.4$, determine where it begins to slip first: at A or B, or both at A and B.

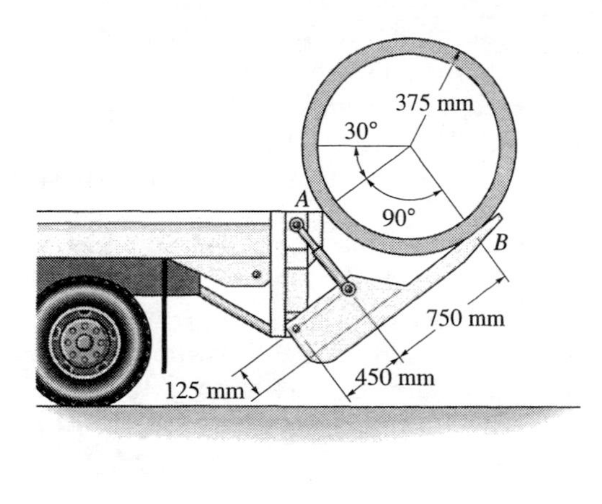

Prob. 4–69

4-70. The friction pawl is pinned at A and rests against the wheel at B. It allows freedom of movement when the wheel is rotating counterclockwise about C. Clockwise rotation is prevented due to friction of the pawl which tends to bind the wheel. If $(\mu_s)_B = 0.6$, determine the design angle θ which will prevent clockwise motion for any value of applied moment M. *Hint:* Neglect the weight of the pawl so that it becomes a two-force member.

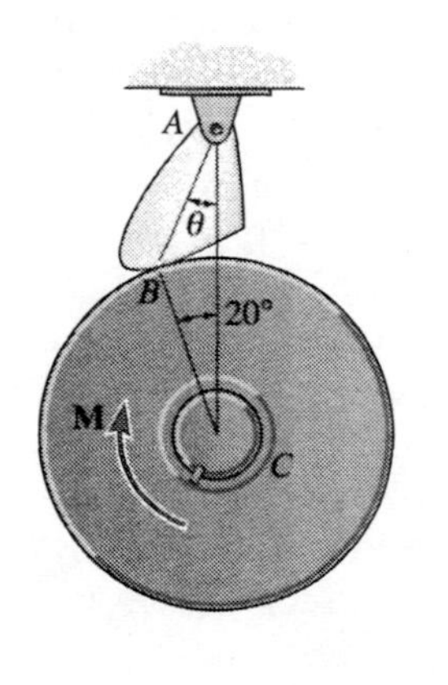

Prob. 4–70

4-71. The semicylinder of mass m and radius r lies on the rough inclined plane for which $\phi = 10°$ and the coefficient of static friction is $\mu_s = 0.3$. Determine if the semicylinder slides down the plane, and if not, find the angle of tip θ of its base AB.

***4-72.** The semicylinder of mass m and radius r lies on the rough inclined plane. If the inclination $\phi = 15°$, determine the smallest coefficient of static friction which will prevent the semicylinder from slipping.

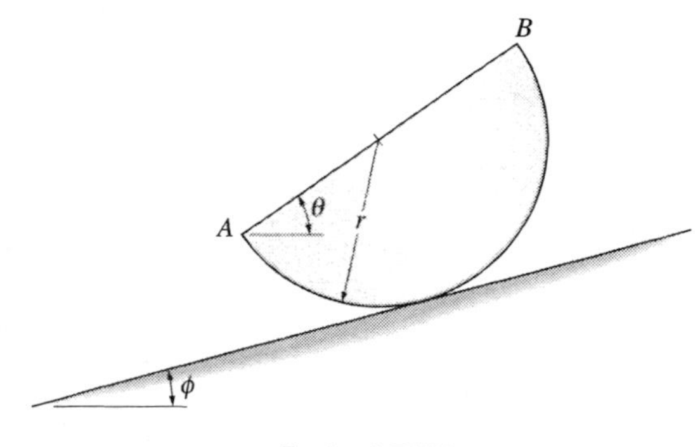

Probs. 4–71/72

4-73. The door brace AB is to be designed to prevent opening the door. If the brace forms a pin connection under the doorknob and the coefficient of static friction with the floor is $\mu_s = 0.5$, determine the largest length L the brace can have to prevent the door from being opened. Neglect the weight of the brace.

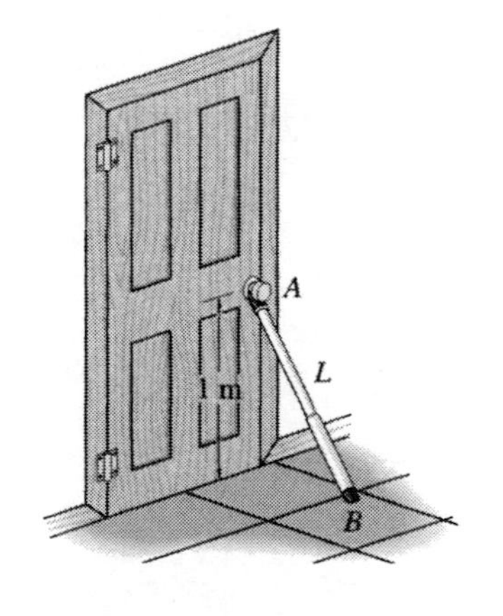

Prob. 4–73

CHAPTER REVIEW

- ***Free-Body Diagram.*** Before analyzing any equilibrium problem it is first necessary to draw a free-body diagram. This is an outlined shape of the body, which shows all the forces and couple moments that act on the body. Remember that a support will exert a *force* on the body in a particular direction if it prevents *translation* of the body in that direction, and it will exert a *couple moment* on the body if it prevents *rotation*. Angles used to resolve forces, and dimensions used to take moments of the forces, should also be shown on the free-body diagram.

- ***Two Dimensions.*** Normally the three scalar equations of equilibrium, $\Sigma F_x = 0$, $\Sigma F_y = 0$, $\Sigma M_o = 0$, can be applied when solving problems in two dimensions, since the geometry is easy to visualize. For the most direct solution, try to sum forces along an axis that will eliminate as many unknown forces as possible. Sum moments about a point O that passes through the line of action of as many unknown forces as possible.

- ***Three Dimensions.*** In three dimensions, it is often advantageous to use a Cartesian vector analysis when applying the equations of equilibrium. To do this, first express each known and unknown force and couple moment shown on the free-body diagram as a Cartesian vector. Then set the force summation equal to zero, $\Sigma \mathbf{F} = \mathbf{0}$. Take moments about a point O that lies on the line of action of as many unknown force components as possible. From point O direct position vectors to each force, and then use the cross product to determine the moment of each force. Require $\Sigma \mathbf{M}_O = \text{E}(\mathbf{r} \times \mathbf{F}) = \mathbf{0}$. The six scalar equations of equilibrium are established by setting the respective **i**, **j**, and **k** components of these force and moment sums equal to zero.

- ***Dry Friction.*** Frictional forces exist at rough surfaces of contact. They act on a body so as to oppose the motion or tendency of motion of the body. A static friction force approaches a maximum value of $F_s = \mu_s N$, where μ_s is the *coefficient of static friction*. In this case motion between the contacting surfaces is about to impend. If slipping occurs, then the friction force remains essentially constant and equal to a value of $F_k = \mu_k N$. Here μ_k is the *coefficient of kinetic friction*. The solution of a problem involving friction requires first drawing the free-body diagram of the body. If the unknowns cannot be determined strictly from the equations of equilibrium, and the possibility of slipping can occur, then the friction equation should be applied at the appropriate points of contact in order to complete the solution. It may also be possible for slender objects to tip over, and this situation should also be investigated.

REVIEW PROBLEMS

4-74. The horizontal beam is supported by springs at its ends. Each spring has a stiffness of $k = 5$ kN/m and is originally unstretched so that the beam is in the horizontal position. Determine the angle of tilt of the beam if a load of 800 N is applied at point C as shown.

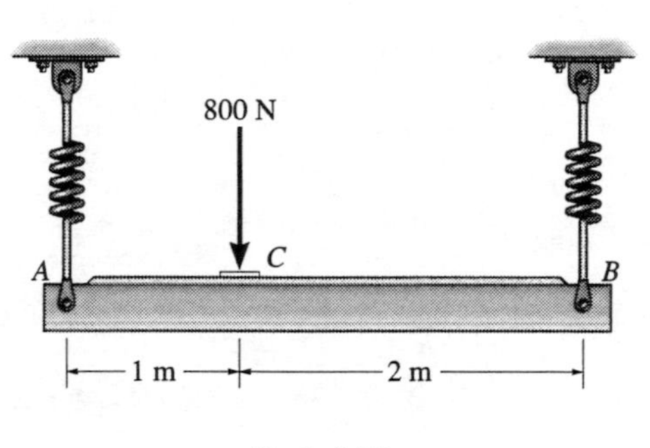

Prob. 4–74

4-75. The horizontal beam is supported by springs at its ends. If the stiffness of the spring at A is $k_A = 5$ kN/m, determine the required stiffness of the spring at B so that if the beam is loaded with the 800-N force it remains in the horizontal position both before and after loading.

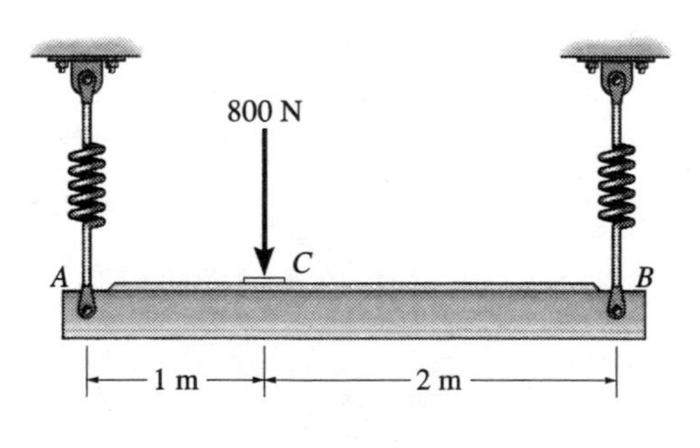

Prob. 4–75

*4-76. A vertical force of 400 N acts on the crankshaft. Determine the horizontal equilibrium force **P** that must be applied to the handle and the x, y, z components of force at the smooth journal bearing A and the thrust bearing B. The bearings are properly aligned and exert only force reactions on the shaft.

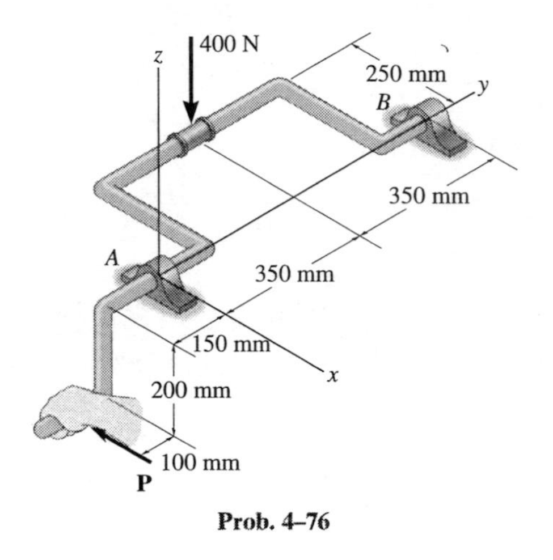

Prob. 4–76

4-77. The spring has a stiffness of $k = 80$ N/m and an unstretched length of 2 m. Determine the force in cables BC and BD when the spring is held in the position shown.

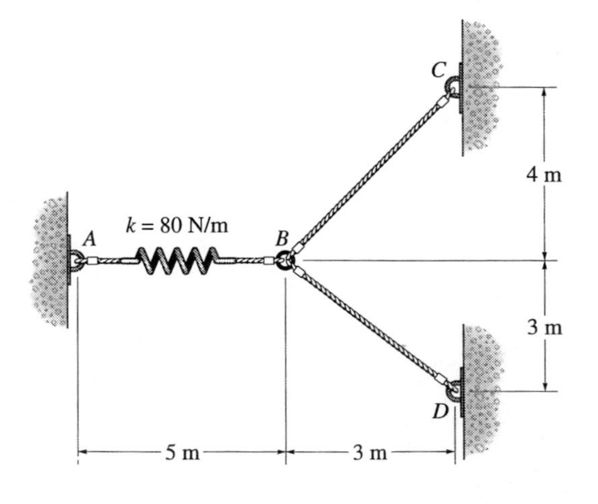

Prob. 4–77

4-78. A skeletal diagram of the lower leg is shown in the lower figure. Here it can be noted that this portion of the leg is lifted by the quadriceps muscle attached to the hip at A and to the patella bone at B. This bone slides freely over cartilage at the knee joint. The quadriceps is further extended and attached to the tibia at C. Using the mechanical system shown in the upper figure to model the lower leg, determine the tension **T** in the quadriceps and the magnitude of the resultant force at the femur (pin), D, in order to hold the lower leg in the position shown. The lower leg has a mass of 3.2 kg and a mass center at G_1, the foot has a mass of 1.6 kg and a mass center at G_2.

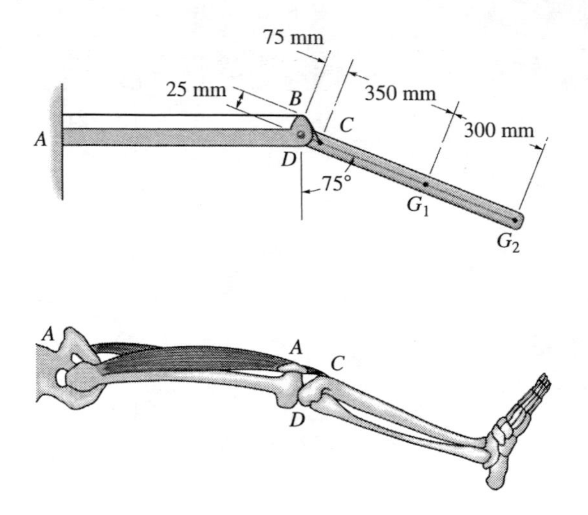

Prob. 4–78

4-79. The man has a mass of 40 kg. He plans to scale the vertical crevice using the method shown. If the coefficient of static friction between his shoes and the rock is $\mu_s = 0.4$ and between his backside and the rock, $\mu_s' = 0.3$, determine the smallest horizontal force his body must exert on the rock in order to do this.

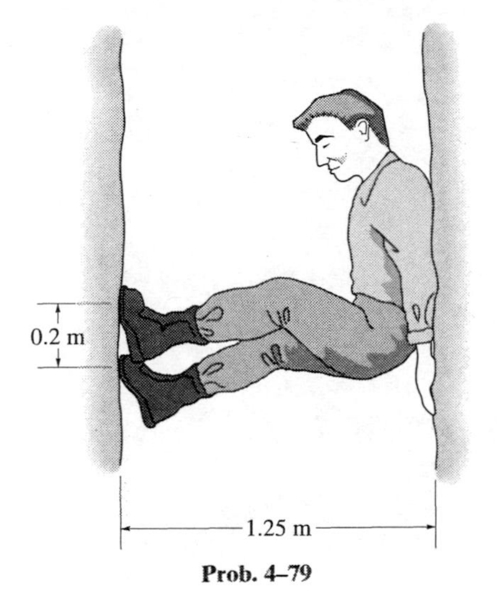

Prob. 4–79

***4-80.** Determine the reactions at the supports A and B of the frame.

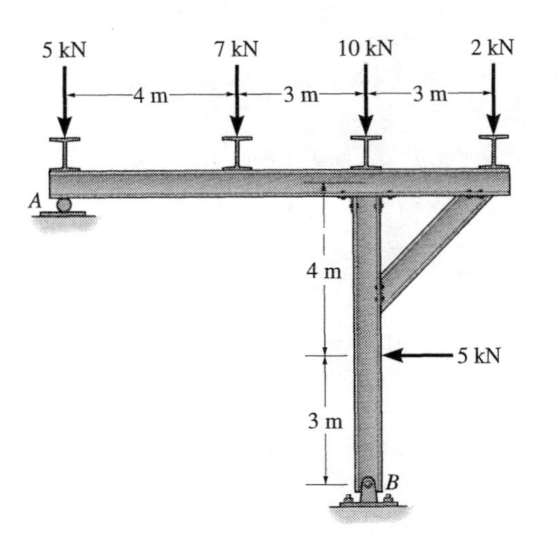

Prob. 4–80

4-81. The stiff-leg derrick used on ships is supported by a ball-and-socket joint at D and two cables BA and BC. The cables are attached to a smooth collar ring at B, which allows rotation of the derrick about the z axis. If the derrick supports a crate having a mass of 100 kg, determine the tension in the supporting cables and the x, y, z components of reaction at D.

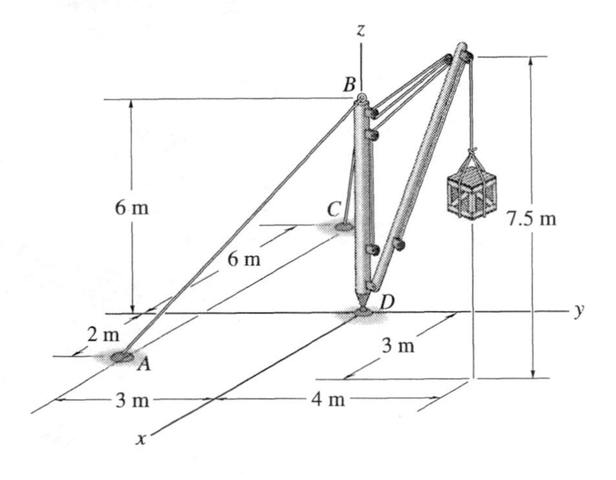

Prob. 4–81

The forces within the members of this truss bridge must be determined if they are to be properly designed.

CHAPTER 5

Structural Analysis

CHAPTER OBJECTIVES

- To show how to determine the forces in the members of a truss using the method of joints and the method of sections.
- To analyze the forces acting on the members of frames and machines composed of pin-connected members.

5.1 Simple Trusses

A *truss* is a structure composed of slender members joined together at their end points. The members commonly used in construction consist of wooden struts or metal bars. The joint connections are usually formed by bolting or welding the ends of the members to a common plate, called a *gusset plate,* as shown in Fig. 5–1*a*, or by simply passing a large bolt or pin through each of the members, Fig. 5–1*b*.

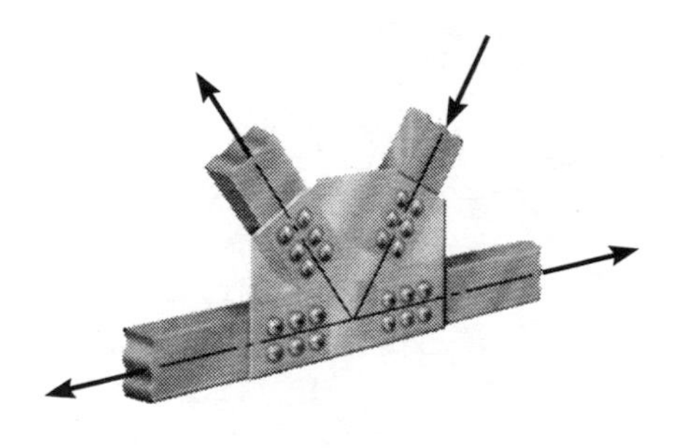

(a)

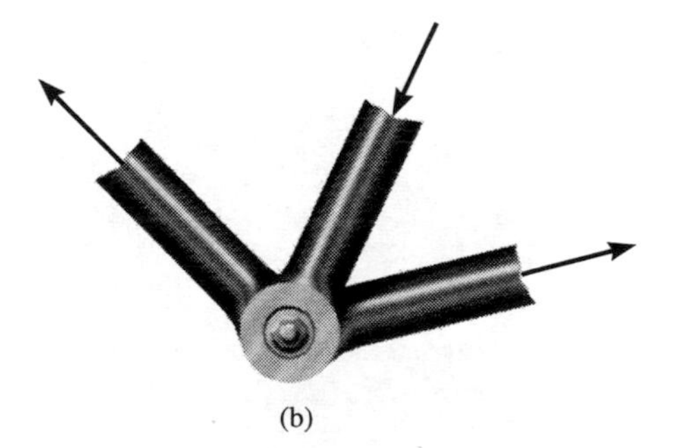

(b)

Fig. 5–1

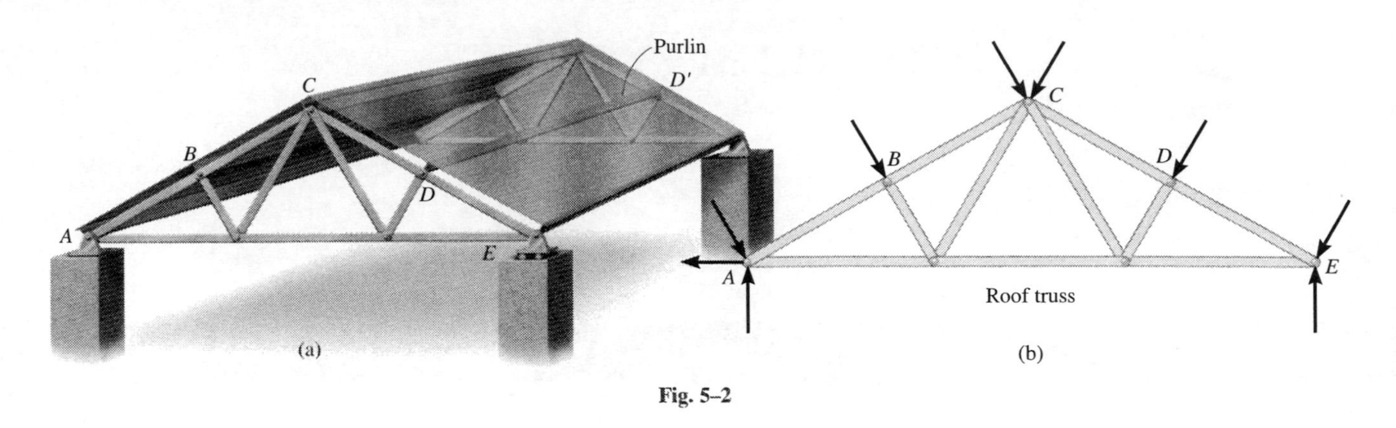

Fig. 5–2

Planar Trusses. *Planar* trusses lie in a single plane and are often used to support roofs and bridges. The truss $ABCDE$, shown in Fig. 5–2a, is an example of a typical roof-supporting truss. In this figure, the roof load is transmitted to the truss *at the joints* by means of a series of *purlins,* such as DD'. Since the imposed loading acts in the same plane as the truss, Fig. 5–2b, the analysis of the forces developed in the truss members is two-dimensional.

In the case of a bridge, such as shown in Fig. 5–3a, the load on the deck is first transmitted to *stringers,* then to *floor beams,* and finally to the *joints B, C,* and *D* of the two supporting side trusses. Like the roof truss, the bridge truss loading is also coplanar, Fig. 5–3b.

When bridge or roof trusses extend over large distances, a rocker or roller is commonly used for supporting one end, e.g., joint E in Figs. 5–2a and 5–3a. This type of support allows freedom for expansion or contraction of the members due to temperature or application of loads.

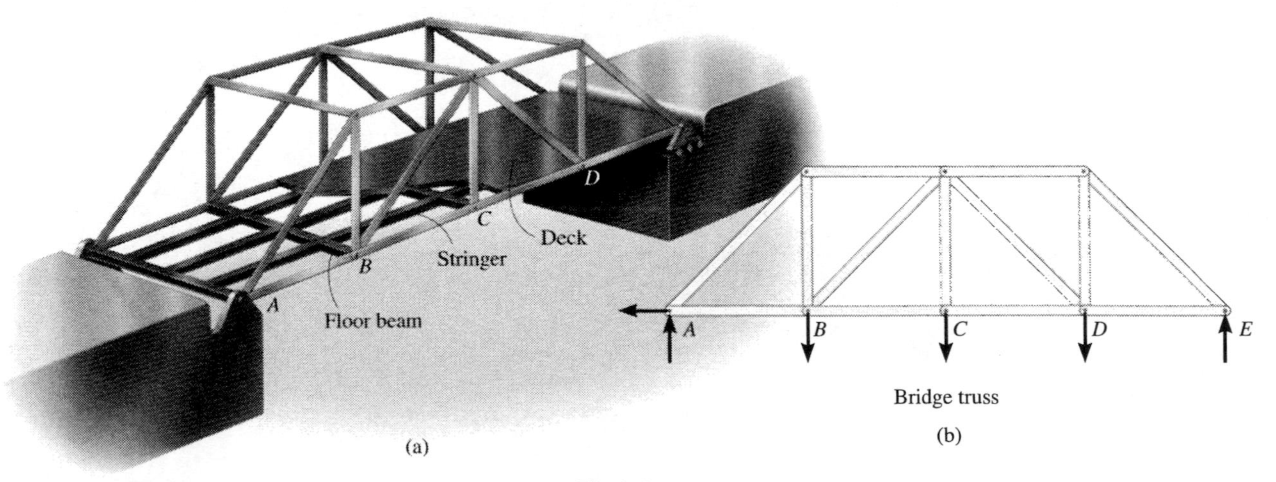

Fig. 5–3

Assumptions for Design. To design both the members and the connections of a truss, it is first necessary to determine the *force* developed in each member when the truss is subjected to a given loading. In this regard, two important assumptions will be made:

1. *All loadings are applied at the joints.* In most situations, such as for bridge and roof trusses, this assumption is true. Frequently in the force analysis the weight of the members is neglected since the forces supported by the members are usually large in comparison with their weight. If the member's weight is to be included in the analysis, it is generally satisfactory to apply it as a vertical force, half of its magnitude applied at each end of the member.
2. *The members are joined together by smooth pins.* In cases where bolted or welded joint connections are used, this assumption is satisfactory provided the center lines of the joining members are *concurrent,* as in Fig. 5–1*a*.

Because of these two assumptions, *each truss member acts as a two-force member,* and therefore the forces at the ends of the member must be directed along the axis of the member. If the force tends to *elongate* the member, it is a *tensile force* (T), Fig. 5–4*a*; whereas if it tends to *shorten* the member, it is a *compressive force* (C), Fig. 5–4*b*. In the actual design of a truss it is important to state whether the nature of the force is tensile or compressive. Often, compression members must be made *thicker* than tension members because of the buckling or column effect that occurs when a member is in compression.

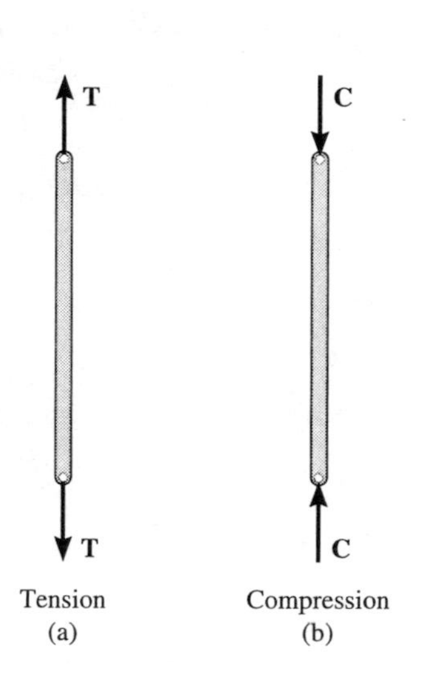

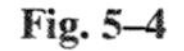
Fig. 5–4

Simple Truss. To prevent collapse, the form of a truss must be rigid. Obviously, the four-bar shape *ABCD* in Fig. 5–5 will collapse unless a diagonal member, such as *AC*, is added for support. The simplest form that is rigid or stable is a *triangle.* Consequently, a *simple truss* is constructed by *starting* with a basic triangular element, such as *ABC* in Fig. 5–6, and connecting two members (*AD* and *BD*) to form an additional element. As each additional element consisting of two members and a joint is placed on the truss, it is possible to construct a simple truss.

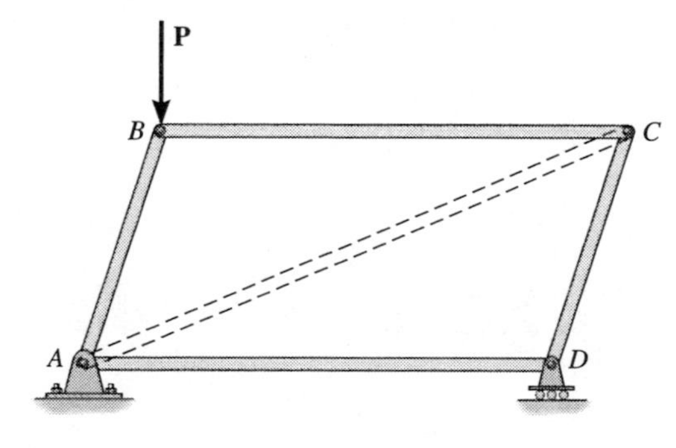

Fig. 5–5

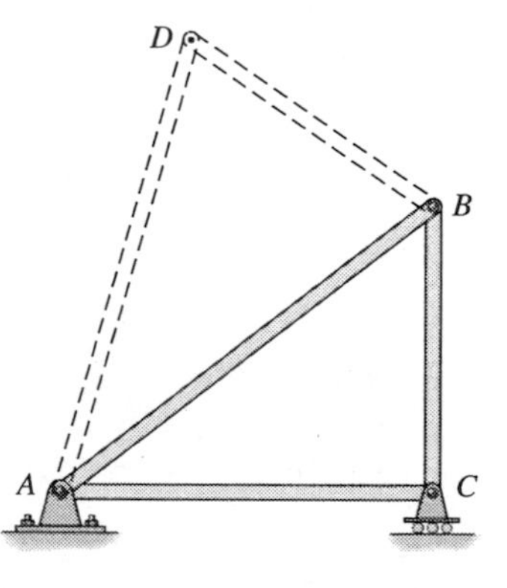

Fig. 5–6

5.2 The Method of Joints

These Howe trusses are used to support the roof of the metal building. Note how the members come together at a common point on the gusset plate and how the roof purlins transmit the load to the joints.

In order to analyze or design a truss, we must obtain the force in each of its members. If we were to consider a free-body diagram of the entire truss, then the forces in the members would be *internal forces,* and they could not be obtained from an equilibrium analysis. Instead, if we consider the equilibrium of a joint of the truss then a member force becomes an *external force* on the joint's free-body diagram, and the equations of equilibrium can be applied to obtain its magnitude. This forms the basis for the *method of joints.*

Because the truss members are all straight two-force members lying in the same plane, the force system acting at each joint is *coplanar and concurrent.* Consequently, rotational or moment equilibrium is automatically satisfied at the joint (or pin), and it is only necessary to satisfy $\Sigma F_x = 0$ and $\Sigma F_y = 0$ to ensure equilibrium.

When using the method of joints, it is *first* necessary to draw the joint's free-body diagram before applying the equilibrium equations. To do this, recall that the *line of action* of each member force acting on the joint is *specified* from the geometry of the truss since the force in a member passes along the axis of the member. As an example, consider the pin at joint B of the truss in Fig. 5–7*a*. Three forces act on the pin, namely, the 500-N force and the forces exerted by members BA and BC. The free-body diagram is shown in Fig. 5–7*b*. As shown, $\mathbf{F}_{BA}$ is "pulling" on the pin, which means that member BA is in *tension;* whereas $\mathbf{F}_{BC}$ is "pushing" on the pin, and consequently member BC is in *compression.* These effects are clearly demonstrated by isolating the joint with small segments of the member connected to the pin, Fig. 5–7*c*. The pushing or pulling on these small segments indicates the effect of the member being either in compression or tension.

In all cases, the analysis should start at a joint having at least one known force and at most two unknown forces, as in Fig. 5–7*b*. In this way, application of $\Sigma F_x = 0$ and $\Sigma F_y = 0$ yields two algebraic equations which can be solved for the two unknowns. When applying these equations, the correct sense of an unknown member force can be determined using one of two possible methods:

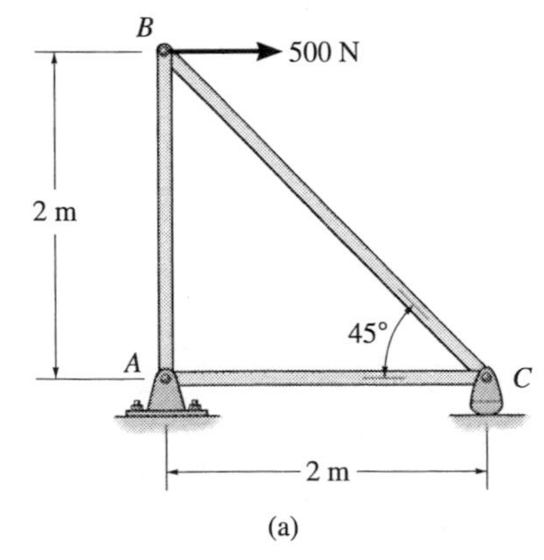

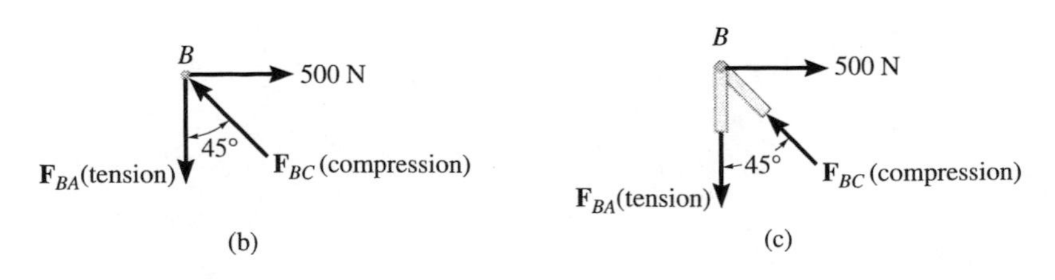

Fig. 5–7

- *Always assume* the *unknown member forces* acting on the joint's free-body diagram to be in *tension,* i.e., "pulling" on the pin. If this is done, then numerical solution of the equilibrium equations will yield *positive scalars for members in tension and negative scalars for members in compression.* Once an unknown member force is found, use its *correct* magnitude and sense (T or C) on subsequent joint free-body diagrams.
- The *correct* sense of direction of an unknown member force can, in many cases, be determined "by inspection." For example, $\mathbf{F}_{BC}$ in Fig. 5–7*b* must push on the pin (compression) since its horizontal component, $F_{BC} \sin 45°$, must balance the 500-N force ($\Sigma F_x = 0$). Likewise, $\mathbf{F}_{BA}$ is a tensile force since it balances the vertical component, $F_{BC} \cos 45°$ ($\Sigma F_y = 0$). In more complicated cases, the sense of an unknown member force can be *assumed;* then, after applying the equilibrium equations, the assumed sense can be verified from the numerical results. A *positive* answer indicates that the sense is *correct,* whereas a *negative* answer indicates that the sense shown on the free-body diagram must be *reversed.* This is the method we will use in the example problems which follow.

PROCEDURE FOR ANALYSIS

The following procedure provides a typical means for analyzing a truss using the method of joints.

- Draw the free-body diagram of a joint having at least one known force and at most two unknown forces. (If this joint is at one of the supports, then it may be necessary to know the external reactions at the truss support.)
- Use one of the two methods described above for establishing the sense of an unknown force.
- Orient the x and y axes such that the forces on the free-body diagram can be easily resolved into their x and y components and then apply the two force equilibrium equations $\Sigma F_x = 0$ and $\Sigma F_y = 0$. Solve for the two unknown member forces and verify their correct sense.
- Continue to analyze each of the other joints, where again it is necessary to choose a joint having at most two unknowns and at least one known force.
- Once the force in a member is found from the analysis of a joint at one of its ends, the result can be used to analyze the forces acting on the joint at its other end. Remember that a member in *compression* "pushes" on the joint and a member in *tension* "pulls" on the joint.

EXAMPLE 5.1

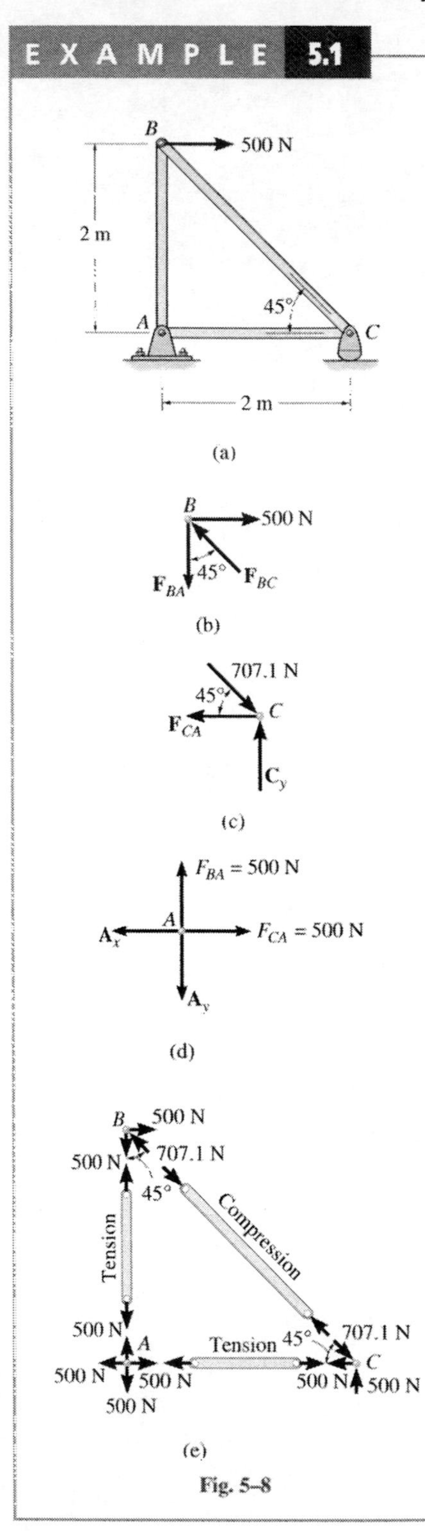

Fig. 5–8

Determine the force in each member of the truss shown in Fig. 5–8*a* and indicate whether the members are in tension or compression.

Solution

By inspection of Fig. 5–8*a*, there are two unknown member forces at joint *B*, two unknown member forces and an unknown reaction force at joint *C*, and two unknown member forces and two unknown reaction forces at joint *A*. Since we should have no more than two unknowns at the joint and at least one known force acting there, we will begin the analysis at joint *B*.

Joint B. The free-body diagram of the pin at *B* is shown in Fig. 5–8*b*. Applying the equations of joint equilibrium, we have

$$\overset{+}{\rightarrow}\Sigma F_x = 0; \quad 500\text{ N} - F_{BC}\sin 45^\circ = 0 \qquad F_{BC} = 707.1\text{ N (C)} \quad Ans.$$

$$+\uparrow\Sigma F_y = 0; \quad F_{BC}\cos 45^\circ - F_{BA} = 0 \qquad F_{BA} = 500\text{ N} \quad \text{(T)} \quad Ans.$$

Since the force in member *BC* has been calculated, we can proceed to analyze joint *C* in order to determine the force in member *CA* and the support reaction at the rocker.

Joint C. From the free-body diagram of joint *C*, Fig. 5–8*c*, we have

$$\overset{+}{\rightarrow}\Sigma F_x = 0; \quad -F_{CA} + 707.1\cos 45^\circ\text{N} = 0 \quad F_{CA} = 500\text{ N} \quad \text{(T)} \quad Ans.$$

$$+\uparrow\Sigma F_y = 0; \quad C_y - 707.1\sin 45^\circ\text{N} = 0 \quad C_y = 500\text{ N} \quad Ans.$$

Joint A. Although it is not necessary, we can determine the support reactions at joint *A* using the results of $F_{CA} = 500$ N and $F_{BA} = 500$ N. From the free-body diagram, Fig. 5–8*d*, we have

$$\overset{+}{\rightarrow}\Sigma F_x = 0; \quad 500\text{ N} - A_x = 0 \quad A_x = 500\text{ N}$$

$$+\uparrow\Sigma F_y = 0; \quad 500\text{ N} - A_y = 0 \quad A_y = 500\text{ N}$$

The results of the analysis are summarized in Fig. 5–8*e*. Note that the free-body diagram of each pin shows the effects of all the connected members and external forces applied to the pin, whereas the free-body diagram of each member shows only the effects of the end pins on the member.

EXAMPLE 5.2

Determine the forces acting in all the members of the truss shown in Fig. 5–9*a*.

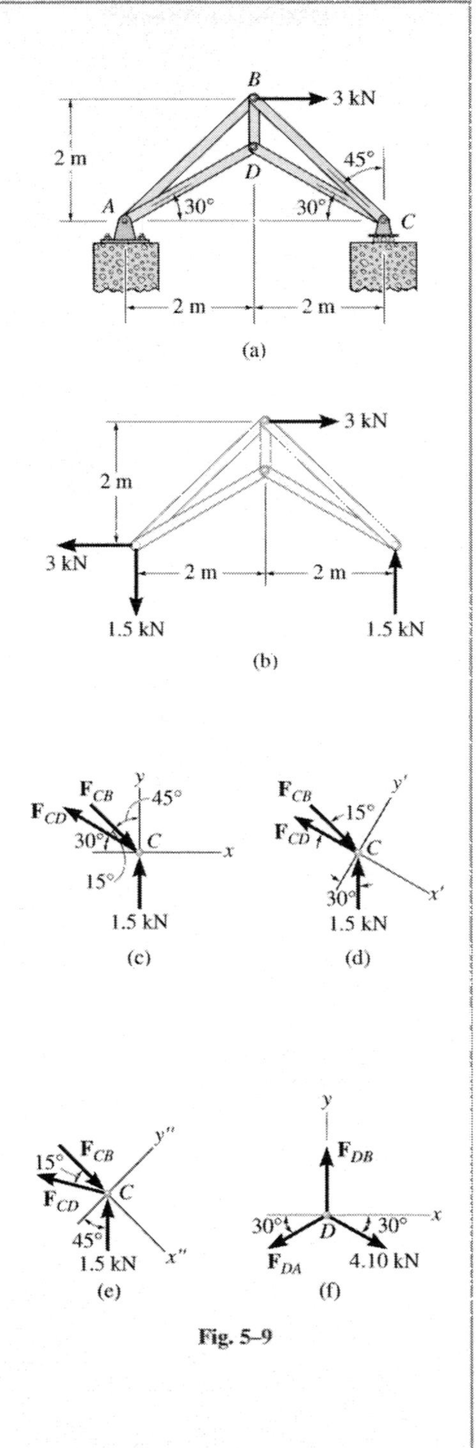

Fig. 5–9

Solution

By inspection, there are more than two unknowns at each joint. Consequently, the support reactions on the truss must first be determined. Show that they have been correctly calculated on the free-body diagram in Fig. 5–9*b*. We can now begin the analysis at joint *C*. Why?

Joint C. From the free-body diagram, Fig. 5–9*c*,

$$\xrightarrow{+} \Sigma F_x = 0; \qquad -F_{CD}\cos 30^\circ + F_{CB}\sin 45^\circ = 0$$

$$+\uparrow \Sigma F_y = 0; \quad 1.5\text{ kN} + F_{CD}\sin 30^\circ - F_{CB}\cos 45^\circ = 0$$

These two equations must be solved *simultaneously* for each of the two unknowns. Note, however, that a *direct solution* for one of the unknown forces may be obtained by applying a force summation along an axis that is *perpendicular* to the direction of the other unknown force. For example, summing forces along the y' axis, which is perpendicular to the direction of $\mathbf{F}_{CD}$, Fig. 5–9*d*, yields a direct solution for F_{CB}.

$$+\nearrow \Sigma F_{y'} = 0;$$

$$1.5\cos 30^\circ\text{kN} - F_{CB}\sin 15^\circ = 0 \quad F_{CB} = 5.02\text{ kN (C)} \qquad \textit{Ans.}$$

In a similar fashion, summing forces along the y'' axis, Fig. 5–9*e*, yields a direct solution for F_{CD}.

$$+\nearrow \Sigma F_{y''} = 0;$$

$$1.5\cos 45^\circ\text{kN} - F_{CD}\sin 15^\circ = 0 \qquad F_{CD} = 4.10\text{ kN (T)} \quad \textit{Ans.}$$

Joint D. We can now proceed to analyze joint *D*. The free-body diagram is shown in Fig. 5–9*f*.

$$\xrightarrow{+} \Sigma F_x = 0; \quad -F_{DA}\cos 30^\circ + 4.10\cos 30^\circ\text{kN} = 0$$

$$F_{DA} = 4.10\text{ kN (T)} \qquad \textit{Ans.}$$

$$+\uparrow \Sigma F_y = 0; \qquad F_{DB} - 2(4.10\sin 30^\circ\text{kN}) = 0$$

$$F_{DB} = 4.10\text{ kN (T)} \qquad \textit{Ans.}$$

The force in the last member, *BA*, can be obtained from joint *B* or joint *A*. As an exercise, draw the free-body diagram of joint *B*, sum the forces in the horizontal direction, and show that $F_{BA} = 0.776$ kN (C).

EXAMPLE 5.3

Determine the force in each member of the truss shown in Fig. 5–10*a*. Indicate whether the members are in tension or compression.

(a)

(b)

Fig. 5–10

Solution

Support Reactions. No joint can be analyzed until the support reactions are determined. Why? A free-body diagram of the entire truss is given in Fig. 5–10*b*. Applying the equations of equilibrium, we have

$$\overset{+}{\rightarrow} \Sigma F_x = 0; \quad 600 \text{ N} - C_x = 0 \quad C_x = 600 \text{ N}$$

$$\circlearrowleft + \Sigma M_C = 0; \quad -A_y(6 \text{ m}) + 400 \text{ N}(3 \text{ m}) + 600 \text{ N}(4 \text{ m}) = 0$$

$$A_y = 600 \text{ N}$$

$$+\uparrow \Sigma F_y = 0; \quad 600 \text{ N} - 400 \text{ N} - C_y = 0 \quad C_y = 200 \text{ N}$$

The analysis can now start at either joint A or C. The choice is arbitrary since there are one known and two unknown member forces acting on the pin at each of these joints.

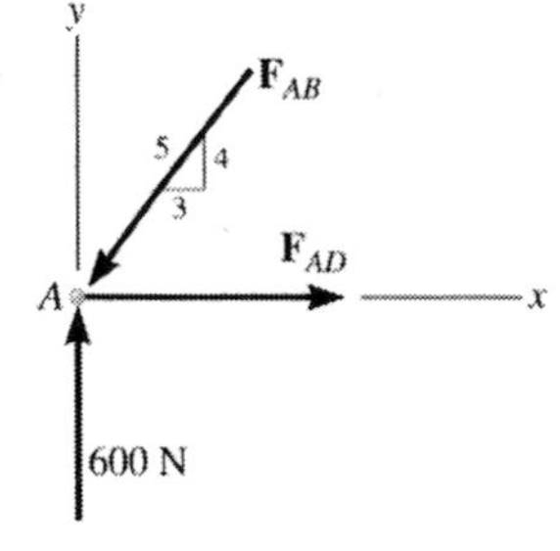

(c)

Joint A (Fig. 5–10*c*). As shown on the free-body diagram, there are three forces that act on the pin at joint A. The inclination of $\mathbf{F}_{AB}$ is determined from the geometry of the truss. By inspection, can you see why this force is assumed to be compressive and $\mathbf{F}_{AD}$ tensile? Applying the equations of equilibrium, we have

$$+\uparrow \Sigma F_y = 0; \quad 600 \text{ N} - \tfrac{4}{5} F_{AB} = 0 \quad F_{AB} = 750 \text{ N (C)} \quad \textit{Ans.}$$

$$\overset{+}{\rightarrow} \Sigma F_x = 0; \quad F_{AD} - \tfrac{3}{5}(750 \text{ N}) = 0 \quad F_{AD} = 450 \text{ N (T)} \quad \textit{Ans.}$$

Joint D (Fig. 5–10*d*). The pin at this joint is chosen next since, by inspection of Fig. 5–10*a*, the force in *AD* is known and the unknown forces in *DB* and *DC* can be determined. Summing forces in the horizontal direction, Fig. 5–10*d*, we have

$$\xrightarrow{+} \Sigma F_x = 0; \quad -450 \text{ N} + \tfrac{3}{5}F_{DB} + 600 \text{ N} = 0 \quad F_{DB} = -250 \text{ N}$$

The negative sign indicates that $\mathbf{F}_{DB}$ acts in the *opposite sense* to that shown in Fig. 5–10*d**. Hence,

$$F_{DB} = 250 \text{ N} \quad \text{(T)} \qquad \textit{Ans.}$$

To determine $\mathbf{F}_{DC}$, we can either correct the sense of $\mathbf{F}_{DB}$ and then apply $\Sigma F_y = 0$, or apply this equation and retain the negative sign for F_{DB}, i.e.,

$$+\uparrow \Sigma F_y = 0; \quad -F_{DC} - \tfrac{4}{5}(-250 \text{ N}) = 0 \qquad F_{DC} = 200 \text{ N} \quad \text{(C)} \quad \textit{Ans.}$$

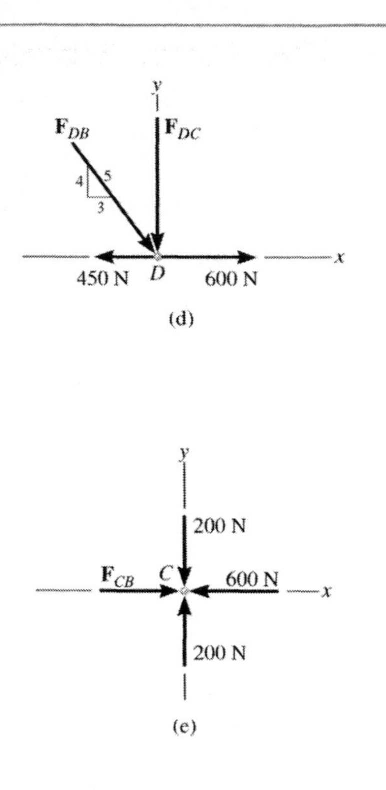

Joint C (Fig. 5–10*e*).

$$\xrightarrow{+} \Sigma F_x = 0; \quad F_{CB} - 600 \text{ N} = 0 \qquad F_{CB} = 600 \text{ N} \quad \text{(C)} \qquad \textit{Ans.}$$

$$+\uparrow \Sigma F_y = 0; \quad 200 \text{ N} - 200 \text{ N} \equiv 0 \quad \text{(check)}$$

The analysis is summarized in Fig. 5–10*f*, which shows the correct free-body diagram for each pin and member.

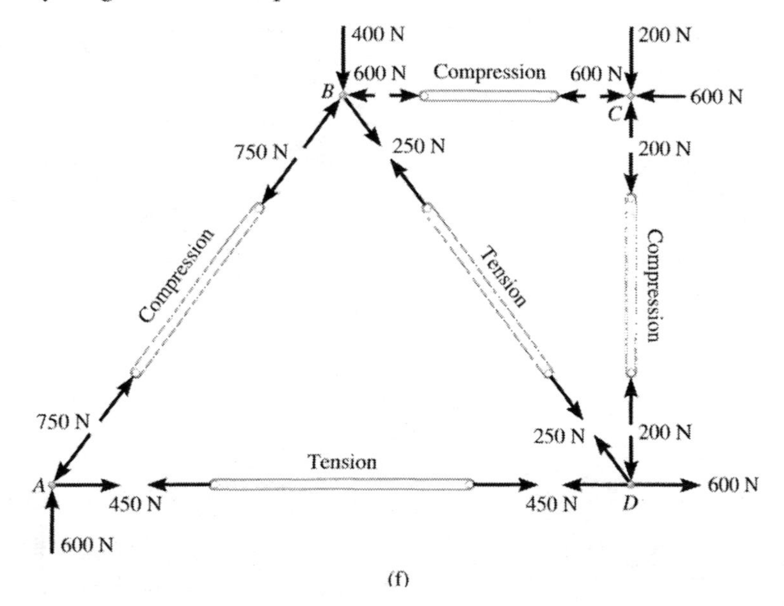

(f)

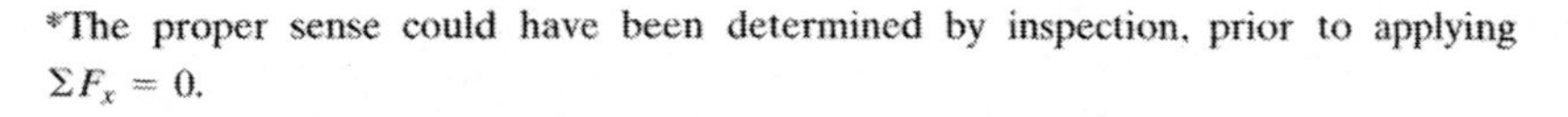

*The proper sense could have been determined by inspection, prior to applying $\Sigma F_x = 0$.

5.3 Zero-Force Members

Truss analysis using the method of joints is greatly simplified if one is first able to determine those members which support *no loading.* These *zero-force members* are used to increase the stability of the truss during construction and to provide support if the applied loading is changed.

The zero-force members of a truss can generally be determined *by inspection* of each of its joints. For example, consider the truss shown in Fig. 5–11*a*. If a free-body diagram of the pin at joint A is drawn, Fig. 5–11*b*, it is seen that members AB and AF are zero-force members. On the other hand, notice that we could not have come to this conclusion if we had considered the free-body diagrams of joints F or B simply because there are five unknowns at each of these joints. In a similar manner, consider the free-body diagram of joint D, Fig. 5–11*c*. Here again it is seen that DC and DE are zero-force members. As a general rule, *if only two members form a truss joint and no external load or support reaction is applied to the joint, the members must be zero-force members.* The load on the truss in Fig. 5–11*a* is therefore supported by only five members as shown in Fig. 5–11*d*.

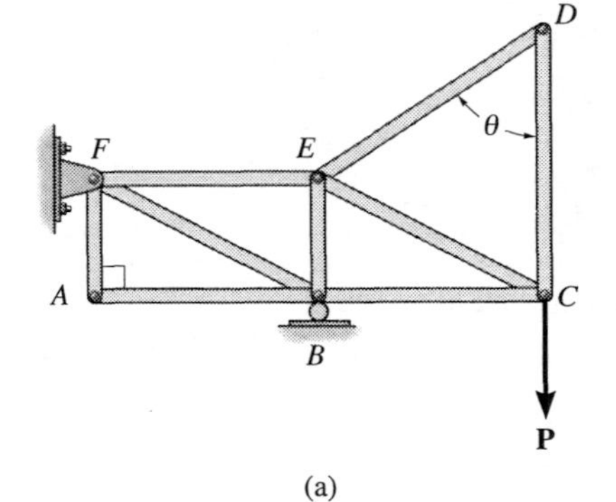

(a)

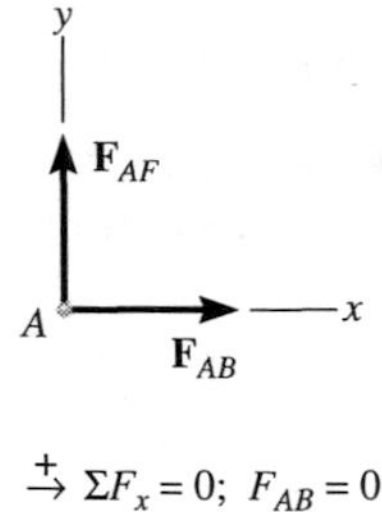

$\xrightarrow{+} \Sigma F_x = 0; \; F_{AB} = 0$

$+\uparrow \Sigma F_y = 0; \; F_{AF} = 0$

(b)

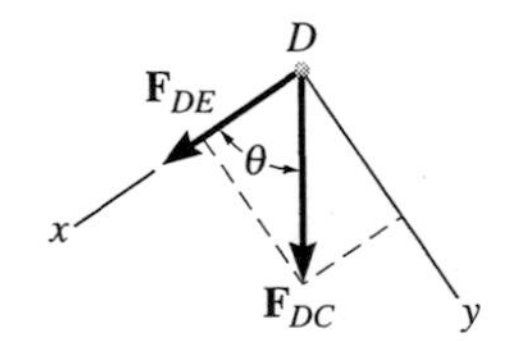

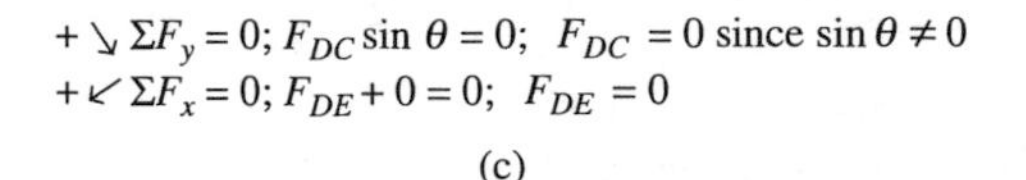

$+\searrow \Sigma F_y = 0; \; F_{DC} \sin\theta = 0; \;\; F_{DC} = 0 \text{ since } \sin\theta \neq 0$

$+\swarrow \Sigma F_x = 0; \; F_{DE} + 0 = 0; \;\; F_{DE} = 0$

(c)

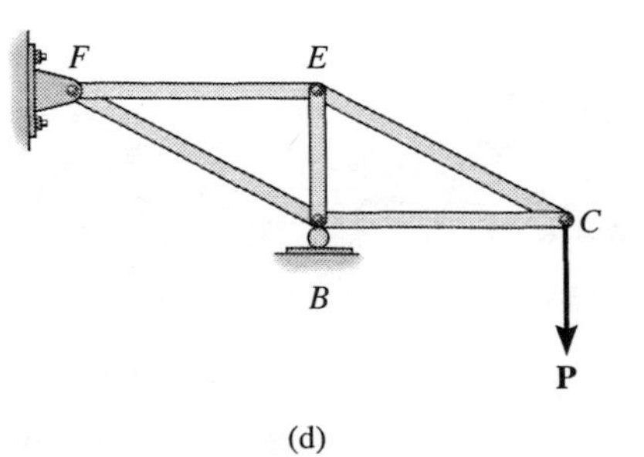

(d)

Fig. 5–11

Now consider the truss shown in Fig. 5–12*a*. The free-body diagram of the pin at joint D is shown in Fig. 5–12*b*. By orienting the y axis along members DC and DE and the x axis along member DA, it is seen that DA is a zero-force member. Note that this is also the case for member CA, Fig. 5–12*c*. In general, *if three members form a truss joint for which two of the members are collinear, the third member is a zero-force member provided no external force or support reaction is applied to the joint.* The truss shown in Fig. 5–12*d* is therefore suitable for supporting the load **P**.

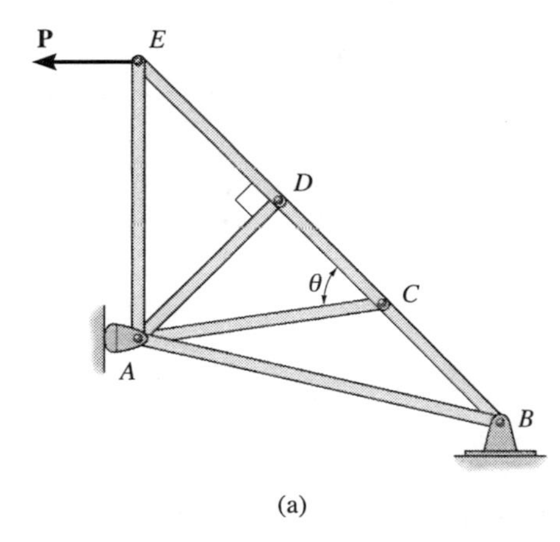

(a)

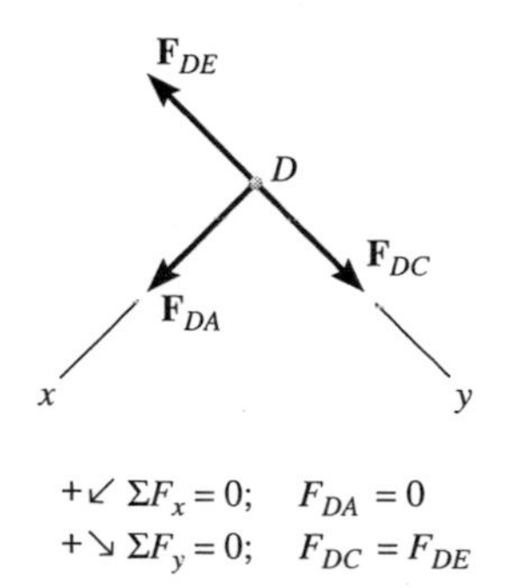

(b)

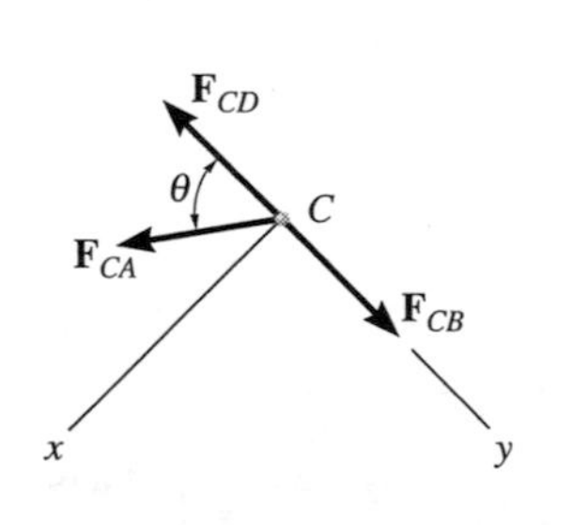

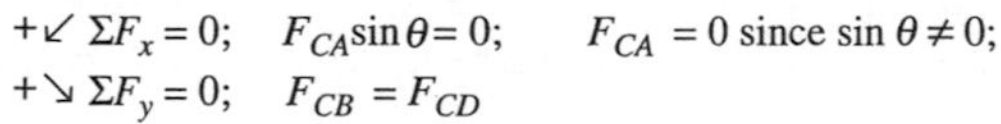

(c)

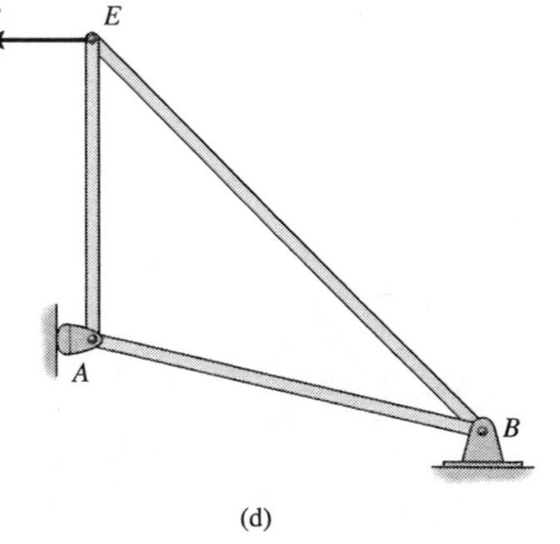

(d)

Fig. 5–12

EXAMPLE 5.4

Using the method of joints, determine all the zero-force members of the *Fink roof truss* shown in Fig. 5–13*a*. Assume all joints are pin connected.

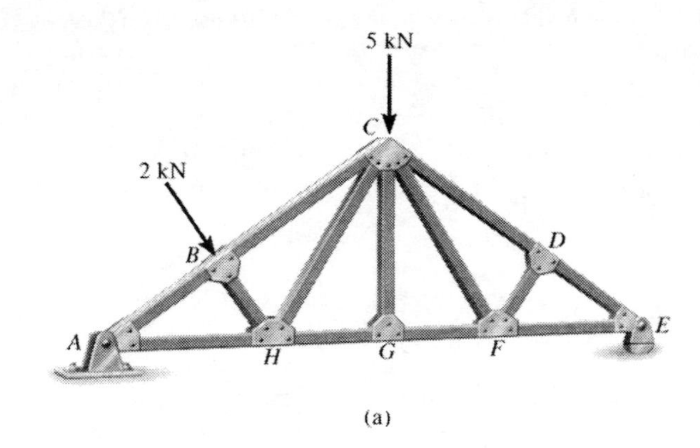

(a)

Fig. 5–13

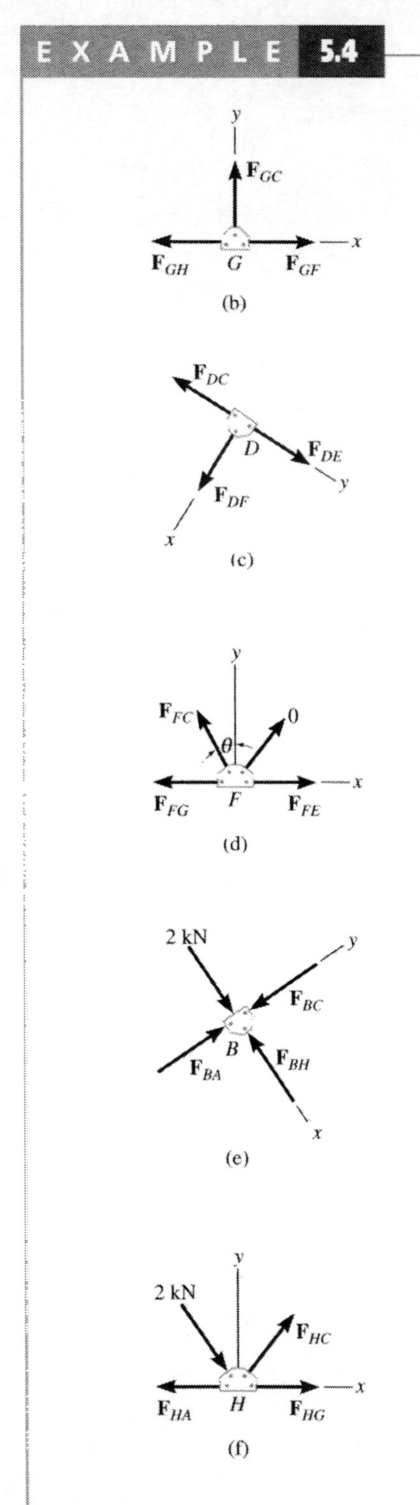

Solution

Look for joint geometries that have three members for which two are collinear. We have

Joint G (Fig. 5–13*b*).

$$+\uparrow \Sigma F_y = 0; \qquad F_{GC} = 0 \qquad \textit{Ans.}$$

Realize that we could not conclude that *GC* is a zero-force member by considering joint *C*, where there are five unknowns. The fact that *GC* is a zero-force member means that the 5-kN load at *C* must be supported by members *CB*, *CH*, *CF*, and *CD*.

Joint D (Fig. 5–13*c*).

$$+\swarrow \Sigma F_x = 0; \qquad F_{DF} = 0 \qquad \textit{Ans.}$$

Joint F (Fig. 5–13*d*).

$$+\uparrow \Sigma F_y = 0: \quad F_{FC}\cos\theta = 0 \qquad \text{Since } \theta \neq 90^\circ, \qquad F_{FC} = 0 \qquad \textit{Ans.}$$

Note that if joint *B* is analyzed, Fig. 5–13*e*,

$$+\searrow \Sigma F_x = 0; \quad 2\text{ kN} - F_{BH} = 0 \quad F_{BH} = 2\text{ kN} \qquad \text{(C)}$$

Note that F_{HC} must satisfy $\Sigma F_y = 0$, Fig. 5–13*f*, and therefore *HC* is *not* a zero-force member.

PROBLEMS

5-1. Determine the force in each member of the truss and state if the members are in tension or compression. Set $P_1 = 800$ kN and $P_2 = 400$ kN.

5-2. Determine the force on each member of the truss and state if the members are in tension or compression. Set $P_1 = 500$ kN and $P_1 = 100$ kN.

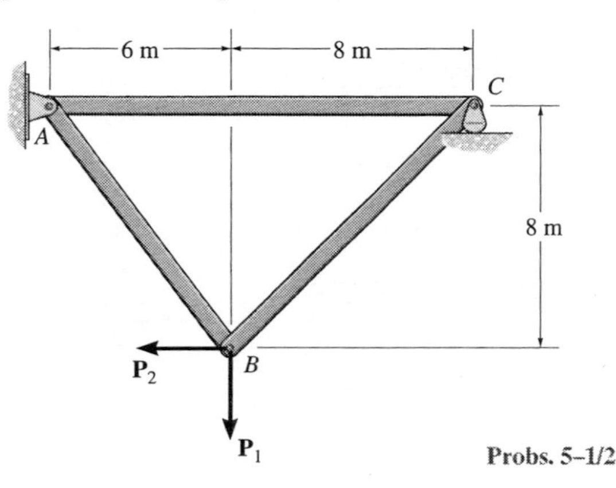

Probs. 5–1/2

5-3. The truss, used to support a balcony, is subjected to the loading shown. Approximate each joint as a pin and determine the force in each member. State whether the members are in tension or compression. Set $P_1 = 600$ kN, $P_2 = 400$ kN.

***5-4.** The truss, used to support a balcony, is subjected to the loading shown. Approximate each joint as a pin and determine the force in each member. State whether the members are in tension or compression. Set $P_1 = 800$ kN, $P_2 = 0$.

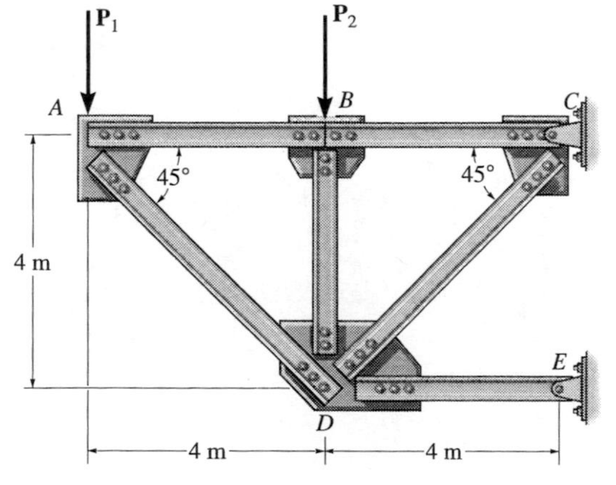

Probs. 5–3/4

5-5. Determine the force in each member of the truss and state if the members are in tension or compression. Assume each joint as a pin. Set $P = 4$ kN.

5-6. Assume that each member of the truss is made of steel having a mass per length of 4 kg/m. Set $P = 0$, determine the force in each member, and indicate if the members are in tension or compression. Neglect the weight of the gusset plates and assume each joint is a pin. Solve the problem by assuming the weight of each member can be represented as a vertical force, half of which is applied at the end of each member.

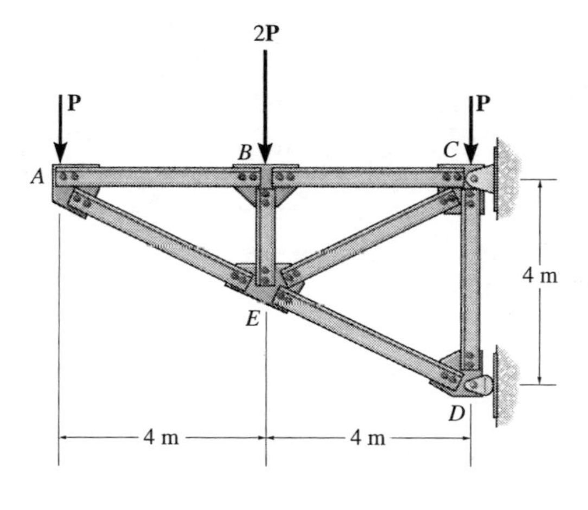

Probs. 5–5/6

5-7. Determine the force in each member of the truss and state if the members are in tension or compression.

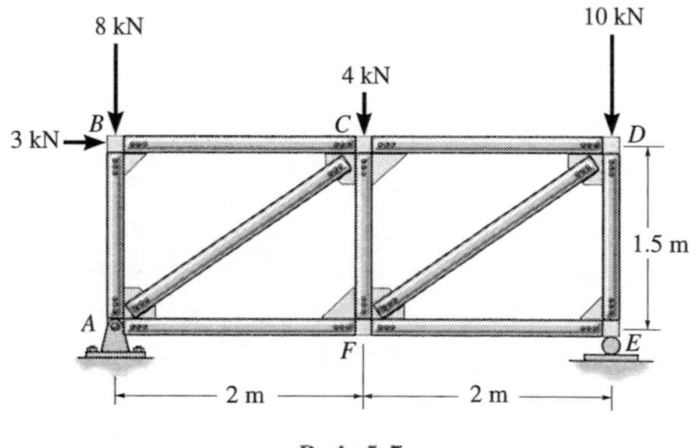

Prob. 5–7

*5-8. Determine the force in each member of the truss and state if the members are in tension or compression. Set $P_1 = 2$ kN and $P_2 = 1.5$ kN.

5-9. Determine the force in each member of the truss and state if the members are in tension or compression. Set $P_1 = P_2 = 4$ kN.

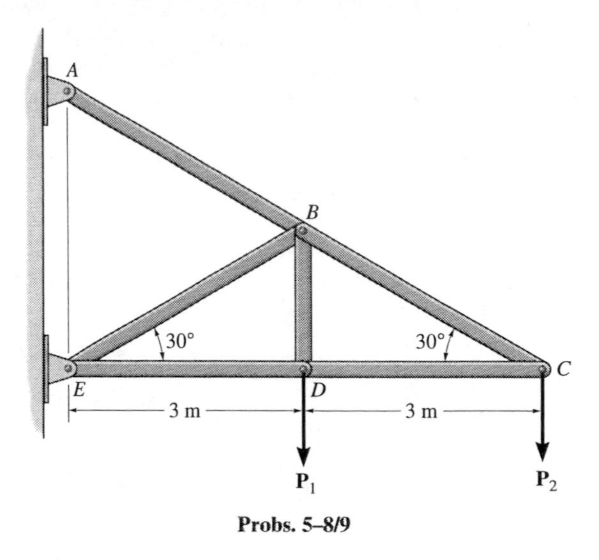

Probs. 5–8/9

*5-12. Determine the force in each member of the truss and state if the members are in tension or compression. Set $P_1 = 10$ kN, $P_2 = 15$ kN.

5-13. Determine the force in each member of the truss and state if the members are in tension or compression. Set $P_1 = 0$, $P_2 = 20$ kN.

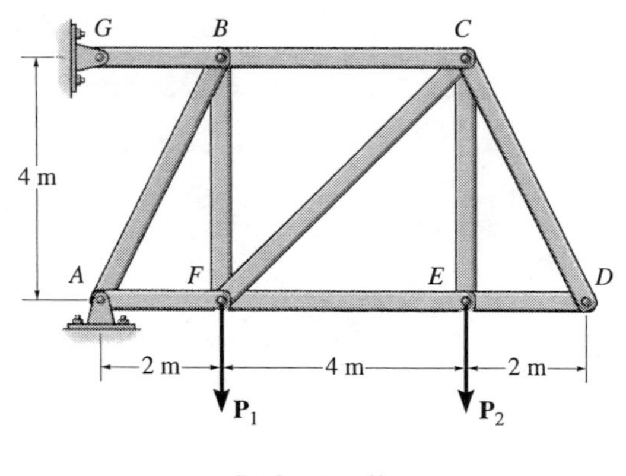

Probs. 5–12/13

5-10. Determine the force in each member of the truss and state if the members are in tension or compression. Set $P_1 = 0$, $P_2 = 100$ kN.

5-11. Determine the force in each member of the truss and state if the members are in tension or compression. Set $P_1 = 50$ kN, $P_2 = 150$ kN.

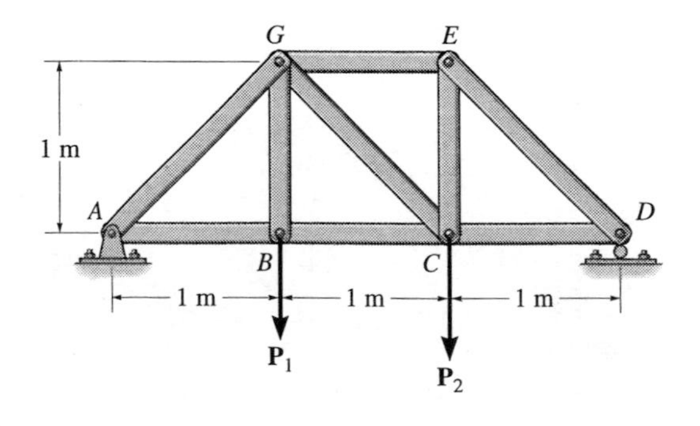

Probs. 5–10/11

5-14. Determine the force in each member of the truss and state if the members are in tension or compression. Set $P_1 = 10$ kN, $P_2 = 20$ kN, $P_3 = 30$ kN.

5-15. Determine the force in each member of the truss and state if the members are in tension or compression. Set $P_1 = 40$ kN, $P_2 = 40$ kN, $P_3 = 0$.

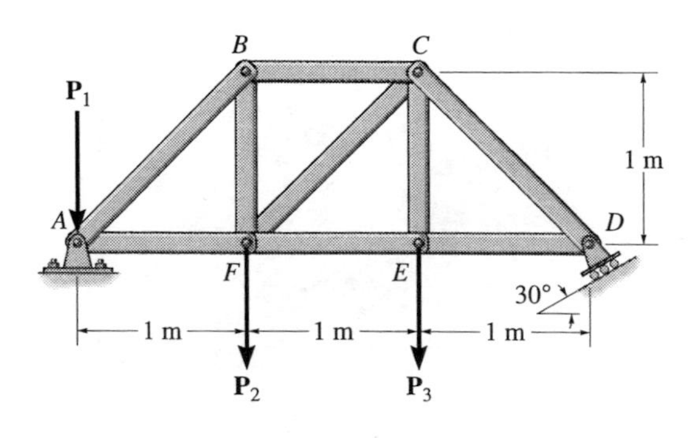

Probs. 5–14/15

5.4 The Method of Sections

The *method of sections* is used to determine the loadings acting within a body. It is based on the principle that if a body is in equilibrium then any part of the body is also in equilibrium. For example, consider the two truss members shown on the left in Fig. 5–14. If the forces within the members are to be determined, then an imaginary section indicated by the blue line, can be used to cut each member into two parts and thereby "expose" each internal force as "external" to the free-body diagrams shown on the right. Clearly, it can be seen that equilibrium requires that the member in tension (T) be subjected to a "pull," whereas the member in compression (C) is subjected to a "push."

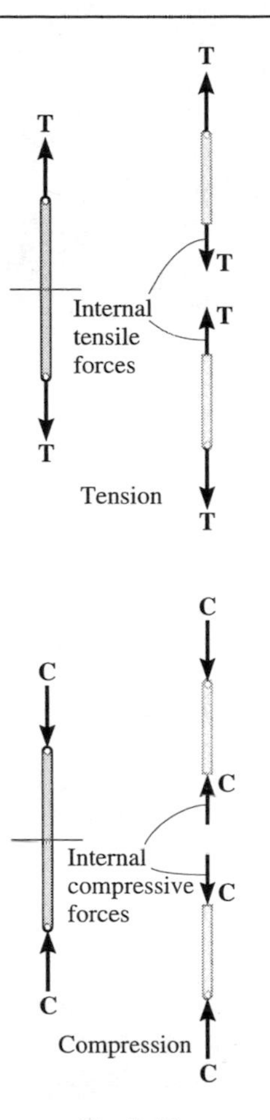

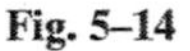
Fig. 5–14

The method of sections can also be used to "cut" or section the members of an entire truss. If the section passes through the truss and the free-body diagram of either of its two parts is drawn, we can then apply the equations of equilibrium to that part to determine the member forces at the "cut section." Since only *three* independent equilibrium equations $(\Sigma F_x = 0, \Sigma F_y = 0, \Sigma M_O = 0)$ can be applied to the isolated part of the truss, try to select a section that, in general, passes through not more than *three* members in which the forces are unknown. For example, consider the truss in Fig. 5–15*a*. If the force in member GC is to be determined, section *aa* would be appropriate. The free-body diagrams of the two parts are shown in Figs. 5–15*b* and 5–15*c*. In particular, note that the line of action of each member force is specified from the *geometry* of the truss, since the force in a member passes along its axis. Also, the member forces acting on one part of the truss are equal but opposite to those acting on the other part—Newton's third law. As noted above, members assumed to be in *tension* (BC and GC) are subjected to a "pull," whereas the member in *compression* (GF) is subjected to a "push."

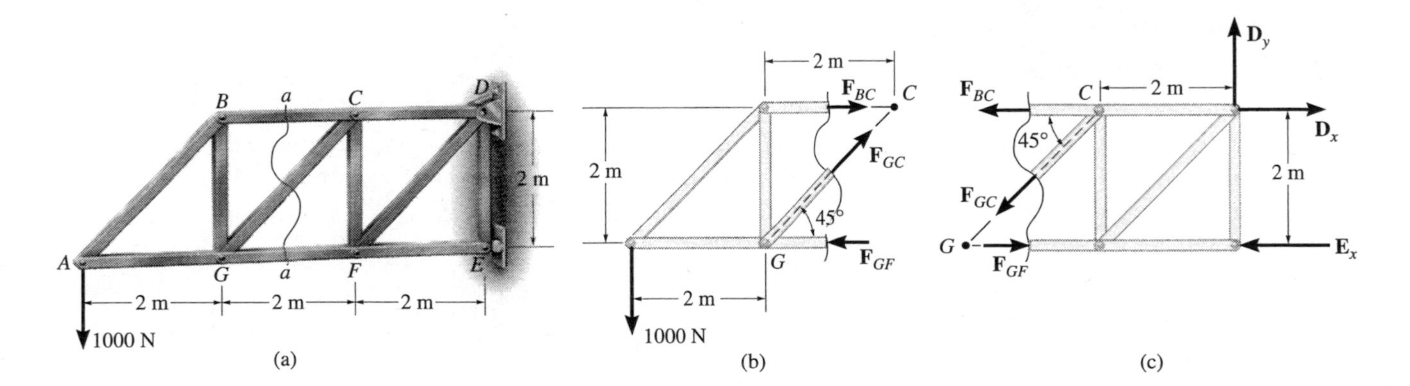

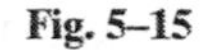
Fig. 5–15

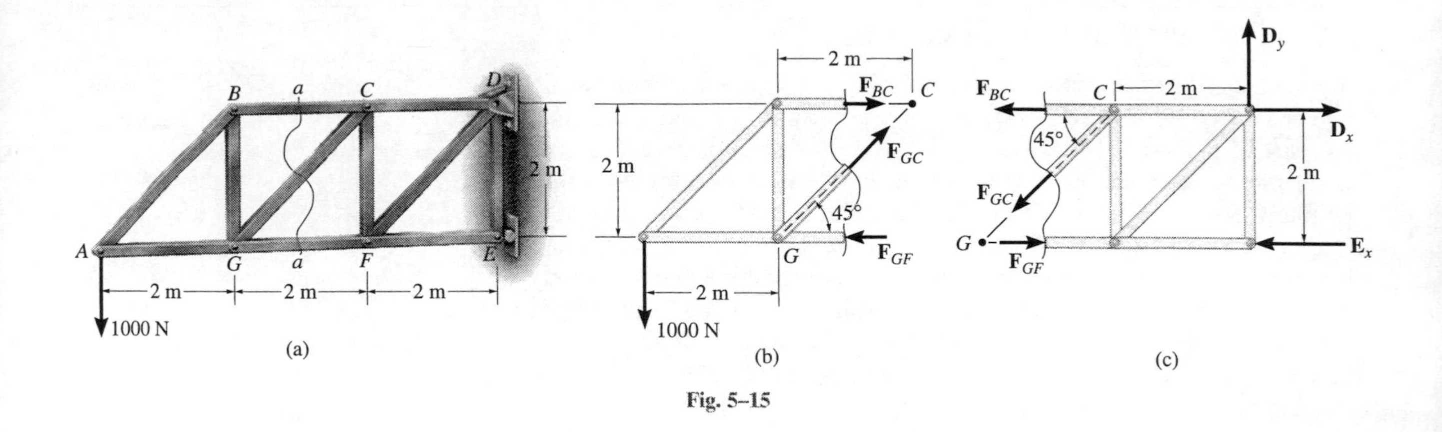

Fig. 5–15

The three unknown member forces $\mathbf{F}_{BC}$, $\mathbf{F}_{GC}$, and $\mathbf{F}_{GF}$ can be obtained by applying the three equilibrium equations to the free-body diagram in Fig. 5–15*b*. If, however, the free-body diagram in Fig. 5–15*c* is considered, the three support reactions $\mathbf{D}_x$, $\mathbf{D}_y$ and $\mathbf{E}_x$ will have to be determined *first.* Why? (This, of course, is done in the usual manner by considering a free-body diagram of the *entire truss.*)

Two Pratt trusses are used to construct this pedestrian bridge.

When applying the equilibrium equations, one should consider ways of writing the equations so as to yield a *direct solution* for each of the unknowns, rather than having to solve simultaneous equations. For example, summing moments about C in Fig. 5–15*b* would yield a direct solution for $\mathbf{F}_{GF}$ since $\mathbf{F}_{BC}$ and $\mathbf{F}_{GC}$ create zero moment about C. Likewise, $\mathbf{F}_{BC}$ can be directly obtained by summing moments about G. Finally, $\mathbf{F}_{GC}$ can be found directly from a force summation in the vertical direction since $\mathbf{F}_{GF}$ and $\mathbf{F}_{BC}$ have no vertical components. This ability to *determine directly* the force in a particular truss member is one of the main advantages of using the method of sections.*

*By comparison, if the method of joints were used to determine, say, the force in member GC, it would be necessary to analyze joints A, B, and G in sequence.

As in the method of joints, there are two ways in which one can determine the correct sense of an unknown member force:

- *Always assume* that the unknown member forces at the cut section are in *tension,* i.e., "pulling" on the member. By doing this, the numerical solution of the equilibrium equations will yield *positive scalars for members in tension and negative scalars for members in compression.*
- The correct sense of an unknown member force can in many cases be determined "by inspection." For example, $\mathbf{F}_{BC}$ is a tensile force as represented in Fig. 5–15*b* since moment equilibrium about *G* requires that $\mathbf{F}_{BC}$ create a moment opposite to that of the 1000-N force. Also, $\mathbf{F}_{GC}$ is tensile since its vertical component must balance the 1000-N force which acts downward. In more complicated cases, the sense of an unknown member force may be *assumed.* If the solution yields a *negative* scalar, it indicates that the force's sense is *opposite* to that shown on the free-body diagram. This is the method we will use in the example problems which follow.

PROCEDURE FOR ANALYSIS

The forces in the members of a truss may be determined by the method of sections using the following procedure.

Free-Body Diagram

- Make a decision as to how to "cut" or section the truss through the members where forces are to be determined.
- Before isolating the appropriate section, it may first be necessary to determine the truss's *external* reactions. Then three equilibrium equations are available to solve for member forces at the cut section.
- Draw the free-body diagram of that part of the sectioned truss which has the least number of forces acting on it.
- Use one of the two methods described above for establishing the sense of an unknown member force.

Equations of Equilibrium

- Moments should be summed about a point that lies at the intersection of the lines of action of two unknown forces, so that the third unknown force is determined directly from the moment equation.
- If two of the unknown forces are *parallel,* forces may be summed *perpendicular* to the direction of these unknowns to determine *directly* the third unknown force.

EXAMPLE 5.5

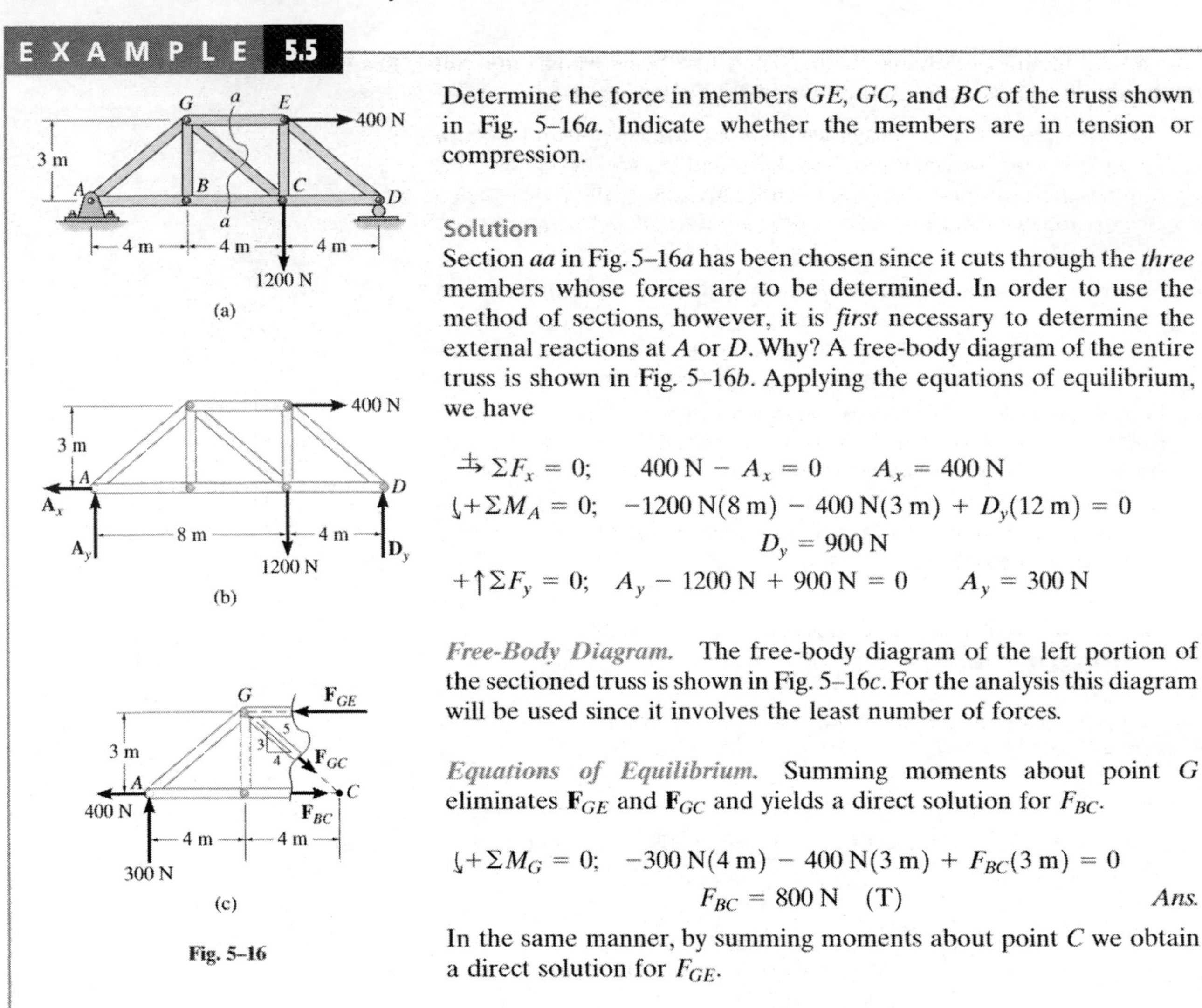

Fig. 5–16

Determine the force in members *GE*, *GC*, and *BC* of the truss shown in Fig. 5–16*a*. Indicate whether the members are in tension or compression.

Solution

Section *aa* in Fig. 5–16*a* has been chosen since it cuts through the *three* members whose forces are to be determined. In order to use the method of sections, however, it is *first* necessary to determine the external reactions at *A* or *D*. Why? A free-body diagram of the entire truss is shown in Fig. 5–16*b*. Applying the equations of equilibrium, we have

$$\overset{+}{\rightarrow}\Sigma F_x = 0; \quad 400\text{ N} - A_x = 0 \quad A_x = 400\text{ N}$$

$$\circlearrowleft + \Sigma M_A = 0; \quad -1200\text{ N}(8\text{ m}) - 400\text{ N}(3\text{ m}) + D_y(12\text{ m}) = 0$$

$$D_y = 900\text{ N}$$

$$+\uparrow\Sigma F_y = 0; \quad A_y - 1200\text{ N} + 900\text{ N} = 0 \quad A_y = 300\text{ N}$$

Free-Body Diagram. The free-body diagram of the left portion of the sectioned truss is shown in Fig. 5–16*c*. For the analysis this diagram will be used since it involves the least number of forces.

Equations of Equilibrium. Summing moments about point *G* eliminates $\mathbf{F}_{GE}$ and $\mathbf{F}_{GC}$ and yields a direct solution for F_{BC}.

$$\circlearrowleft + \Sigma M_G = 0; \quad -300\text{ N}(4\text{ m}) - 400\text{ N}(3\text{ m}) + F_{BC}(3\text{ m}) = 0$$

$$F_{BC} = 800\text{ N} \quad (\text{T}) \qquad \textit{Ans.}$$

In the same manner, by summing moments about point *C* we obtain a direct solution for F_{GE}.

$$\circlearrowleft + \Sigma M_C = 0; \quad -300\text{ N}(8\text{ m}) + F_{GE}(3\text{ m}) = 0$$

$$F_{GE} = 800\text{ N} \quad (\text{C}) \qquad \textit{Ans.}$$

Since $\mathbf{F}_{BC}$ and $\mathbf{F}_{GE}$ have no vertical components, summing forces in the *y* direction directly yields F_{GC}, i.e.,

$$+\uparrow\Sigma F_y = 0 \quad 300\text{N} - \tfrac{3}{5}F_{GC} = 0$$

$$F_{GC} = 500\text{ N} \quad (\text{T}) \qquad \textit{Ans.}$$

As an exercise, obtain these results by applying the equations of equilibrium to the free-body diagram of the right portion of the sectioned truss.

EXAMPLE 5.6

Determine the force in member *CF* of the bridge truss shown in Fig. 5–17*a*. Indicate whether the member is in tension or compression. Assume each member is pin-connected.

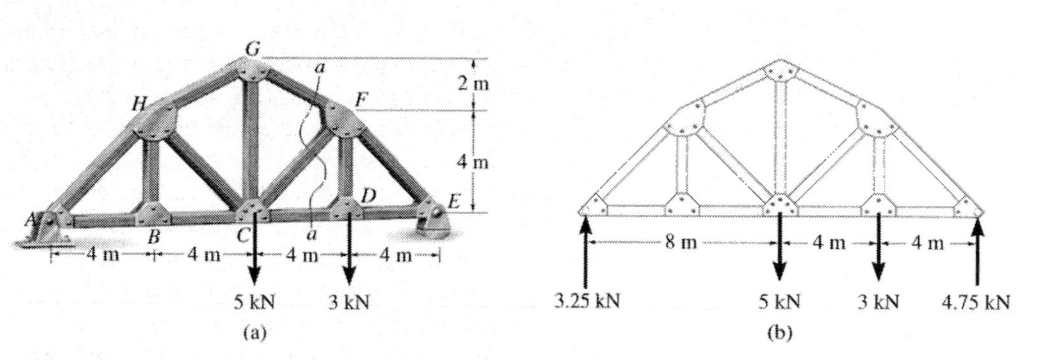

Fig. 5–17

Solution

Free-Body Diagram. Section *aa* in Fig. 5–17*a* will be used since this section will "expose" the internal force in member *CF* as "external" on the free-body diagram of either the right or left portion of the truss. It is first necessary, however, to determine the external reactions on either the left or right side. Verify the results shown on the free-body diagram in Fig. 5–17*b*.

The free-body diagram of the right portion of the truss, which is the easiest to analyze, is shown in Fig. 5–17*c*. There are three unknowns, F_{FG}, F_{CF}, and F_{CD}.

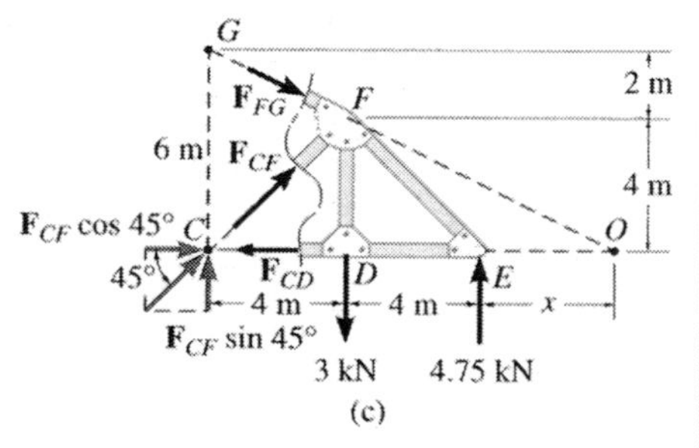

Equations of Equilibrium. The most direct method for solving this problem requires application of the moment equation about a point that eliminates two of the unknown forces. Hence, to obtain $\mathbf{F}_{CF}$, we will eliminate $\mathbf{F}_{FG}$ and $\mathbf{F}_{CD}$ by summing moments about point *O*, Fig. 5–17*c*. Note that the location of point *O* measured from *E* is determined from proportional triangles, i.e., $4/(4 + x) = 6/(8 + x)$, $x = 4$ m. Or, stated in another manner, the slope of member *GF* has a drop of 2 m to a horizontal distance of 4 m. Since *FD* is 4 m, Fig. 5–17*c*, then from *D* to *O* the distance must be 8 m.

An easy way to determine the moment of $\mathbf{F}_{CF}$ about point *O* is to use the principle of transmissibility and move $\mathbf{F}_{CF}$ to point *C*, and then resolve $\mathbf{F}_{CF}$ into its two rectangular components. We have

$\circlearrowleft + \Sigma M_O = 0;$

$$-F_{CF} \sin 45°(12 \text{ m}) + (3 \text{ kN})(8 \text{ m}) - (4.75 \text{ kN})(4 \text{ m}) = 0$$

$$F_{CF} = 0.589 \text{ kN} \quad \text{(C)} \qquad \textit{Ans.}$$

EXAMPLE 5.7

Determine the force in member EB of the roof truss shown in Fig. 5–18a. Indicate whether the member is in tension or compression.

Solution

Free-Body Diagrams. By the method of sections, any imaginary vertical section that cuts through EB, Fig. 5–18a, will also have to cut through three other members for which the forces are unknown. For example, section aa cuts through ED, EB, FB, and AB. If the components of reaction at A are calculated first ($A_x = 0$, $A_y = 4000$ N) and a free-body diagram of the left side of this section is considered, Fig. 5–18b, it is possible to obtain $\mathbf{F}_{ED}$ by summing moments about B to eliminate the other three unknowns; however, $\mathbf{F}_{EB}$ cannot be determined from the remaining two equilibrium equations. One possible way of obtaining $\mathbf{F}_{EB}$ is first to determine $\mathbf{F}_{ED}$ from section aa, then use this result on section bb, Fig. 5–18a, which is shown in Fig. 5–18c. Here the force system is concurrent and our sectioned free-body diagram is the same as the free-body diagram for the pin at E (method of joints).

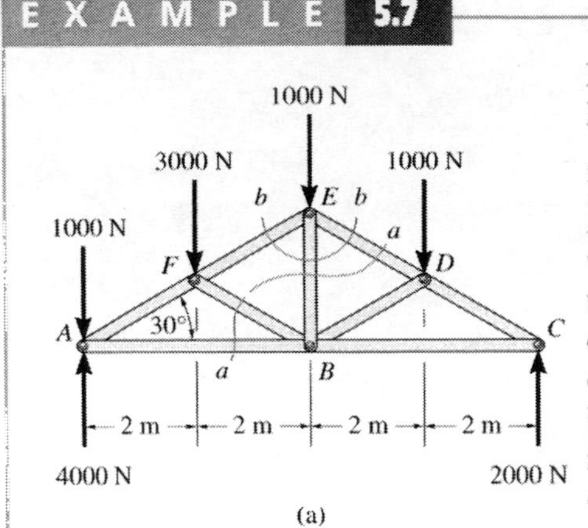

(a)

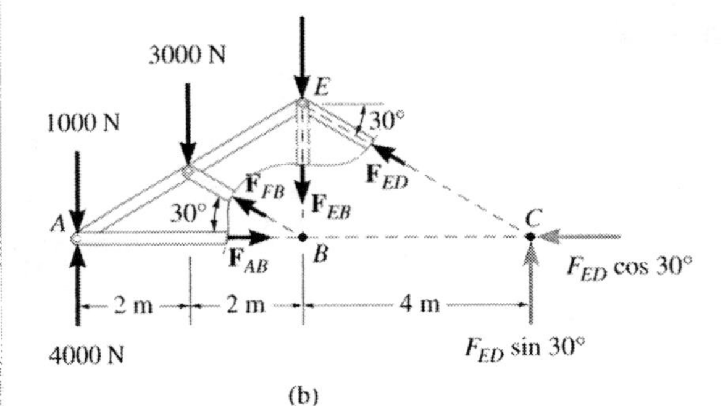

(b)

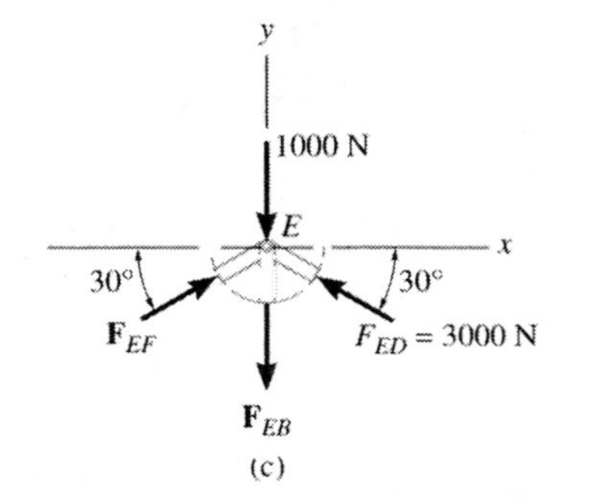

(c)

Fig. 5–18

Equations of Equilibrium. In order to determine the moment of $\mathbf{F}_{ED}$ about point B, Fig. 5–18b, we will resolve the force into its rectangular components and, by the principle of transmissibility, extend it to point C as shown. The moments of 1000 N, F_{AB}, F_{FB}, F_{EB}, and F_{ED} cos 30° are all zero about B. Therefore,

$$\curvearrowright + \Sigma M_B = 0; \quad 1000 \text{ N}(4 \text{ m}) + 3000 \text{ N}(2 \text{ m}) - 4000 \text{ N}(4 \text{ m}) + F_{ED} \sin 30°(4) = 0$$

$$F_{ED} = 3000 \text{ N} \quad \text{(C)}$$

Considering now the free-body diagram of section bb, Fig. 5–18c, we have

$$\overset{+}{\rightarrow} \Sigma F_x = 0; \quad F_{EF} \cos 30° - 3000 \cos 30° \text{ N} = 0$$

$$F_{EF} = 3000 \text{ N} \quad \text{(C)}$$

$$+\uparrow \Sigma F_y = 0; \; 2(3000 \sin 30° \text{ N}) - 1000 \text{ N} - F_{EB} = 0$$

$$F_{EB} = 2000 \text{ N} \quad \text{(T)} \qquad \textit{Ans.}$$

PROBLEMS

5-16. Determine the force in members BC, HC, and HG of the bridge truss, and indicate whether the members are in tension or compression.

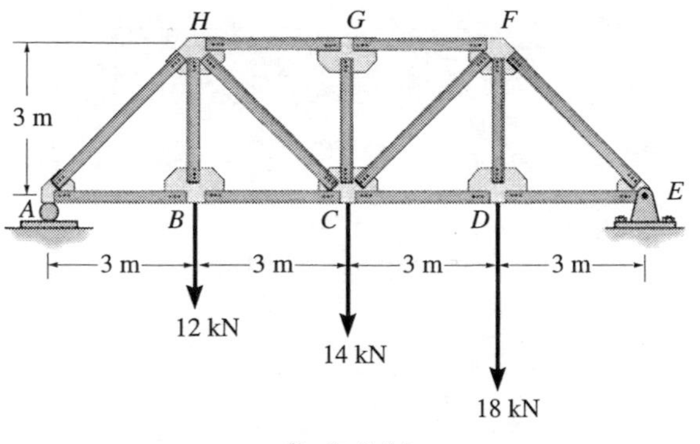

Prob. 5–16

5-17. Determine the force in members GF, CF, and CD of the bridge truss, and indicate whether the members are in tension or compression

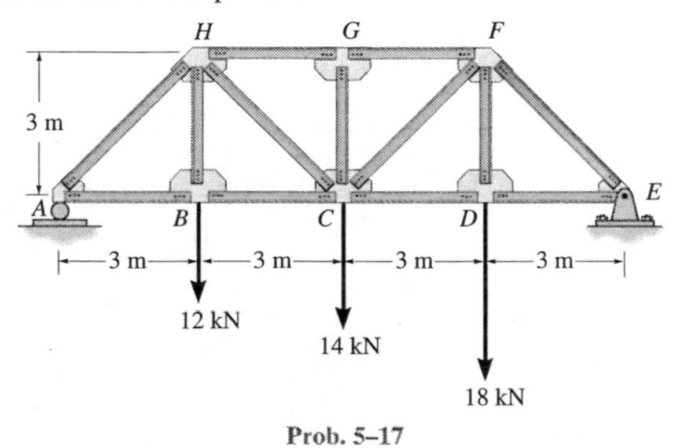

Prob. 5–17

***5-18.** Determine the force in members DE, DF, and GF of the cantilevered truss and state if the members are in tension or compression.

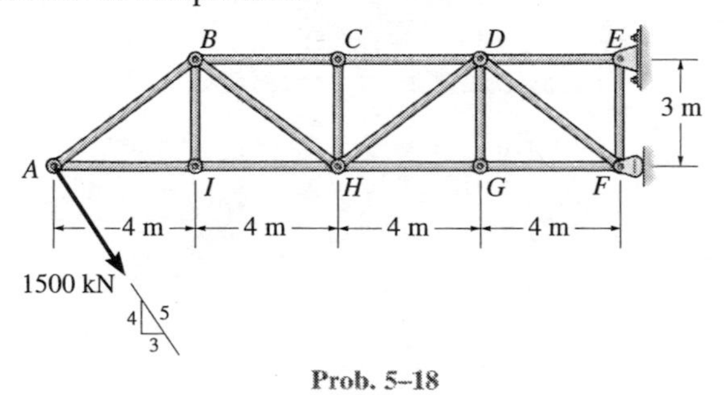

Prob. 5–18

5-19. The roof truss supports the vertical loading shown. Determine the force in members BC, CK, and KJ and state if these members are in tension or compression.

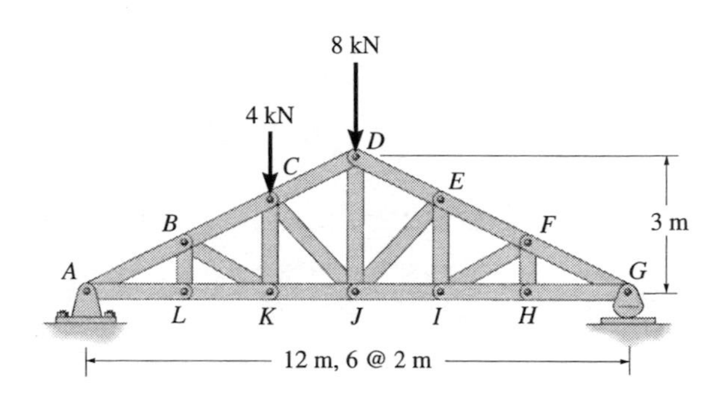

Prob. 5–19

5-20. Determine the force in members CD, CJ, KJ, and DJ of the truss which serves to support the deck of a bridge. State if these members are in tension or compression.

5-21. Determine the force in members EI and JI of the truss which serves to support the deck of a bridge. State if these members are in tension or compression.

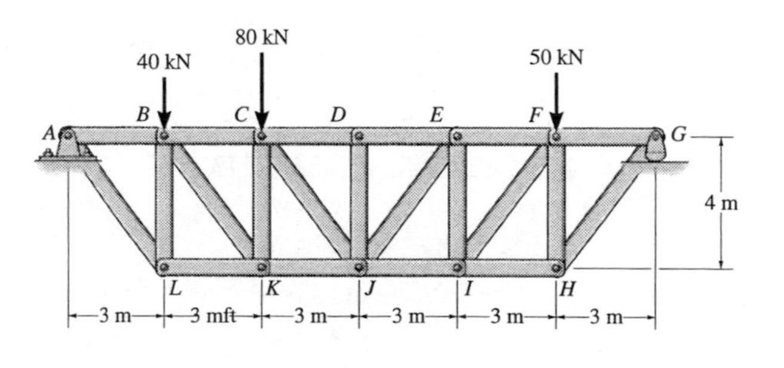

Probs. 5–20/21

***5-22.** Determine the force in members *BC, CG*, and *GF* of the *Warren truss*. Indicate if the members are in tension or compression.

5-23. Determine the force in members *CD, CF*, and *FG* of the *Warren truss*. Indicate if the members are in tension or compression.

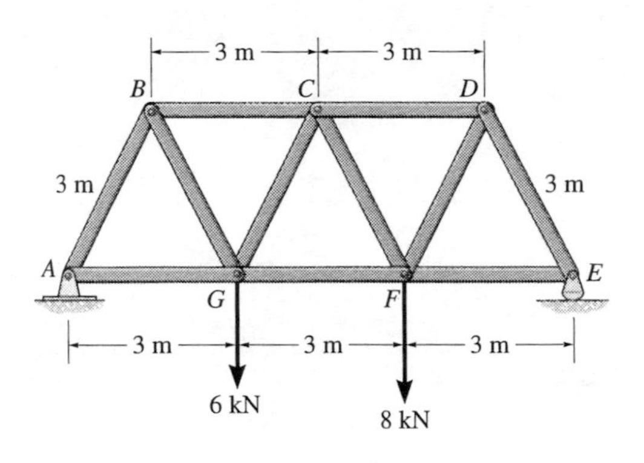

Probs. 5–22/23

■5-25. The truss supports the vertical load of 600 N. Determine the force in members *BC, BG*, and *HG* as the dimension *L* varies. Plot the results of *F* (ordinate with tension as positive) versus *L* (abscissa) for $0 \le L \le 3$ m.

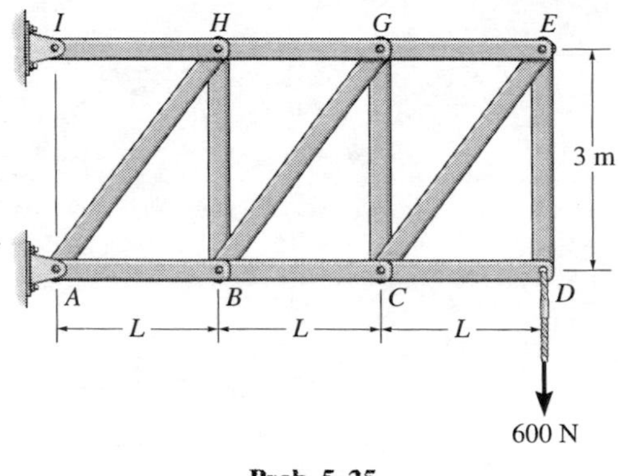

Prob. 5–25

***5-26.** Determine the force in members *IC* and *CG* of the truss and state if these members are in tension or compression. Also, indicate all zero-force members.

5-27. Determine the force in members *JE* and *GF* of the truss and state if these members are in tension or compression. Also, indicate all zero-force members.

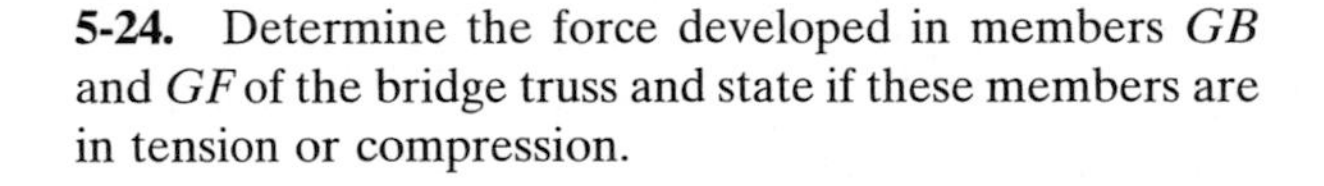

5-24. Determine the force developed in members *GB* and *GF* of the bridge truss and state if these members are in tension or compression.

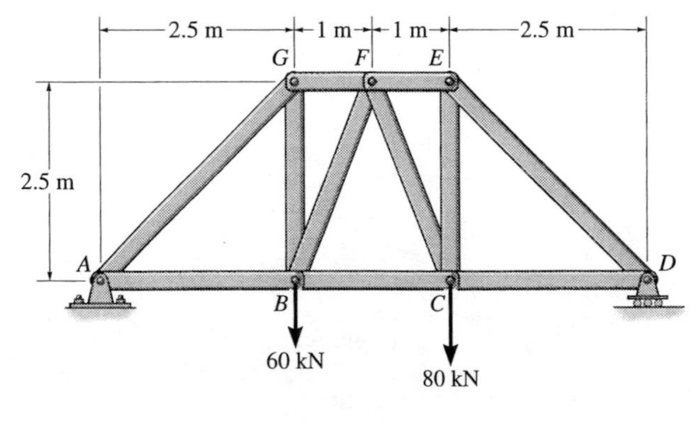

Prob. 5–24

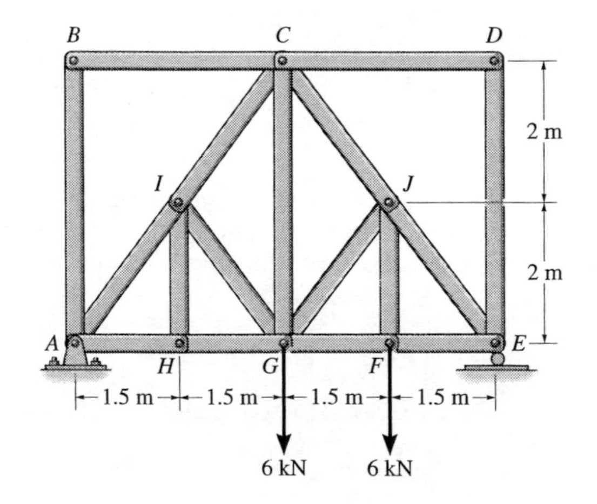

Probs. 5–26/27

5-28. Determine the force in members *BC*, *HC*, and *HG*. After the truss is sectioned use a single equation of equilibrium for the calculation of each force. State if these members are in tension or compression.

5-29. Determine the force in members *CD*, *CF*, and *CG* and state if these members are in tension or compression.

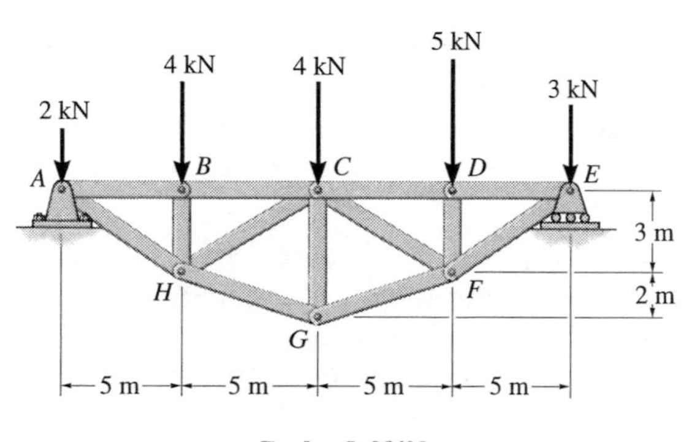

Probs. 5–28/29

5-31. Determine the force in member *GJ* of the truss and state if this member is in tension or compression.

5-32. Determine the force in member *GC* of the truss and state if this member is in tension or compression.

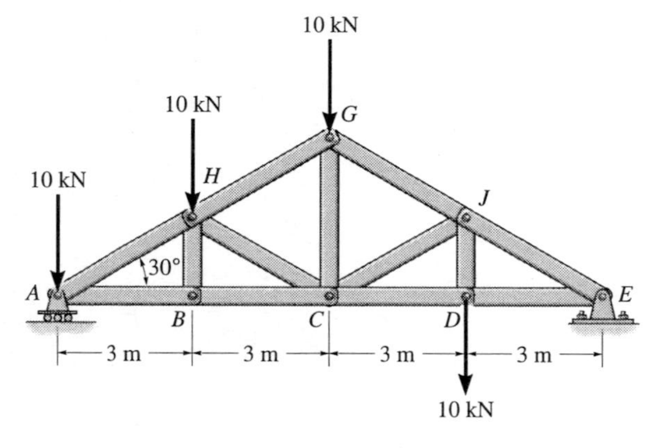

Probs. 5–31/32

***5-30.** Determine the force in members *GF*, *FB*, and *BC* of the *Fink truss* and state if the members are in tension or compression.

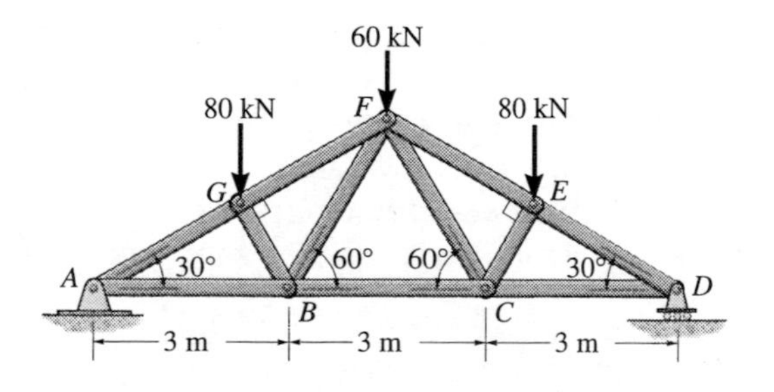

Prob. 5–30

5-33. Determine the force in members *GF*, *CF*, and *CD* of the roof truss and indicate if the members are in tension or compression.

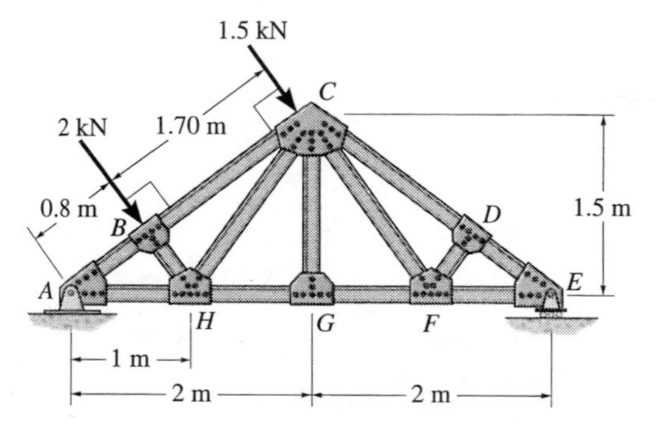

Prob. 5–33

5.5 Frames and Machines

Frames and machines are two common types of structures which are often composed of pin-connected *multiforce members*, i.e., members that are subjected to more than two forces. *Frames* are generally stationary and are used to support loads, whereas *machines* contain moving parts and are designed to transmit and alter the effect of forces. Provided a frame or machine is properly constrained and contains no more supports or members than are necessary to prevent collapse, the forces acting at the joints and supports can be determined by applying the equations of equilibrium to each member. Once the forces at the joints are obtained, it is then possible to *design* the size of the members, connections, and supports using the theory of mechanics of materials and an appropriate engineering design code.

Free-Body Diagrams. In order to determine the forces acting at the joints and supports of a frame or machine, the structure must be disassembled and the free-body diagrams of its parts must be drawn. The following important points *must* be observed:

- Isolate each part by drawing its *outlined shape*. Then show all the forces and/or couple moments that act on the part. Make sure to *label* or *identify* each known and unknown force and couple moment with reference to an established x, y coordinate system. Also, indicate any dimensions used for taking moments. Most often the equations of equilibrium are easier to apply if the forces are represented by their rectangular components. As usual, the sense of an unknown force or couple moment can be assumed.
- Identify all the two-force members in the structure and represent their free-body diagrams as having two equal but opposite collinear forces acting at their points of application. (See Sec. 4.4.) By recognizing the two-force members, we can avoid solving an unnecessary number of equilibrium equations.
- Forces common to any two *contacting* members act with equal magnitudes but opposite sense on the respective members. If the two members are treated as a *"system" of connected members*, then these forces are *"internal"* and are *not shown* on the *free-body diagram of the system*; however, if the free-body diagram of *each member* is drawn, the forces are *"external"* and *must* be shown on each of the free-body diagrams.

The following examples graphically illustrate application of these points in drawing the free-body diagrams of a dismembered frame or machine. In all cases, the weight of the members is neglected.

EXAMPLE 5.8

For the frame shown in Fig. 5–19*a*, draw the free-body diagram of (a) each member, (b) the pin at *B*, and (c) the two members connected together.

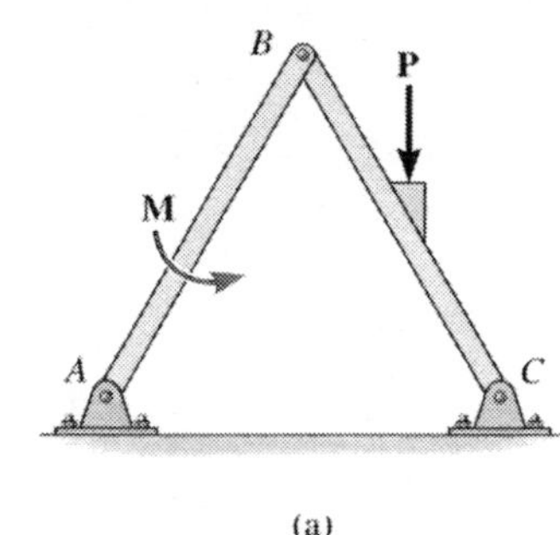

(a)

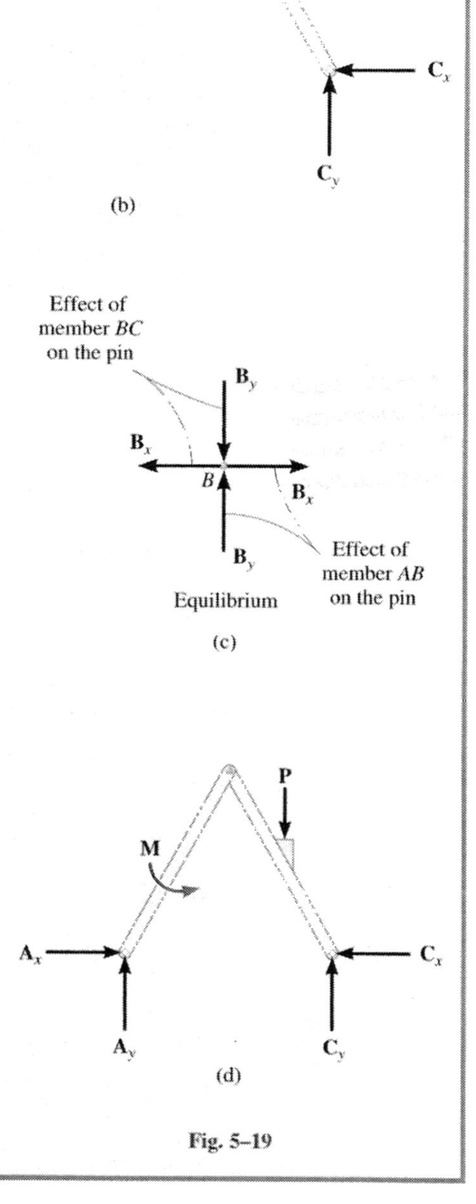

Fig. 5–19

Solution

Part (a). By inspection, members *BA* and *BC* are *not* two-force members. Instead, as shown on the free-body diagrams, Fig. 5–19*b*, *BC* is subjected to *not* five but *three forces*, namely, the resultant force from pins *B* and *C* and the external force **P**. Likewise, *AB* is subjected to the *resultant* forces from the pins at *A* and *B* and the external couple moment **M**.

Part (b). It can be seen in Fig. 5–19*a* that the pin at *B* is subjected to only *two forces*, i.e., the force of member *BC* on the pin and the force of member *AB* on the pin. For *equilibrium* these forces and therefore their respective components must be equal but opposite, Fig. 5–19*c*. Notice carefully how Newton's third law is applied between the pin and its contacting members, i.e., the effect of the pin on the two members, Fig. 5–19*b*, and the equal but opposite effect of the two members on the pin, Fig. 5–19*c*. Also note that $\mathbf{B}_x$ and $\mathbf{B}_y$, shown equal but opposite in Fig. 5–19*b* on members *AB* and *BC*, is *not* the effect of Newton's third law; instead, this results from the *equilibrium* analysis of the pin, Fig. 5–19*c*.

Part (c). The free-body diagram of both members connected together, yet removed from the supporting pins at *A* and *C*, is shown in Fig. 5–19*d*. The force components $\mathbf{B}_x$ and $\mathbf{B}_y$ are *not shown* on this diagram since they form equal but opposite collinear pairs of *internal* forces (Fig. 5–19*b*) and therefore cancel out. Also, to be consistent when later applying the equilibrium equations, the unknown force components at *A* and *C* must act in the *same sense* as those shown in Fig. 5–19*b*. Here the couple moment **M** can be applied at any point on the frame in order to determine the reactions at *A* and *C*. Note, however, that it must act on member *AB* in Fig. 5–19*b* and *not* on member *BC*.

EXAMPLE 5.9

A constant tension in the conveyor belt is maintained by using the device shown in Fig. 5–20*a*. Draw the free-body diagrams of the frame and the cylinder which supports the belt. The suspended block has a weight of W.

(a)

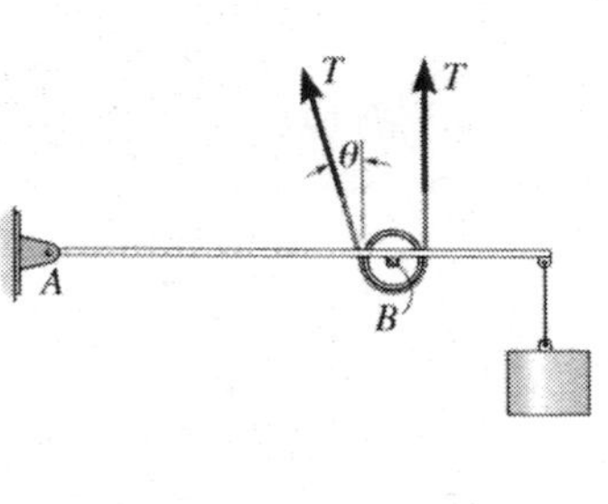

(b)

Fig. 5–20

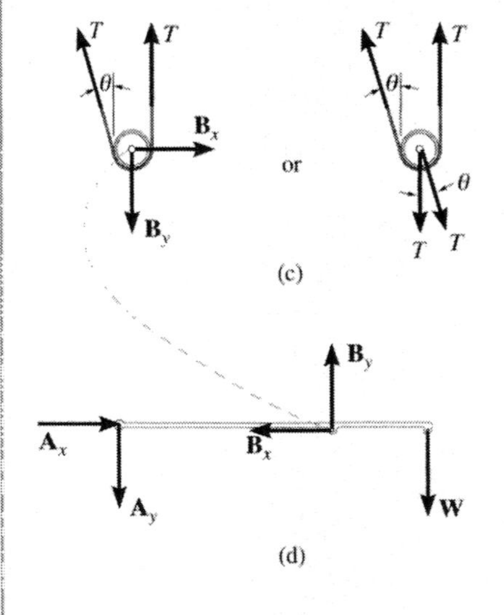

Solution

The idealized model of the device is shown in Fig. 5–20*b*. Here the angle θ is assumed to be known. Notice that the tension in the belt is the same on each side of the cylinder, since the cylinder is free to turn. From this model, the free-body diagrams of the frame and cylinder are shown in Figs. 5–20*c* and 5–20*d*, respectively. Note that the force that the pin at B exerts on the cylinder can be represented by either its horizontal and vertical components $\mathbf{B}_x$ and $\mathbf{B}_y$, which can be determined by using the force equations of equilibrium applied to the cylinder, or by the two components T, which provide equal but opposite couple moments on the cylinder and thus keep it from turning. Also, realize that once the pin reactions at A have been determined, half of their values act on each side of the frame since pin connections occur on each side, Fig. 5–20*a*.

EXAMPLE 5.10

Draw the free-body diagram of each part of the smooth piston and link mechanism used to crush recycled cans, which is shown in Fig. 5–21*a*.

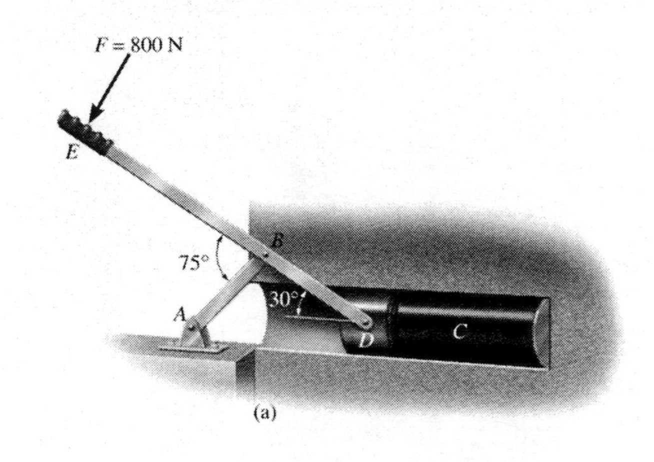

(a)

Solution

By inspection, member AB is a two-force member. The free-body diagrams of the parts are shown in Fig. 5–21*b*. Since the pins at B and D *connect only two parts together,* the forces there are shown as equal but opposite on the separate free-body diagrams of their connected members. In particular, four components of force act on the piston: $\mathbf{D}_x$ and $\mathbf{D}_y$ represent the effect of the pin (or lever EBD), $\mathbf{N}_w$ is the *resultant force* of the floor, and $\mathbf{P}$ is the resultant compressive force caused by the can C.

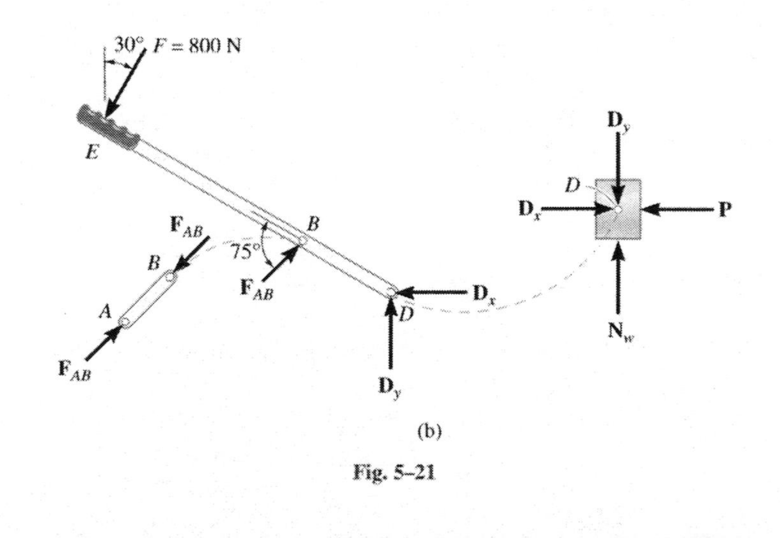

(b)

Fig. 5–21

EXAMPLE 5.11

For the frame shown in Fig. 5–22*a*, draw the free-body diagrams of (a) the entire frame including the pulleys and cords, (b) the frame without the pulleys and cords, and (c) each of the pulleys.

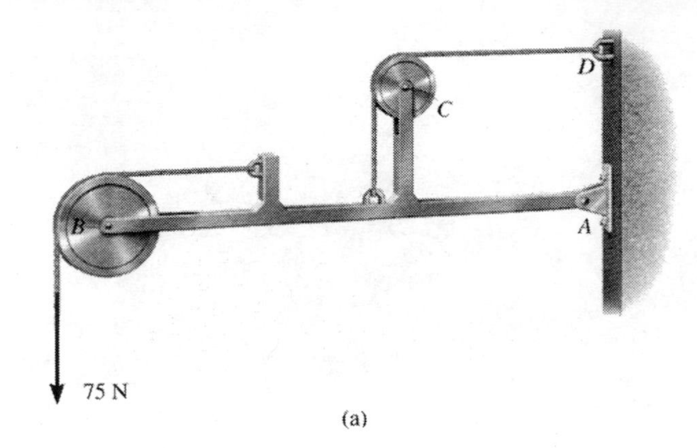

(a)

Solution

Part (a). When the entire frame including the pulleys and cords is considered, the interactions at the points where the pulleys and cords are connected to the frame become pairs of *internal forces* which cancel each other and therefore are not shown on the free-body diagram, Fig. 5–22*b*.

Part (b). When the cords and pulleys are removed, their effect *on the frame* must be shown, Fig. 5–22*c*.

Part (c). The force components $\mathbf{B}_x$, $\mathbf{B}_y$, $\mathbf{C}_x$, $\mathbf{C}_y$ of the pins on the pulleys, Fig. 5–22*d*, are equal but opposite to the force components exerted by the pins on the frame, Fig. 5–22*c*. Why?

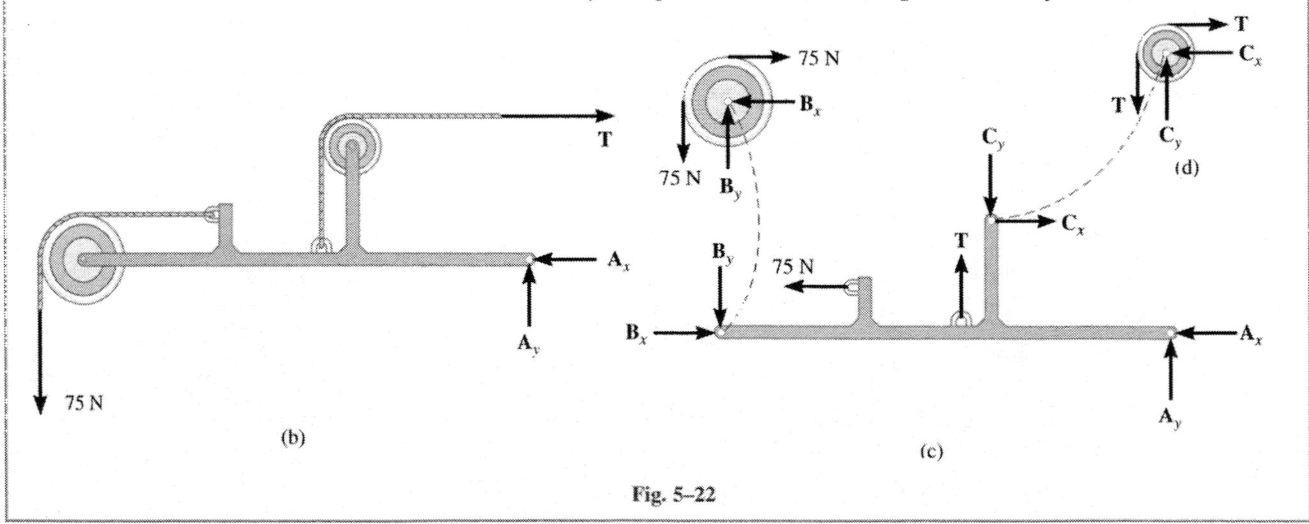

Fig. 5–22

Before proceeding, it is recommended to cover the solutions to the previous examples and attempt to draw the requested free-body diagrams. When doing so, make sure the work is neat and that all the forces and couple moments are properly labeled.

(a)

Equations of Equilibrium. Provided the structure (frame or machine) is properly supported and contains no more supports or members than are necessary to prevent its collapse, then the unknown forces at the supports and connections can be determined from the equations of equilibrium. If the structure lies in the x–y plane, then for *each* free-body diagram drawn the loading must satisfy $\Sigma F_x = 0$, $\Sigma F_y = 0$, and $\Sigma M_O = 0$. The selection of the free-body diagrams used for the analysis is *completely arbitrary*. They may represent each of the members of the structure, a portion of the structure, or its entirety. For example, consider finding the six components of the pin reactions at A, B, and C for the frame shown in Fig. 5–23*a*. If the frame is dismembered, as it is in Fig. 5–23*b*, these unknowns can be determined by applying the three equations of equilibrium to each of the two members (total of six equations). The free-body diagram of the *entire frame* can also be used for part of the analysis, Fig. 5–23*c*. Hence, if so desired, all six unknowns can be determined by applying the three equilibrium equations to the entire frame, Fig. 5–23*c*, and also to either one of its members. Furthermore, the answers can be checked in part by applying the three equations of equilibrium to the remaining "second" member. In general, then, this problem can be solved by writing *at most* six equilibrium equations using free-body diagrams of the members and/or the combination of connected members. Any more than six equations written would *not* be unique from the original six and would only serve to check the results.

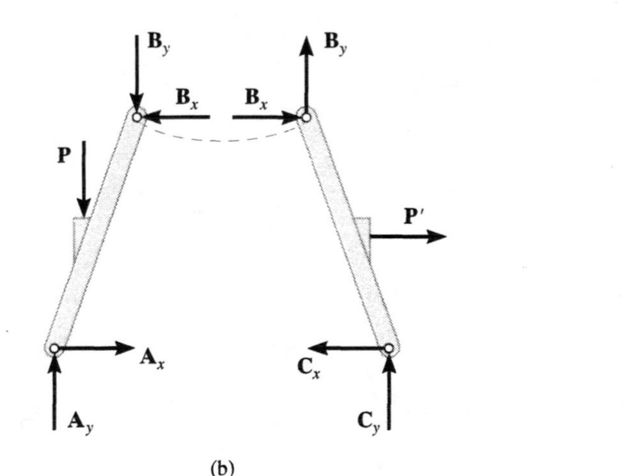

(b)

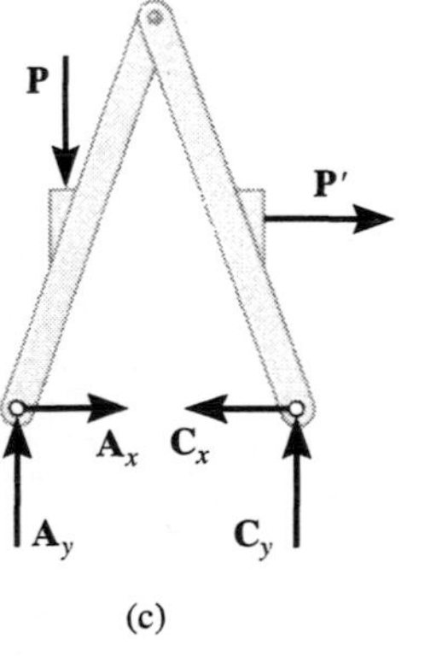

(c)

Fig. 5–23

PROCEDURE FOR ANALYSIS

The joint reactions on frames or machines (structures) composed of multiforce members can be determined using the following procedure.

Free-Body Diagram.

- Draw the free-body diagram of the entire structure, a portion of the structure, or each of its members. The choice should be made so that it leads to the most direct solution of the problem.
- When the free-body diagram of a group of members of a structure is drawn, the forces at the connected parts of this group are internal forces and are not shown on the free-body diagram of the group.
- Forces common to two members which are in contact act with equal magnitude but opposite sense on the respective free-body diagrams of the members.
- Two-force members, regardless of their shape, have equal but opposite collinear forces acting at the ends of the member.
- In many cases it is possible to tell by inspection the proper sense of the unknown forces acting on a member; however, if this seems difficult, the sense can be assumed.
- A couple moment is a free vector and can act at any point on the free-body diagram. Also, a force is a sliding vector and can act at any point along its line of action.

Equations of Equilibrium.

- Count the number of unknowns and compare it to the total number of equilibrium equations that are available. In two dimensions, there are three equilibrium equations that can be written for each member.
- Sum moments about a point that lies at the intersection of the lines of action of as many unknown forces as possible.
- If the solution of a force or couple moment magnitude is found to be negative, it means the sense of the force is the reverse of that shown on the free-body diagrams.

EXAMPLE 5.12

Determine the horizontal and vertical components of force which the pin at C exerts on member CB of the frame in Fig. 5–24*a*.

Solution I

Free-Body Diagrams. By inspection it can be seen that AB is a two-force member. The free-body diagrams are shown in Fig. 5–24*b*.

Equations of Equilibrium. The *three unknowns*, C_x, C_y, and F_{AB}, can be determined by applying the three equations of equilibrium to member CB.

$$\circlearrowleft + \Sigma M_C = 0;\ 2000\text{ N}(2\text{ m}) - (F_{AB}\sin 60^\circ)(4\text{ m}) = 0\quad F_{AB} = 1154.7\text{ N}$$

$$\xrightarrow{+} \Sigma F_x = 0;\quad 1154.7\cos 60^\circ\text{N} - C_x = 0\quad C_x = 577\text{ N}\quad \textit{Ans.}$$

$$+\uparrow \Sigma F_y = 0;\ 1154.7\sin 60^\circ\text{N} - 2000\text{ N} + C_y = 0\quad C_y = 1000\text{ N}\quad \textit{Ans.}$$

Solution II

Free-Body Diagrams. If one does not recognize that AB is a two-force member, then more work is involved in solving this problem. The free-body diagrams are shown in Fig. 5–24*c*.

Equations of Equilibrium. The *six unknowns*, A_x, A_y, B_x, B_y, C_x, C_y, are determined by applying the three equations of equilibrium to each member.

Member AB

$$\circlearrowleft + \Sigma M_A = 0;\quad B_x(3\sin 60^\circ\text{ m}) - B_y(3\cos 60^\circ\text{ m}) = 0 \qquad (1)$$

$$\xrightarrow{+} \Sigma F_x = 0;\quad A_x - B_x = 0 \qquad (2)$$

$$+\uparrow \Sigma F_y = 0;\quad A_y - B_y = 0 \qquad (3)$$

Member BC

$$\circlearrowleft + \Sigma M_C = 0;\quad 2000\text{ N}(2\text{ m}) - B_y(4\text{ m}) = 0 \qquad (4)$$

$$\xrightarrow{+} \Sigma F_x = 0;\quad B_x - C_x = 0 \qquad (5)$$

$$+\uparrow \Sigma F_y = 0;\quad B_y - 2000\text{ N} + C_y = 0 \qquad (6)$$

The results for C_x and C_y can be determined by solving these equations in the following sequence: 4, 1, 5, then 6. The results are

$$B_y = 1000\text{ N}$$

$$B_x = 577\text{ N}$$

$$C_x = 577\text{ N}\qquad \textit{Ans.}$$

$$C_y = 1000\text{ N}\qquad \textit{Ans.}$$

By comparison, Solution I is simpler since the requirement that F_{AB} in Fig. 5–24*b* be equal, opposite, and collinear at the ends of member AB automatically satisfies Eqs. 1, 2, and 3 above and therefore eliminates the need to write these equations. *As a result, always identify the two-force members before starting the analysis!*

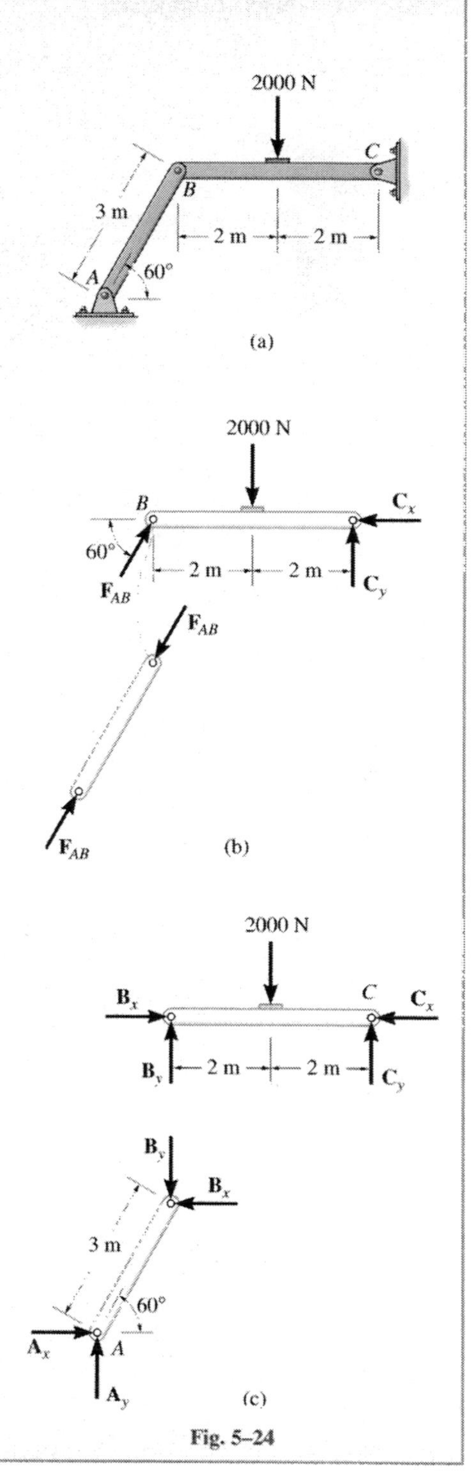

Fig. 5–24

EXAMPLE 5.13

The compound beam shown in Fig. 5–25*a* is pin connected at *B*. Determine the reactions at its supports. Neglect its weight and thickness.

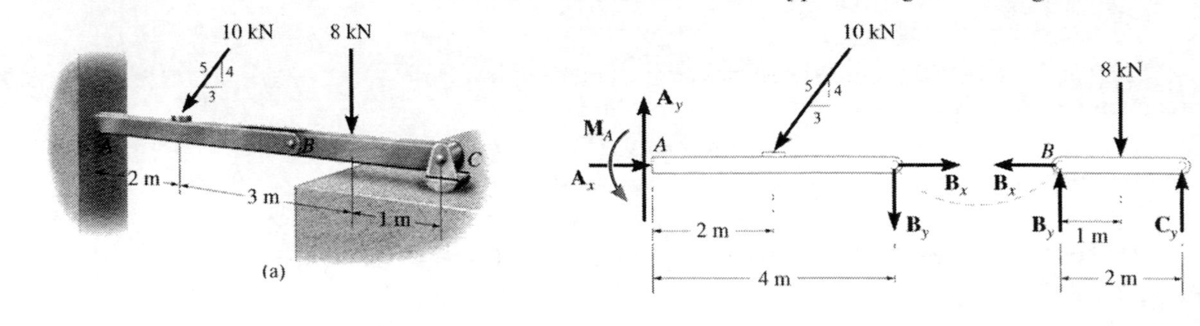

Fig. 5–25

Solution

Free-Body Diagrams. By inspection, if we consider a free-body diagram of the entire beam *ABC*, there will be three unknown reactions at *A* and one at *C*. These four unknowns cannot all be obtained from the three equations of equilibrium, and so it will become necessary to dismember the beam into its two segments as shown in Fig. 5–25*b*.

Equations of Equilibrium. The six unknowns are determined as follows:

Segment BC

$$\overset{+}{\rightarrow}\Sigma F_x = 0; \qquad B_x = 0$$

$$\circlearrowleft + \Sigma M_B = 0; \qquad -8\text{ kN}(1\text{ m}) + C_y(2\text{ m}) = 0$$

$$+\uparrow \Sigma F_y = 0; \qquad B_y - 8\text{ kN} + C_y = 0$$

Segment AB

$$\overset{+}{\rightarrow}\Sigma F_x = 0; \qquad A_x - (10\text{ kN})(\tfrac{3}{5}) + B_x = 0$$

$$\circlearrowleft + \Sigma M_A = 0; \qquad M_A - (10\text{ kN})(\tfrac{4}{5})(2\text{ m}) - B_y(4\text{ m}) = 0$$

$$+\uparrow \Sigma F_y = 0; \qquad A_y - (10\text{ kN})(\tfrac{4}{5}) - B_y = 0$$

Solving each of these equations successively, using previously calculated results, we obtain

$A_x = 6\text{ kN}$ $\quad A_y = 12\text{ kN}$ $\quad M_A = 32\text{ kN}\cdot\text{m}$ *Ans.*

$B_x = 0$ $\quad B_y = 4\text{ kN}$

$C_y = 4\text{ kN}$ *Ans.*

EXAMPLE 5.14

The smooth disk shown in Fig. 5–26*a* is pinned at D and has a weight of 20 N. Neglecting the weights of the other members, determine the horizontal and vertical components of reaction at pins B and D.

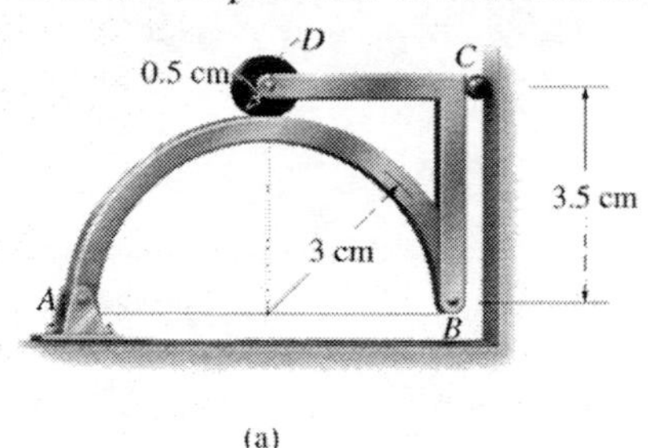

(a)

Solution

Free-Body Diagrams. By inspection, the three components of reaction at the supports can be determined from a free-body diagram of the entire frame, Fig. 5–26*b*. Also, free-body diagrams of the members are shown in Fig. 5–26*c*.

Equations of Equilibrium. The eight unknowns can of course be obtained by applying the eight equilibrium equations to each member—three to member AB, three to member BCD, and two to the disk. (Moment equilibrium is automatically satisfied for the disk.) If this is done, however, all the results can be obtained only from a simultaneous solution of some of the equations. (Try it and find out.) To avoid this situation, it is best to first determine the three support reactions on the *entire* frame; then, using these results, the remaining five equilibrium equations can be applied to two other parts in order to solve successively for the other unknowns.

Entire Frame

$$\circlearrowleft+\Sigma M_A = 0; \quad -20\text{ N}(3\text{ cm}) + C_x(3.5\text{ cm}) = 0 \quad C_x = 17.1\text{ N}$$

$$\xrightarrow{+} \Sigma F_x = 0; \quad A_x - 17.1\text{ N} = 0 \quad A_x = 17.1\text{ N}$$

$$+\uparrow \Sigma F_y = 0; \quad A_y - 20\text{ N} = 0 \quad A_y = 20\text{ N}$$

Member AB

$$\xrightarrow{+} \Sigma F_x = 0; \quad 17.1\text{ N} - B_x = 0 \quad B_x = 17.1\text{ N} \quad \textit{Ans}$$

$$\circlearrowleft+\Sigma M_B = 0; \quad -20\text{ N}(6\text{ cm}) + N_D(3\text{ cm}) = 0 \quad N_D = 40\text{ N}$$

$$+\uparrow \Sigma F_y = 0; \quad 20\text{ N} - 40\text{ N} + B_y = 0 \quad B_y = 20\text{ N} \quad \textit{Ans}$$

Disk

$$\xrightarrow{+} \Sigma F_x = 0; \quad D_x = 0 \quad \textit{Ans.}$$

$$+\uparrow \Sigma F_y = 0; \quad 40\text{ N} - 20\text{ N} - D_y = 0 \quad D_y = 20\text{ N} \quad \textit{Ans.}$$

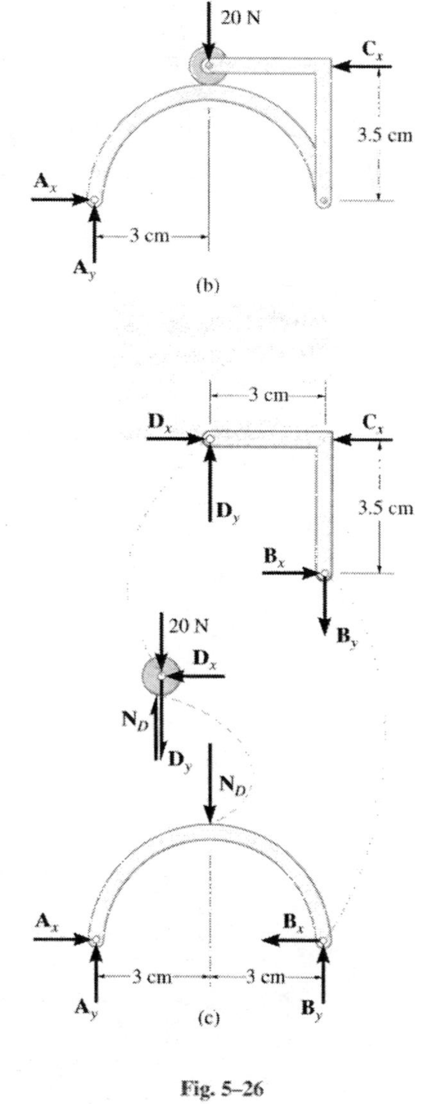

Fig. 5–26

EXAMPLE 5.15

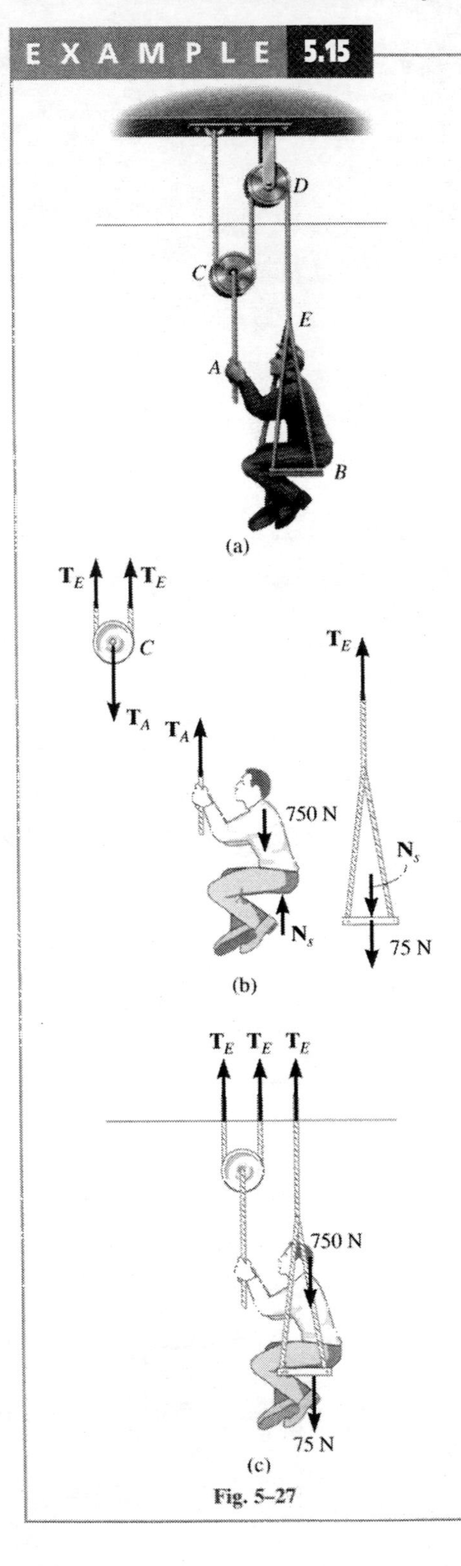

(a)
(b)
(c)
Fig. 5–27

A man having a weight of 750 N ($\approx$ 75 kg) supports himself by means of the cable and pulley system shown in Fig. 5–27*a*. If the seat has a weight of 75 N ($\approx$ 7.5 kg), determine the force that he must exert on the cable at *A* and the force he exerts on the seat. Neglect the weight of the cables and pulleys.

Solution I

Free-Body Diagrams. The free-body diagrams of the man, seat, and pulley *C* are shown in Fig. 5–27*b*. The *two* cables are subjected to tensions $\mathbf{T}_A$ and $\mathbf{T}_E$, respectively. The man is subjected to three forces: his weight, the tension $\mathbf{T}_A$ of cable *AC*, and the reaction $\mathbf{N}_s$ of the seat.

Equations of Equilibrium. The three unknowns are obtained as follows:

Man

$$+\uparrow \Sigma F_y = 0; \qquad T_A + N_s - 750\text{ N} = 0 \qquad (1)$$

Seat

$$+\uparrow \Sigma F_y = 0; \qquad T_E + N_s - 75\text{ N} = 0 \qquad (2)$$

Pulley C

$$+\uparrow \Sigma F_y = 0; \qquad 2T_E - T_A = 0 \qquad (3)$$

Here T_E can be determined by adding Eqs. 1 and 2 to eliminate N_s and then using Eq. 3. The other unknowns are then obtained by resubstitution of T_E.

$$T_A = 550\text{ N} \qquad \textit{Ans.}$$
$$T_E = 275\text{ N}$$
$$N_E = 200\text{ N} \qquad \textit{Ans.}$$

Solution II

Free-Body Diagrams. By using the blue section shown in Fig. 5–27*a*, the man, pulley, and seat can be considered as a *single system*, Fig. 5–27*c*. Here $\mathbf{N}_s$ and $\mathbf{T}_A$ are *internal* forces and hence are not included on this "combined" free-body diagram.

Equations of Equilibrium. Applying $\Sigma F_y = 0$ yields a *direct* solution for T_E.

$$+\uparrow \Sigma F_y = 0; \qquad 3T_E - 75\text{ N} - 750\text{ N} = 0 \qquad T_E = 275\text{ N}$$

The other unknowns can be obtained from Eqs. 2 and 3.

EXAMPLE 5.16

The hand exerts a force of 35 N on the grip of the spring compressor shown in Fig. 5–28*a*. Determine the force in the spring needed to maintain equilibrium of the mechanism.

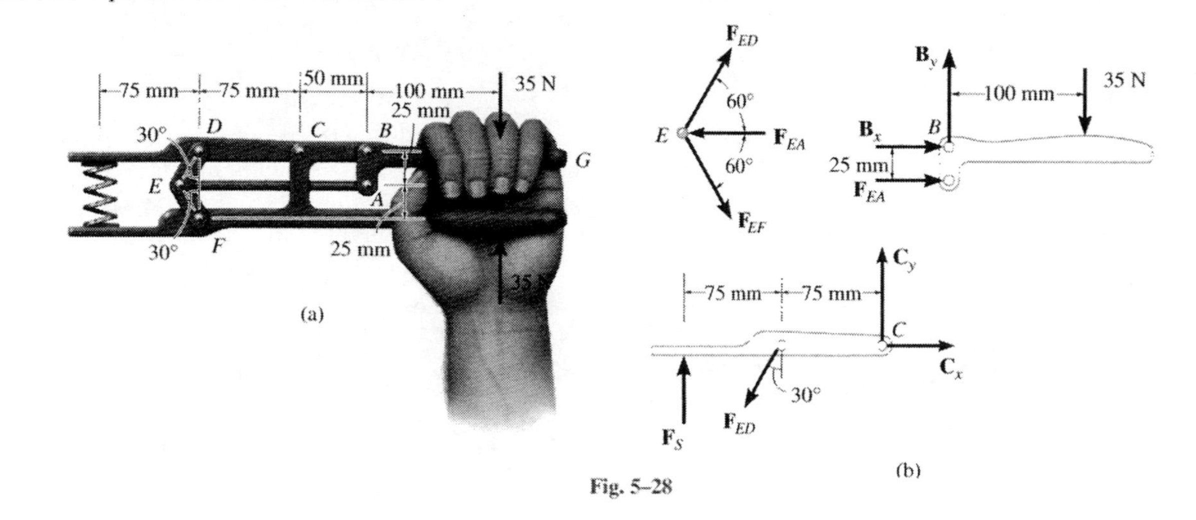

Fig. 5–28

Solution

Free-Body Diagrams. By inspection, members *EA*, *ED*, and *EF* are all two-force members. The free-body diagrams for parts *DC* and *ABG* are shown in Fig. 5–28*b*. The pin at *E* has also been included here since *three* force interactions occur on this pin. They represent the effects of members *ED*, *EA*, and *EF*. Note carefully how equal and opposite force reactions occur between each of the parts.

Equations of Equilibrium. By studying the free-body diagrams, the most direct way to obtain the spring force is to apply the equations of equilibrium in the following sequence:

Lever ABG

$$\circlearrowleft + \Sigma M_B = 0; \quad F_{EA}(25\text{ mm}) - 35\text{ N}(100\text{ mm}) = 0 \qquad F_{EA} = 140\text{ N}$$

Pin E

$$+\uparrow \Sigma F_y = 0; \quad F_{ED}\sin 60^\circ - F_{EF}\sin 60^\circ = 0 \quad F_{ED} = F_{EF} = F$$

$$\overset{+}{\rightarrow} \Sigma F_x = 0; \quad 2F\cos 60^\circ - 140\text{ N} = 0 \qquad F = 140\text{ N}$$

Arm DC

$$\circlearrowleft + \Sigma M_C = 0; \quad -F_s(150\text{ mm}) + 140\cos 30^\circ\text{ N}(75\text{ mm}) = 0$$

$$F_s = 60.62\text{ N} \qquad \textit{Ans.}$$

EXAMPLE 5.17

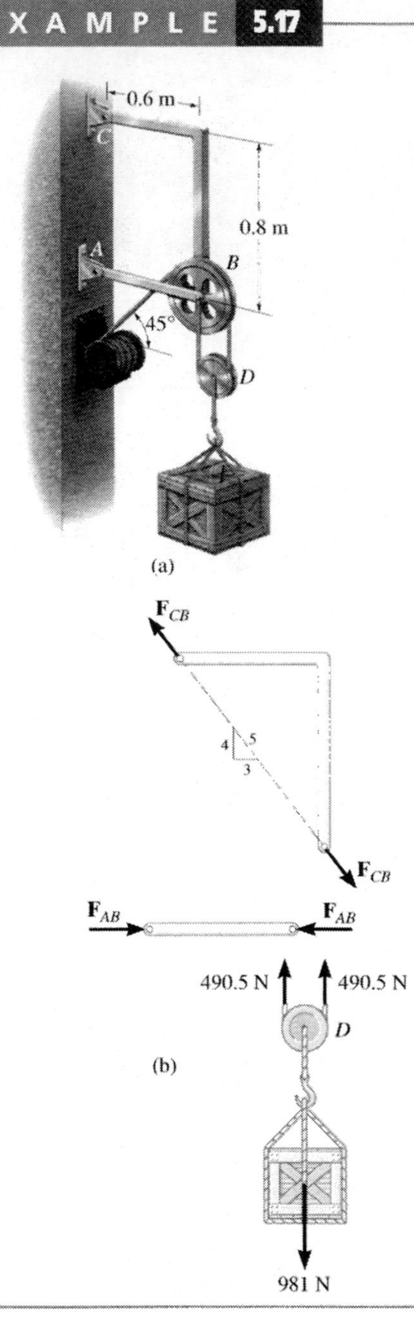

The 100-kg block is held in equilibrium by means of the pulley and continuous cable system shown in Fig. 5–29*a*. If the cable is attached to the pin at *B*, compute the forces which this pin exerts on each of its connecting members.

Solution

Free-Body Diagrams. A free-body diagram of each member of the frame is shown in Fig. 5–29*b*. By inspection, members *AB* and *CB* are two-force members. Furthermore, the cable must be subjected to a force of 490.5 N in order to hold pulley *D* and the block in equilibrium. A free-body diagram of the pin at *B* is needed since *four interactions* occur at this pin. These are caused by the attached cable (490.5 N), member *AB* ($\mathbf{F}_{AB}$), member *CB* ($\mathbf{F}_{CB}$), and pulley *B* ($\mathbf{B}_x$ and $\mathbf{B}_y$).

Equations of Equilibrium. Applying the equations of force equilibrium to pulley *B*, we have

$\overset{+}{\rightarrow} \Sigma F_x = 0;\quad B_x - 490.5 \cos 45° \text{ N} = 0 \quad B_x = 346.8 \text{ N}$ *Ans.*

$+\uparrow \Sigma F_y = 0;\quad B_y - 490.5 \sin 45° \text{ N} - 490.5 \text{ N} = 0$

$B_y = 837.3 \text{ N}$ *Ans.*

Using these results, equilibrium of the pin requires that

$+\uparrow \Sigma F_y = 0;\quad \frac{4}{5}F_{CB} - 837.3 \text{ N} - 490.5 \text{ N} \quad F_{CB} = 1660 \text{ N}$ *Ans.*

$\overset{+}{\rightarrow} \Sigma F_x = 0;\ F_{AB} - \frac{3}{5}(1660 \text{ N}) - 346.8 \text{ N} = 0 \quad F_{AB} = 1343 \text{ N}$ *Ans.*

It may be noted that the two-force member *CB* is subjected to bending as caused by the force $\mathbf{F}_{CB}$. From the standpoint of design, it would be better to make this member *straight* (from *C* to *B*) so that the force $\mathbf{F}_{CB}$ would create only tension in the member.

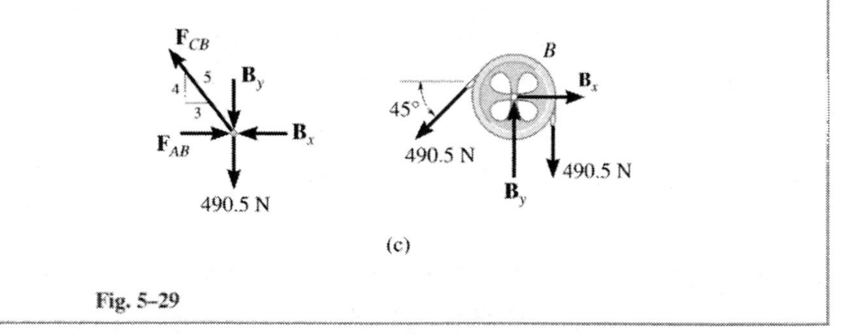

Fig. 5–29

Before solving the following problems, it is suggested that a brief review be made of all the previous examples. This may be done by covering each solution, trying to locate the two-force members, drawing the free-body diagrams, and conceiving ways of applying the equations of equilibrium to obtain the solution.

PROBLEMS

5-34. In each case, determine the force **P** required to maintain equilibrium. The block weighs 100 N ($\approx$ 10 kg).

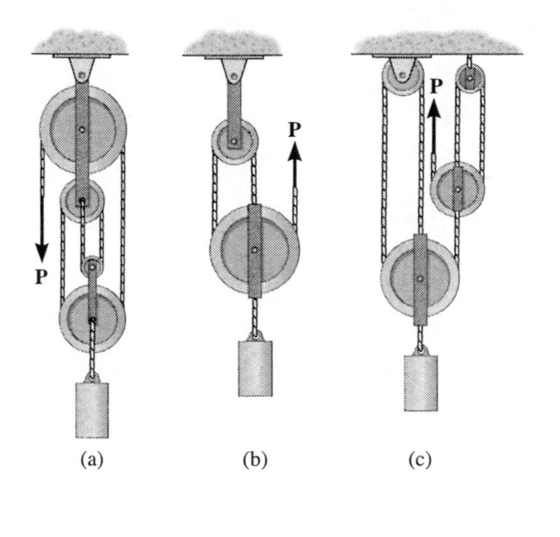

Prob. 5–34

5-35. The eye hook has a positive locking latch when it supports the load because its two parts are pin-connected at A and they bear against one another along the smooth surface at B. Determine the resultant force at the pin and the normal force at B when the eye hook supports a load of 800 N.

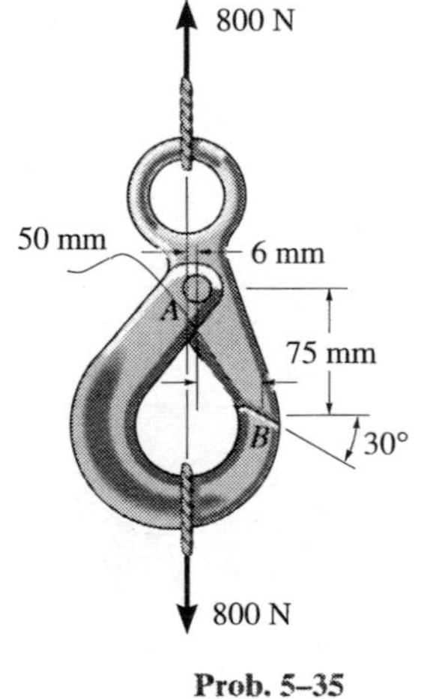

Prob. 5–35

***5-36.** Determine the force **P** needed to support the 100-N ($\approx$ 10-kg) weight. Each pulley has a weight of 10 N ($\approx$ 1 kg). Also, what are the cord reactions at A and B?

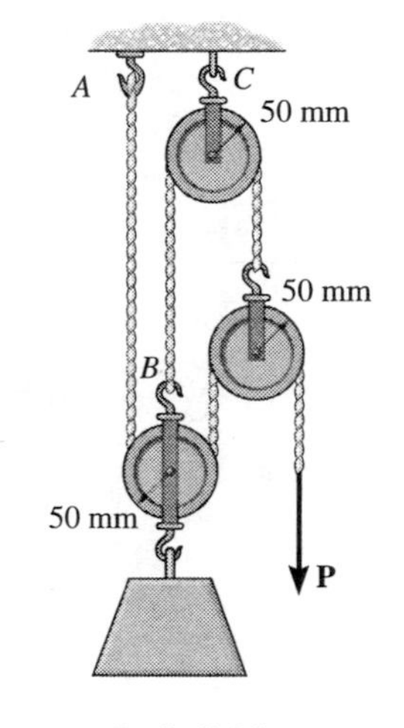

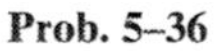

Prob. 5–36

5-37. The link is used to hold the rod in place. Determine the required axial force on the screw at E if the largest force to be exerted on the rod at B, C or D is to be 100 N. Also, find the magnitude of the force reaction at pin A. Assume all surfaces of contact are smooth.

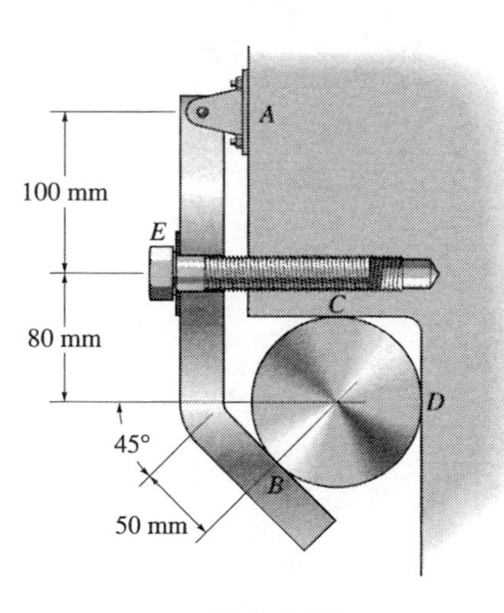

Prob. 5–37

5-38. The principles of a *differential chain block* are indicated schematically in the figure. Determine the magnitude of force **P** needed to support the 800-N force. Also, find the distance *x* where the cable must be attached to bar *AB* so the bar remains horizontal. All pulleys have a radius of 60 mm.

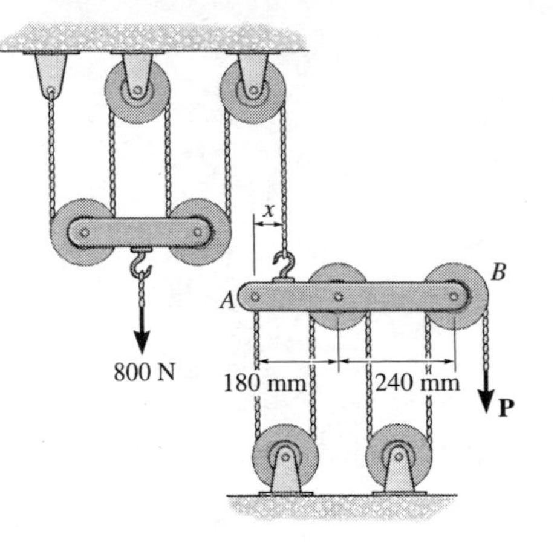

Prob. 5–38

5-39. Determine the force *P* needed to support the 20-kg mass using the *Spanish Burton rig*. Also, what are the reactions at the supporting hooks *A*, *B*, and *C*?

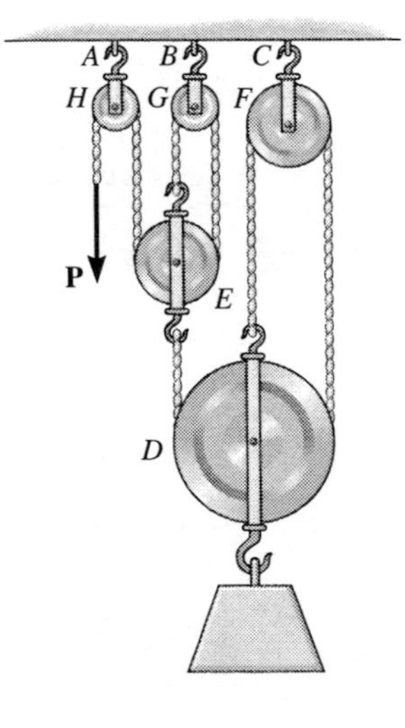

Prob. 5–39

***5-40.** The compound beam is fixed at *A* and supported by a rocker at *B* and *C*. There are hinges (pins) at *D* and *E*. Determine the reactions at the supports.

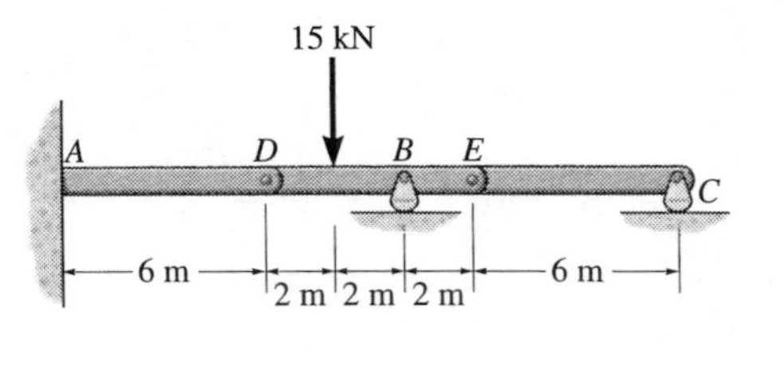

Prob. 5–40

5-41. The compound beam is pin-supported at *C* and supported by a roller at *A* and *B*. There is a hinge (pin) at *D*. Determine the reactions at the supports. Neglect the thickness of the beam.

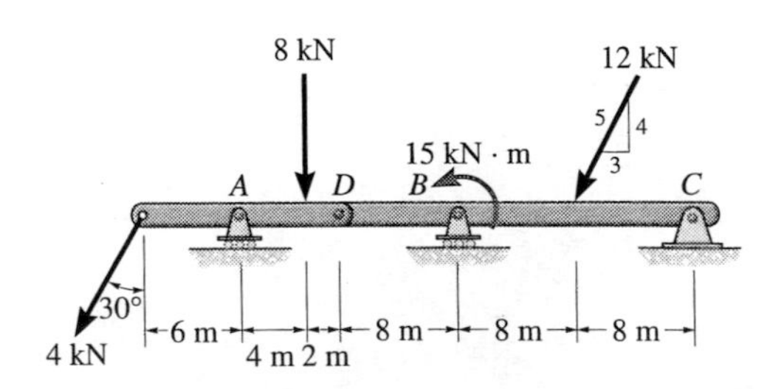

Prob 5–41

5-42. Determine the greatest force P that can be applied to the frame if the largest force resultant acting at A can have a magnitude of 2 kN.

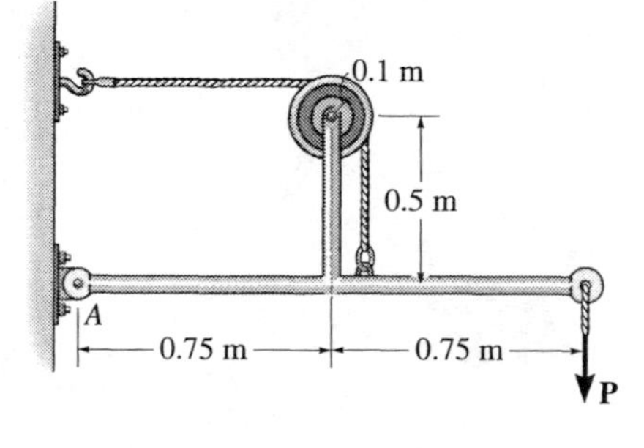

Prob. 5–42

***5-44.** The three-hinged arch supports the loads $F_1 = 8$ kN and $F_2 = 5$ kN. Determine the horizontal and vertical components of reaction at the pin supports A and B. Take $h = 2$ m.

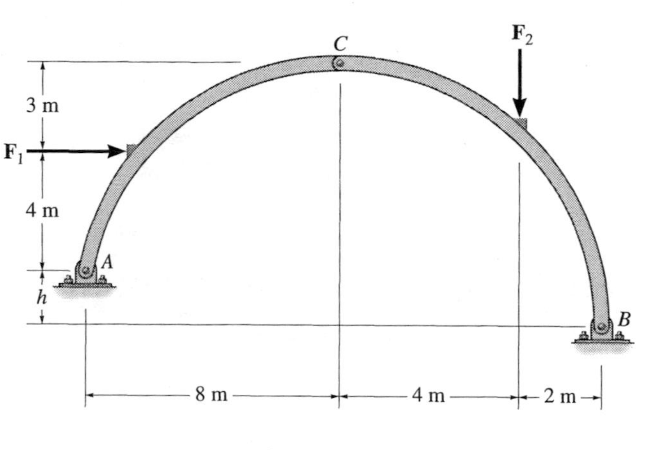

Prob. 5–44

5-43. Determine the horizontal and vertical components force at pins A and C of the two-member frame.

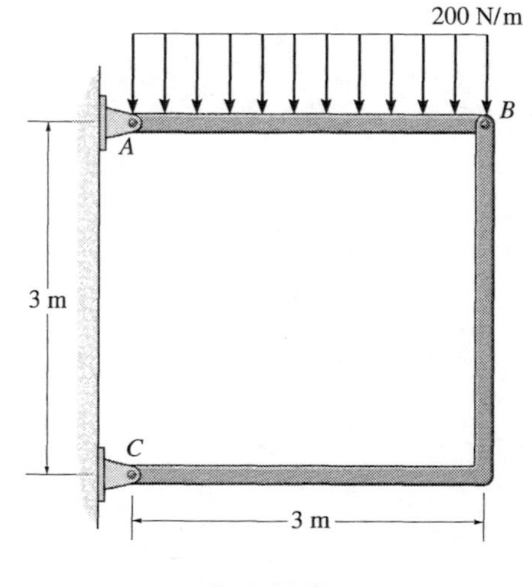

Prob. 5–43

5-45. Determine the horizontal and vertical components of force at pins A, B, and C, and the reactions to the fixed support D of the three-member frame.

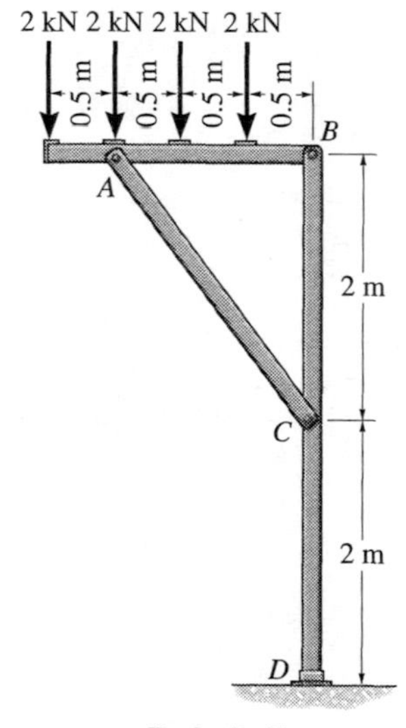

Prob. 5–45

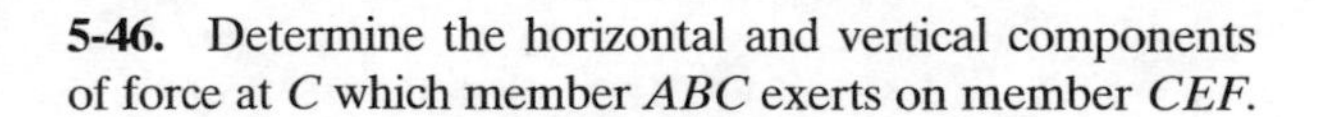

5-46. Determine the horizontal and vertical components of force at C which member ABC exerts on member CEF.

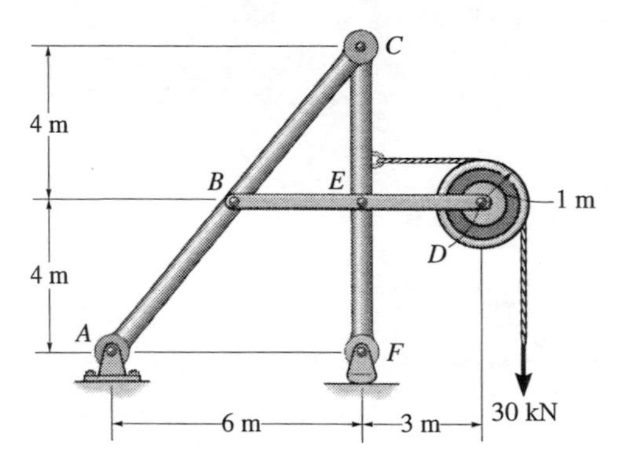

Prob. 5–46

5-47. Determine the horizontal and vertical components of force that the pins at A, B, and C exert on their connecting members.

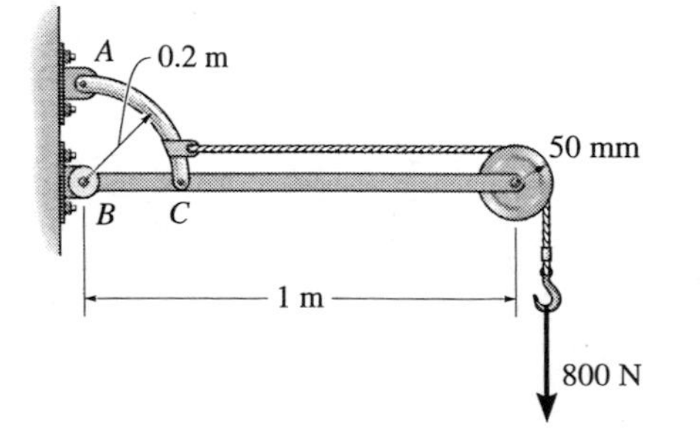

Prob. 5–47

***5-48.** The hoist supports the 125-kg engine. Determine the force the load creates in member DB and in member FB, which contains the hydraulic cylinder H.

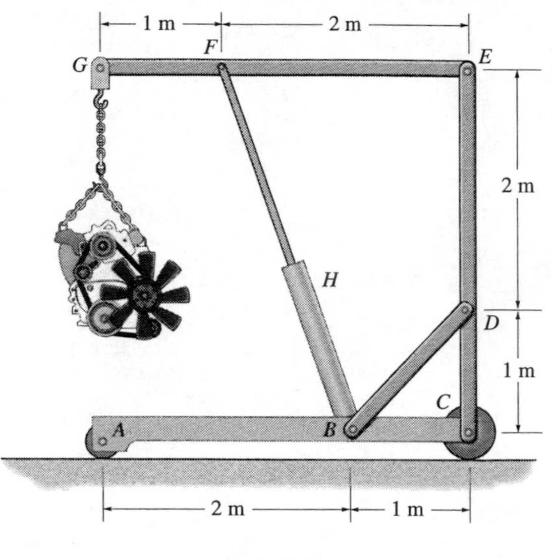

Prob. 5–48

5-49. Determine the force P on the cord, and the angle θ that the pulley-supporting link AB makes with the vertical. Neglect the mass of the pulleys and the link. The block has a weight of 200 N ($\approx$ 20 kg) and the cord is attached to the pin at B. The pulleys have radii of $r_1 = 2$ cm, and $r_2 = 1$ cm.

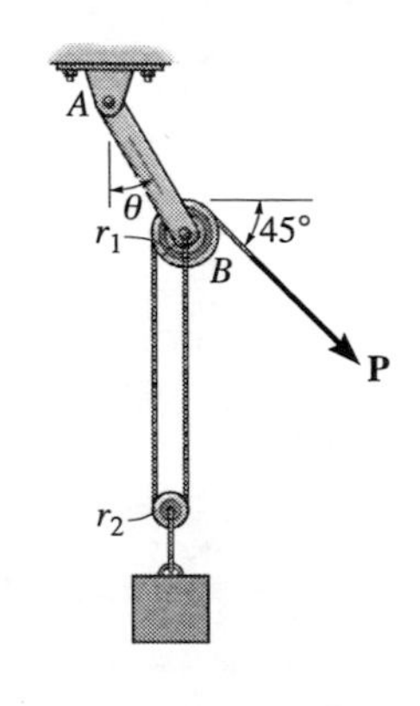

Prob. 5–49

5-50. The front of the car is to be lifted using a smooth, rigid 3.5 m long board. The car has a weight of 17.5 kN and a center of gravity at G. Determine the position x of the fulcrum so that an applied force of 500 N at E will lift the front wheels of the car.

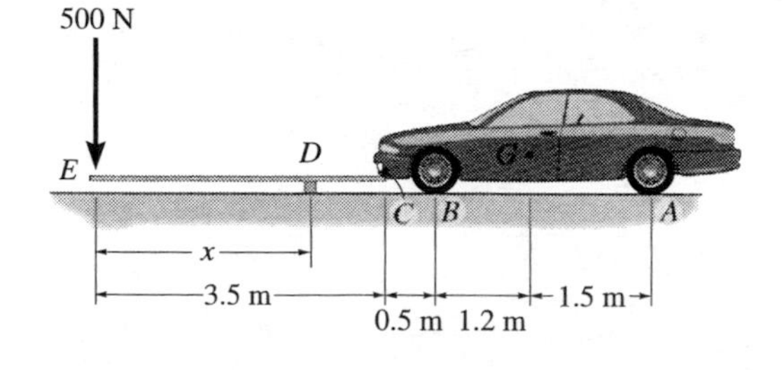

Prob. 5–50

5-51. The wall crane supports a load of 700 N. Determine the horizontal and vertical components of reaction at the pins A and D. Also, what is the force in the cable at the winch W?

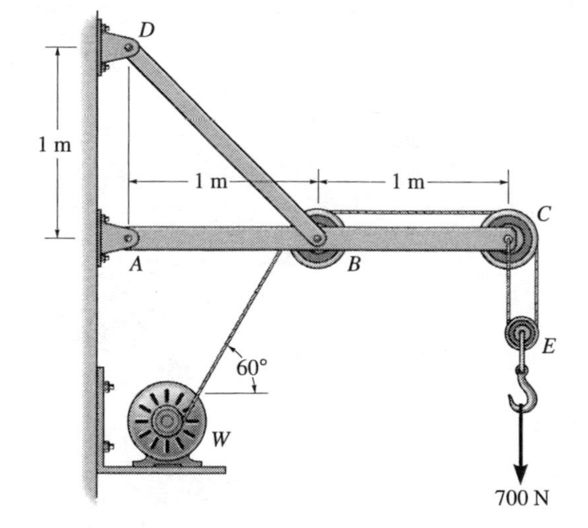

Prob. 5–51

***5-52.** Determine the force that the smooth roller C exerts on beam AB. Also, what are the horizontal and vertical components of reaction at pin A? Neglect the weight of the frame and roller.

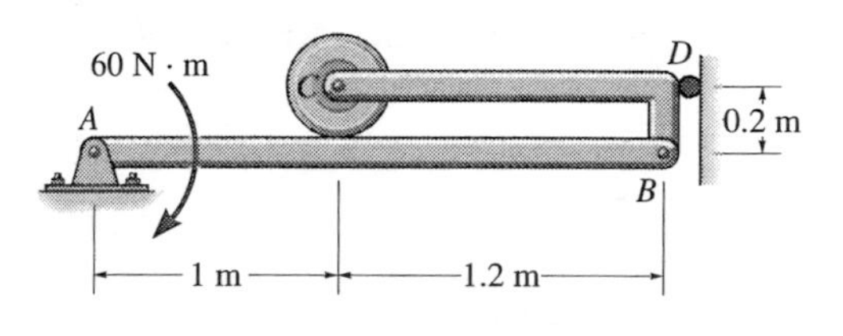

Prob. 5–52

5-53. Determine the horizontal and vertical components of force which the pins exert on member ABC.

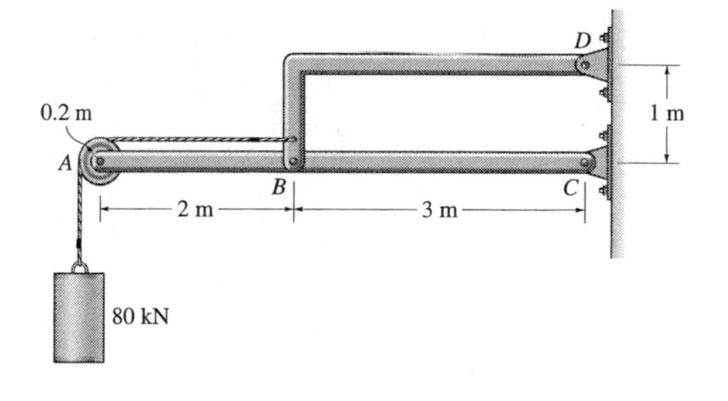

Prob. 5–53

5-54. The engine hoist is used to support the 200-kg engine. Determine the force acting in the hydraulic cylinder AB, the horizontal and vertical components of force at the pin C, and the reactions at the fixed support D.

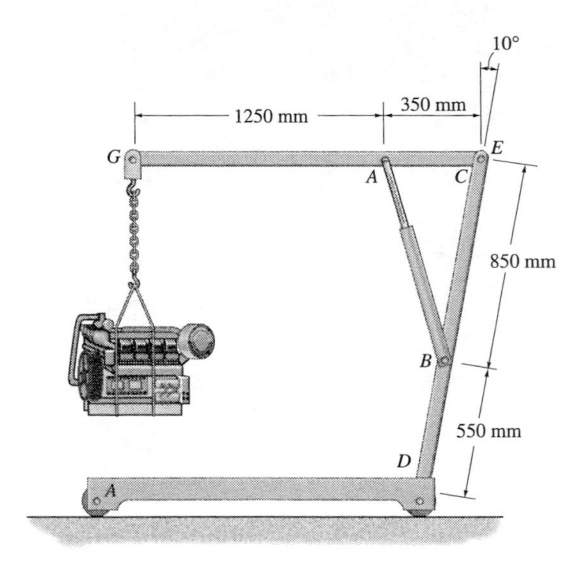

Prob. 5–54

5-55. Determine the horizontal and vertical components of force at pins B and C.

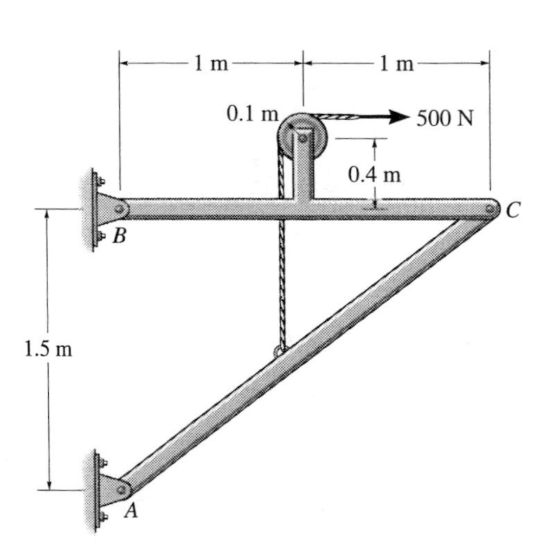

Prob. 5–55

***5-56.** The pipe cutter is clamped around the pipe P. If the wheel at A exerts a normal force of $F_A = 80$ N on the pipe, determine the normal forces of wheels B and C on the pipe. Also compute the pin reaction on the wheel at C. The three wheels each have a radius of 7 mm and the pipe has an outer radius of 10 mm.

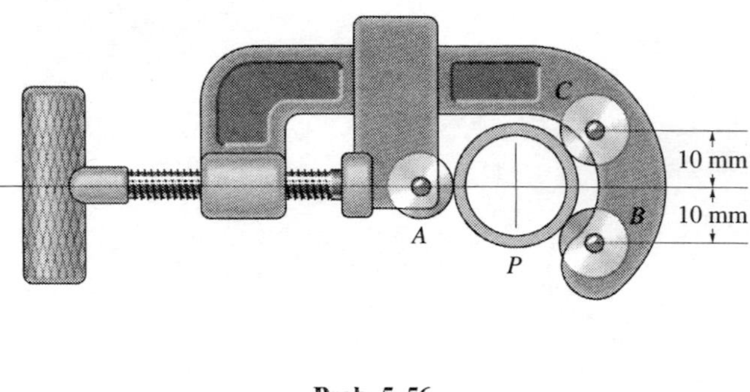

Prob. 5–56

5-57. Determine the horizontal and vertical components of force at each pin. The suspended cylinder has a weight of 800 N (≈ 80 kg).

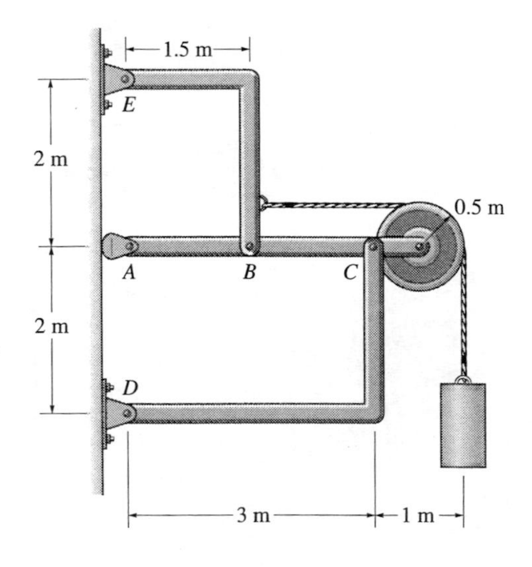

Prob. 5–57

5-58. The toggle clamp is subjected to a force **F** at the handle. Determine the vertical clamping force acting at E.

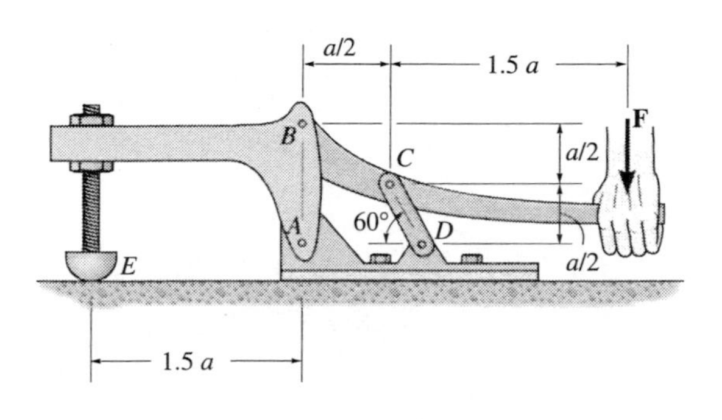

Prob. 5–58

5-59. Determine the horizontal and vertical components of force which the pins at A, B, and C exert on member ABC of the frame.

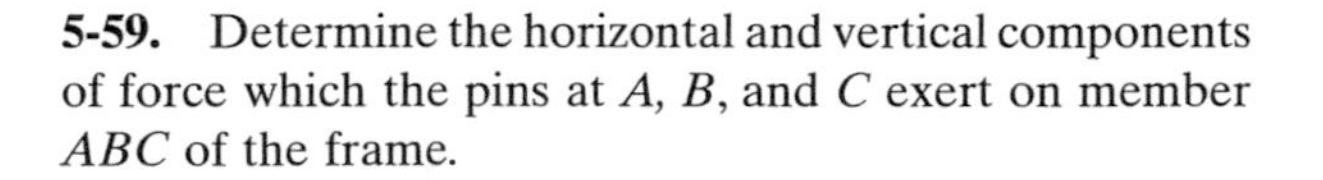

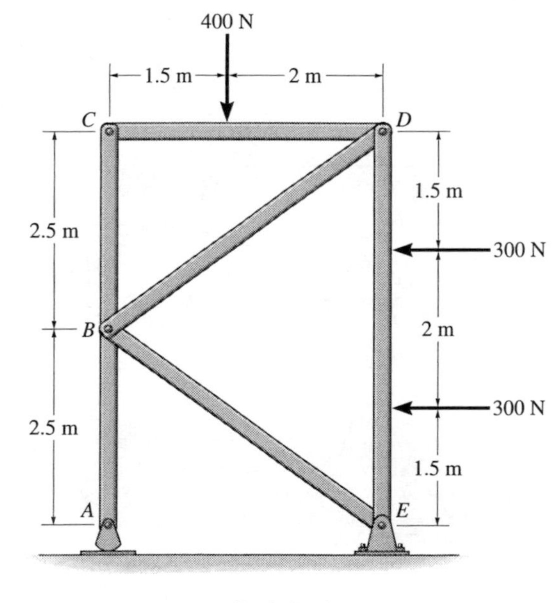

Prob. 5–59

***5-60.** The derrick is pin-connected to the pivot at A. Determine the largest mass that can be supported by the derrick if the maximum force that can be sustained by the pin at A is 18 kN.

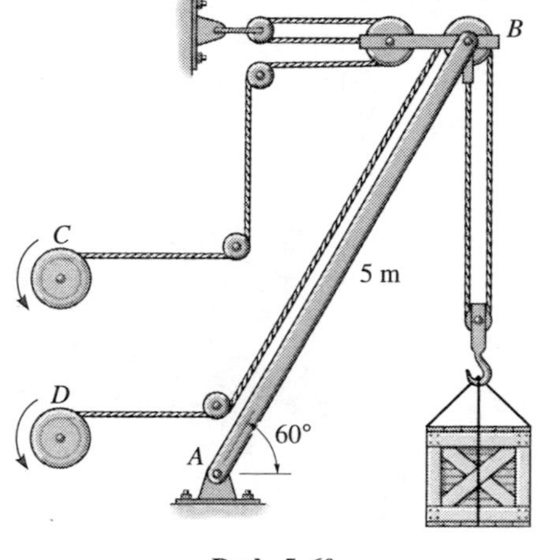

Prob. 5–60

5-61. Determine the required mass of the suspended cylinder if the tension in the chain wrapped around the freely turning gear is to be 2 kN. Also, what is the magnitude of the resultant force on pin A?

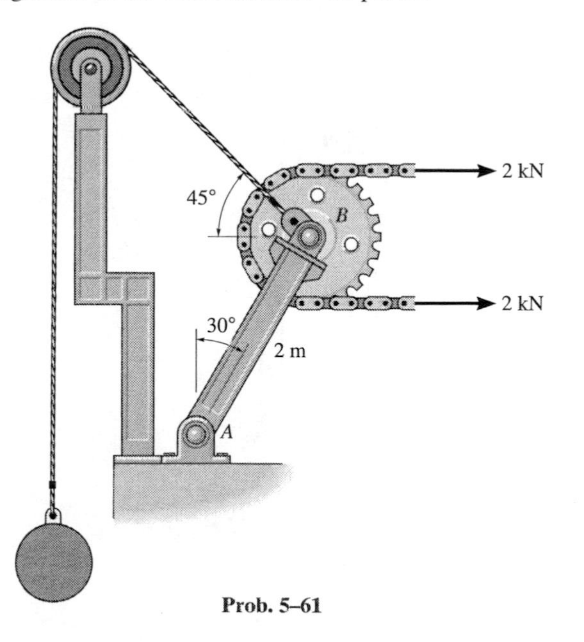

Prob. 5–61

5-62. The pumping unit is used to recover oil. When the walking beam ABC is horizontal, the force acting in the wireline at the well head is 1000 N. Determine the torque **M** which must be exerted by the motor in order to overcome this load. The horse-head C weighs 240 N and has a center of gravity at G_C. The walking beam ABC has a weight of 520 N and a center of gravity at G_B, and the counterweight has a weight of 800 N and a center of gravity at G_W. The pitman, AD, is pin-connected at its ends and has negligible weight.

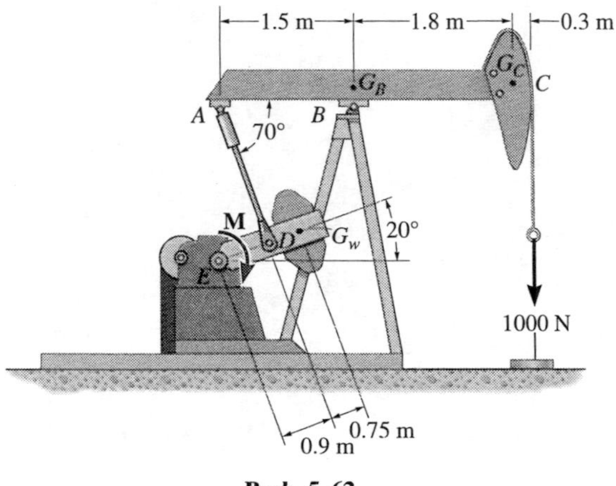

Prob. 5–62

5-63. Determine the force P on the cable if the spring is compressed 10 mm when the mechanism is in the position shown. The spring has a stiffness of $k = 12$ kN/m.

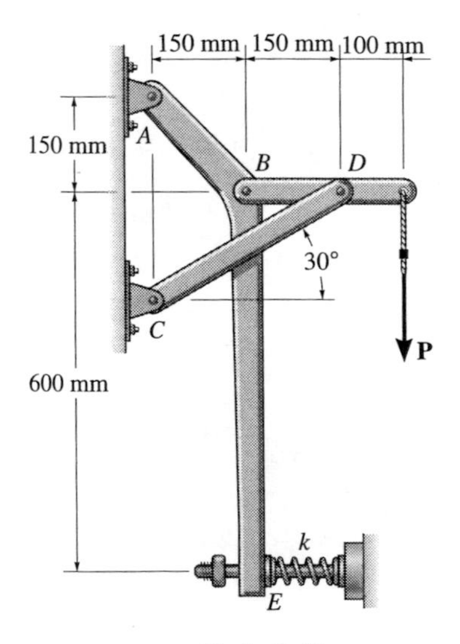

Prob. 5–63

***5-64.** Determine the force that the jaws J of the metal cutters exert on the smooth cable C if 100-N forces are applied to the handles. The jaws are pinned at E and A, and D and B. There is also a pin at F.

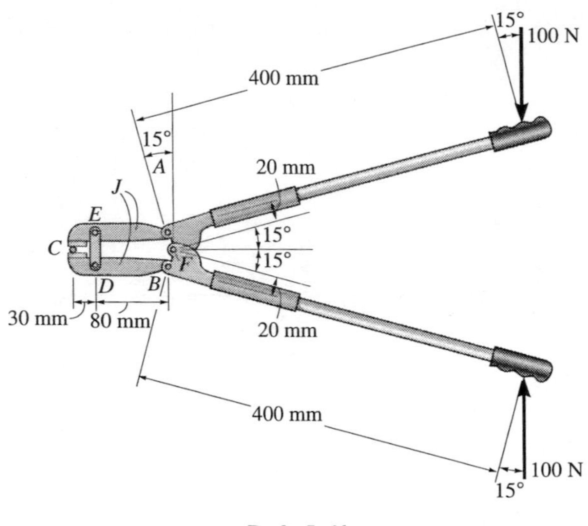

Prob. 5–64

5-65. The compound arrangement of the pan scale is shown. If the mass on the pan is 4 kg, determine the horizontal and vertical components at pins A, B, and C and the distance x of the 25-g mass to keep the scale in balance.

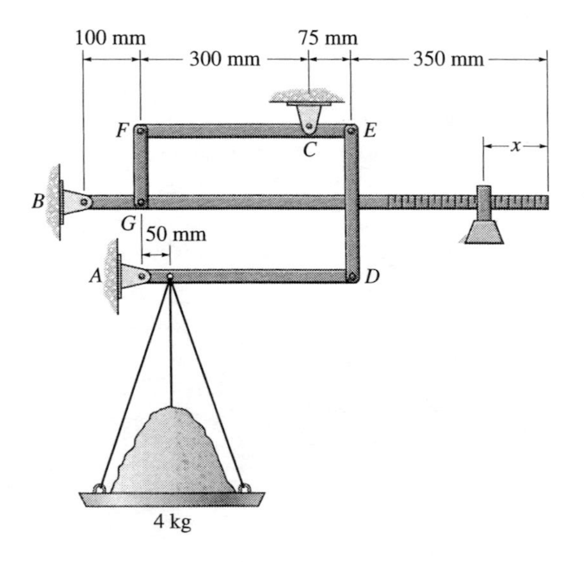

Prob. 5–65

5-66. The scissors lift consists of *two* sets of cross members and *two* hydraulic cylinders, DE, symmetrically located on *each side* of the platform. The platform has a uniform mass of 60 kg, with a center of gravity at G_1. The load of 85 kg, with center of gravity at G_2, is centrally located between each side of the platform. Determine the force in each of the hydraulic cylinders for equilibrium. Rollers are located at B and D.

Prob. 5–66

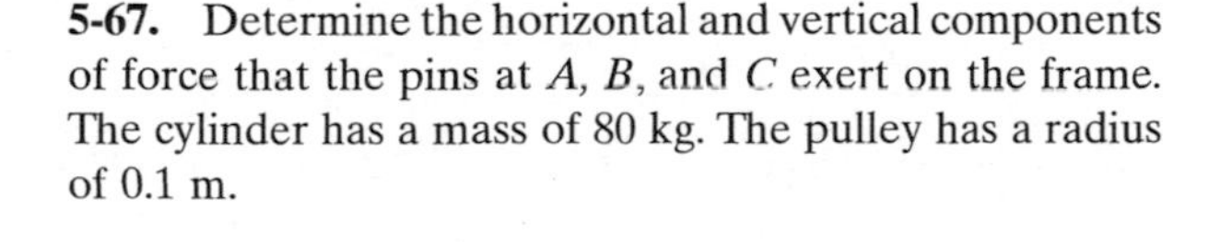

5-67. Determine the horizontal and vertical components of force that the pins at A, B, and C exert on the frame. The cylinder has a mass of 80 kg. The pulley has a radius of 0.1 m.

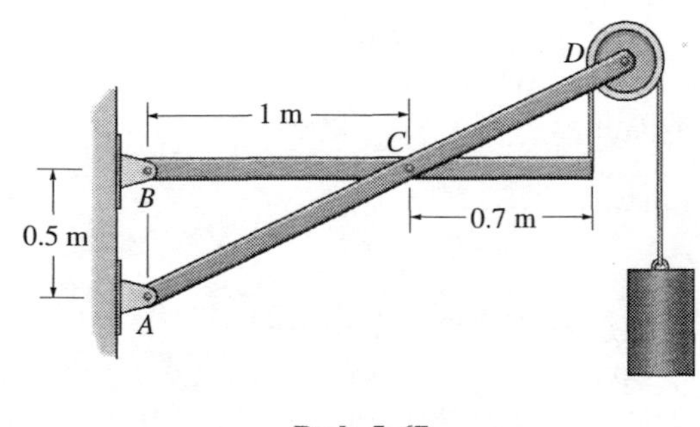

Prob. 5–67

***5-68.** By squeezing on the hand brake of the bicycle, the rider subjects the brake cable to a tension of 200 N. If the caliper mechanism is pin-connected to the bicycle frame at B, determine the normal force each brake pad exerts on the rim of the wheel. Is this the force that stops the wheel from turning? Explain.

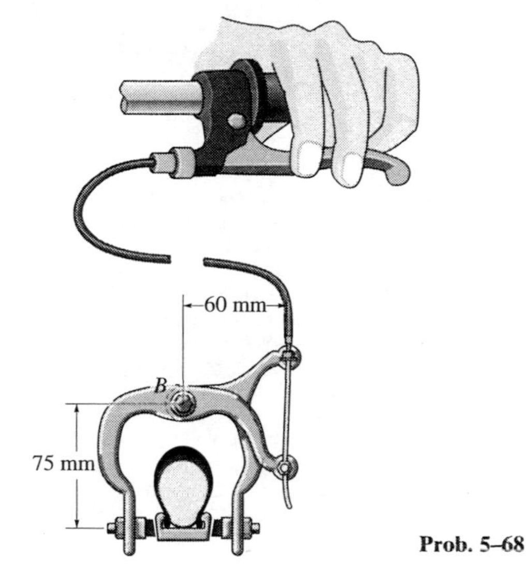

Prob. 5–68

5-69. If a force of $P = 30$ N is applied perpendicular to the handle of the mechanism, determine the magnitude of force **F** for equilibrium. The members are pin-connected at A, B, C, and D.

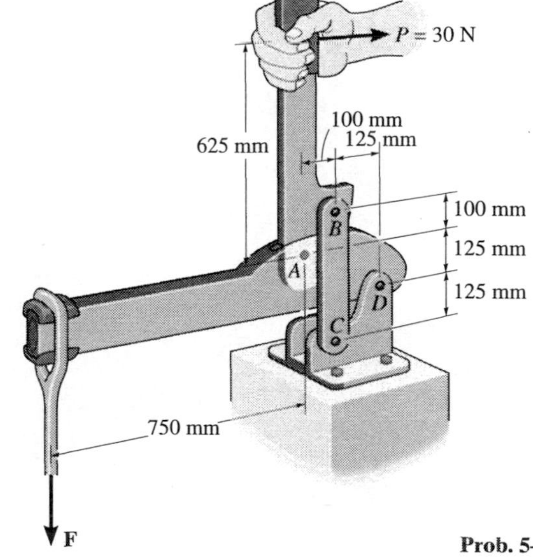

Prob. 5–69

5-70. The bucket of the backhoe and its contents have a weight of 3000 N ($\approx$ 300 kg) and a center of gravity at G. Determine the forces of the hydraulic cylinder AB and in links AC and AD in order to hold the load in the position shown. The bucket is pinned at E.

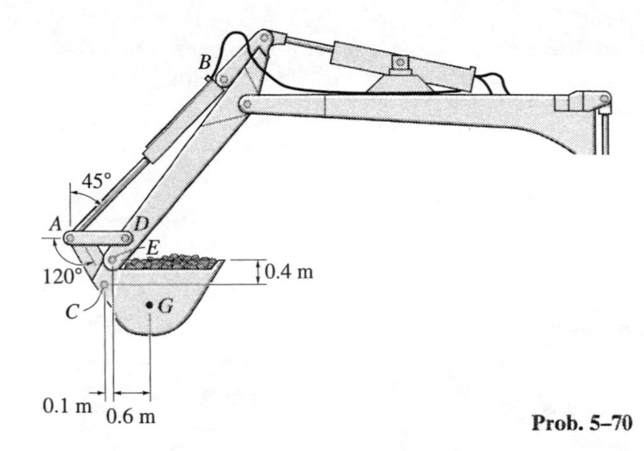

Prob. 5–70

CHAPTER REVIEW

- ***Truss Analysis.*** A simple truss consists of triangular elements connected together by pin joints. The forces within it members can be determined by assuming the members are all two-force members, connected concurrently at each joint.

- ***Method of Joints.*** If a truss is in equilibrium, then each of its joints is also in equilibrium. For a coplanar truss, the concurrent force system at each joint must satisfy force equilibrium, $\Sigma F_x = 0$, $\Sigma F_y = 0$. To obtain a numerical solution for the forces in the members, select a joint that has a free-body diagram with at most two unknown forces and one known force. (This may require first finding the reactions at the supports.) Once a member force is determined, use its value and apply it to an adjacent joint. Remember that forces that are found to *pull* on the joint are in *tension*, and those that *push* on the joint are in *compression*. To avoid a simultaneous solution of two equations, try to sum forces in a direction that is perpendicular to one of the unknowns. This will allow a direct solution for the other unknown. To further simplify the analysis, first identify all the zero-force members.

- ***Method of Sections.*** If a truss is in equilibrium, then each section of the truss is also in equilibrium. Pass a section through the member whose force is to be determined. Then draw the free-body diagram of the sectioned part having the least number of forces on it. Sectioned members subjected to *pulling* are in *tension*, and those that are subjected to *pushing* are in *compression*. If the force system is coplanar, then three equations of equilibrium are available to determine the unknowns. If possible, sum forces in a direction that is perpendicular to two of the three unknown forces. This will yield a direct solution for the third force. Likewise, sum moments about a point that passes through the line of action of two of the three unknown forces, so that the third unknown force can be determined directly.

- ***Frames and Machines.*** The forces acting at the joints of a frame or machine can be determined by drawing the free-body diagrams of each of its members or parts. The principle of action-reaction should be carefully observed when drawing these forces on each adjacent member or pin. For a coplanar force system, there are three equilibrium equations available for each member.

REVIEW PROBLEMS

5-71. Determine the reactions at the supports of the compound beam. There is a short vertical link at C.

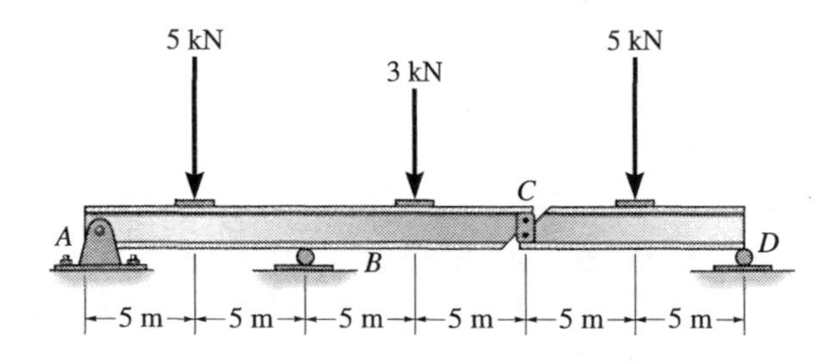

Prob. 5–71

5-72. The two-bar mechanism consists of a lever arm AB and smooth link CD, which has a fixed collar at its end C and a roller at the other end D. Determine the force $\mathbf{P}$ needed to hold the lever in the position θ. The spring has a stiffness k and unstretched length $2L$. The roller contacts either the top or bottom portion of the horizontal guide.

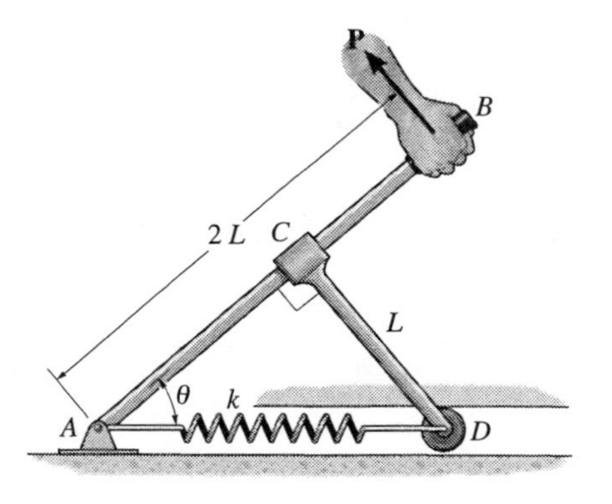

Prob. 5–72

5-73. Determine the force in each member of the truss and indicate whether the members are in tension or compression.

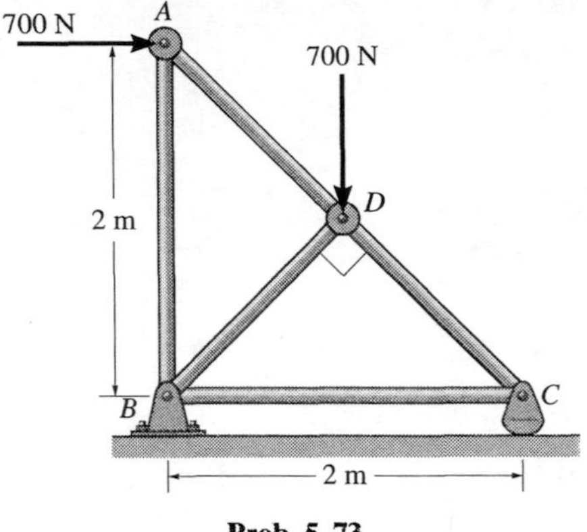

Prob. 5–73

5-74. The *Howe bridge truss* is subjected to the loading shown. Determine the force in members *HD, CD*, and *GD*, and indicate whether the members are in tension or compression.

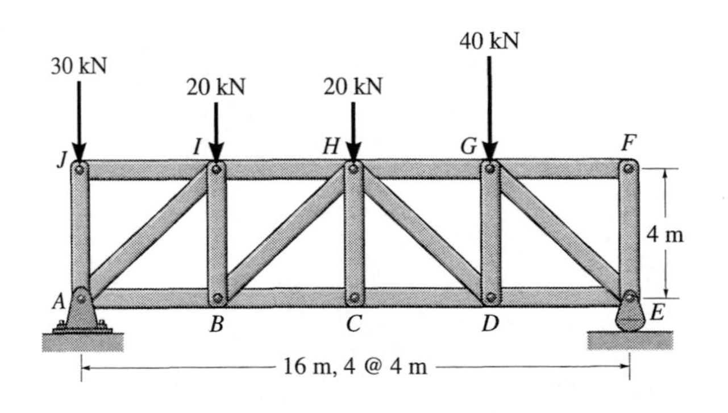

Prob. 5–74

5-75. The *Howe bridge truss* is subjected to the loading shown. Determine the force in members. *HI, HB*, and *BC*, and indicate whether the members are in tension or compression.

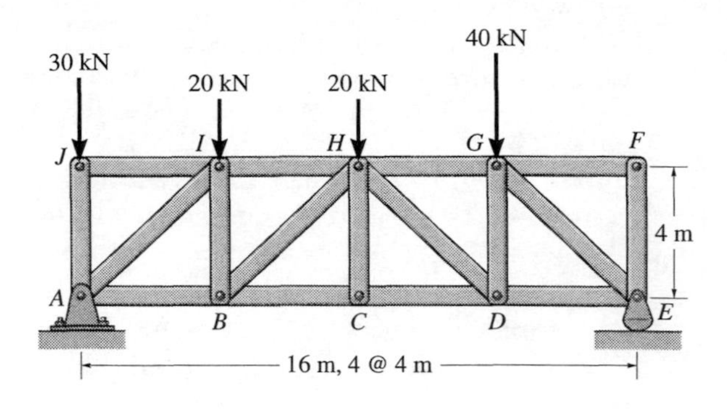

Prob. 5–75

***5-76.** Determine the horizontal and vertical components of force at pins *A, B*, and *C* of the two-member frame.

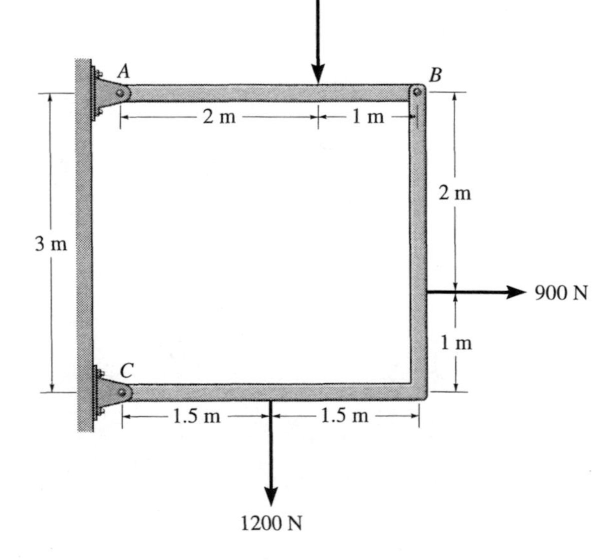

Prob. 5–76

5-77. The compound beam is supported by a rocker at B and fixed to the wall at A. If it is hinged (pinned) together at C, determine the reactions at the supports.

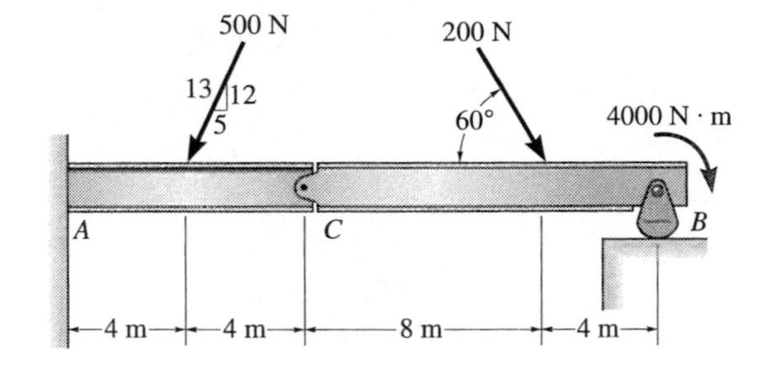

Prob. 5–77

5-78. Determine the horizontal and vertical components of reaction at A and B. The pin at C is fixed to member AE and fits through a smooth slot in member BD.

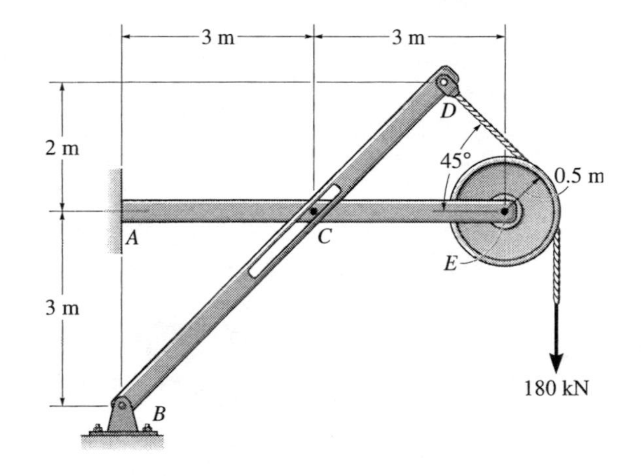

Prob. 5–78

When a pressure vessel is designed, it is important to be able to determine the center of gravity of its component parts, calculate its volume and surface area, and reduce three-dimensional distributed loadings to their resultants. These topics are discussed in this chapter.

CHAPTER 6

Geometric Properties and Distributed Loadings

CHAPTER OBJECTIVES

- To discuss the concept of the center of gravity, center of mass, and the centroid.
- To show how to determine the location of the center of gravity and centroid for a system of discrete particles and a body of arbitrary shape.
- To present a method for finding the resultant of a general distributed loading.
- To develop a method for determining the moment of inertia for an area.

6.1 Center of Gravity and Center of Mass for a System of Particles

Center of Gravity. The *center of gravity* G is a point which locates the resultant weight of a system of particles. To show how to determine this point consider the system of n particles fixed within a region of space as shown in Fig. 6–1a. The weights of the particles comprise a system of parallel forces* which can be replaced by a single (equivalent) resultant weight having the defined point G of application. To find the $\bar{x}$, $\bar{y}$, $\bar{z}$ coordinates of G, we must use the principles outlined in Sec. 3.9.

*This is not true in the exact sense, since the weights are not parallel to each other; rather they are all *concurrent* at the earth's center. Furthermore, the acceleration of gravity g is actually different for each particle since it depends on the distance from the earth's center to the particle. For all practical purposes, however, both of these effects can generally be neglected.

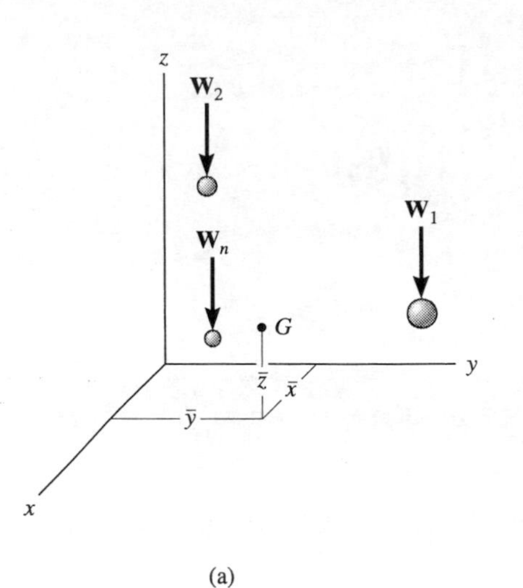

(b)

Fig. 6–1

This requires that the resultant weight be equal to the total weight of all n particles; that is,

$$W_R = \Sigma W$$

The sum of the moments of the weights of all the particles about the x, y, and z axes is then equal to the moment of the resultant weight about these axes. Thus, to determine the $\bar{x}$ coordinate of G, we can sum moments about the y axis. This yields

$$\bar{x}W_R = \tilde{x}_1W_1 + \tilde{x}_2W_2 + \cdots + \tilde{x}_nW_n$$

Likewise, summing moments about the x axis, we can obtain the $\bar{y}$ coordinate; i.e.,

$$\bar{y}W_R = \tilde{y}_1W_1 + \tilde{y}_2W_2 + \cdots + \tilde{y}_nW_n$$

Although the weights do not produce a moment about the z axis, we can obtain the $\bar{z}$ coordinate of G by imagining the coordinate system, with the particles fixed in it, as being rotated 90° about the x (or y) axis, Fig. 6–1b. Summing moments about the x axis, we have

$$\bar{z}W_R = \tilde{z}_1W_1 + \tilde{z}_2W_2 + \cdots + \tilde{z}_nW_n$$

We can generalize these formulas, and write them symbolically in the form

$$\bar{x} = \frac{\Sigma\tilde{x}W}{\Sigma W} \qquad \bar{y} = \frac{\Sigma\tilde{y}W}{\Sigma W} \qquad \bar{z} = \frac{\Sigma\tilde{z}W}{\Sigma W} \tag{6–1}$$

Here

$\bar{x}, \bar{y}, \bar{z}$ represent the coordinates of the center of gravity G of the system of particles.

$\tilde{x}, \tilde{y}, \tilde{z}$ represent the coordinates of each particle in the system.

ΣW is the resultant sum of the weights of all the particles in the system.

These equations are easily remembered if it is kept in mind that they simply represent a balance between the sum of the moments of the weights of each particle of the system and the moment of the *resultant* weight for the system.

Center of Mass. To study problems concerning the motion of *matter* under the influence of force, i.e., dynamics, it is necessary to locate a point called the *center of mass*. Provided the acceleration due to gravity g for every particle is constant, then $W = mg$. Substituting into Eqs. 6–1 and canceling g from both the numerator and denominator yields

$$\bar{x} = \frac{\Sigma\tilde{x}m}{\Sigma m} \qquad \bar{y} = \frac{\Sigma\tilde{y}m}{\Sigma m} \qquad \bar{z} = \frac{\Sigma\tilde{z}m}{\Sigma m} \tag{6–2}$$

By comparison, then, the location of the center of gravity *coincides* with that of the center of mass.* Recall, however, that particles have "weight" only when under the influence of a gravitational attraction, whereas the center of mass is independent of gravity. For example, it would be meaningless to define the center of gravity of a system of particles representing the planets of our solar system, while the center of mass of this system is important.

6.2 Center of Gravity and Centroid for a Body

Center of Gravity. A rigid body is composed of an infinite number of particles, and so if the principles used to determine Eqs. 6–1 are applied to the system of particles composing a rigid body, it becomes necessary to use integration rather than a discrete summation of the terms. Considering the arbitrary particle located at $(\tilde{x}, \tilde{y}, \tilde{z})$ and having a weight dW, Fig. 6–2, the resulting equations are

$$\bar{x} = \frac{\int \tilde{x}\, dW}{\int dW} \qquad \bar{y} = \frac{\int \tilde{y}\, dW}{\int dW} \qquad \bar{z} = \frac{\int \tilde{z}\, dW}{\int dW} \qquad (6\text{–}3)$$

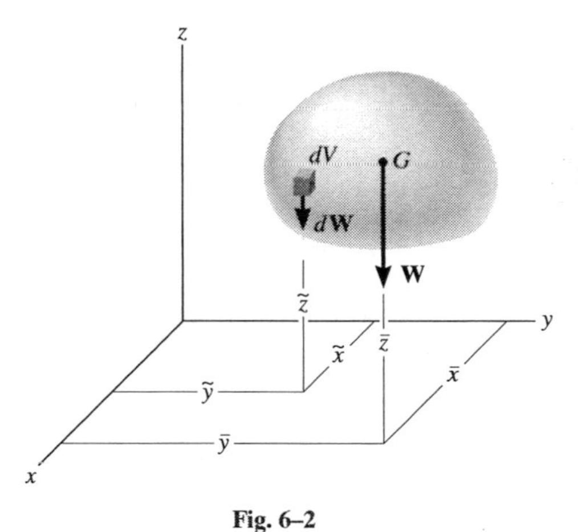

Fig. 6–2

In order to apply these equations properly, the differential weight dW must be expressed in terms of its associated volume dV. If γ represents the *specific weight* of the body, measured as a weight per unit volume, then $dW = \gamma\, dV$ and therefore

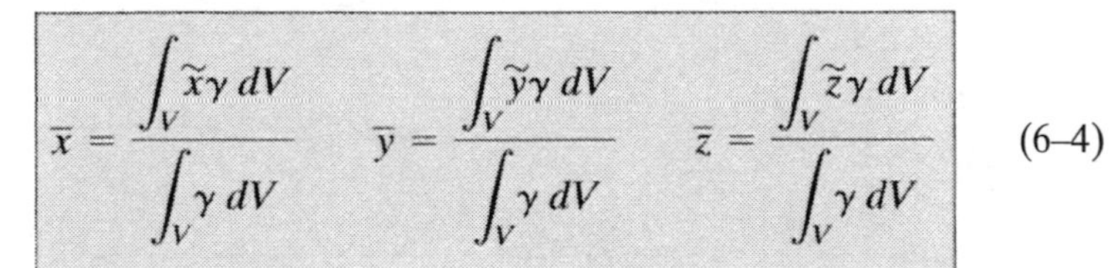

$$\bar{x} = \frac{\int_V \tilde{x}\gamma\, dV}{\int_V \gamma\, dV} \qquad \bar{y} = \frac{\int_V \tilde{y}\gamma\, dV}{\int_V \gamma\, dV} \qquad \bar{z} = \frac{\int_V \tilde{z}\gamma\, dV}{\int_V \gamma\, dV} \qquad (6\text{–}4)$$

Here integration must be performed throughout the entire volume of the body.

Center of Mass. The *density* ρ, or mass per unit volume, is related to γ by the equation $\gamma = \rho g$, where g is the acceleration due to gravity. Substituting this relationship into Eqs. 6–4 and canceling g from both the numerators and denominators yields similar equations (with ρ replacing γ) that can be used to determine the body's *center of mass*.

*This is true as long as the gravity field is assumed to have the same magnitude and direction everywhere. That assumption is appropriate for most engineering applications, since gravity does not vary appreciably between, for instance, the bottom and the top of a building.

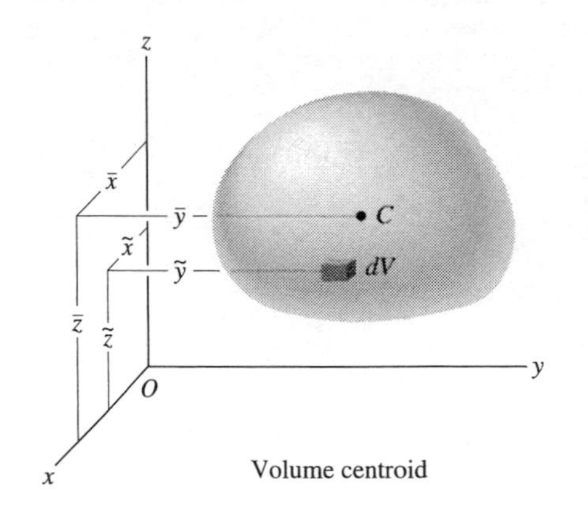

Fig. 6–3

Centroid. The *centroid* C is a point which defines the *geometric center* of an object. Its location can be determined from formulas similar to those used to determine the body's center of gravity or center of mass. In particular, if the material composing a body is uniform or *homogeneous*, the *density or specific weight* will be *constant* throughout the body, and therefore this term will factor out of the integrals and *cancel* from both the numerators and denominators of Eqs. 6–4. The resulting formulas define the centroid of the body since they are independent of the body's weight and instead depend only on the body's geometry. Three specific cases will be considered.

Volume. If an object is subdivided into volume elements dV, Fig. 6–3, the location of the centroid $C(\bar{x}, \bar{y}, \bar{z})$ for the volume of the object can be determined by computing the "moments" of the elements about each of the coordinate axes. The resulting formulas are

$$\bar{x} = \frac{\int_V \tilde{x}\, dV}{\int_V dV} \qquad \bar{y} = \frac{\int_V \tilde{y}\, dV}{\int_V dV} \qquad \bar{z} = \frac{\int_V \tilde{z}\, dV}{\int_V dV} \tag{6–5}$$

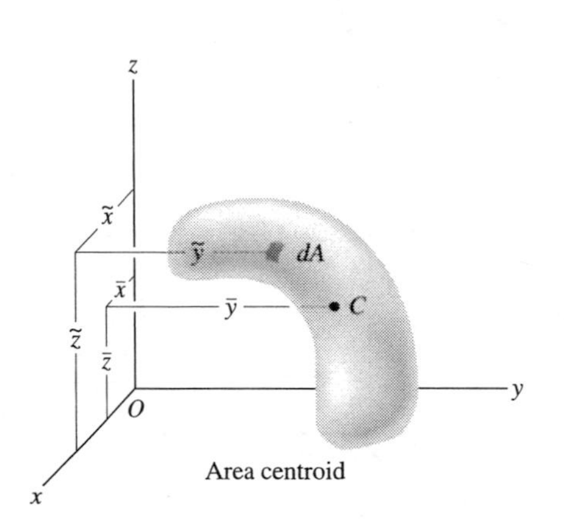

Fig. 6–4

Area. In a similar manner, the centroid for the surface area of an object, such as a plate or shell, Fig. 6–4, can be found by subdividing the area into differential elements dA and computing the "moments" of these area elements about each of the coordinate axes, namely,

$$\bar{x} = \frac{\int_A \tilde{x}\, dA}{\int_A dA} \qquad \bar{y} = \frac{\int_A \tilde{y}\, dA}{\int_A dA} \qquad \bar{z} = \frac{\int_A \tilde{z}\, dA}{\int_A dA} \tag{6–6}$$

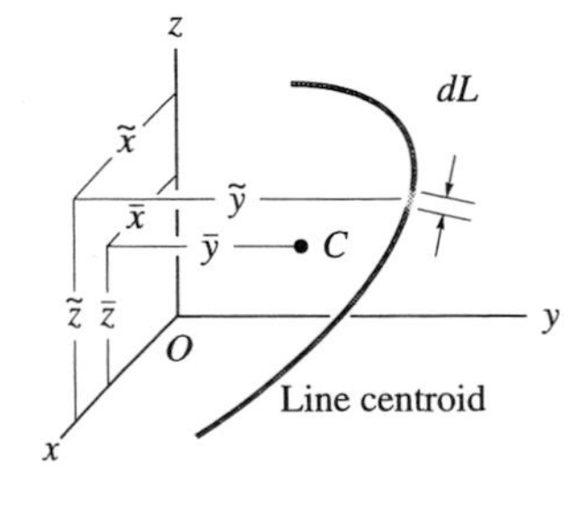

Fig. 6–5

Line. If the geometry of the object, such as a thin rod or wire, takes the form of a line, Fig. 6–5, the balance of moments of the differential elements dL about each of the coordinate axes yields

$$\bar{x} = \frac{\int_L \tilde{x}\, dL}{\int_L dL} \qquad \bar{y} = \frac{\int_L \tilde{y}\, dL}{\int_L dL} \qquad \bar{z} = \frac{\int_L \tilde{z}\, dL}{\int_L dL} \tag{6–7}$$

Remember that when applying Eqs. 6–4 through 6–7 it is best to choose a coordinate system that simplifies as much as possible the equation used to describe the object's boundary. For example, polar coordinates are generally appropriate for areas having circular boundaries. Also, the terms $\tilde{x}, \tilde{y}, \tilde{z}$ in the equations refer to the "moment arms" or coordinates of the *center of gravity or centroid for the differential element* used. If possible, this differential element should be chosen such that it has a differential size or thickness in only *one direction*. When this is done, only a single integration is required to cover the entire region.

Integration must be used to determine the location of the center of gravity of this goal post.

Symmetry. The *centroids* of some shapes may be partially or completely specified by using conditions of *symmetry*. In cases where the shape has an axis of symmetry, the centroid of the shape will lie along that axis. For example, the centroid C for the line shown in Fig. 6–6 must lie along the y axis since for every elemental length dL at a distance $+\tilde{x}$ to the right of the y axis there is an identical element at a distance $-\tilde{x}$ to the left. The total moment for all the elements about the axis of symmetry will therefore cancel; i.e., $\int \tilde{x}\, dL = 0$ (Eq. 6–7), so that $\bar{x} = 0$. In cases where a shape has two or three axes of symmetry, it follows that the centroid lies at the intersection of these axes, Fig. 6–7 and Fig. 6–8.

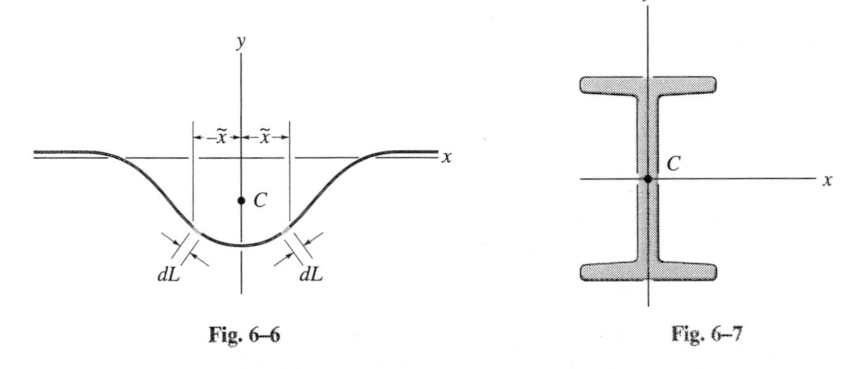

Fig. 6–6

Fig. 6–7

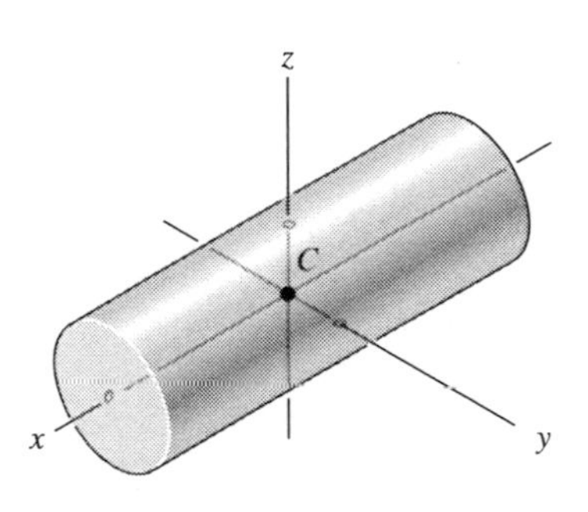

Fig. 6–8

IMPORTANT POINTS

- The centroid represents the geometric center of a body. This point coincides with the center of mass or the center of gravity only if the material composing the body is uniform or homogeneous.
- Formulas used to locate the center of gravity or the centroid simply represent a balance between the sum of moments of all the parts of the system and the moment of the "resultant" for the system.
- In some cases the centroid is located at a point that is not on the object, as in the case of a ring, where the centroid is at its center. Also, this point will lie on any axis of symmetry for the body.

PROCEDURE FOR ANALYSIS

The center of gravity or centroid of an object or shape can be determined by single integrations using the following procedure.

Differential Element.

- Select an appropriate coordinate system, specify the coordinate axes, and then choose a differential element for integration.
- For lines the element dL is represented as a differential line segment.
- For areas the element dA is generally a rectangle having a finite length and differential width.
- For volumes the element dV is either a circular disk having a finite radius and differential thickness, or a shell having a finite length and radius and a differential thickness.
- Locate the element at an arbitrary point (x, y, z) on the curve that defines the shape.

Size and Moment Arms.

- Express the length dL, area dA, or volume dV of the element in terms of the coordinates of the curve used to define the geometric shape.
- Determine the coordinates or moment arms $\tilde{x}, \tilde{y}, \tilde{z}$ for the centroid or center of gravity of the element.

Integrations.

- Substitute the formulations for $\tilde{x}, \tilde{y}, \tilde{z}$ and dL, dA, or dV into the appropriate equations (Eqs. 6–4 through 6–7) and perform the integrations.*
- Express the function in the integrand in terms of the *same variable as the differential thickness of the element* in order to perform the integration.
- The limits of the integral are defined from the two extreme locations of the element's differential thickness, so that when the elements are "summed" or the integration performed, the entire region is covered.

*Formulas for integration are given in Appendix A.

EXAMPLE 6.1

Determine the distance $\bar{y}$ from the x axis to the centroid of the area of the triangle shown in Fig. 6–9.

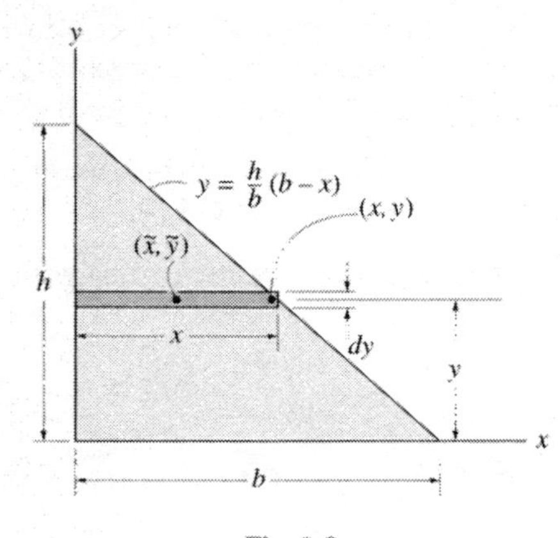

Fig. 6–9

Solution

Differential Element. Consider a rectangular element having thickness dy which intersects the boundary at (x, y), Fig. 6–9.

Area and Moment Arms. The area of the element is $dA = x\,dy = \dfrac{b}{h}(h - y)\,dy$, and its centroid is located a distance $\tilde{y} = y$ from the x axis.

Integrations. Applying the second of Eqs. 6–6 and integrating with respect to y yields

$$\bar{y} = \frac{\int_A \tilde{y}\,dA}{\int_A dA} = \frac{\int_0^h y\frac{b}{h}(h - y)\,dy}{\int_0^h \frac{b}{h}(h - y)\,dy} = \frac{\frac{1}{6}bh^2}{\frac{1}{2}bh}$$

$$= \frac{h}{3} \qquad \textit{Ans.}$$

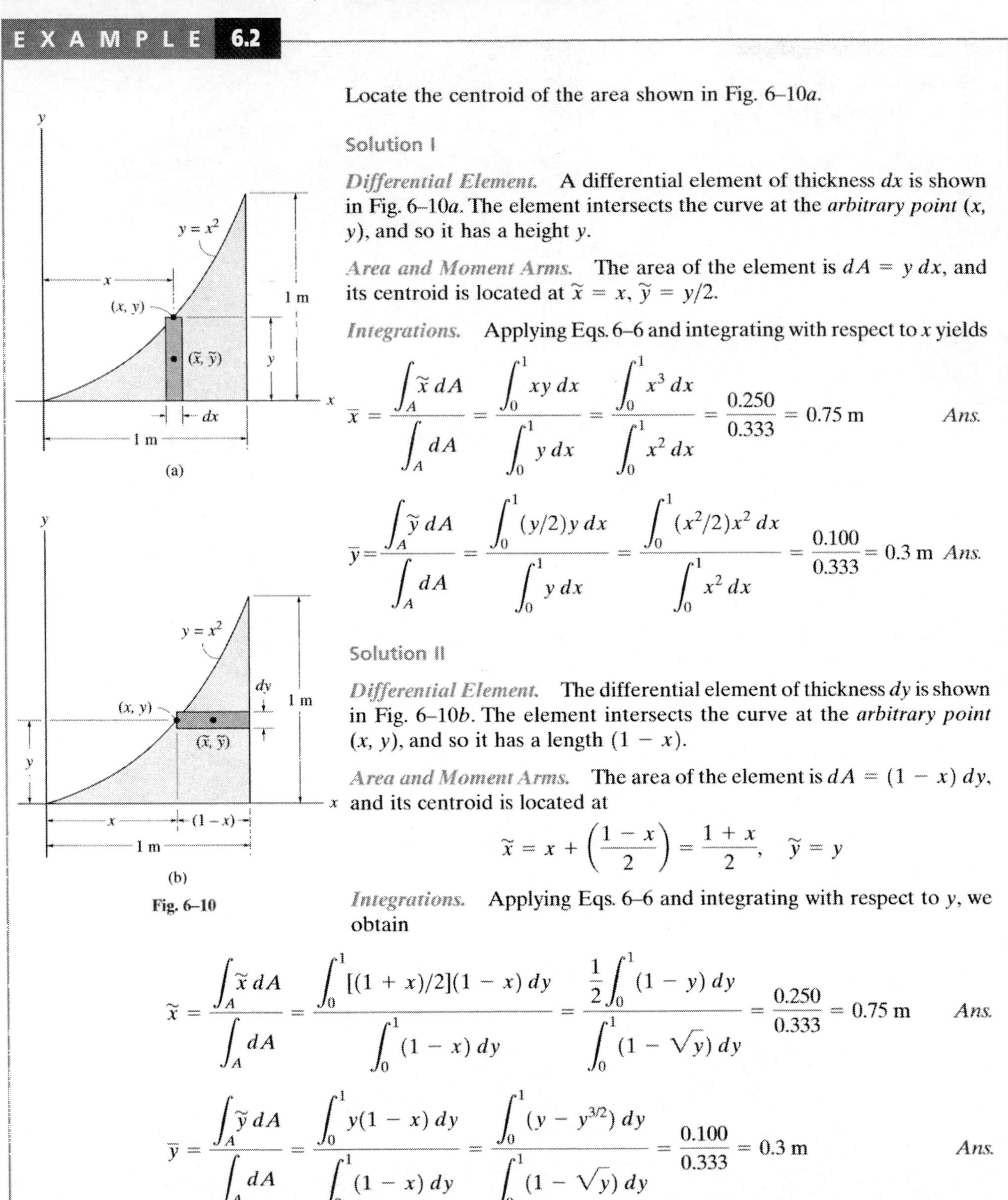

Fig. 6–10

EXAMPLE 6.2

Locate the centroid of the area shown in Fig. 6–10*a*.

Solution I

Differential Element. A differential element of thickness dx is shown in Fig. 6–10*a*. The element intersects the curve at the *arbitrary point* (x, y), and so it has a height y.

Area and Moment Arms. The area of the element is $dA = y\,dx$, and its centroid is located at $\tilde{x} = x$, $\tilde{y} = y/2$.

Integrations. Applying Eqs. 6–6 and integrating with respect to x yields

$$\bar{x} = \frac{\int_A \tilde{x}\,dA}{\int_A dA} = \frac{\int_0^1 xy\,dx}{\int_0^1 y\,dx} = \frac{\int_0^1 x^3\,dx}{\int_0^1 x^2\,dx} = \frac{0.250}{0.333} = 0.75\text{ m} \qquad \textit{Ans.}$$

$$\bar{y} = \frac{\int_A \tilde{y}\,dA}{\int_A dA} = \frac{\int_0^1 (y/2)y\,dx}{\int_0^1 y\,dx} = \frac{\int_0^1 (x^2/2)x^2\,dx}{\int_0^1 x^2\,dx} = \frac{0.100}{0.333} = 0.3\text{ m} \qquad \textit{Ans.}$$

Solution II

Differential Element. The differential element of thickness dy is shown in Fig. 6–10*b*. The element intersects the curve at the *arbitrary point* (x, y), and so it has a length $(1 - x)$.

Area and Moment Arms. The area of the element is $dA = (1 - x)\,dy$, and its centroid is located at

$$\tilde{x} = x + \left(\frac{1 - x}{2}\right) = \frac{1 + x}{2}, \qquad \tilde{y} = y$$

Integrations. Applying Eqs. 6–6 and integrating with respect to y, we obtain

$$\tilde{x} = \frac{\int_A \tilde{x}\,dA}{\int_A dA} = \frac{\int_0^1 [(1 + x)/2](1 - x)\,dy}{\int_0^1 (1 - x)\,dy} = \frac{\frac{1}{2}\int_0^1 (1 - y)\,dy}{\int_0^1 (1 - \sqrt{y})\,dy} = \frac{0.250}{0.333} = 0.75\text{ m} \qquad \textit{Ans.}$$

$$\bar{y} = \frac{\int_A \tilde{y}\,dA}{\int_A dA} = \frac{\int_0^1 y(1 - x)\,dy}{\int_0^1 (1 - x)\,dy} = \frac{\int_0^1 (y - y^{3/2})\,dy}{\int_0^1 (1 - \sqrt{y})\,dy} = \frac{0.100}{0.333} = 0.3\text{ m} \qquad \textit{Ans.}$$

EXAMPLE 6.3

Locate the $\bar{y}$ centroid for the paraboloid of revolution, which is generated by revolving the shaded area shown in Fig. 6–11*a* about the *y* axis.

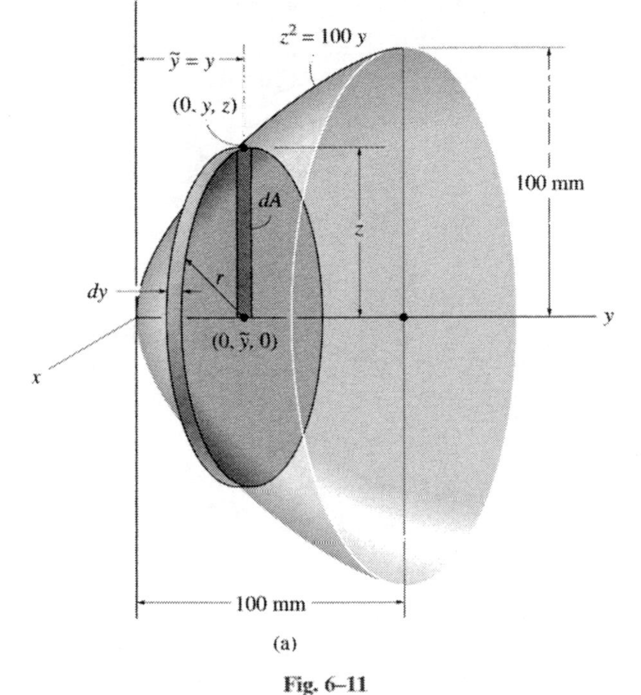

(a)

Fig. 6–11

Solution

Differential Element. An element having the shape of a *thin disk* is chosen, Fig. 6–11*a*. This element has a thickness *dy*. In this "disk" method of analysis, the element of planar area, *dA*, is always taken *perpendicular* to the axis of revolution. Here the element intersects the generating curve at the *arbitrary point* (0, *y*, *z*), and so its radius is $r = z$.

Area and Moment Arm. The volume of the element is $dV = (\pi z^2)\,dy$, and its centroid is located at $\tilde{y} = y$.

Integration Applying the second of Eqs. 6–5 and integrating with respect to *y* yields

$$\bar{y} = \frac{\int_V \tilde{y}\,dV}{\int_V dV} = \frac{\int_0^{100} y(\pi z^2)\,dy}{\int_0^{100} (\pi z^2)\,dy} = \frac{100\pi \int_0^{100} y^2\,dy}{100\pi \int_0^{100} y\,dy} = 66.7 \text{ mm} \quad \textit{Ans.}$$

EXAMPLE 6.4

Determine the location of the center of mass of the cylinder shown in Fig. 6–12 if its density varies directly with its distance from the base, i.e., $\rho = 200z \text{ kg/m}^3$.

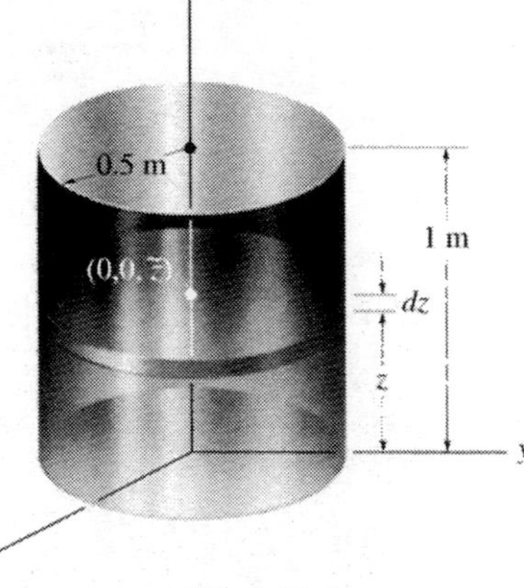

Fig. 6–12

Solution

For reasons of material symmetry,

$$\bar{x} = \bar{y} = 0 \qquad \textit{Ans.}$$

Differential Element. A disk element of radius 0.5 m and thickness dz is chosen for integration, Fig. 6–12, since the *density of the entire element is constant* for a given value of z. The element is located along the z axis at the *arbitrary point* $(0, 0, z)$.

Volume and Moment Arm. The volume of the element is $dV = \pi(0.5)^2\,dz$, and its centroid is located at $\tilde{z} = z$.

Integrations. Using an equation similar to the third of Eqs. 6–4 and integrating with respect to z, noting that $\rho = 200z$, we have

$$\bar{z} = \frac{\displaystyle\int_v \tilde{z}\rho\,dV}{\displaystyle\int_v \rho\,dV} = \frac{\displaystyle\int_0^1 z(200z)\pi(0.5)^2\,dz}{\displaystyle\int_0^1 (200z)\pi(0.5)^2\,dz}$$

$$= \frac{\displaystyle\int_0^1 z^2\,dz}{\displaystyle\int_0^1 z\,dz} = 0.667 \text{ m} \qquad \textit{Ans.}$$

PROBLEMS

6-1. Locate the centroid $(\overline{x}, \overline{y})$ of the shaded area.

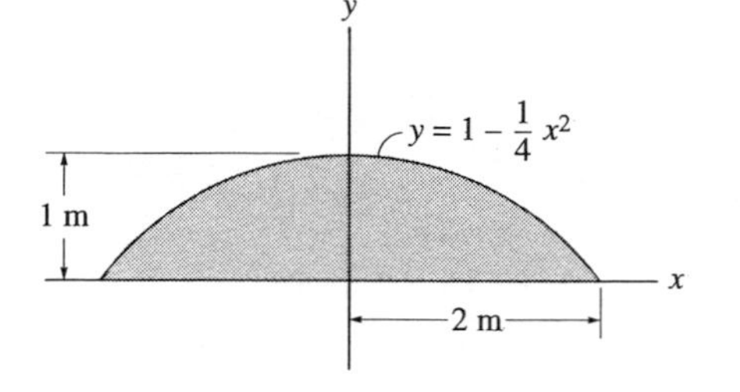

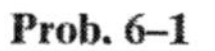

6-2. The plate has a thickness of 2.5 cm and a specific weight of $\gamma = 80\ \text{kN/m}^3$. Determine the location of its center of gravity. Also, find the tension in each of the cords used to support it.

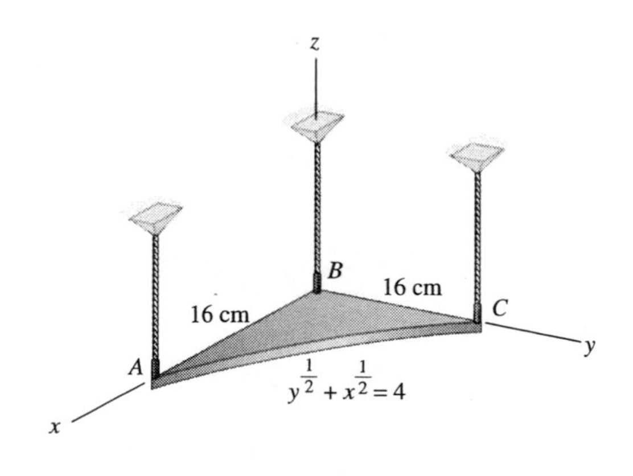

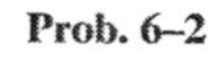

6-3. Locate the centroid $\overline{y}$ of the shaded area.

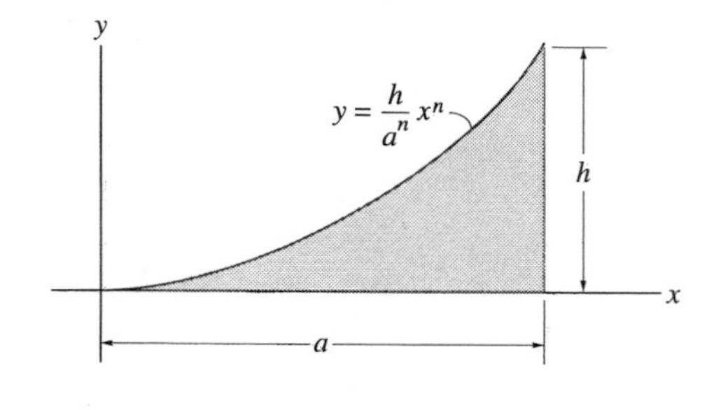

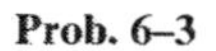

***6-4.** Locate the centroid of the shaded area bounded by the parabola and the line $y = a$.

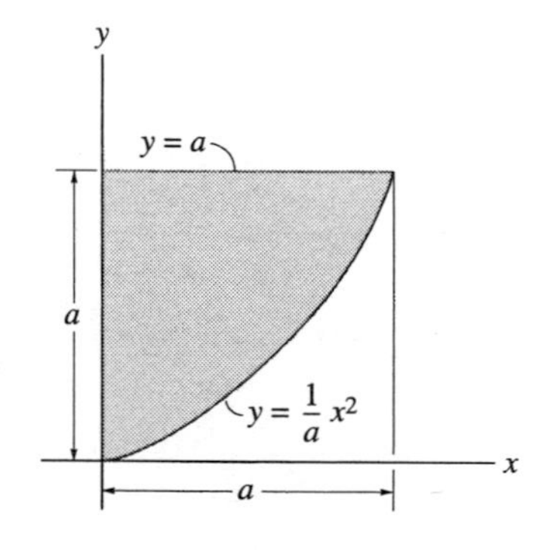

Prob. 6–4

6-5. Locate the centroid of the quarter elliptical area.

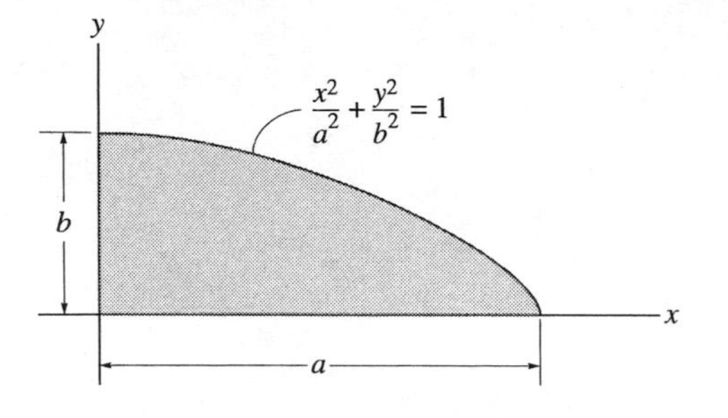

Prob. 6–5

6-6. Locate the centroid ($\bar{x}$, $\bar{y}$) of the shaded area.

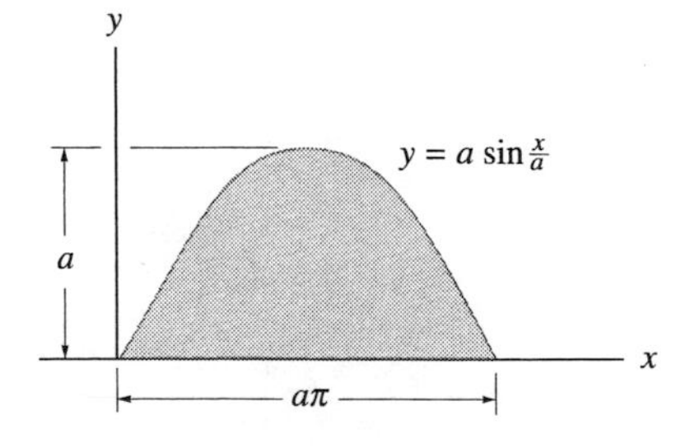

Prob. 6–6

6-7. Locate the centroid of the shaded area.

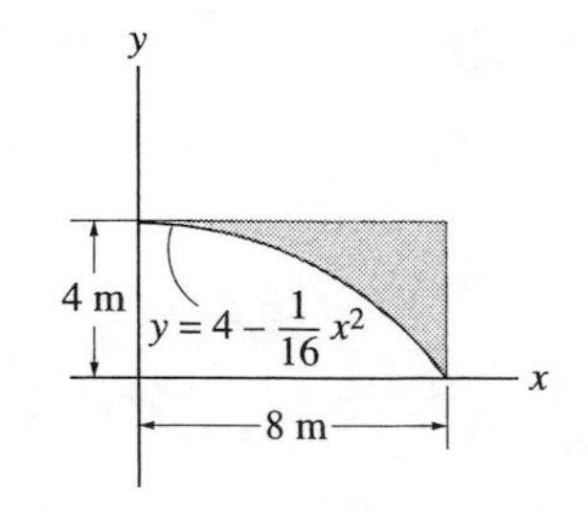

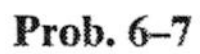

Prob. 6–7

*■ **6-8.** Locate the centroid $\bar{x}$ of the shaded area. Solve the problem by evaluating the integrals using Simpson's rule.

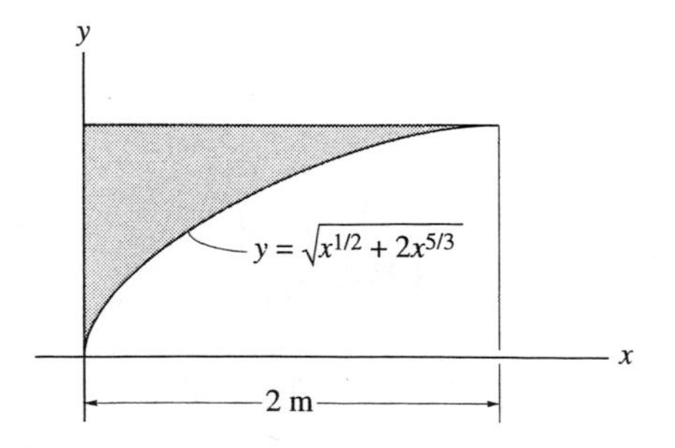

Prob. 6–8

6-9. Locate the center of gravity of the volume. The material is homogeneous.

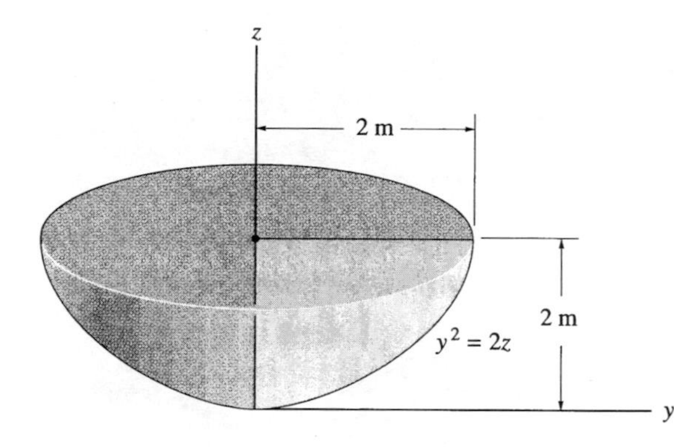

Prob. 6–9

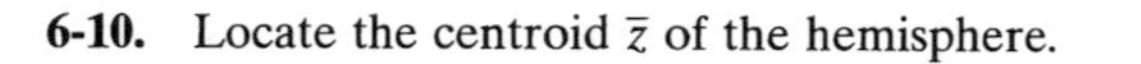

6-10. Locate the centroid $\bar{z}$ of the hemisphere.

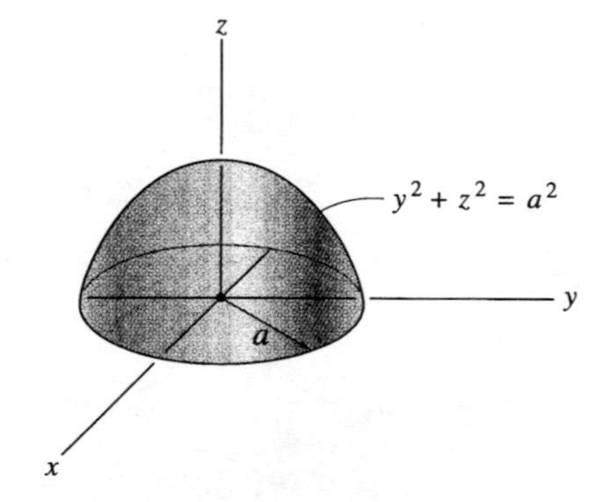

Prob. 6–10

6-11. Locate the centroid of the solid.

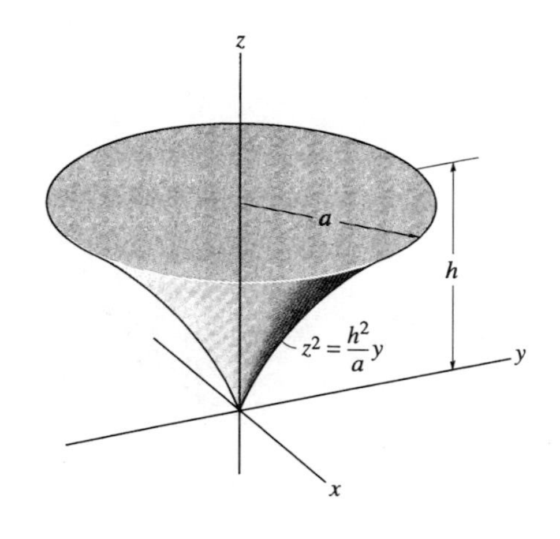

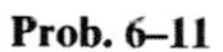

Prob. 6–11

***6-12.** Locate the centroid of the quarter-cone.

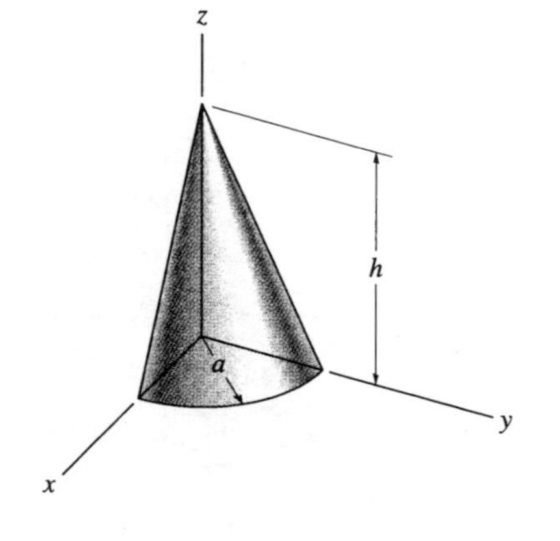

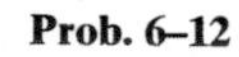

Prob. 6–12

6-13. Locate the center of mass $\bar{x}$ of the hemisphere. The density of the material varies linearly from zero at the origin O to ρ_0 at the surface. *Suggestion:* Choose a hemispherical shell element for integration.

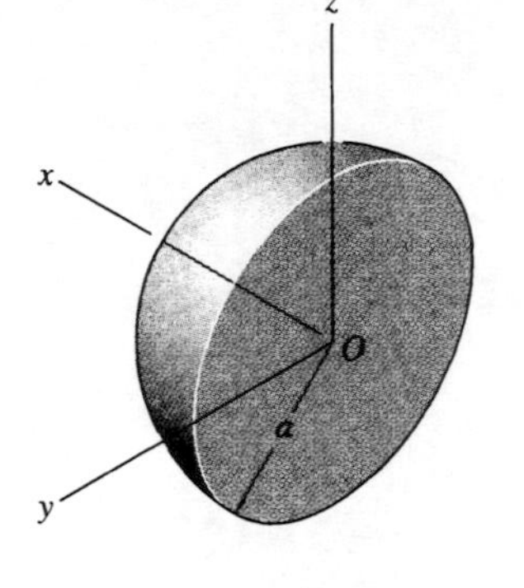

Prob. 6–13

6-14. Locate the centroid $\bar{z}$ of the right-elliptical cone.

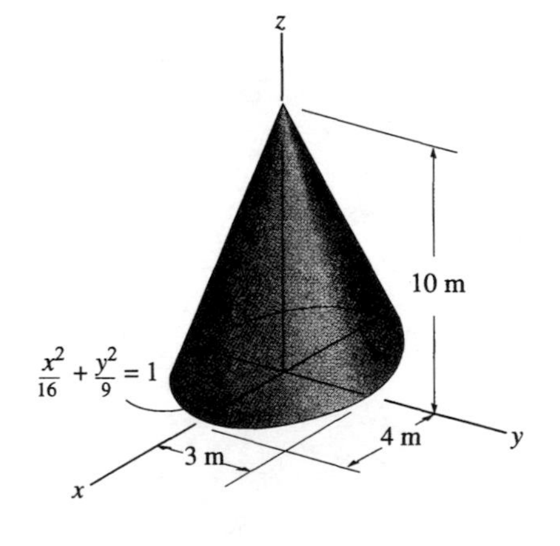

Prob. 6–14

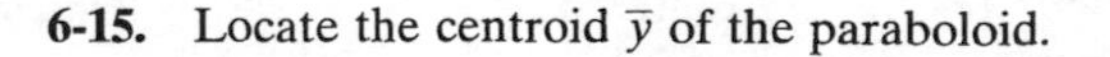

6-15. Locate the centroid $\bar{y}$ of the paraboloid.

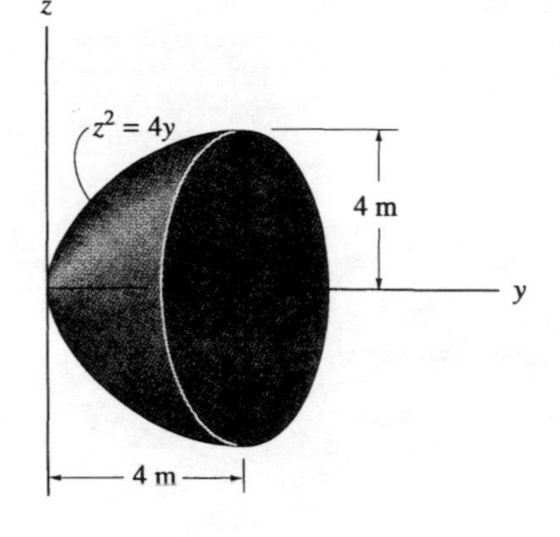

Prob. 6–15

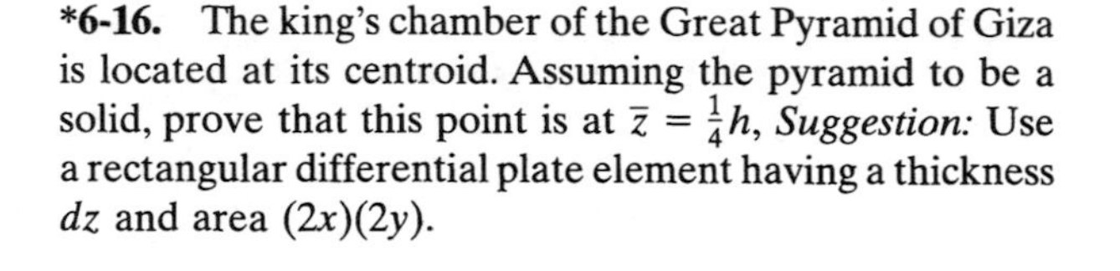

***6-16.** The king's chamber of the Great Pyramid of Giza is located at its centroid. Assuming the pyramid to be a solid, prove that this point is at $\bar{z} = \frac{1}{4}h$, *Suggestion:* Use a rectangular differential plate element having a thickness dz and area $(2x)(2y)$.

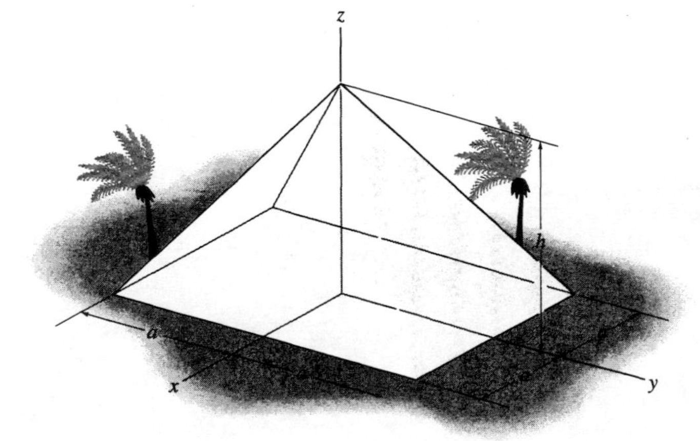

Prob. 6–16

6.3 Composite Bodies

A *composite body* consists of a series of connected "simpler" shaped bodies, which may be rectangular, triangular, semicircular, etc. Such a body can often be sectioned or divided into its composite parts and, provided the *weight* and location of the center of gravity of each of these parts are known, we can eliminate the need for integration to determine the center of gravity for the entire body. The method for doing this requires treating each composite part like a particle and following the procedure outlined in Sec. 6.1. Formulas analogous to Eqs. 6–1 result since we must account for a finite number of weights. Rewriting these formulas, we have

$$\bar{x} = \frac{\Sigma \tilde{x} W}{\Sigma W} \qquad \bar{y} = \frac{\Sigma \tilde{y} W}{\Sigma W} \qquad \bar{z} = \frac{\Sigma \tilde{z} W}{\Sigma W} \tag{6–8}$$

Here

$\bar{x}, \bar{y}, \bar{z}$ represent the coordinates of the center of gravity G of the composite body.

$\tilde{x}, \tilde{y}, \tilde{z}$ represent the coordinates of the center of gravity of each composite part of the body.

ΣW is the sum of the weights of all the composite parts of the body, or simply the total weight of the body.

In order to determine the force required to tip over this concrete barrier it is first necessary to determine the location of its center of gravity.

When the body has a *constant density or specific weight*, the center of gravity *coincides* with the centroid of the body. The centroid for composite lines, areas, and volumes can be found using relations analogous to Eqs. 6–8; however, the W's are replaced by L's, A's, and V's, respectively. Centroids for common shapes of lines, areas, shells, and volumes that often make up a composite body are given in the table in Appendix C.

PROCEDURE FOR ANALYSIS

The location of the center of gravity of a body or the centroid of a composite geometrical object represented by a line, area, or volume can be determined using the following procedure.

Composite Parts.

- Using a sketch, divide the body or object into a finite number of composite parts that have simpler shapes.
- If a composite part has a *hole*, or a geometric region having no material, then consider the composite part without the hole and consider the hole as an *additional* composite part having *negative* weight or size.

Moment Arms.

- Establish the coordinate axes on the sketch and determine the coordinates $\tilde{x}, \tilde{y}, \tilde{z}$ of the center of gravity or centroid of each part.

Summations.

- Determine $\bar{x}, \bar{y}, \bar{z}$ by applying the center of gravity equations, Eqs. 6–8, or the analogous centroid equations.
- If an object is *symmetrical* about an axis, the centroid of the object lies on this axis.

If desired, the calculations can be arranged in tabular form, as indicated in the following two examples.

EXAMPLE 6.5

Locate the centroid of the plate area shown in Fig. 6–13*a*.

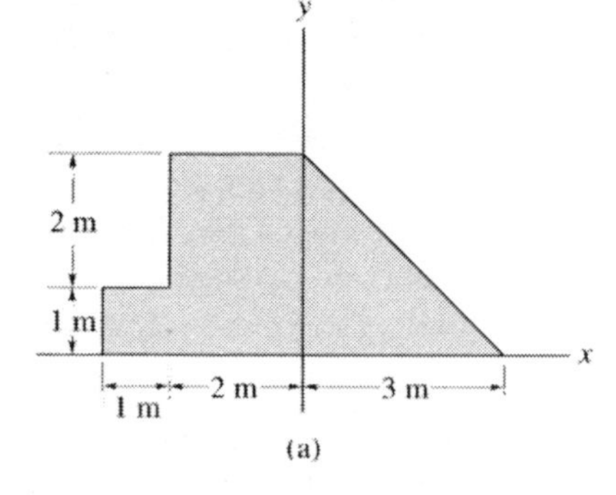

Fig. 6–13

Solution

Composite Parts. The plate is divided into three segments as shown in Fig. 6–13*b*. Here the area of the small rectangle ③ is considered "negative" since it must be subtracted from the larger one ②.

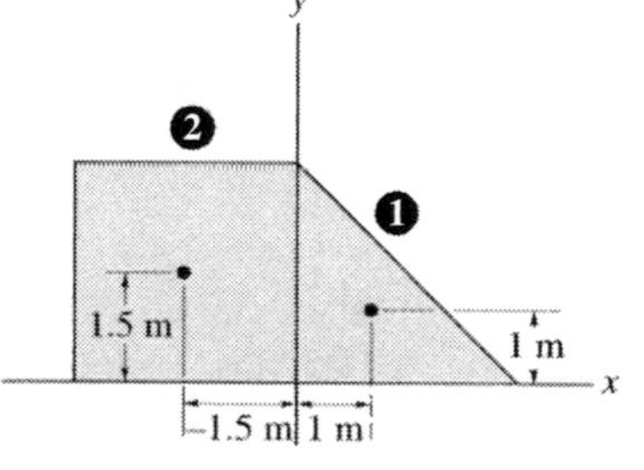

Moment Arms. The centroid of each segment is located as indicated in the figure. Note that the $\tilde{x}$ coordinates of ② and ③ are *negative*.

Summations. Taking the data from Fig. 6–13*b*, the calculations are tabulated as follows:

Segment	A (m²)	$\tilde{x}$ (m)	$\tilde{y}$ (m)	$\tilde{x}A$ (m³)	$\tilde{y}A$ (m³)
1	$\frac{1}{2}(3)(3) = 4.5$	1	1	4.5	4.5
2	$(3)(3) = 9$	−1.5	1.5	−13.5	13.5
3	$-(2)(1) = -2$	−2.5	2	5	−4
	$\Sigma A = 11.5$			$\Sigma \tilde{x}A = -4$	$\Sigma \tilde{y}A = 14$

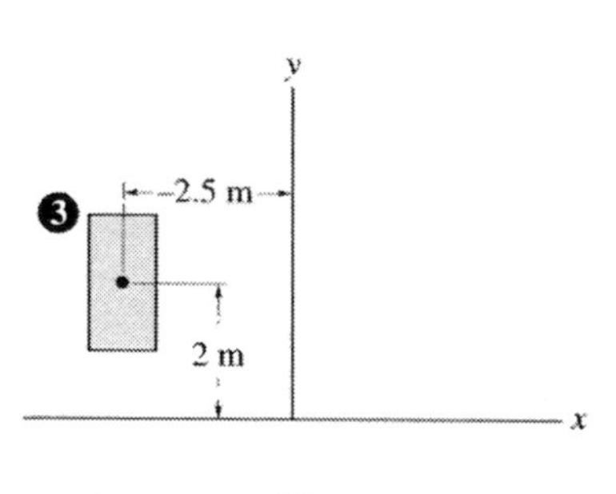

Thus,

$$\bar{x} = \frac{\Sigma \tilde{x}A}{\Sigma A} = \frac{-4}{11.5} = -0.348 \text{ m} \qquad \textit{Ans.}$$

$$\bar{y} = \frac{\Sigma \tilde{y}A}{\Sigma A} = \frac{14}{11.5} = 1.22 \text{ m} \qquad \textit{Ans.}$$

EXAMPLE 6.6

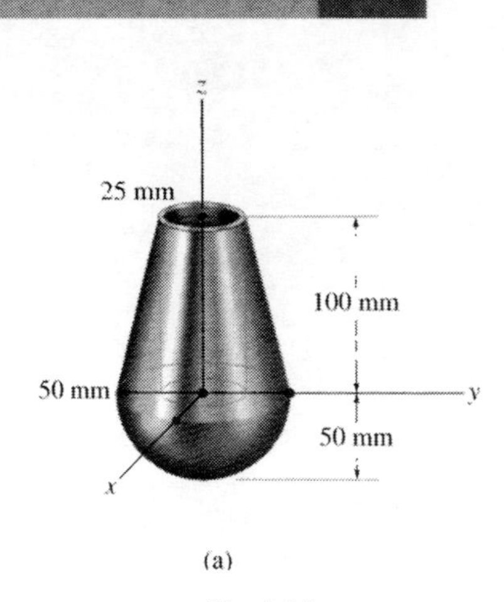

(a)

Fig. 6–14

Locate the center of mass of the composite assembly shown in Fig. 6–14*a*. The conical frustum has a density of $\rho_c = 8\ \text{Mg/m}^3$, and the hemisphere has a density of $\rho_h = 4\ \text{Mg/m}^3$. There is a 25-mm radius cylindrical hole in the center.

Solution

Composite Parts. The assembly can be thought of as consisting of four segments as shown in Fig. 6–14*b*. For the calculations, ③ and ④ must be considered as "negative" volumes in order that the four segments, when added together, yield the total composite shape shown in Fig. 6–14*a*.

Moment Arm. Using the table on the inside back cover, the computations for the centroid $\tilde{z}$ of each piece are shown in the figure.

Summations. Because of *symmetry*, note that

$$\bar{x} = \bar{y} = 0 \qquad \textit{Ans.}$$

Since $W = mg$ and g is constant, the third of Eqs. 6–8 becomes $\bar{z} = \Sigma\tilde{z}m/\Sigma m$. The mass of each piece can be computed from $m = \rho V$ and used for the calculations. Also, $1\ \text{Mg/m}^3 = 10^{-6}\ \text{kg/mm}^3$, so that

Segment	m (kg)	$\tilde{z}$ (mm)	$\tilde{z}m$ (kg · mm)
1	$8(10^{-6})(\frac{1}{3})\pi(50)^2(200) = 4.189$	50	209.440
2	$4(10^{-6})(\frac{2}{3})\pi(50)^3 = 1.047$	−18.75	−19.635
3	$-8(10^{-6})(\frac{1}{3})\pi(25)^2(100) = -0.524$	100 + 25 = 125	−65.450
4	$-8(10^{-6})\pi(25)^2(100) = -1.571$	50	−78.540
	$\Sigma m = 3.141$		$\Sigma\tilde{z}m = 45.815$

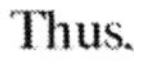

Thus,

$$\bar{z} = \frac{\Sigma\tilde{z}m}{\Sigma m} = \frac{45.815}{3.141} = 14.6\ \text{mm} \qquad \textit{Ans.}$$

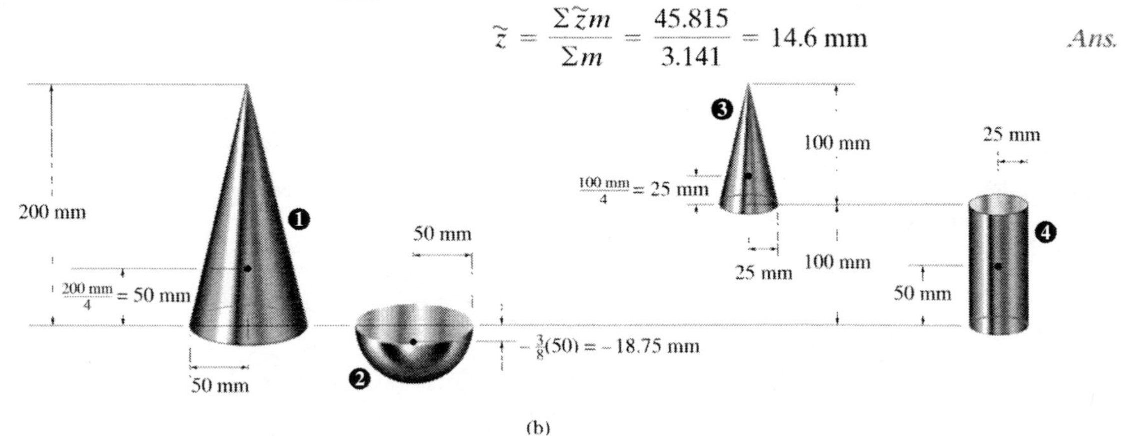

(b)

PROBLEMS

6-17. Determine the location $\bar{y}$ of the centroidal axis $\bar{x}\,\bar{x}$ of the beam's cross-sectional area. Neglect the size of the corner welds at A and B for the calculation.

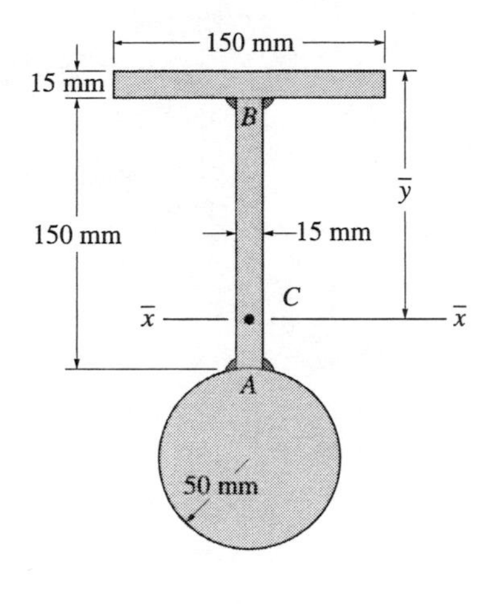

Prob. 6–17

6-18. Locate the centroid $\bar{y}$ of the cross-sectional area of the beam.

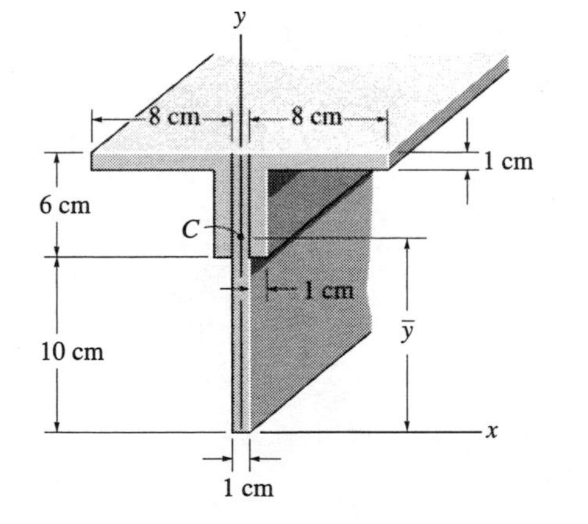

Prob. 6–18

6-19. Determine the location $\bar{x}$ of the centroid C of the shaded area which is part of a circle having a radius r.

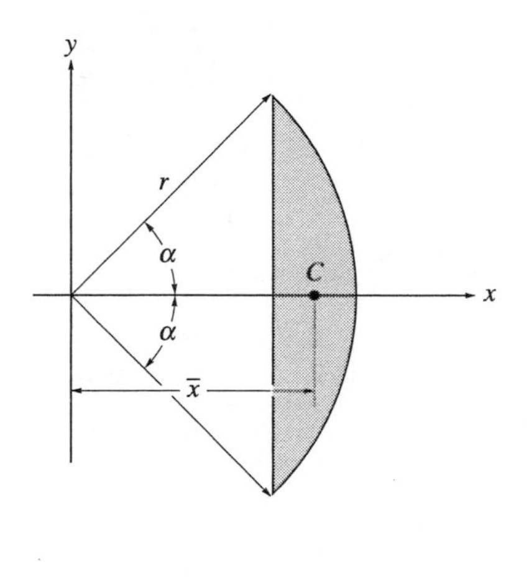

Prob. 6–19

6-20. Locate the centroid $\bar{y}$ of the channel's cross-sectional area.

Prob. 6–20

***6-21.** Locate the centroid $\bar{y}$ of the cross-sectional area of the beam constructed from a channel and a plate. Assume all corners are square and neglect the size of the weld at A.

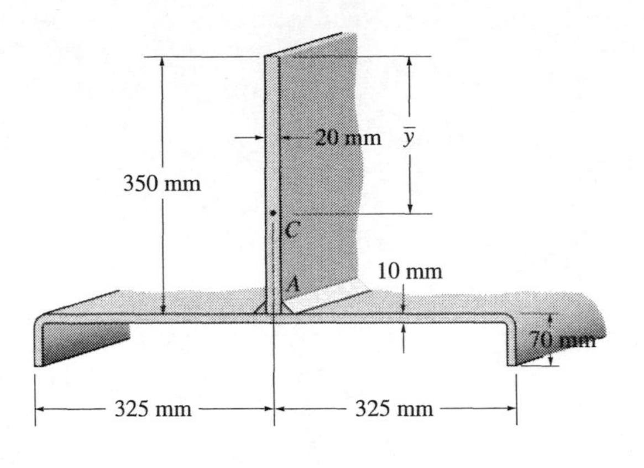

Prob. 6–21

6-22. Locate the centroid $(\bar{x}, \bar{y})$ of the member's cross-sectional area.

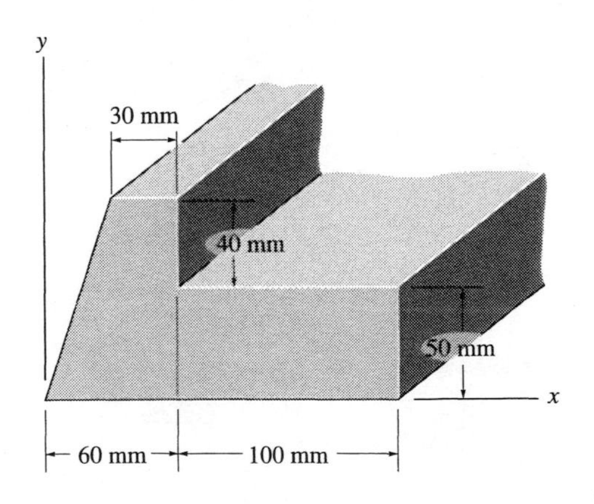

Prob. 6–22

6-23. Locate the centroid $\bar{y}$ of the concrete beam having the tapered cross section shown.

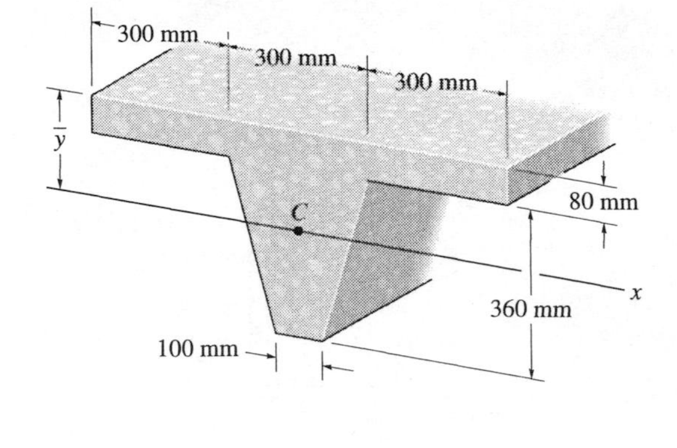

Prob. 6–23

6-24. Locate the centroid $\bar{y}$ of the beam's cross-section built up from a channel and a wide-flange beam.

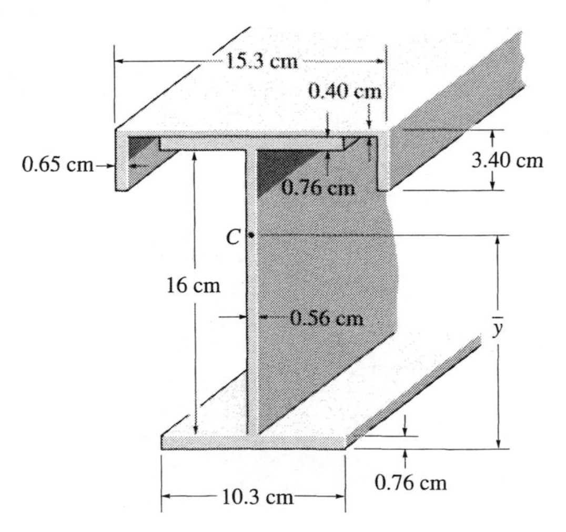

Prob. 6–24

***6-25.** Locate the centroid $\overline{y}$ of the bulb-tee cross section.

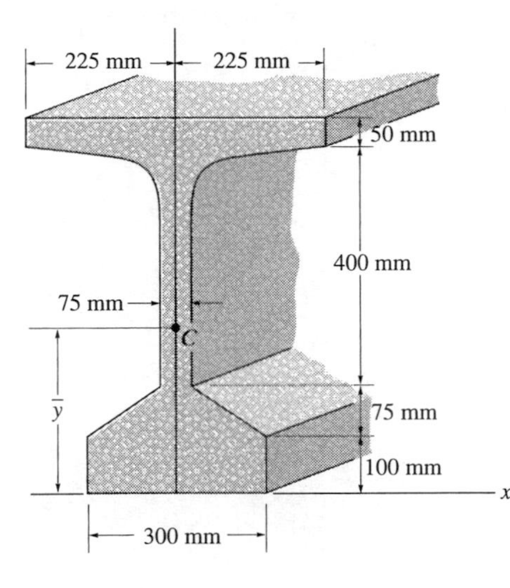

Prob. 6–25

6-26. Determine the distance h to which a 100-mm-diameter hole must be bored into the base of the cone so that the center of mass of the resulting shape is located at $\overline{z} = 115$ mm. The material has a density of 8 Mg/m^3.

6-27. Determine the distance $\overline{z}$ to the centroid of the shape which consists of a cone with a hole of height $h = 50$ mm bored into its base.

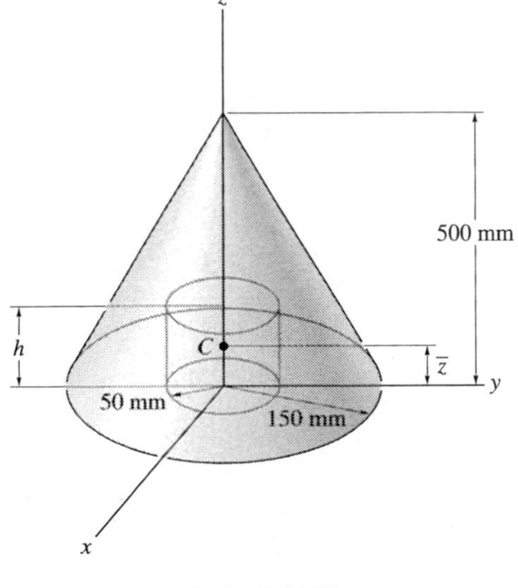

Probs. 6–26/27

6-28. The sheet metal part has the dimensions shown. Determine the location $(\overline{x}, \overline{y}, \overline{z})$ of its centroid.

***6-29.** The sheet metal part has a weight per unit area of 0.01 N/cm^2 and is supported by the smooth rod and at C. If the cord is cut, the part will rotate about the y axis until it reaches equilibrium. Determine the equilibrium angle of tilt, measured downward from the negative x axis, that AD makes with the $-x$ axis.

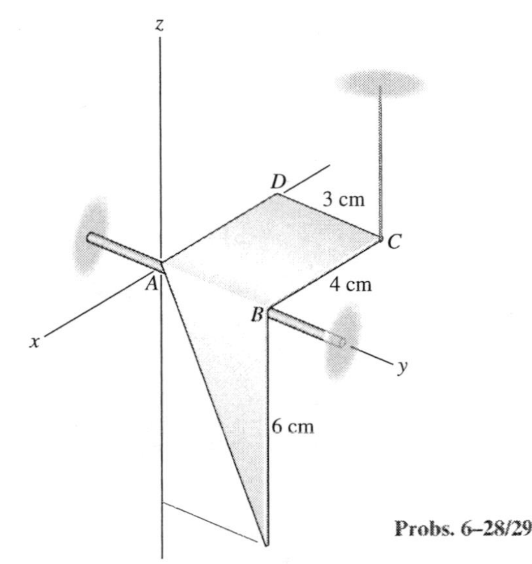

Probs. 6–28/29

6-30. Determine the location $(\overline{x}, \overline{y})$ of the centroid C of the cross-sectional area for the structural member constructed from two equal-sized channels welded together as shown. Assume all corners are square. Neglect the size of the welds.

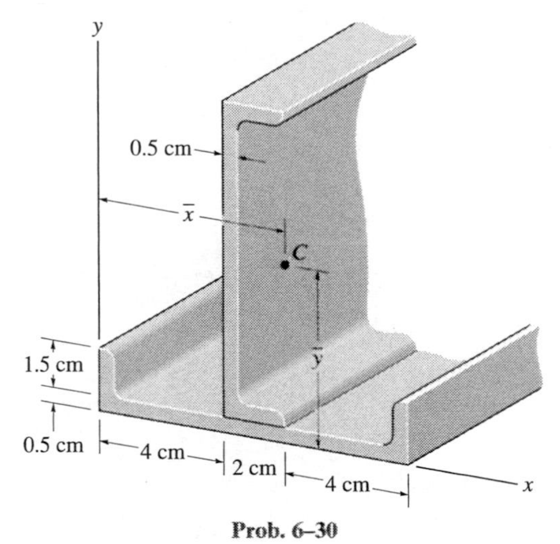

Prob. 6–30

6-31. Locate the centroid $\bar{z}$ of the top made from a hemisphere and a cone.

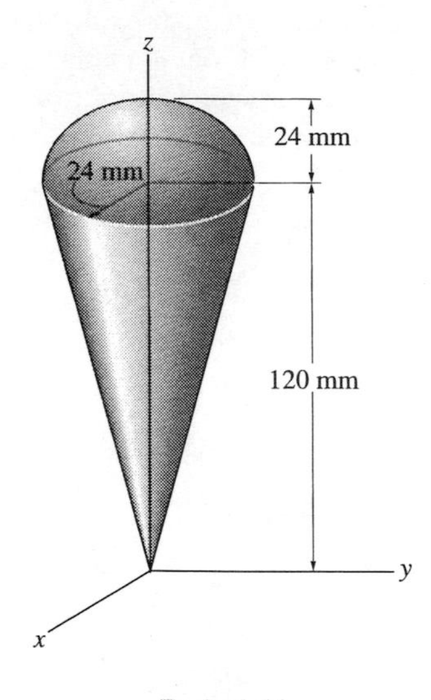

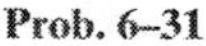
Prob. 6–31

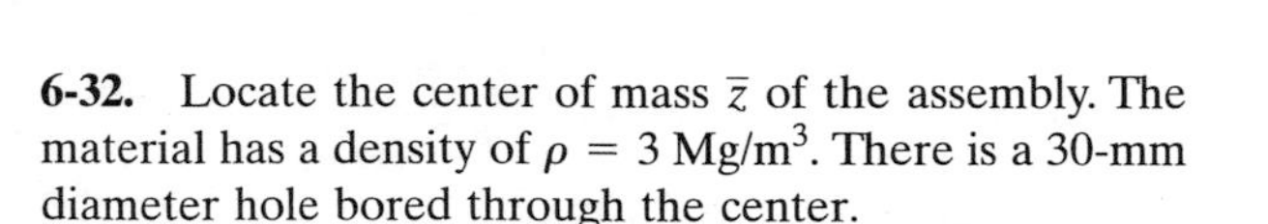
6-32. Locate the center of mass $\bar{z}$ of the assembly. The material has a density of $\rho = 3\ \mathrm{Mg/m^3}$. There is a 30-mm diameter hole bored through the center.

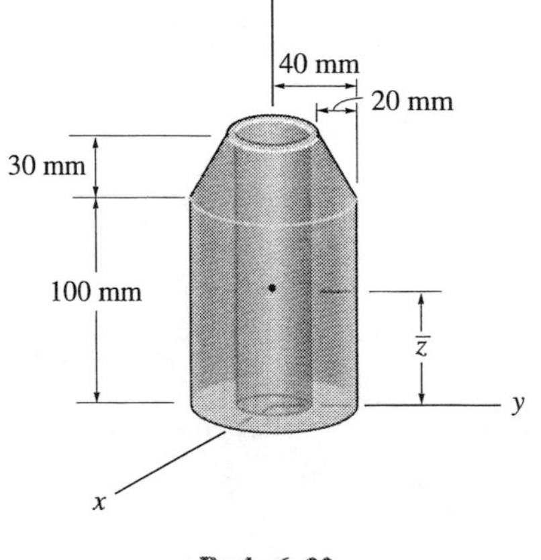

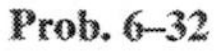
Prob. 6–32

***6-33.** Locate the center of gravity of the two-block assembly. The specific weights of the materials A and B are $\gamma_A = 24\ \mathrm{kN/m^3}$ and $\gamma_B = 64\ \mathrm{kN/m^3}$, respectively.

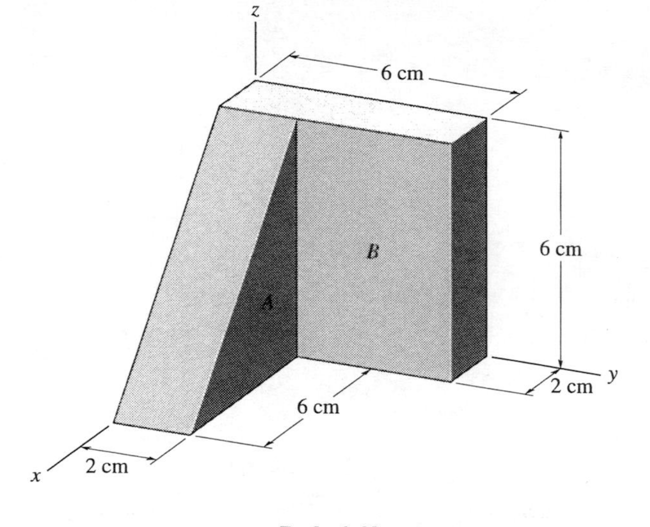

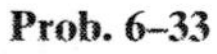
Prob. 6–33

6-34. The buoy is made from two homogeneous cones each having a radius of 1.5 m. If $h = 1.2$ m, find the distance $\bar{z}$ to the buoy's center of gravity G.

6-35. The buoy is made from two homogeneous cones each having a radius of 1.5 m. If it is required that the buoy's center of gravity G be located at $\bar{z} = 0.5$ m, determine the height h of the top cone.

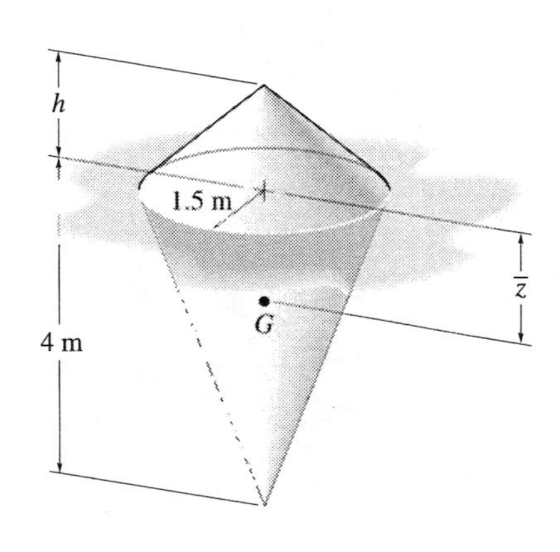

Probs. 6–34/35

6.4 Resultant of a Distributed Force System

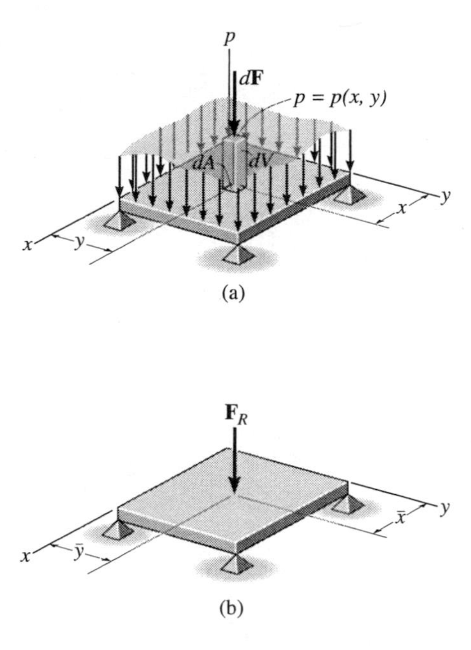

Fig. 6–15

In Chapter 4 we considered ways of simplifying a system of concentrated forces which act on a body. In many practical situations, however, the body may be subjected to loadings distributed over its surface. We have already encountered this situation in Sec. 4.7, while studying frictional and normal forces acting on the bottom of a block resting on a flat surface. Other examples of distributed loadings result from wind and hydrostatic pressure. The effects of these loadings can be studied in a simple manner if we replace them by their resultants. Here we will use the methods of Sec. 3.8 and show how to compute the resultant force of a distributed loading and specify its line of action. As a specific application, in Sec. 6.5 we will find the resultant loading acting on the surface of a body that is submerged in a fluid.

Pressure Distribution over a Surface. Consider the flat plate shown in Fig. 6–15*a*, which is subjected to the loading function $p = p(x, y)$ Pa, where Pa (pascal) = 1 N/m^2. Knowing this function, we can determine the force dF acting on the differential area dA m^2 of the plate, located at the arbitrary point (x, y). This force magnitude is simply $dF = [p(x, y)\text{ N/m}^2](dA\text{ m}^2) = [p(x, y)\,dA]$ N. The entire loading on the plate is therefore represented as a system of *parallel forces* infinite in number and each acting on a separate differential area dA. This system will now be simplified to a single resultant force $\mathbf{F}_R$ acting through a unique point $(\bar{x}, \bar{y})$ on the plate, Fig. 6–15*b*.

Magnitude of Resultant Force. To determine the *magnitude* of $\mathbf{F}_R$, it is necessary to sum each of the differential forces $d\mathbf{F}$ acting over the plate's *entire surface area A*. This sum may be expressed mathematically as an integral:

$$F_R = \Sigma F; \qquad F_R = \int_A p(x, y)\,dA = \int_V dV \tag{6–9}$$

Here $p(x, y)\,dA = dV$, the colored differential *volume element* shown in Fig. 6–15*a*. Therefore, the result indicates that the *magnitude of the resultant force is equal to the total volume under the distributed-loading diagram.*

Location of Resultant Force. The location $(\bar{x}, \bar{y})$ of $\mathbf{F}_R$ is determined by setting the moments of $\mathbf{F}_R$ equal to the moments of all the forces $d\mathbf{F}$ about the respective y and x axes: From Figs. 6–15*a* and 6–15*b*, using Eq. 6–9, this results in

$$\bar{x} = \frac{\int_A x p(x, y)\,dA}{\int_A p(x, y)\,dA} = \frac{\int_V x\,dV}{\int_V dV} \qquad \bar{y} = \frac{\int_A y p(x, y)\,dA}{\int_A p(x, y)\,dA} = \frac{\int_V y\,dV}{\int_V dV} \tag{6–10}$$

Hence, it can be seen that the *line of action of the resultant force passes through the geometric center or centroid of the volume under the distributed loading diagram.*

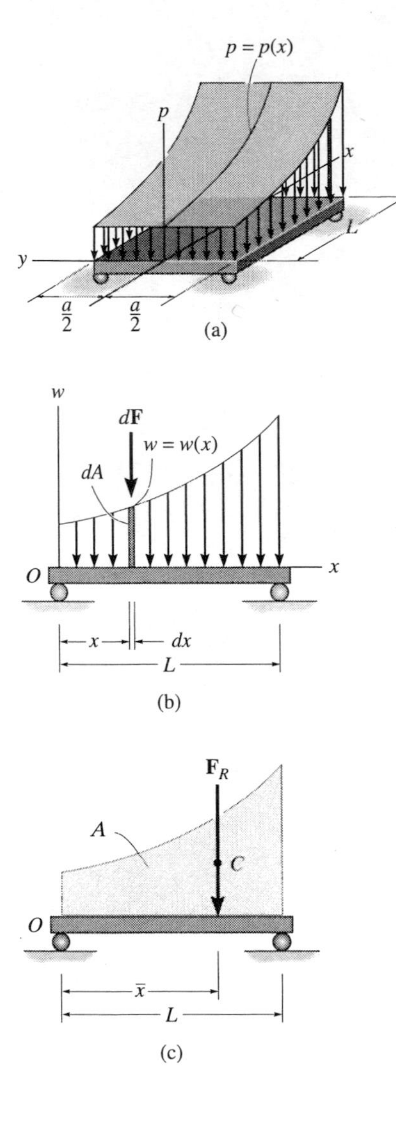

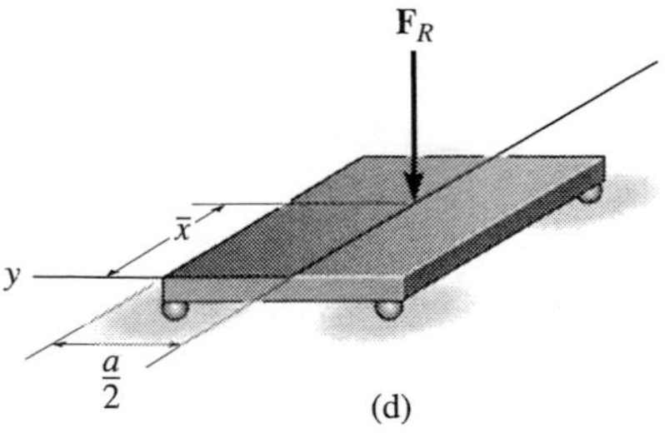

Fig. 6–16

Linear Distribution of Load Along a Straight Line. In many situations a very large surface area of a body may be subjected to *distributed loadings* such as those caused by wind, fluids, or simply the weight of material supported over the body's surface. The *intensity* of these loadings at each point on the surface is defined as the *pressure p* (force per unit area), which can be measured in unit of pascals (Pa), where 1 Pa = 1 N/m^2.

We will consider the most common case of a distributed pressure loading, which is *uniform* along one axis of a flat rectangular body upon which the loading is applied. An example of such a loading is shown in Fig. 6–16*a*. The direction of the intensity of the pressure load is indicated by arrows shown on the *load-intensity diagram*. The entire loading on the plate is therefore a system of parallel forces, infinite in number and each acting on a separate differential area of the plate. Here the *loading function*, $p = p(x)$ Pa, is only a function of x since the pressure is uniform along the y axis. If we multiply $p = p(x)$ by the *width a* m of the plate, we obtain $\mathbf{w} = [p(x)\ \text{N/m}^2]a\ \text{m} = \mathbf{w}(x)$ N/m. This loading function, shown in Fig. 6–16*b*, is a measure of load distribution along the line $y = 0$ which is in the plane of symmetry of the loading, Fig. 6–16*a*. As noted, it is measured as a force per unit length, rather than a force per unit area. Consequently, the load-intensity diagram for $\mathbf{w} = \mathbf{w}(x)$ can be represented by a system of *coplanar* parallel forces, shown in two dimensions in Fig. 6–16*b*. Using the methods of Sec. 3.9, this system of forces can be simplified to a single resultant force $\mathbf{F}_R$ and its location $\bar{x}$ can be specified, Fig. 6–16*c*.

Magnitude of Resultant Force. From Eq. 3–17 ($F_R = \Sigma F$), the magnitude of $\mathbf{F}_R$ is equivalent to the sum of all the forces in the system. In this case integration must be used since there is an infinite number of parallel forces $d\mathbf{F}$ acting along the plate, Fig. 6–16*b*. Since $d\mathbf{F}$ is acting on an element of length dx and $\mathbf{w}(x)$ is a force per unit length, then at the location x, $dF = \mathbf{w}(x)\,dx = dA$. In other words, the magnitude of $d\mathbf{F}$ is determined from the colored differential *area dA* under the loading curve. For the entire plate length,

$$+\downarrow F_R = \Sigma F; \qquad F_R = \int_L \mathbf{w}(x)\,dx = \int_A dA = A \qquad (6\text{–}11)$$

Hence, the magnitude of the resultant force is equal to the total area A under the loading diagram $\mathbf{w} = \mathbf{w}(x)$, *Fig. 6–16c.*

Location of Resultant Force. Applying Eq. 3–17 ($M_{R_O} = \Sigma M_O$), the location $\overline{x}$ of the line of action of $\mathbf{F}_R$ can be determined by equating the moments of the force resultant and the force distribution about point O (the y axis). Since $d\mathbf{F}$ produces a moment of $x\,dF = x\,\mathbf{w}(x)\,dx$ about O, Fig. 6–16*b*, then for the entire plate, Fig. 6–16*c*,

$$\curvearrowleft + M_{R_O} = \Sigma M_O; \qquad \overline{x}F_R = \int_L x\,\mathbf{w}(x)\,dx$$

Solving for $\overline{x}$, using Eq. 6–11, we can write

$$\overline{x} = \frac{\displaystyle\int_L x\,\mathbf{w}(x)\,dx}{\displaystyle\int_L \mathbf{w}(x)\,dx} = \frac{\displaystyle\int_A x\,dA}{\displaystyle\int_A dA} \tag{6–12}$$

Setting $dA = \mathbf{w}(x)\,dx$, we can also write

$$\overline{x} = \frac{\displaystyle\int_A x\,dA}{\displaystyle\int_A dA} \tag{6–13}$$

This equation represents the x coordinate for the geometric center or *centroid* of the *area* under the distributed-loading diagram $w(x)$. *Therefore, the resultant force has a line of action which passes through the centroid C (geometric center) of the area defined by the distributed-loading diagram* $w(x)$, Fig. 6–16*c*.

Once $\overline{x}$ is determined, F_R by symmetry passes through point $(\overline{x}, 0)$ on the surface of the plate, Fig. 6–16*d*. If we now consider the three-dimensional pressure loading $p(x)$, Fig. 6–16*a*, we can therefore conclude that *the resultant force has a magnitude equal to the volume under the distributed-loading curve* $p = p(x)$ *and a line of action which passes through the centroid (geometric center) of this volume.* In many cases, however, the distributed-loading diagram is in the shape of a rectangle, triangle, or some other simple geometric form. The centroids for such common shapes do not have to be determined from Eq. 6–12; rather, they can be obtained directly from the table in Appendix C.

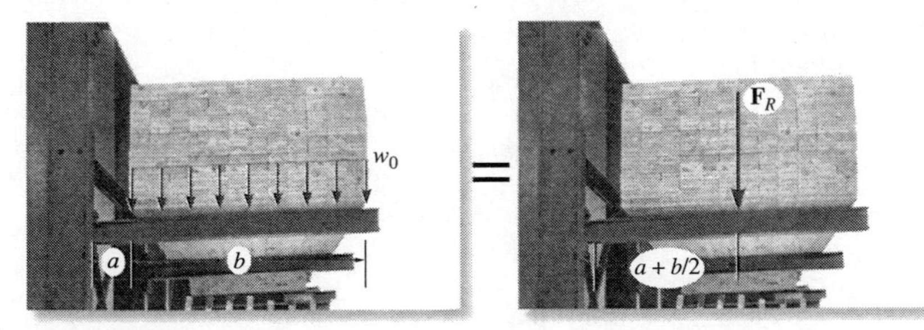

The beam supporting this stack of lumber is subjected to a *uniform* distributed loading, and so the load-intensity diagram has a rectangular shape. If the load intensity is $\mathbf{w}_0$, then the resultant force is determined from the area of the rectangle, $F_R = \mathbf{w}_0 b$. The line of action of this force passes through the centroid or center of this area, $\overline{x} = a + b/2$. This resultant is equivalent to the distributed load, and so both loadings produce the same "external" effects or support reactions on the beam.

EXAMPLE 6.7

In each case, determine the magnitude and location of the resultant of the distributed load acting on the beams in Fig. 6–17.

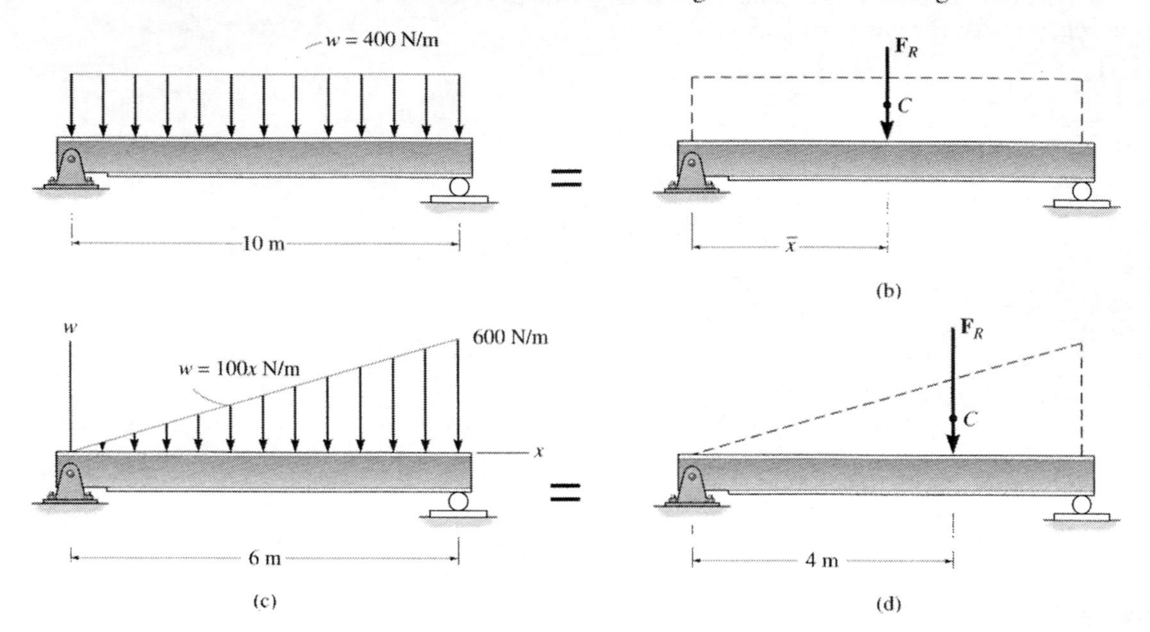

Fig. 6–17

Solution

Uniform Loading. As indicated $w = 400$ N/m, which is constant over the entire beam, Fig. 6–17*a*. This loading forms a rectangle, the area of which is equal to the resultant force, Fig. 6–17*b*; i.e.,

$$F_R = (400\text{ N/m})(10\text{ m}) = 4000\text{ N} \qquad \textit{Ans.}$$

The location of $\mathbf{F}_R$ passes through the geometric center or centroid C of this rectangular area, so

$$\bar{x} = 5\text{ m} \qquad \textit{Ans.}$$

Triangular Loading. Here the loading varies uniformly in intensity from 0 to 600 N/m, Fig. 6–17*c*. These values can be verified by substitution of $x = 0$ and $x = 6$ m into the loading function $\mathbf{w} = 100x$ N/m. The area of this triangular loading is equal to $\mathbf{F}_R$, Fig. 6–17*d*. From Appendix C, $A = \frac{1}{2}bh$, so that

$$F_R = \tfrac{1}{2}(6\text{ m})(600\text{ N/m}) = 1800\text{ N} \qquad \textit{Ans.}$$

The line of action of $\mathbf{F}_R$ passes through the centroid C of the triangle. Using Appendix B, this point lies at a distance of one third the length of the beam, measured from the right side. Hence,

$$\bar{x} = 6\text{ m} - \tfrac{1}{3}(6\text{ m}) = 4\text{ m} \qquad \textit{Ans.}$$

EXAMPLE 6.8

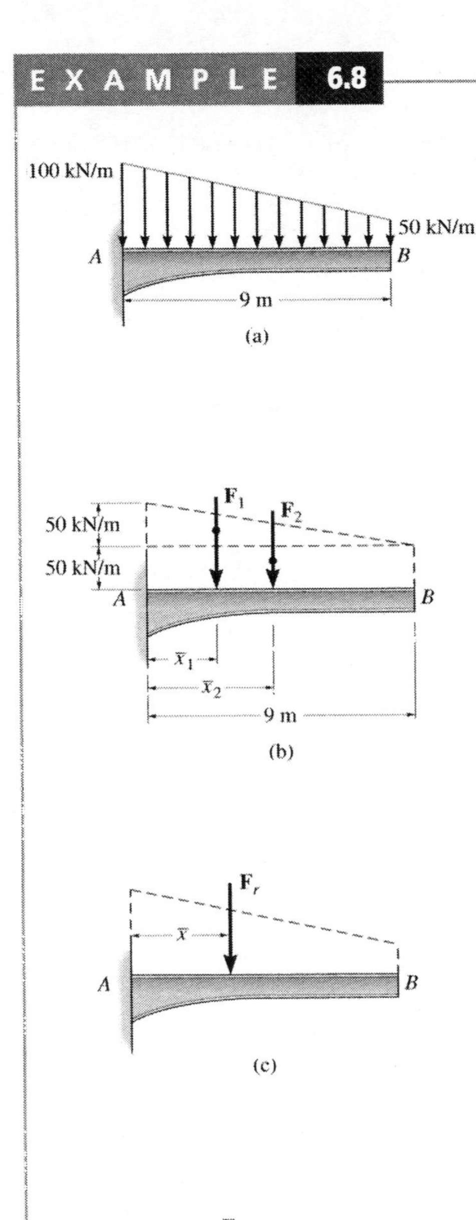

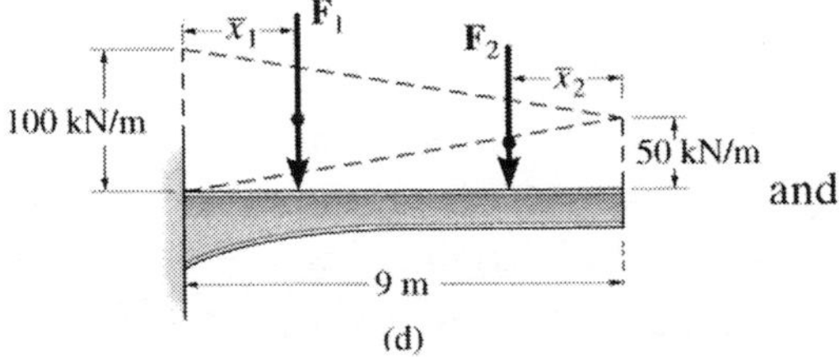

Fig. 6–18

The granular material exerts the distributed loading on the beam as shown in Fig. 6–18*a*. Determine the magnitude and location of the equivalent resultant of this load.

Solution

The area of the loading diagram is a *trapezoid*, and therefore the solution can be obtained directly from the area and centroid formulas for a trapezoid listed in Appendix C. Since these formulas are not easily remembered, instead we will solve this problem by using "composite" areas. In this regard, we can divide the trapezoidal loading into a rectangular and triangular loading as shown in Fig. 6–18*b*. The magnitude of the force represented by each of these loadings is equal to its associated *area*.

$$F_1 = \tfrac{1}{2}(9\text{ m})(50\text{ kN/m}) = 225\text{ kN}$$

$$F_2 = \tfrac{1}{2}(9\text{ m})(50\text{ kN/m}) = 450\text{ kN}$$

The lines of action of these parallel forces act through the *centroid* of their associated areas and therefore intersect the beam at

$$\bar{x}_1 = \tfrac{1}{3}(9\text{ m}) = 3\text{ m}$$

$$\bar{x}_2 = \tfrac{1}{2}(9\text{ m}) = 4.5\text{ m}$$

The two parallel forces $\mathbf{F}_1$ and $\mathbf{F}_2$ can be reduced to a single resultant $\mathbf{F}_R$. The magnitude of $\mathbf{F}_R$ is

$$+\downarrow F_R = \Sigma F; \qquad F_R = 225 + 450 = 675\text{ kN} \qquad \textit{Ans.}$$

With reference to point A, Fig. 6–18*b* and 6–18*c*, we can find the location of $\mathbf{F}_R$. We require

$$\curvearrowleft + M_{R_A} = \Sigma M_A; \qquad \bar{x}(675) = 3(225) + 4.5(450)$$

$$\bar{x} = 4\text{ m} \qquad \textit{Ans.}$$

Note: The trapezoidal area in Fig. 6–18*a* can also be divided into two triangular areas as shown in Fig. 6–18*d*. In this case

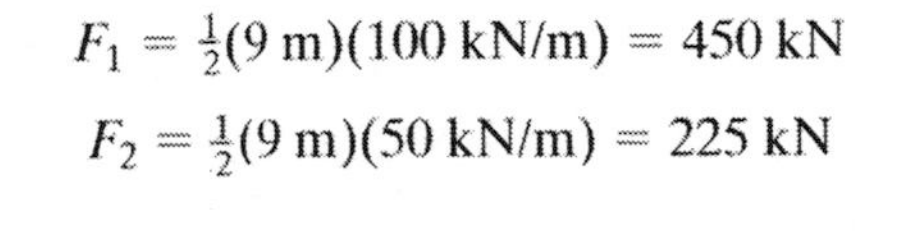

$$F_1 = \tfrac{1}{2}(9\text{ m})(100\text{ kN/m}) = 450\text{ kN}$$

$$F_2 = \tfrac{1}{2}(9\text{ m})(50\text{ kN/m}) = 225\text{ kN}$$

and

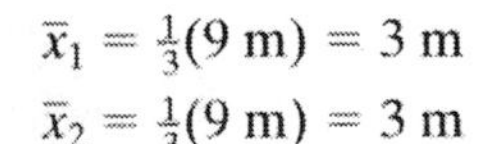

$$\bar{x}_1 = \tfrac{1}{3}(9\text{ m}) = 3\text{ m}$$

$$\bar{x}_2 = \tfrac{1}{3}(9\text{ m}) = 3\text{ m}$$

Using these results, show that again $F_R = 675$ kN and $\bar{x} = 4$ m.

EXAMPLE 6.9

Determine the magnitude and location of the equivalent resultant force acting on the shaft in Fig. 6–19*a*.

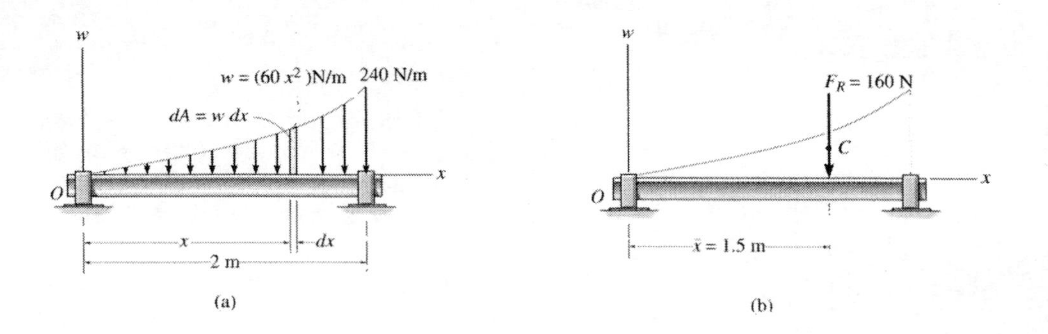

Fig. 6–19

Solution

Since $\mathbf{w} = \mathbf{w}(x)$ is given, this problem will be solved by integration. The colored differential area element $dA = \mathbf{w}\,dx = 60x^2\,dx$. Applying Eq. 6–11, by summing these elements from $x = 0$ to $x = 2$ m, we obtain the resultant force $\mathbf{F}_R$.

$F_R = \Sigma F;$

$$F_R = \int_A dA = \int_0^2 60x^2\,dx = 60\left[\frac{x^3}{3}\right]_0^2 = 60\left[\frac{2^3}{3} - \frac{0^3}{3}\right]$$
$$= 160 \text{ N} \qquad \textit{Ans.}$$

Since the element of area dA is located an arbitrary distance x from O, the location $\bar{x}$ of $\mathbf{F}_R$ *measured from O*, Fig. 6–19*b*, is determined from Eq. 6–12.

$$\bar{x} = \frac{\int_A x\,dA}{\int_A dA} = \frac{\int_0^2 x(60x^2)dx}{160} = \frac{60\left[\frac{x^4}{4}\right]_0^2}{160} = \frac{60\left[\frac{2^4}{4} - \frac{0^4}{4}\right]}{160}$$
$$= 1.5 \text{ m} \qquad \textit{Ans.}$$

These results may be checked by using Appendix C, where it is shown that for an exparabolic area of length a, height b, and shape shown in Fig. 6–19*a*,

$$A = \frac{ab}{3} = \frac{2\text{ m}(240\text{ N/m})}{3} = 160\text{ N and } \bar{x} = \frac{3}{4}a = \frac{3}{4}(2\text{ m}) = 1.5\text{ m}$$

EXAMPLE 6.10

A distributed loading of $p = 800x$ Pa acts over the top surface of the beam shown in Fig. 6–20*a*. Determine the magnitude and location of the equivalent resultant force.

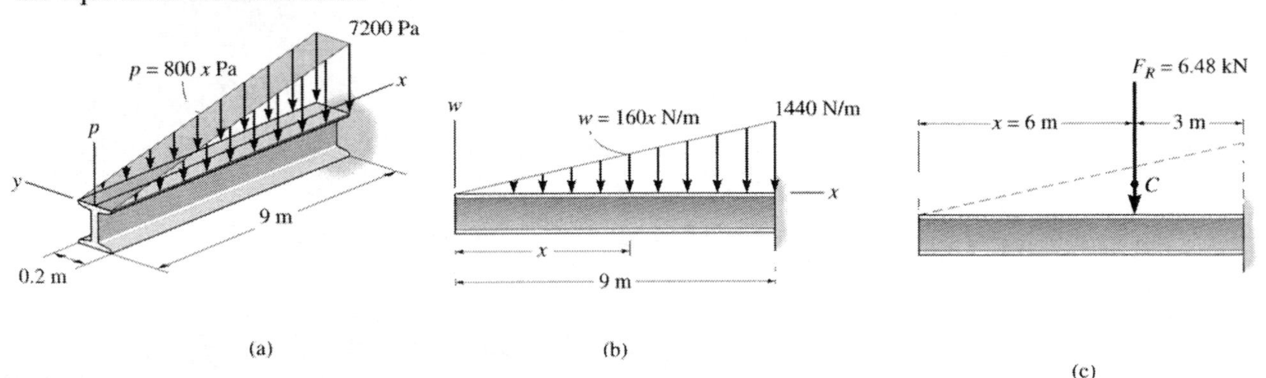

Fig. 6–20

Solution

The loading function $p = 800x$ Pa indicates that the load intensity varies uniformly from $p = 0$ at $x = 0$ to $p = 7200$ Pa at $x = 9$ m. Since the intensity is uniform along the width of the beam (the y axis), the loading may be viewed in two dimensions as shown in Fig. 6–20*b*. Here

$$\mathbf{w} = (800x \text{ N/m}^2)(0.2 \text{ m})$$
$$= (160x) \text{ N/m}$$

At $x = 9$ m, note that $\mathbf{w} = 1440$ N/m. Although we may again apply Eqs. 6–11 and 6–12 as in Example 6–9, it is simpler to use Appendix C.

The magnitude of the resultant force is equivalent to the area under the triangle.

$$F_R = \tfrac{1}{2}(9 \text{ m})(1440 \text{ N/m}) = 6480 \text{ N} = 6.48 \text{ kN} \qquad \textit{Ans.}$$

The line of action of $\mathbf{F}_R$ passes through the *centroid* C of the triangle. Hence,

$$\bar{x} = 9 \text{ m} - \tfrac{1}{3}(9 \text{ m}) = 6 \text{ m} \qquad \textit{Ans.}$$

The results are shown in Fig. 6–20*c*.

We may also view the resultant $\mathbf{F}_R$ as *acting* through the *centroid* of the *volume* of the loading diagram $p = p(x)$ in Fig. 6–20*a*. Hence $\mathbf{F}_R$ intersects the x–y plane at the point (6 m, 0). Furthermore, the magnitude of $\mathbf{F}_R$ is equal to the volume under the loading diagram; i.e.,

$$F_R = V = \tfrac{1}{2}(7200 \text{ N/m}^2)(9 \text{ m})(0.2 \text{ m}) = 6.48 \text{ kN} \qquad \textit{Ans.}$$

PROBLEMS

***6-36.** Determine the resultant moment of both the 100-kN force and the triangular distributed load about point O.

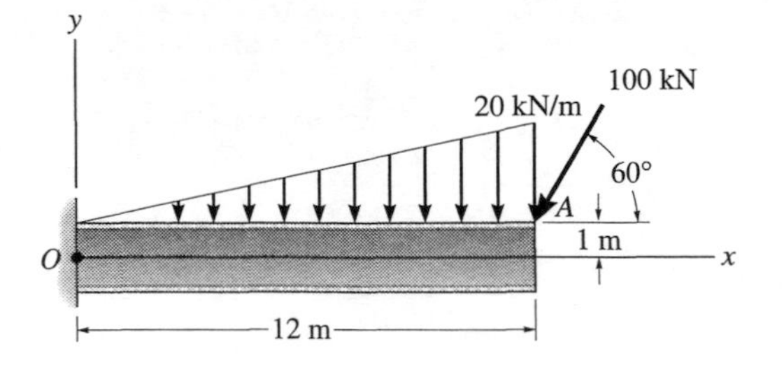

Prob. 6–36

6-37. Replace the loading by an equivalent resultant force and specify the location of the force on the beam, measured from point B.

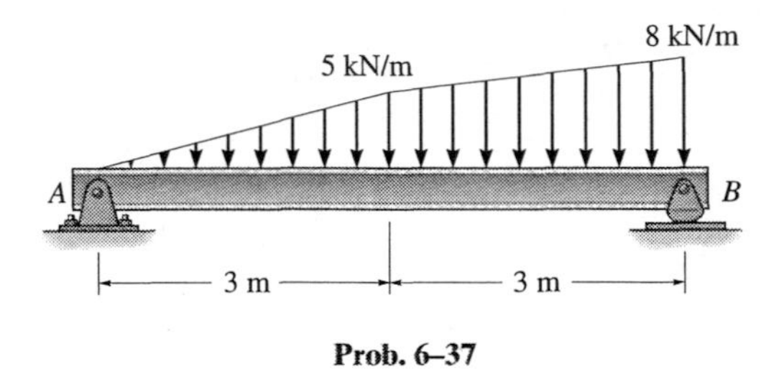

Prob. 6–37

6-38. Replace the distributed loading by an equivalent resultant force, and specify its location on the beam measured from the pin at C.

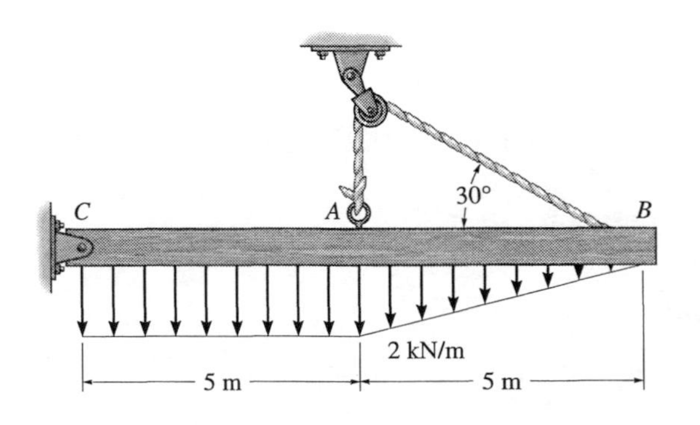

Prob. 6–38

6-39. Determine the magnitude of the equivalent resultant force of the distributed loading and specify its location on the beam, measured from point A.

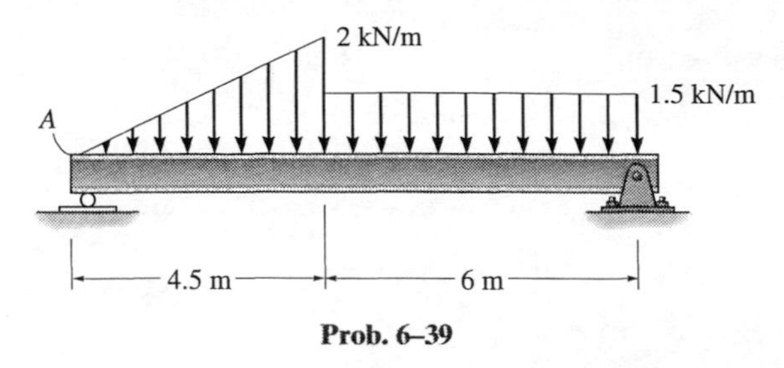

Prob. 6–39

***6-40.** The column is used to support the floor which exerts a force of 15 kN on the top of the column. The effect of soil pressure along the side of the column is distributed as shown. Replace this loading by an equivalent resultant force and specify where it acts along the column measured from its base A.

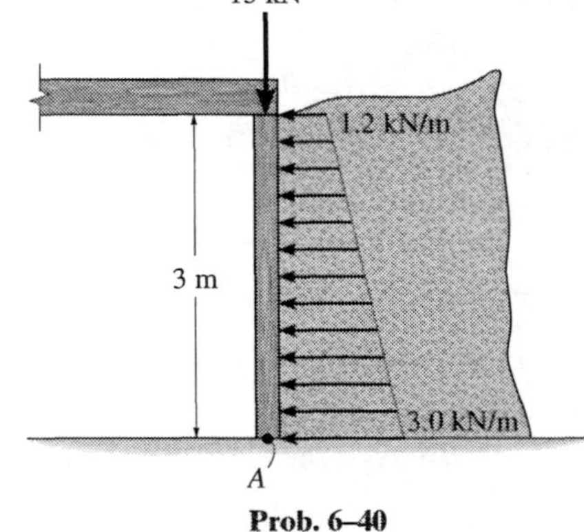

Prob. 6–40

6-41. The beam is subjected to the distributed loading. Determine the length b of the uniform load and its position a on the beam such that the resultant force and couple moment acting on the beam are zero.

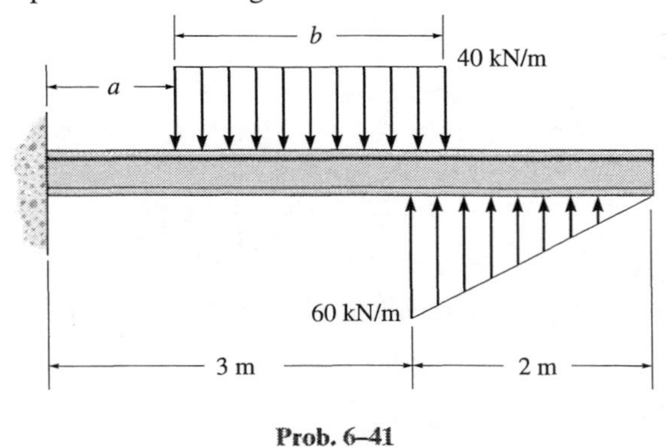

Prob. 6–41

6-42. Wet concrete exerts a pressure distribution along the wall of the form. Determine the resultant force of this distribution and specify the height h where the bracing strut should be placed so that it lies through the line of action of the resultant force. The wall has a width of 5 m.

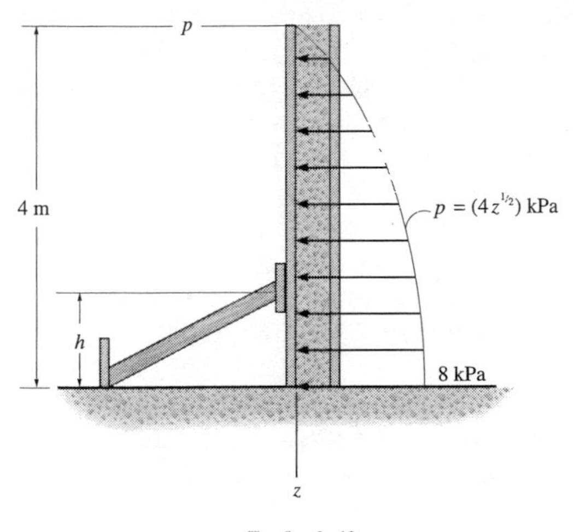

Prob. 6–42

6-43. Determine the magnitude of the resultant force of the loading acting on the beam and specify where it acts from point O.

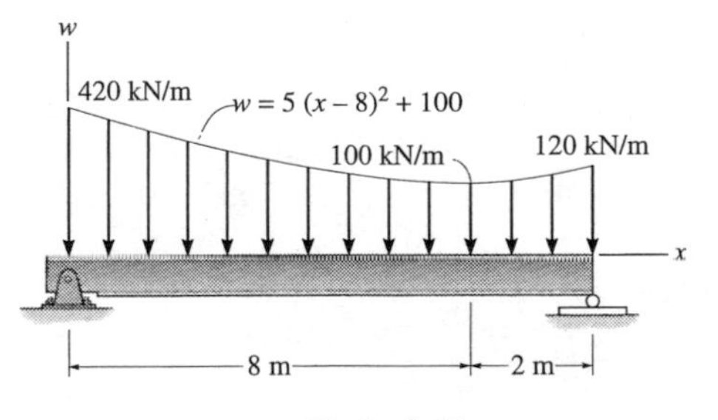

Prob. 6–43

***6-44.** The load over the plate varies linearly along the sides of the plate such that $p = \frac{2}{3}[x(4 - y)]$ kPa. Determine the resultant force and its position $(\bar{x}, \bar{y})$ on the plate.

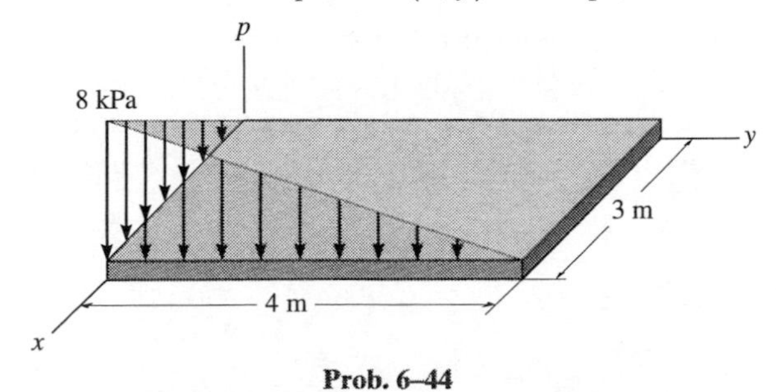

Prob. 6–44

6-45. Determine the magnitude and location of the resultant force of the parabolic loading acting on the plate.

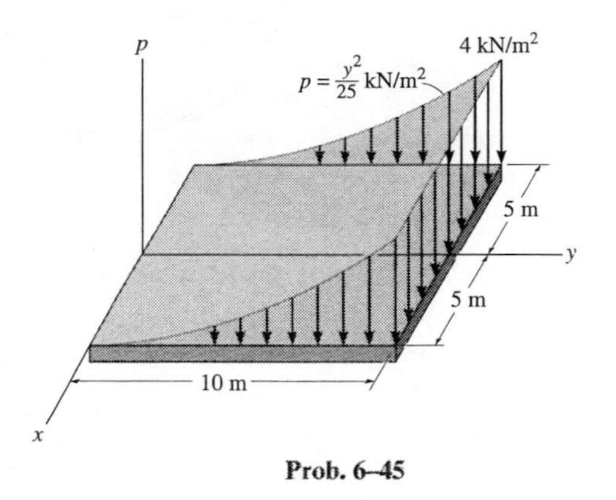

Prob. 6–45

6-46. The loading acting on a square plate is represented by a parabolic pressure distribution. Determine the magnitude of the resultant force and the coordinates $(\bar{x}, \bar{y})$ of the point where the line of action of the force intersects the plate. Also, what are the reactions at the rollers B and C and the ball-and-socket joint A? Neglect the weight of the plate.

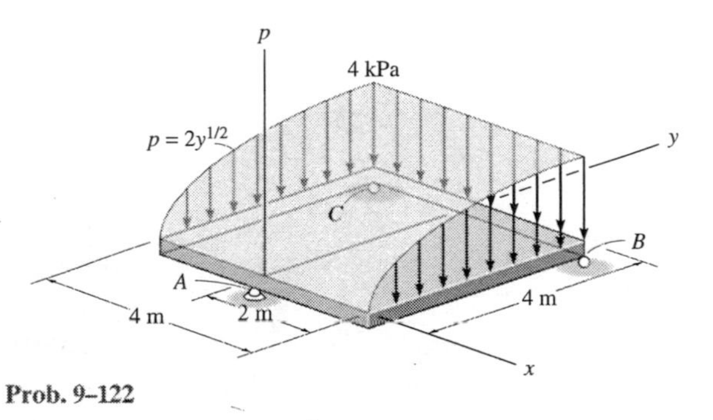

Prob. 9–122

6-47. The pressure loading on the plate is described by the function $p = [-240/(x + 1) + 340]$ Pa. Determine the magnitude of the resultant force and coordinates of the point where the line of action of the force intersects the plate.

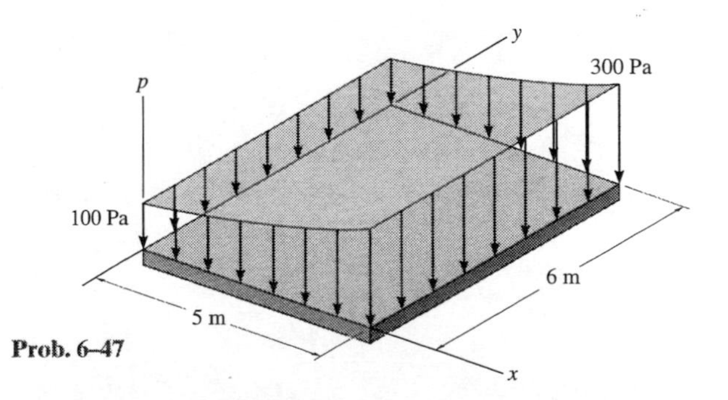

Prob. 6–47

6.5 Moments of Inertia for Areas

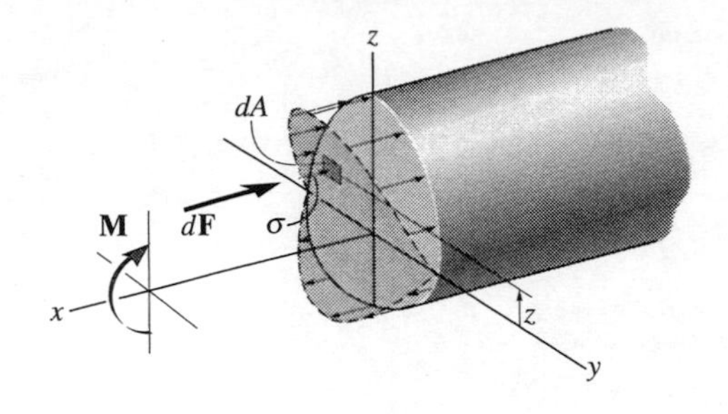

Fig. 6–21

In the first few sections of this chapter, we determined the centroid for an area by considering the first moment of the area about an axis; that is, for the computation we had to evaluate an integral of the form $\int x\,dA$. An integral of the second moment of an area, such as $\int x^2\,dA$, is referred to as the *moment of inertia* for the area. The terminology "moment of inertia" as used here is actually a misnomer; however, it has been adopted because of the similarity with integrals of the same form related to mass.

The moment of inertia of an area orginates whenever one relates the normal stress σ (sigma), or force per unit area, acting on the transverse cross section of an elastic beam, to the applied external moment **M**, which causes bending of the beam. From the theory of mechanics of materials, it can be shown that the stress within the beam varies linearly with its distance from an axis passing through the centroid C of the beam's cross-sectional area; i.e., $\sigma = kz$, Fig. 6–21. The magnitude of force acting on the area element dA, shown in the figure, is therefore $dF = \sigma\,dA = kz\,dA$. Since this force is located a distance z from the y axis, the moment of $d\mathbf{F}$ about the y axis is $dM = dF z = kz^2\,dA$. The resulting moment of the entire stress distribution is equal to the applied moment **M**; hence, $M = k\int z^2\,dA$. Here the integral represents the moment of inertia of the area about the y axis. Since integrals of this form often arise in formulas used in mechanics of materials, structural mechanics, fluid mechanics, and machine design, the engineer should become familiar with the methods used for their computation.

Moment of Inertia. Consider the area A, shown in Fig. 6–22, which lies in the x–y plane. By definition, the moments of inertia of the differential planar area dA about the x and y axes are $dI_x = y^2\,dA$ and $dI_y = x^2\,dA$, respectively. For the entire area the *moments of inertia* are determined by integration; i.e.,

$$I_x = \int_A y^2\,dA$$
$$I_y = \int_A x^2\,dA \qquad (6\text{–}14)$$

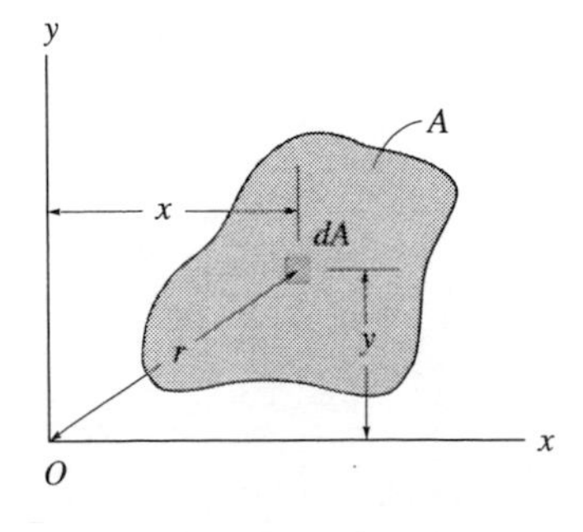

Fig. 6–22

We can also formulate the second moment of dA about the pole O or z axis, Fig. 6–22. This is referred to as the polar moment of inertia, $dJ_O = r^2\,dA$. Here r is the perpendicular distance from the pole (z axis) to the element dA. For the entire area the *polar moment of inertia* is

$$J_O = \int_A r^2\, dA = I_x + I_y \qquad (6\text{–}15)$$

The relationship between J_O and I_x, I_y is possible since $r^2 = x^2 + y^2$, Fig. 6-22.

From the above formulations it is seen that I_x, I_y, and J_O will *always* be *positive* since they involve the product of distance squared and area. Furthermore, the units for moment of inertia involve length raised to the fourth power, e.g., m^4, mm^4.

6.6 Parallel-Axis Theorem

If the moment of inertia for an area is known about an axis passing through its centroid, which is often the case, it is convenient to determine the moment of inertia of the area about a corresponding parallel axis using the *parallel-axis theorem*. To derive this theorem, consider finding the moment of inertia of the shaded area shown in Fig. 6–23 about the x axis. In this case, a differential element dA is located at an arbitrary distance y' from the *centroidal* x' axis, whereas the *fixed distance* between the parallel x and x' axes is defined as d_y. Since the moment of inertia of dA about the x axis is $dI_x = (y' + d_y)^2\, dA$, then for the entirc arca,

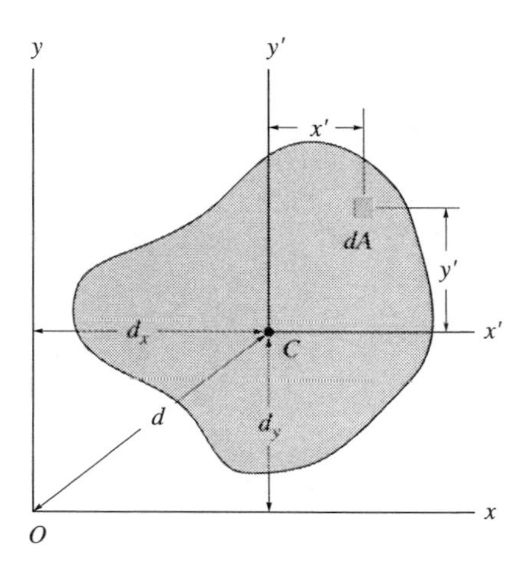

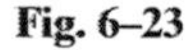

Fig. 6–23

$$I_x = \int_A (y' + d_y)^2\, dA$$

$$= \int_A y'^2\, dA + 2d_y \int_A y'\, dA + d_y^2 \int_A dA$$

The first integral represents the moment of inertia of the area about the centroidal axis, $\bar{I}_{x'}$. The second integral is zero since the x' axis passes through the area's centroid C; i.e., $\int y'\, dA = \bar{y} \int dA = 0$ since $\bar{y} = 0$. Realizing that the third integral represents the total area A, the final result is therefore

$$I_x = \bar{I}_{x'} + Ad_y^2 \qquad (6\text{–}16)$$

A similar expression can be written for I_y; i.e.,

$$I_y = \bar{I}_{y'} + Ad_x^2 \qquad (6\text{–}17)$$

And finally, for the polar moment of inertia about an axis perpendicular to the x–y plane and passing through the pole O (z axis), Fig. 6–23, we have

$$J_O = \bar{J}_C + Ad^2 \qquad (6\text{–}18)$$

The form of each of these three equations states that *the moment of inertia of an area about an axis is equal to the moment of inertia of the area about a parallel axis passing through the area's centroid plus the product of the area and the square of the perpendicular distance between the axes.*

6.7 Moments of Inertia for an Area by Integration

When the boundaries for a planar area are expressed by mathematical functions, Eqs. 6–14 may be integrated to determine the moments of inertia for the area. If the element of area chosen for integration has a differential size in two directions as shown in Fig. 6–22, a double integration must be performed to evaluate the moment of inertia. Most often, however, it is easier to perform only a single integration by choosing an element having a differential size or thickness in only one direction.

PROCEDURE FOR ANALYSIS

- If a single integration is performed to determine the moment of inertia of an area about an axis, it will be necessary to specify the differential element dA.
- Most often this element will be rectangular, such that it will have a finite length and differential width.
- The element should be located so that it intersects the boundary of the area at the *arbitrary point* (x, y). There are two possible ways to orient the element with respect to the axis about which the moment of inertia is to be determined.

Case 1

- The *length* of the element can be oriented *parallel* to the axis. This situation occurs when the rectangular element shown in Fig. 6–24 is used to determine I_y for the area. Direct application of Eq. 6–14, i.e., $I_y = \int x^2\,dA$, can be made in this case since the element has an infinitesimal thickness dx and therefore *all parts* of the element lie at the *same* moment-arm distance x from the y axis.*

Case 2

- The *length* of the element can be oriented *perpendicular* to the axis. Here Eq. 6–14 *does not apply* since all parts of the element will *not* lie at the same moment-arm distance from the axis. For example, if the rectangular element in Fig. 6–24 is used for determining I_x for the area, it will first be necessary to calculate the moment of inertia of the *element* about a horizontal axis passing through the element's centroid and then determine the moment of inertia of the *element* about the x axis by using the parallel-axis theorem. Integration of this result will yield I_x.

*In the case of the element $dA = dx\,dy$, Fig. 6–22, the moment arms y and x are appropriate for the formulation of I_x and I_y (Eq. 6–14) since the *entire* element, because of its infinitesimal size, lies at the specified y and x perpendicular distances from the x and y axes.

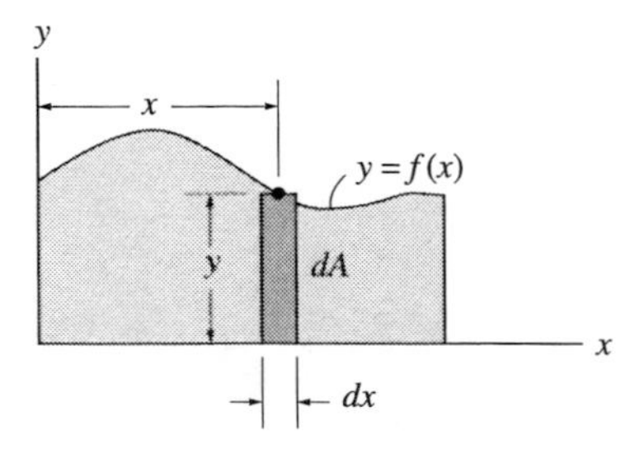

Fig. 6–24

EXAMPLE 6.11

Determine the moment of inertia for the rectangular area shown in Fig. 6–25 with respect to (a) the centroidal x' axis, (b) the axis x_b passing through the base of the rectangle, and (c) the pole or z' axis perpendicular to the $x'-y'$ plane and passing through the centroid C.

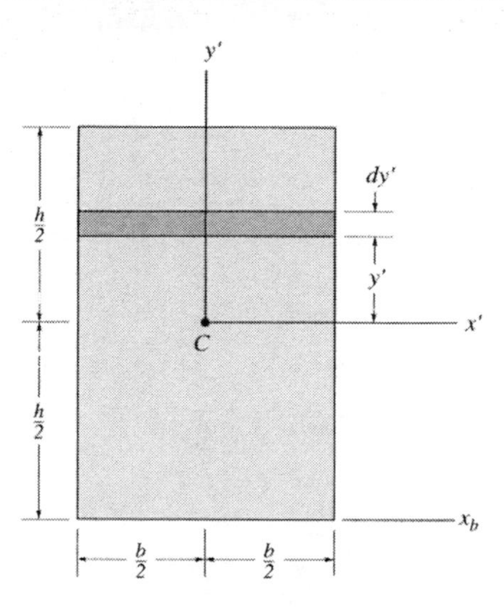

Fig. 6–25

Solution (Case 1)

Part (a). The differential element shown in Fig. 6–25 is chosen for integration. Because of its location and orientation, the *entire element* is at a distance y' from the x' axis. Here it is necessary to integrate from $y' = -h/2$ to $y' = h/2$. Since $dA = b\,dy'$, then

$$\bar{I}_{x'} = \int_A y'^2\,dA = \int_{-h/2}^{h/2} y'^2(b\,dy') = b\int_{-h/2}^{h/2} y'^2\,dy$$

$$= \frac{1}{12}bh^3 \qquad \textit{Ans.}$$

Part (b). The moment of inertia about an axis passing through the base of the rectangle can be obtained by using the result of part (a) and applying the parallel-axis theorem, Eq. 6–16.

$$I_{x_b} = \bar{I}_{x'} + Ad_y^2$$

$$= \frac{1}{12}bh^3 + bh\left(\frac{h}{2}\right)^2 = \frac{1}{3}bh^3 \qquad \textit{Ans.}$$

Part (c). To obtain the polar moment of inertia about point C, we must first obtain $\bar{I}_{y'}$, which may be found by interchanging the dimensions b and h in the result of part (a), i.e.,

$$\bar{I}_{y'} = \frac{1}{12}hb^3$$

Using Eq. 6–15, the polar moment of inertia about C is therefore

$$\bar{J}_C = \bar{I}_{x'} + \bar{I}_{y'} = \frac{1}{12}bh(h^2 + b^2) \qquad \textit{Ans.}$$

EXAMPLE 6.12

Determine the moment of inertia of the shaded area shown in Fig. 6–26*a* about the *x* axis.

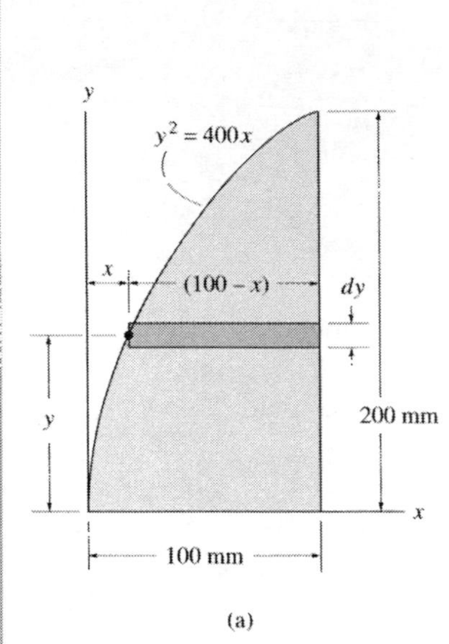

(a)

Solution I *(Case 1)*

A differential element of area that is *parallel* to the *x* axis, as shown in Fig. 6–26*a*, is chosen for integration. Since the element has a thickness dy and intersects the curve at the *arbitrary point* (x, y), the area is $dA = (100 - x)\,dy$. Furthermore, all parts of the element lie at the same distance y from the x axis. Hence, integrating with respect to y, from $y = 0$ to $y = 200$ mm, yields

$$I_x = \int_A y^2\,dA = \int_A y^2(100 - x)\,dy$$

$$= \int_0^{200} y^2\left(100 - \frac{y^2}{400}\right)dy = 100\int_0^{200} y^2\,dy - \frac{1}{400}\int_0^{200} y^4\,dy$$

$$= 107(10^6)\text{ mm}^4 \qquad \textit{Ans.}$$

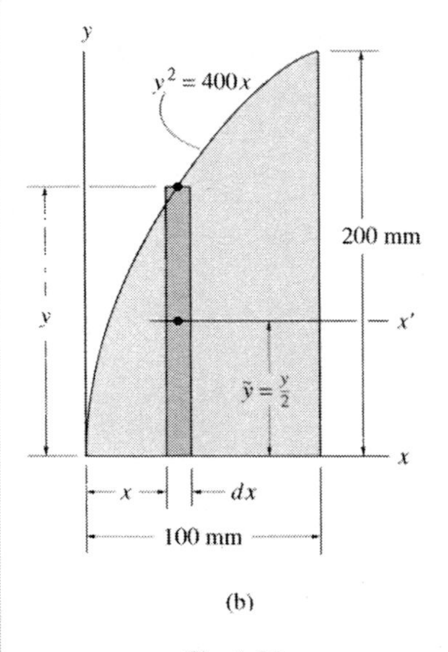

(b)

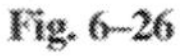
Fig. 6–26

Solution II *(Case 2)*

A differential element *parallel* to the *y* axis, as shown in Fig. 6–26*b*, is chosen for integration. It intersects the curve at the *arbitrary point* (x, y). In this case, all parts of the element do *not* lie at the same distance from the *x* axis, and therefore the parallel-axis theorem must be used to determine the *moment of inertia of the element* with respect to this axis. For a rectangle having a base b and height h, the moment of inertia about its centroidal axis has been determined in part (a) of Example 6.11. There it was found that $\bar{I}_{x'} = \frac{1}{12}bh^3$. For the differential element shown in Fig. 6–26*b*, $b = dx$ and $h = y$, and thus $d\bar{I}_{x'} = \frac{1}{12}dx\,y^3$. Since the centroid of the element is at $\tilde{y} = y/2$ from the x axis, the moment of inertia of the element about this axis is

$$dI_x = d\bar{I}_{x'} + dA\,\tilde{y}^2 = \frac{1}{12}dx\,y^3 + y\,dx\left(\frac{y}{2}\right)^2 = \frac{1}{3}y^3\,dx$$

This result can also be concluded from part (b) of Example 6.11. Integrating with respect to x, from $x = 0$ to $x = 100$ mm, yields

$$I_x = \int dI_x = \int_A \frac{1}{3}y^3\,dx = \int_0^{100}\frac{1}{3}(400x)^{3/2}\,dx$$

$$= 107(10^6)\text{ mm}^4 \qquad \textit{Ans.}$$

EXAMPLE 6.13

Determine the moment of inertia with respect to the x axis of the circular area shown in Fig. 6–27a.

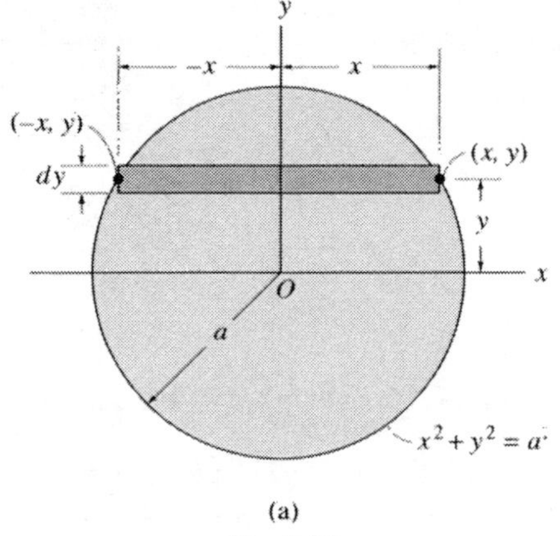

(a)

Fig. 6–27

Solution I *(Case 1)*

Using the differential element shown in Fig. 6–27a, since $dA = 2x\,dy$, we have

$$I_x = \int_A y^2\,dA = \int_A y^2(2x)\,dy$$

$$= \int_{-a}^{a} y^2\left(2\sqrt{a^2 - y^2}\right)dy = \frac{\pi a^4}{4} \qquad \textit{Ans.}$$

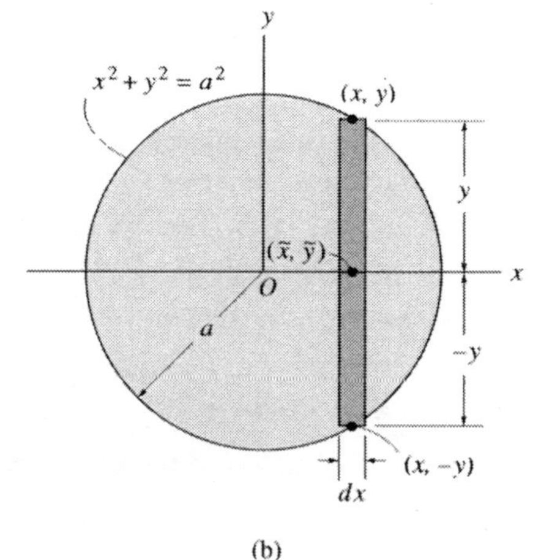

(b)

Solution II *(Case 2)*

When the differential element is chosen as shown in Fig. 6–27b, the centroid for the element happens to lie on the x axis, and so, applying Eq. 6–16, noting that $d_y = 0$ and for a rectangle $\bar{I}_{x'} = \frac{1}{12}bh^3$, we have

$$dI_x = \frac{1}{12}dx\,(2y)^3$$

$$= \frac{2}{3}y^3\,dx$$

Integrating with respect to x yields

$$I_x = \int_{-a}^{a}\frac{2}{3}(a^2 - x^2)^{3/2}\,dx = \frac{\pi a^4}{4} \qquad \textit{Ans.}$$

PROBLEMS

6-48. Determine the moment of inertia of the shaded area about the x axis.

6-49. Determine the moment of inertia of the shaded area about the y axis.

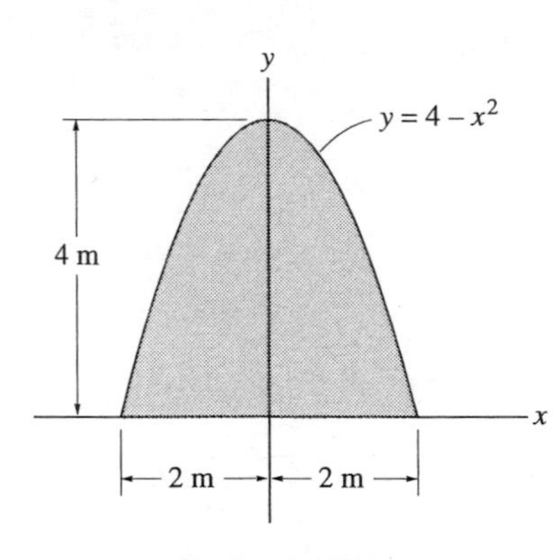

Probs. 6–48/49

6-50. Determine the moment of inertia of the area about the x axis. Solve the problem in two ways, using rectangular differential elements: (a) having a thickness dx and (b) having a thickness of dy.

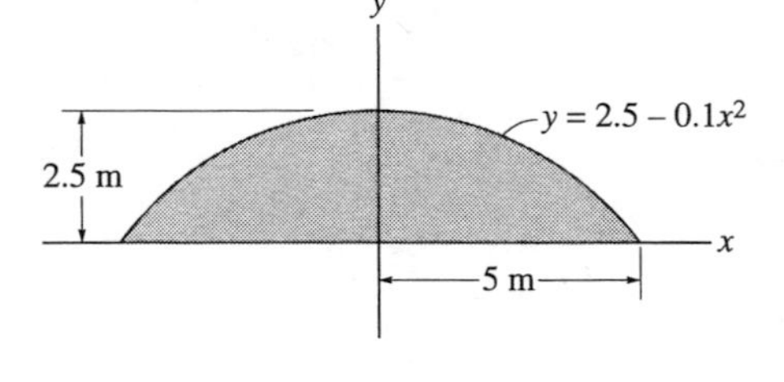

Prob. 6–50

***6-51.** Determine the moment of inertia of the area about the x axis. Solve the problem in two ways, using rectangular differential elements: (a) having a thickness of dx, and (b) having a thickness of dy.

6-52. Determine the moment of inertia of the area about the y axis. Solve the problem in two ways, using rectangular differential elements: (a) having a thickness of dx, and (b) having a thickness of dy.

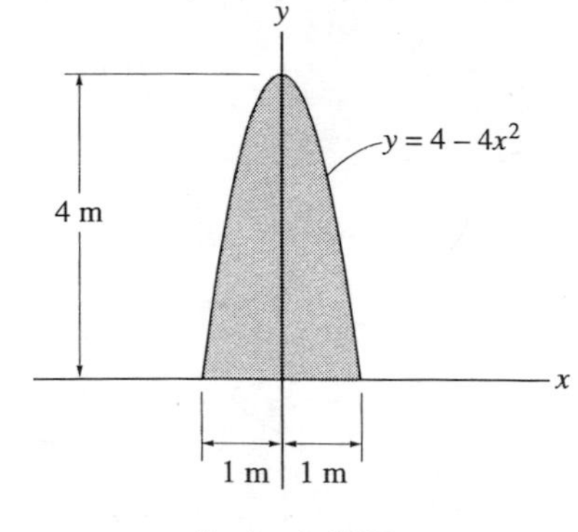

Probs. 6–51/52

6-53. Determine the moment of inertia of the shaded area about the x axis.

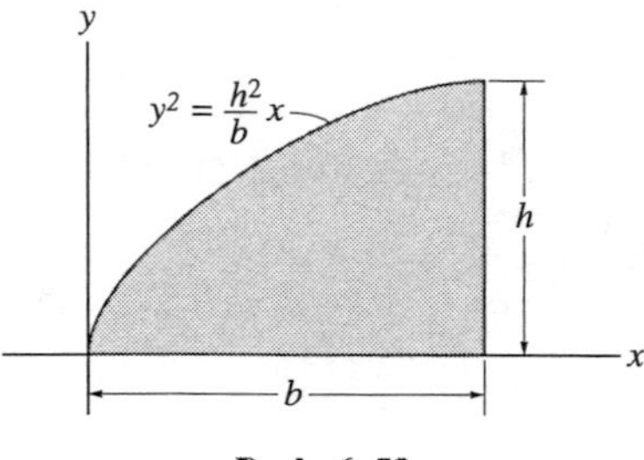

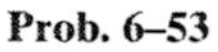

Prob. 6–53

6-54. Determine the moment of inertia of the shaded area about the x axis.

***6-55.** Determine the moment of inertia of the shaded area about the y axis.

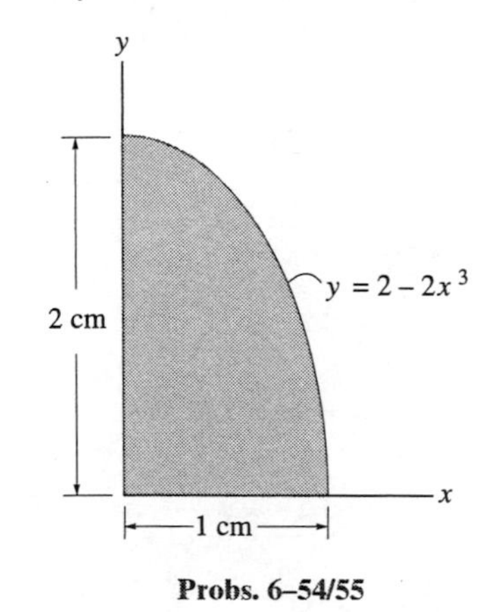

Probs. 6–54/55

6-56. Determine the moment of inertia of the shaded area about the x axis.

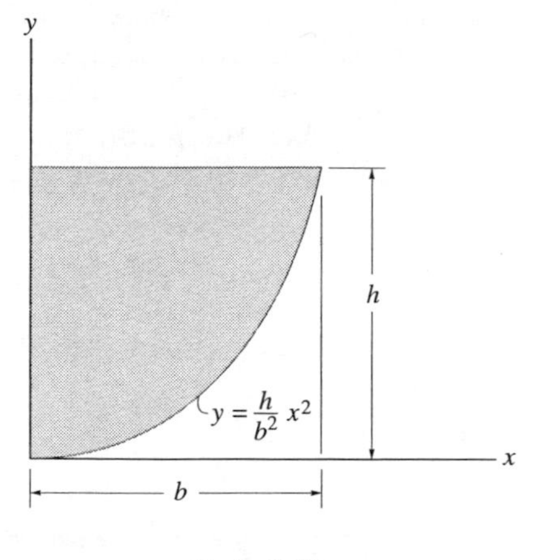

Prob. 6–56

6-57. Determine the moment of inertia of the shaded area about the y axis.

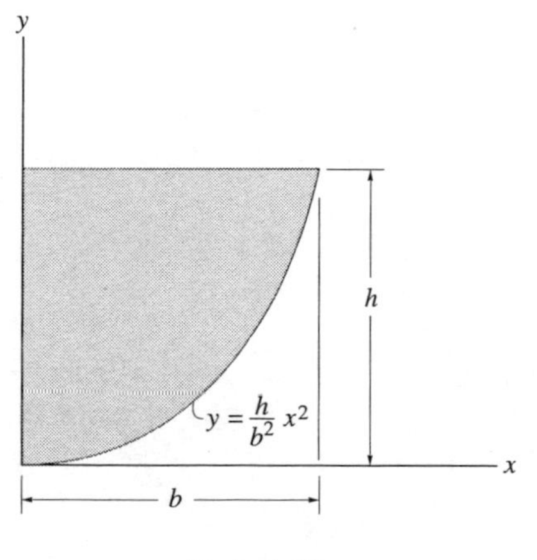

Prob. 6–57

6-58. Determine the moment of inertia of the shaded area about the x axis.

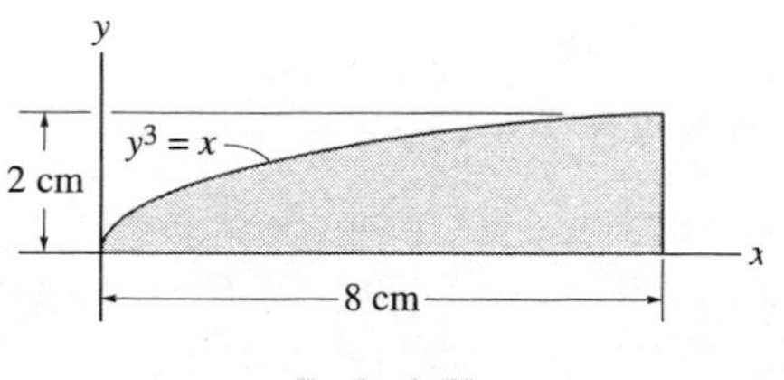

Prob. 6–58

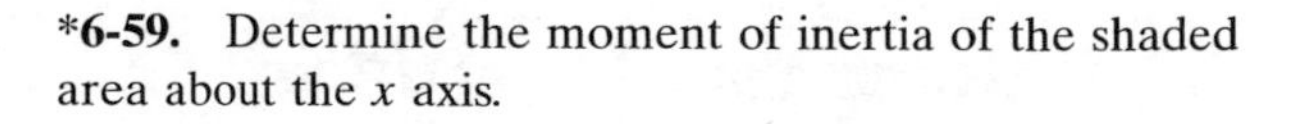

***6-59.** Determine the moment of inertia of the shaded area about the x axis.

6-60. Determine the moment of inertia of the shaded area about the y axis.

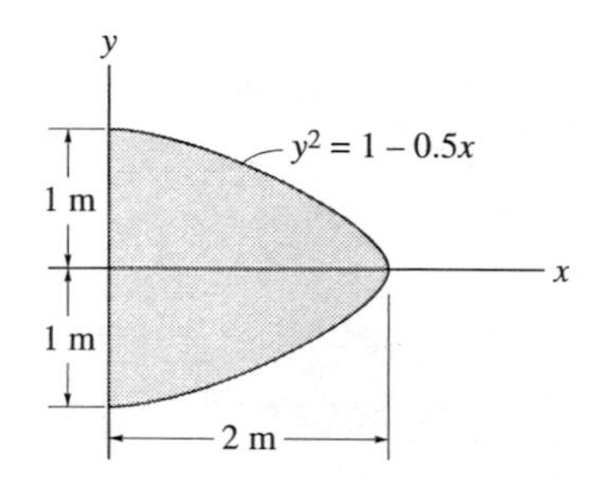

Probs. 6–59/60

6-61. Determine the moment of inertia of the shaded area about the x axis.

6-63. Determine the moment of inertia of the shaded area about the y axis.

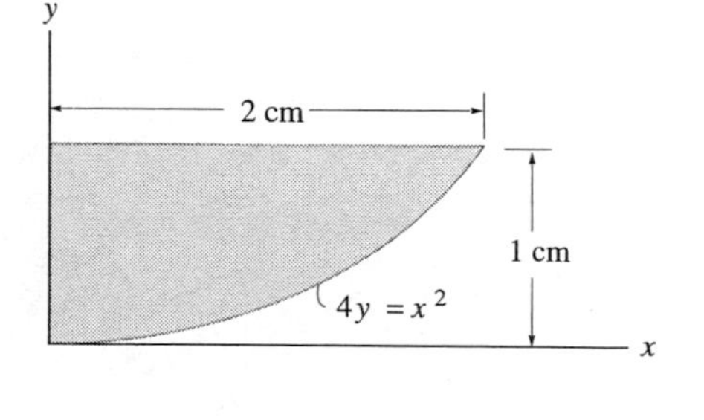

Probs. 6–61/62

6.8 Moments of Inertia for Composite Areas

Structural members have various cross-sectional shapes, and it is necessary to calculate their moments of inertia in order to determine the stress in these members.

A composite area consists of a series of connected "simpler" parts or shapes, such as semicircles, rectangles, and triangles. Provided the moment of inertia of each of these parts is known or can be determined about a common axis, then the moment of inertia of the composite area equals the *algebraic sum* of the moments of inertia of all its parts.

PROCEDURE FOR ANALYSIS

The moment of inertia of a composite area about a reference axis can be determined using the following procedure.

Composite Parts.

- Using a sketch, divide the area into its composite parts and indicate the perpendicular distance from the *centroid* of each part to the reference axis.

Parallel-Axis Theorem.

- The moment of inertia of each part should be determined about its centroidal axis, which is parallel to the reference axis. For the calculation use the table given on the inside back cover.
- If the centroidal axis does not coincide with the reference axis, the parallel-axis theorem, $I = \bar{I} + Ad^2$, should be used to determine the moment of inertia of the part about the reference axis.

Summation.

- The moment of inertia of the entire area about the reference axis is determined by summing the results of its composite parts.
- If a composite part has a "hole," its moment of inertia is found by "subtracting" the moment of inertia for the hole from the moment of inertia of the entire part including the hole.

EXAMPLE 6.14

Compute the moment of inertia of the composite area shown in Fig. 6–28*a* about the *x* axis.

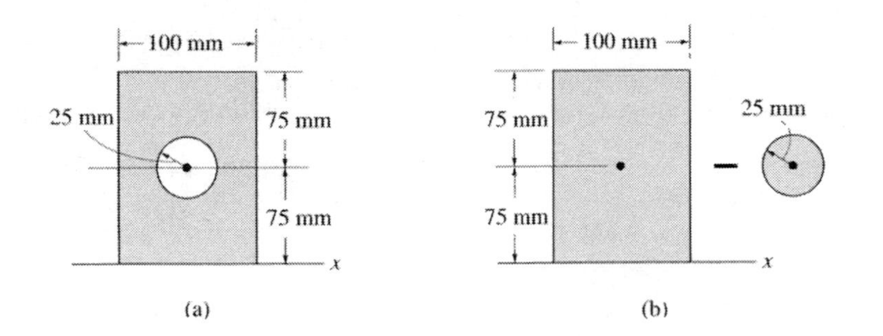

Fig. 6–28

Solution

Composite Parts. The composite area is obtained by *subtracting* the circle from the rectangle as shown in Fig. 6–28*b*. The centroid of each area is located in the figure.

Parallel-Axis Theorem. The moments of inertia about the *x* axis are determined using the parallel-axis theorem and the data in Appendix C.

Circle

$$I_x = \bar{I}_{x'} + Ad_y^2$$

$$= \frac{1}{4}\pi(25)^4 + \pi(25)^2(75)^2 = 11.4(10^6)\text{ mm}^4$$

Rectangle

$$I_x = \bar{I}_{x'} + Ad_y^2$$

$$= \frac{1}{12}(100)(150)^3 + (100)(150)(75)^2 = 112.5(10^6)\text{ mm}^4$$

Summation. The moment of inertia for the composite area is thus

$$I_x = -11.4(10^6) + 112.5(10^6)$$

$$= 101(10^6)\text{ mm}^4 \qquad \textit{Ans.}$$

EXAMPLE 6.15

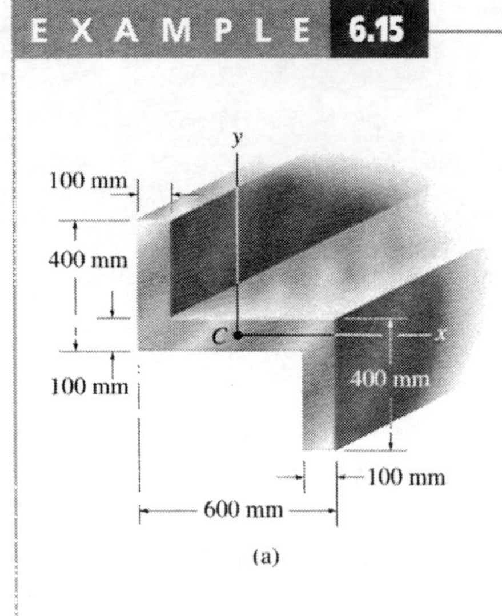

(a)

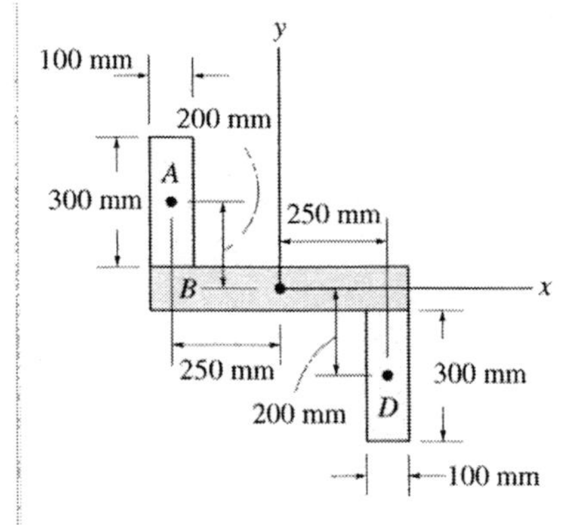

(b)

Fig. 6–29

Determine the moments of inertia of the beam's cross-sectional area shown in Fig. 6–29*a* about the x and y centroidal axes.

Solution

Composite Parts. The cross section can be considered as three composite rectangular areas A, B, and D shown in Fig. 6–29*b*. For the calculation, the centroid of each of these rectangles is located in the figure.

Parallel-Axis Theorem. From the table in Appendix C, or Example 6.11, the moment of inertia of a rectangle about its centroidal axis is $\bar{I} = \frac{1}{12}bh^3$. Hence, using the parallel-axis theorem for rectangles A and D, the calculations are as follows:

Rectangle A

$$I_x = \bar{I}_{x'} + Ad_y^2 = \frac{1}{12}(100)(300)^3 + (100)(300)(200)^2$$
$$= 1.425(10^9)\text{ mm}^4$$
$$I_y = \bar{I}_{y'} + Ad_x^2 = \frac{1}{12}(300)(100)^3 + (100)(300)(250)^2$$
$$= 1.90(10^9)\text{ mm}^4$$

Rectangle B

$$I_x = \frac{1}{12}(600)(100)^3 = 0.05(10^9)\text{ mm}^4$$
$$I_y = \frac{1}{12}(100)(600)^3 = 1.80(10^9)\text{ mm}^4$$

Rectangle D

$$I_x = \bar{I}_{x'} + Ad_y^2 = \frac{1}{12}(100)(300)^3 + (100)(300)(200)^2$$
$$= 1.425(10^9)\text{ mm}^4$$
$$I_y = \bar{I}_{y'} + Ad_x^2 = \frac{1}{12}(300)(100)^3 + (100)(300)(250)^2$$
$$= 1.90(10^9)\text{ mm}^4$$

Summation. The moments of inertia for the entire cross section are thus

$$I_x = 1.425(10^9) + 0.05(10^9) + 1.425(10^9)$$
$$= 2.90(10^9)\text{ mm}^4 \qquad \textit{Ans.}$$
$$I_y = 1.90(10^9) + 1.80(10^9) + 1.90(10^9)$$
$$= 5.60(10^9)\text{ mm}^4 \qquad \textit{Ans.}$$

PROBLEMS

6-63. Locate the centroid $\bar{y}$ of the cross-sectional area for the angle. Then find the moment of inertia $\bar{I}_{x'}$ about the x' centroidal axis.

6-64. Locate the centroid $\bar{x}$ of the cross-sectional area for the angle. Then find the moment of inertia $\bar{I}_{y'}$ about the y' centroidal axis.

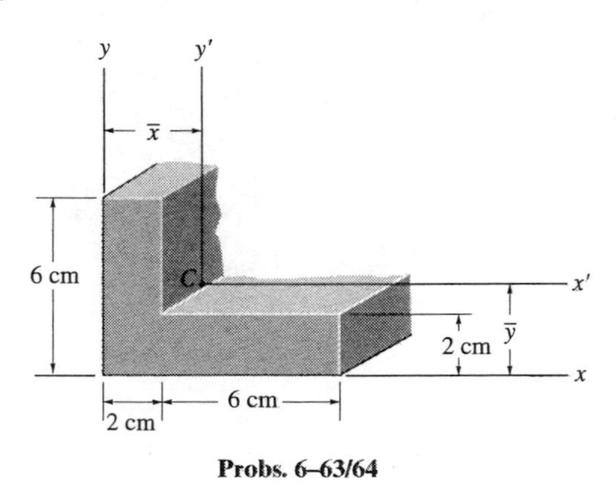

Probs. 6–63/64

***6-65.** Determine the distance $\bar{x}$ to the centroid of the beam's cross-sectional area: then find the moment of inertia about the y' axis.

6-66. Determine the moment of inertia of the beam's cross-sectional area about the x' axis.

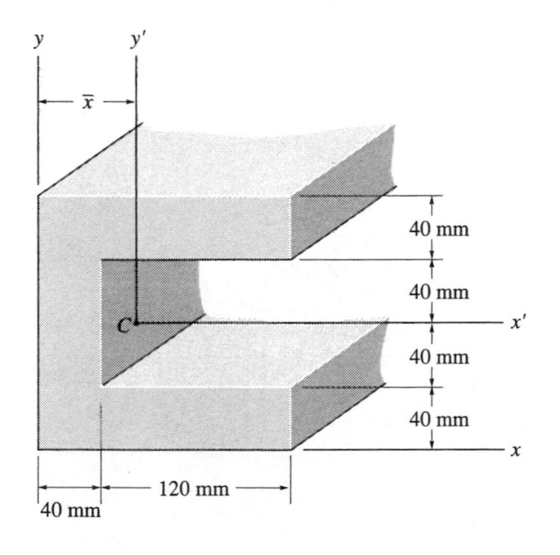

Probs. 6–65/66

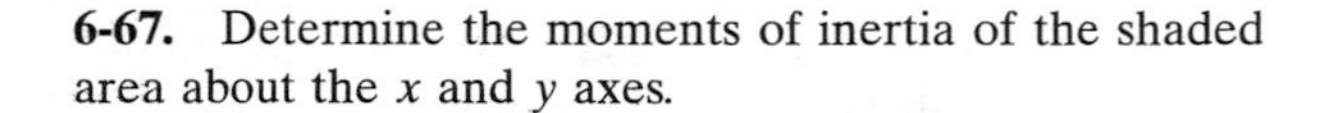

6-67. Determine the moments of inertia of the shaded area about the x and y axes.

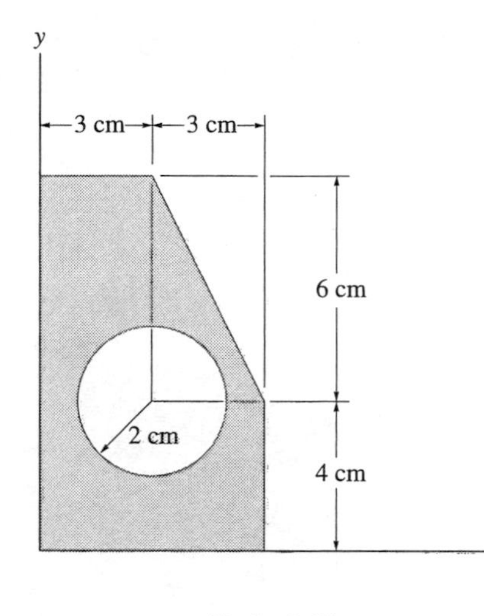

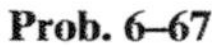

Prob. 6–67

6-68. Determine the moment of inertia of the beam's cross-sectional area about the x' axis. Neglect the size of the corner welds at A and B for the calculation, $\bar{y} = 154.4$ mm.

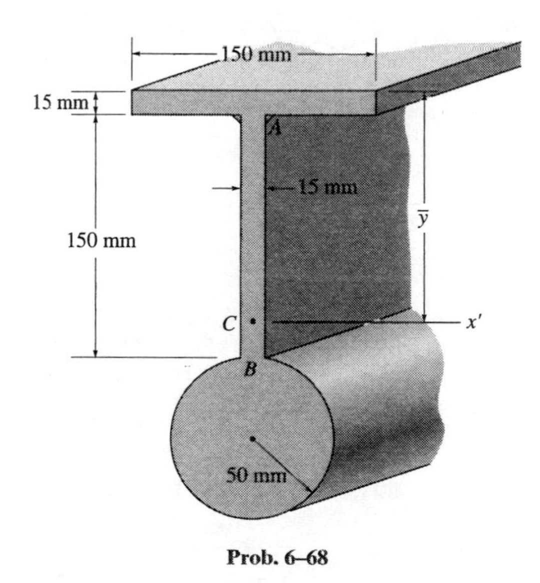

Prob. 6–68

***6-69.** Compute the moments of inertia I_x and I_y for the beam's cross-sectional area about the x and y axes.

6-70. Determine the distance $\bar{y}$ to the centroid C of the beam's cross-sectional area and then compute the moment of inertia $\bar{I}_{x'}$ about the x' axis.

6-61. Determine the distance $\bar{x}$ to the centroid C of the beam's cross-sectional area and then compute the moment of inertia $\bar{I}_{y'}$ about the y' axis.

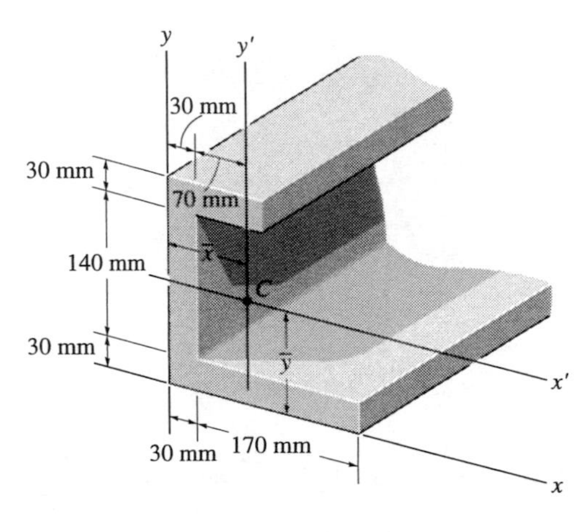

Probs. 6–69/70/71

6-72. Locate the centroid $\bar{y}$ of the cross section and determine the moment of inertia of the section about the x' axis.

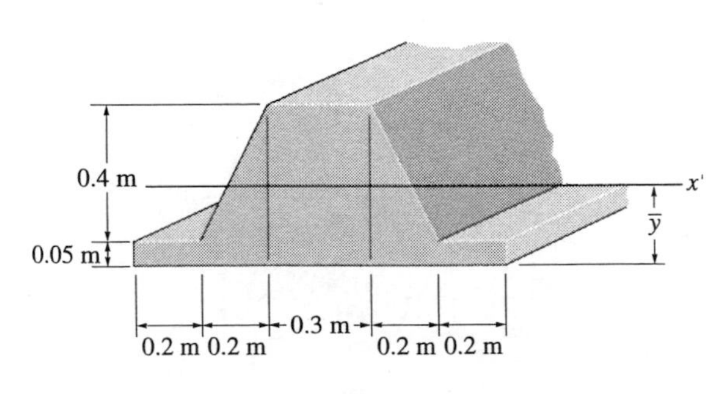

Prob. 6–72

***6-73.** Determine $\bar{y}$, which locates the centroidal axis x' for the cross-sectional area of the T-beam, and then find the moments of inertia $\bar{I}_{x'}$ and $\bar{I}_{y'}$.

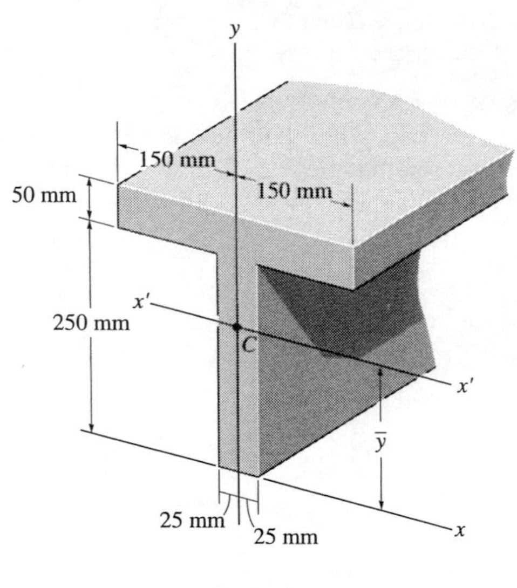

Prob. 6–73

6-74. Determine the distance $\bar{y}$ to the centroid for the beam's cross-sectional area; then determine the moment of inertia about the x' axis.

6-75. Determine the moment of inertia of the beam's cross-sectional area about the y axis.

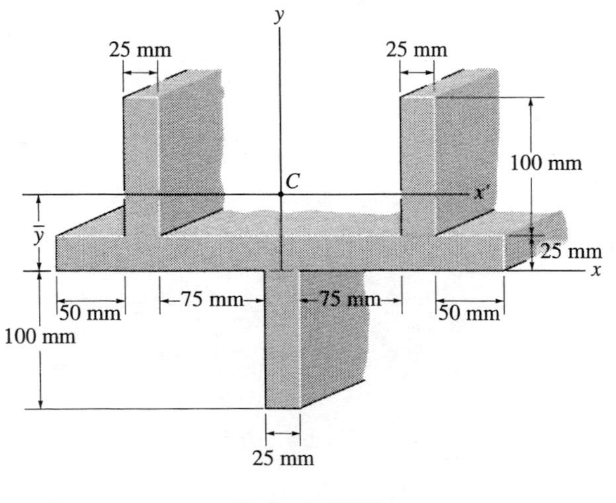

Probs. 6–74/75

6-76. Determine the moment of inertia I_x of the shaded area about the x axis.

***6-77.** Determine the moment of inertia I_y of the shaded area about the y axis.

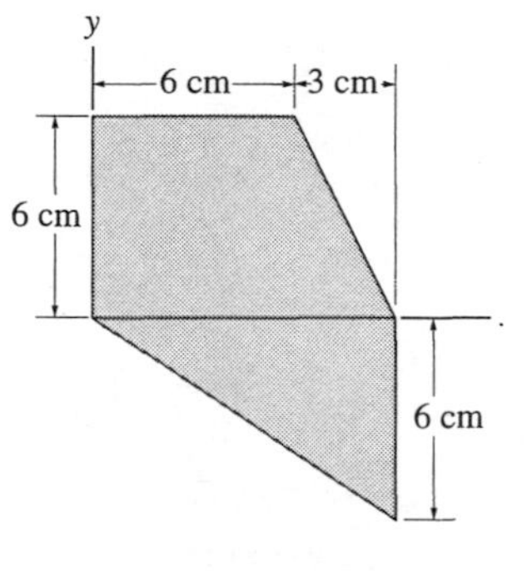

Probs. 6–76/77

6-78. Locate the centroid $\bar{y}$ of the channel's cross-sectional area, and then determine the moment of inertia with respect to the x' axis passing through the centroid.

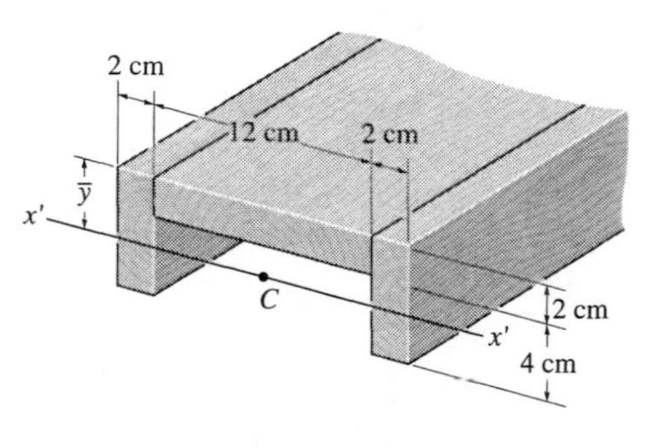

Prob. 6–78

6-79. Determine the moments of inertia I_x and I_y of the shaded area.

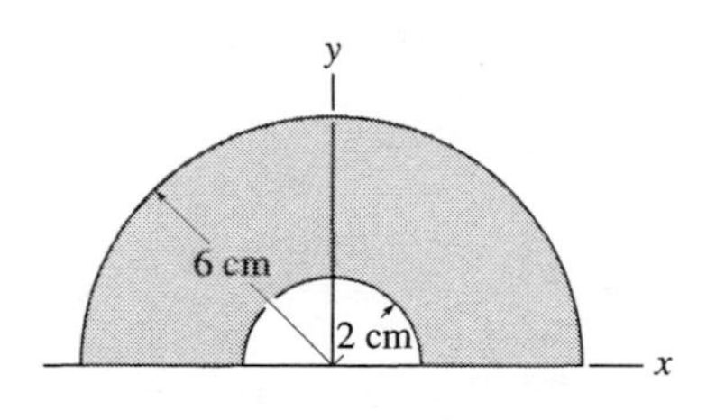

Prob. 6–79

6-80. Determine the moment of inertia of the parallelogram about the x' axis, which passes through the centroid C of the area.

***6-81.** Determine the moment of inertia of the parallelogram about the y' axis, which passes through the centroid C of the area.

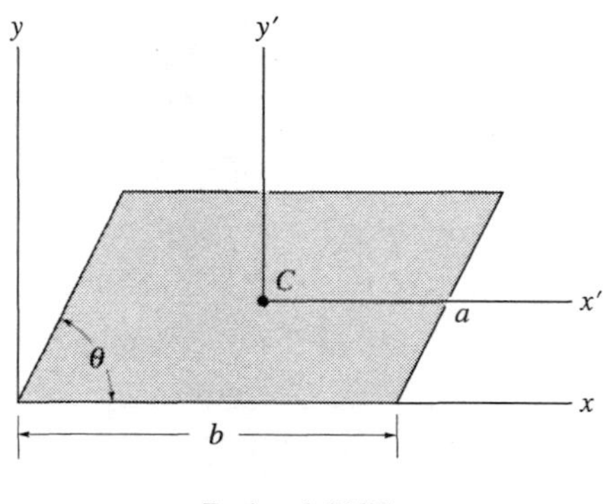

Probs. 6–80/81

6-82. An aluminum strut has a cross section referred to as a deep hat. Determine the location $\bar{y}$ of the centroid of its area and the moment of inertia of the area about the x' axis. Each segment has a thickness of 10 mm.

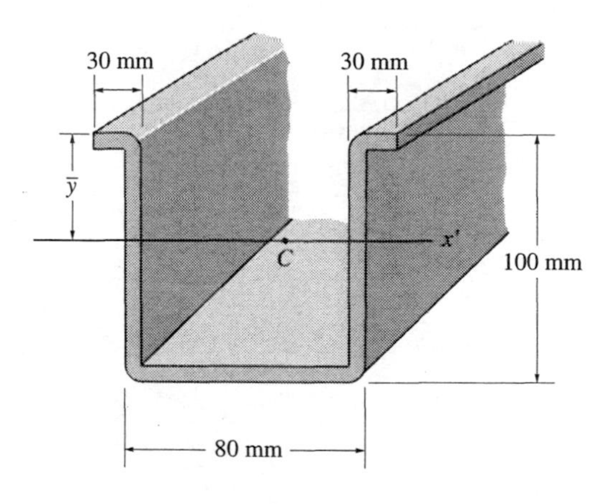

Prob. 6–82

6-83. Determine the moment of inertia of the beam's cross-sectional area with respect to the x' axis passing through the centroid C of the cross section. Neglect the size of the corner welds at A and B for the calculation, $\bar{y} = 104.3$ mm.

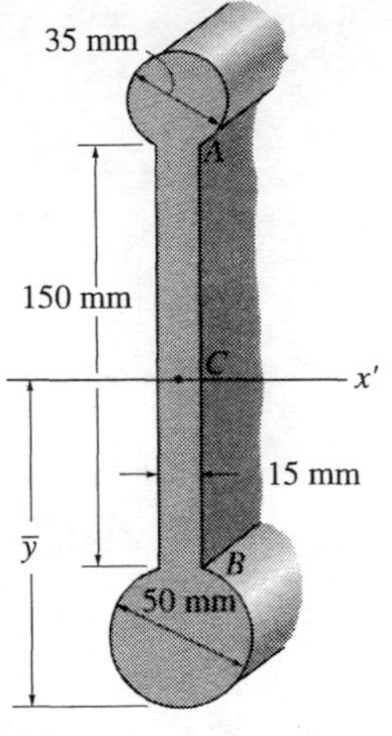

Prob. 6–83

6-84. Determine the location $\bar{y}$ of the centroid of the channel's cross-sectional area and then calculate the moment of inertia of the area about this axis.

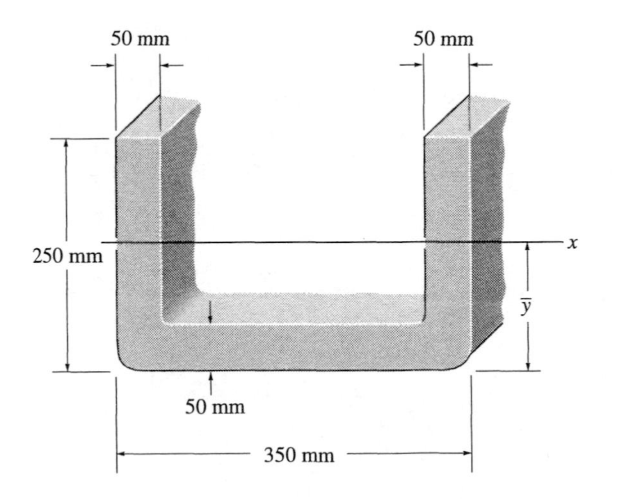

Prob. 6–84

6-85. Determine the moments of inertia of the triangular area about the x' and y' axes, which pass through the centroid C of the area.

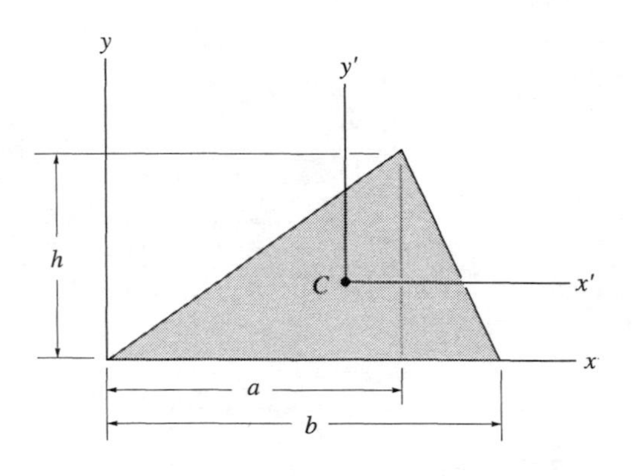

Prob. 6–85

CHAPTER REVIEW

- ***Center of Gravity and Centroid.*** The *center of gravity* represents a point where the weight of the body can be considered concentrated. The distance $\bar{s}$ to this point can be determined from a balance of moments. This requires that the moment of the weight of all the particles of the body about some point must equal the moment of the entire body about the point, $\bar{s}W = \Sigma\tilde{s}W$. The *centroid* is the location of the geometric center for the body. It is determined in a similar manner, using a moment balance of geometric elements such as line, area, or volume segments. For bodies having a continuous shape, moments are summed (integrated) using differential elements. If the body is a composite of several shapes, each having a known location for its center of gravity or centroid, then the location is determined from a discrete summation using its composite parts.

- ***Distributed Force System.*** A distributed load can be replaced by resultant force that is equivalent to the area or volume under the loading diagram. This resultant has a line of action that passes through the centroid or geometric center of the area or volume in the diagram.

- ***Area Moment of Inertia.*** The *area moment of inertia* represents the second moment of the area about an axis, $I = \int r^2\,dA$. It is frequently used in formulas related to strength and stability of structural members or mechanical elements. If the area shape is irregular, then a differential element must be selected and integration over the entire area must be performed. Tabular values of the moment of inertia of common shapes about their *centroidal axis* are available. To determine the moment of inertia of these shapes about some *other axis*, the parallel-axis theorem must be used, $I = \bar{I} + Ad^2$. If an area is a composite of these shapes, then its moment of inertia is equal to the sum of the moments of inertia of each of its parts.

REVIEW PROBLEMS

6-86. Determine the distance $\bar{y}$ to the centroidal axis $\bar{x}-\bar{x}$ of the beam's cross-sectional area. Neglect the size of the corner welds at A and B for the calculation.

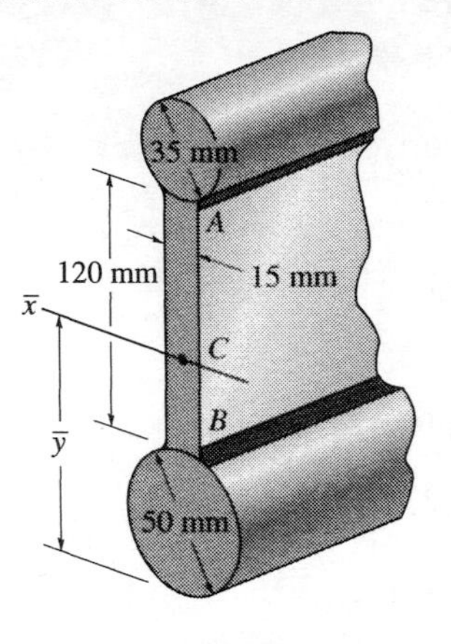

Prob. 6–86

6-87. Determine the distance $\bar{y}$ to the centroid of the plate area.

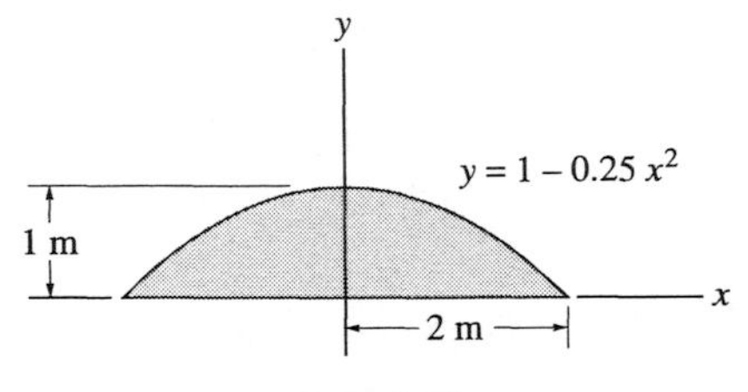

Prob. 6–87

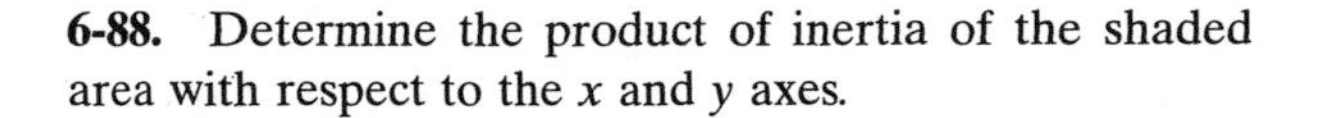

6-88. Determine the product of inertia of the shaded area with respect to the x and y axes.

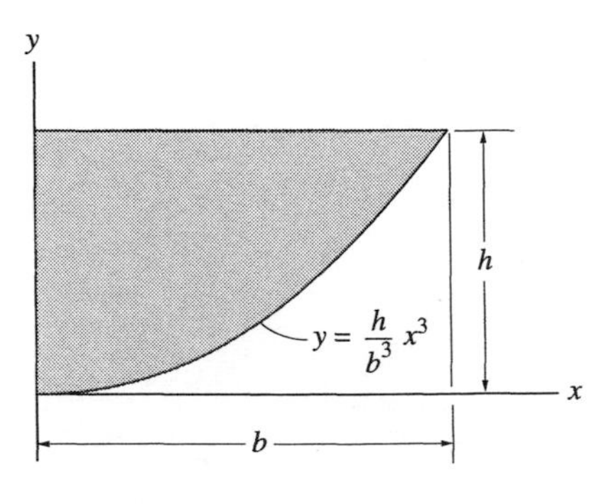

Prob. 6–88

6-89. Determine the distance $\bar{z}$ to the center of gravity for the frustum of the paraboloid. The material is homogeneous.

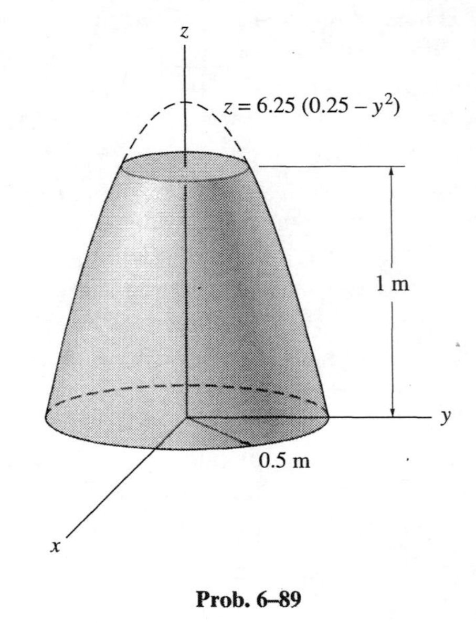

Prob. 6–89

6-90. Determine the moments of inertia of the "Z" section with respect to the x and y centroidal axes.

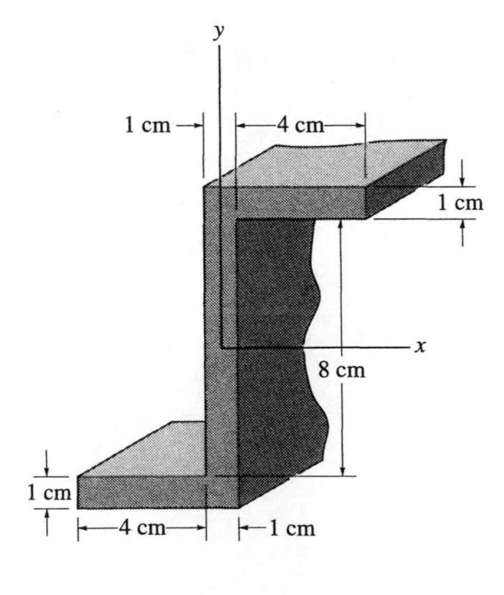

Prob. 6–90

6-91. The form is used to cast concrete columns. Determine the resultant force that wet concrete exerts along the plate A, $0.5 \text{ m} \leq z \leq 3 \text{ m}$, if the pressure due to the concrete varies as shown. Specify the location of the resultant force, measured from the top of the column.

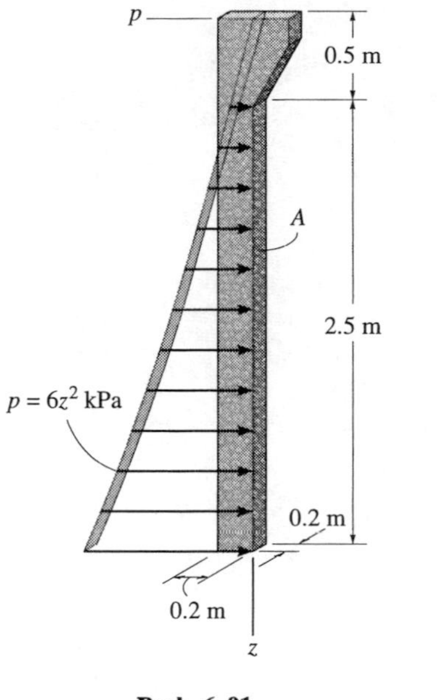

Prob. 6–91

*6-92. Determine the moment of inertia of the beam's cross-sectional area about the x axis.

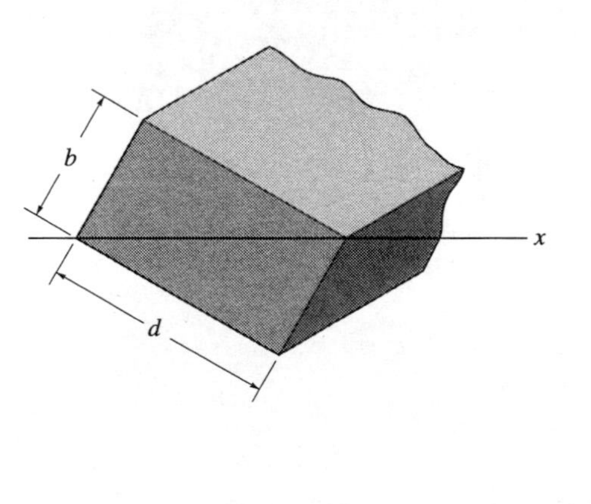

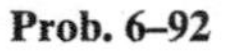

Prob. 6–92

6-93. Determine the location $(\bar{x}, \bar{y})$ of the centroid of the area.

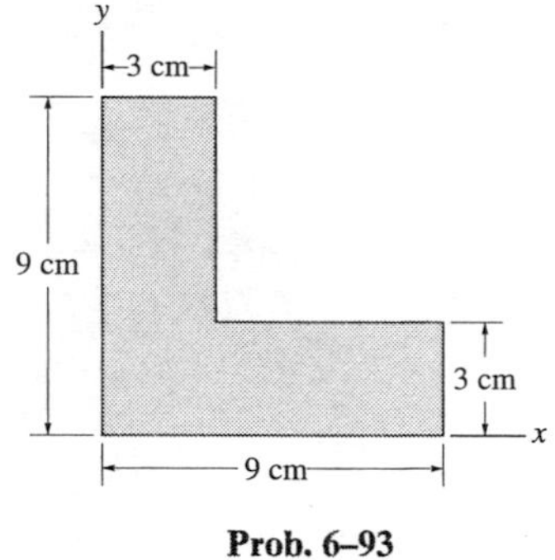

Prob. 6–93

6-94. Determine the location $(\bar{x}, \bar{y})$ of the centroid of the homogeneous plate.

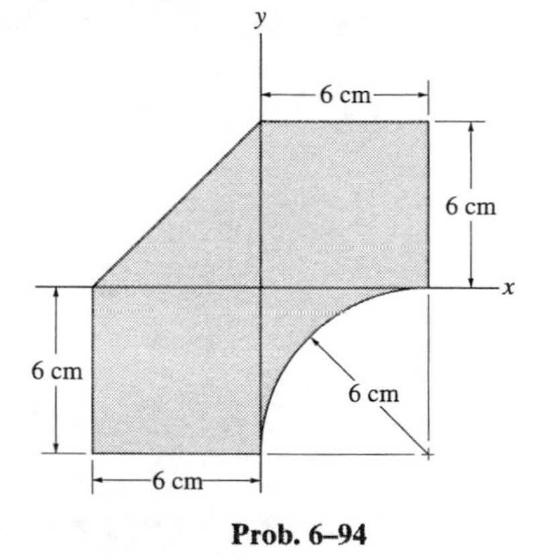

Prob. 6–94

6-95. Determine the area moment of inertia of the beam's cross-sectional area about the x axis which passes through the centroid C.

6-96. Determine the area moment of inertia of the beam's cross-sectional area about the y axis which passes through the centroid C.

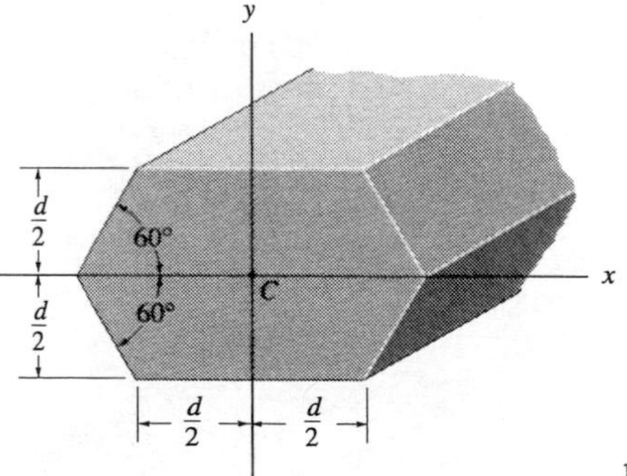

Probs. 6–95/96

The design and analysis of any structural member requires knowledge of the internal loadings acting within it, not only when it is in place and subjected to service loads, but also when it is being hoisted as shown here. In this chapter, we will discuss how engineers determine these loadings.

CHAPTER 7

Internal Loadings

CHAPTER OBJECTIVES

- To show how to use the method of sections for determining the internal loadings in a member.
- To generalize this procedure by formulating equations that can be plotted so that they describe the internal shear and moment throughout a member.

7.1 Internal Forces Developed in Structural Members

The design of any structural or mechanical member requires an investigation of the loading acting within the member in order to be sure the material can resist this loading. These internal loadings can be determined by using the *method of sections*. To illustrate the procedure, consider the "simply supported" beam shown in Fig. 7–1*a*, which is subjected to the forces $\mathbf{F}_1$ and $\mathbf{F}_2$ and the *support reactions* A_x, $\mathbf{A}_y$, and $\mathbf{B}_y$, Fig. 7–1*b*. If the *internal loadings* acting on the cross section at *C* are to be determined, then an imaginary section is passed through the beam, cutting it into two segments. By doing this the internal loadings at the section become *external* on the free-body diagram of each segment,

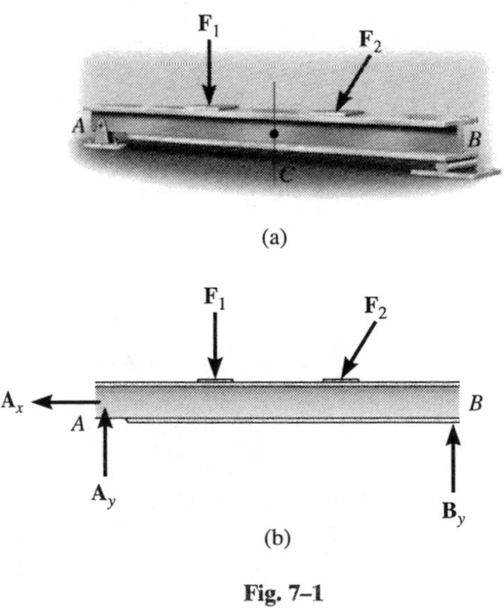

Fig. 7–1

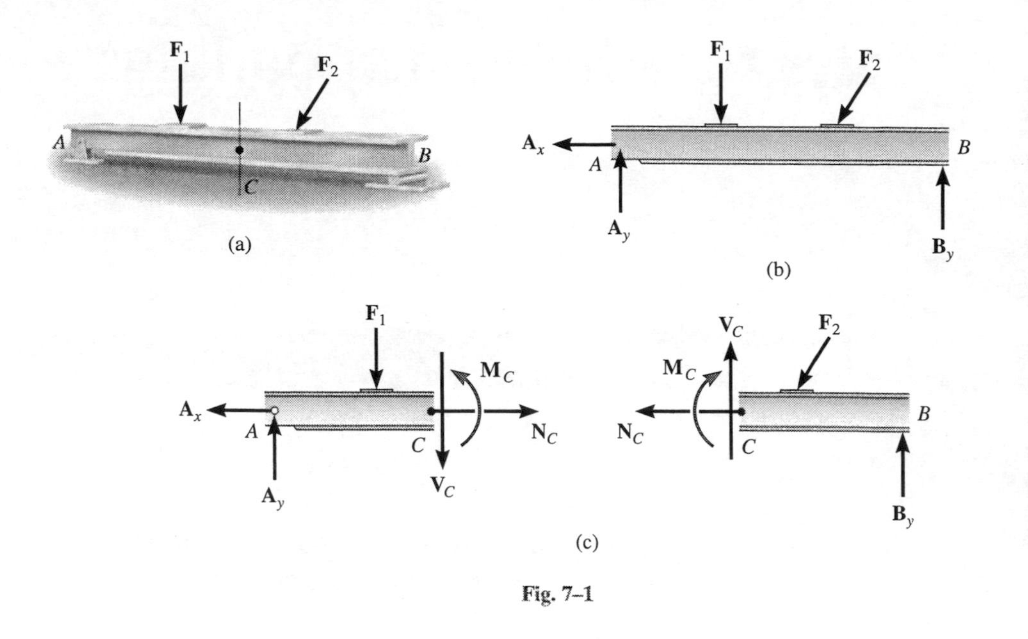

Fig. 7–1

Fig. 7–1*c*. Since both segments (AC and CB) were in equilibrium *before* the beam was sectioned, equilibrium of each segment is maintained provided rectangular force components $\mathbf{N}_C$ and $\mathbf{V}_C$ and a resultant couple moment $\mathbf{M}_C$ are developed at the section. Note that these loadings must be equal in magnitude and opposite in direction on each of the segments (Newton's third law). The magnitude of each of these loadings can now be determined by applying the three equations of equilibrium to either segment AC or CB. A *direct solution* for $\mathbf{N}_C$ is obtained by applying $\Sigma F_x = 0$; $\mathbf{V}_C$ is obtained directly from $\Sigma F_y = 0$; and $\mathbf{M}_C$ is determined by summing moments about point C, $\Sigma M_C = 0$, in order to eliminate the moments of the unknowns $\mathbf{N}_C$ and $\mathbf{V}_C$.

To save on material the beams used to support the roof of this shelter were tapered since the roof loading will produce a larger internal moment at the beams' centers than at their ends.

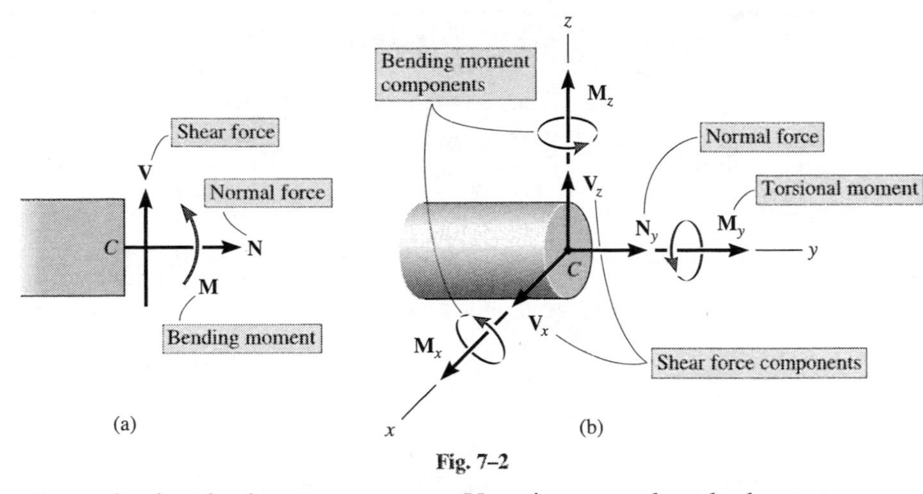

Fig. 7–2

In mechanics, the force components **N**, acting normal to the beam at the cut section, and **V**, acting tangent to the section, are termed the *normal or axial force* and the *shear force*, respectively. The couple moment **M** is referred to as the *bending moment*, Fig. 7–2*a*. In three dimensions, a general internal force and couple moment resultant will act at the section. The *x, y, z* components of these loadings are shown in Fig. 7–2*b*. Here $\mathbf{N}_y$ is the *normal force*, and $\mathbf{V}_x$ and $\mathbf{V}_z$ are *shear force components*. $\mathbf{M}_y$ is a *torsional or twisting moment*, and $\mathbf{M}_x$ and $\mathbf{M}_z$ are *bending moment components*. For most applications, these *resultant loadings* will act at the geometric center or centroid (*C*) of the section's cross-sectional area. Although the magnitude for each loading generally will be different at various points along the axis of the member, the method of sections can always be used to determine their values.

Free-Body Diagrams. Since frames and machines are composed of *multiforce members*, each of these members will generally be subjected to internal normal, shear, and bending loadings. For example, consider the frame shown in Fig. 7–3*a*. If the blue section is passed through the frame to determine the internal loadings at points *H, G*, and *F*, the resulting free-body diagram of the top portion of this section is shown in Fig. 7–3*b*. At each point where a member is sectioned there is an unknown normal force, shear force, and bending moment. As a result, we cannot apply the *three* equations of equilibrium to this section in order to obtain these *nine unknowns*.*Instead, to solve this problem we must *first dismember* the frame and determine the reactions at the connections of the members using the techniques of Sec. 5.5. Once this is done, *each member* may then be sectioned at its appropriate point, and the three equations of equilibrium can be applied to determine **N**, **V**, and **M**. For example, the free-body diagram of segment *DG*, Fig. 7–3*c*, can be used to determine the internal loadings at *G* provided the reactions of the pin, $\mathbf{D}_x$ and $\mathbf{D}_y$, are known.

*Recall that this method of analysis worked well for trusses since truss members are *straight two-force members* which support only an axial or normal load.

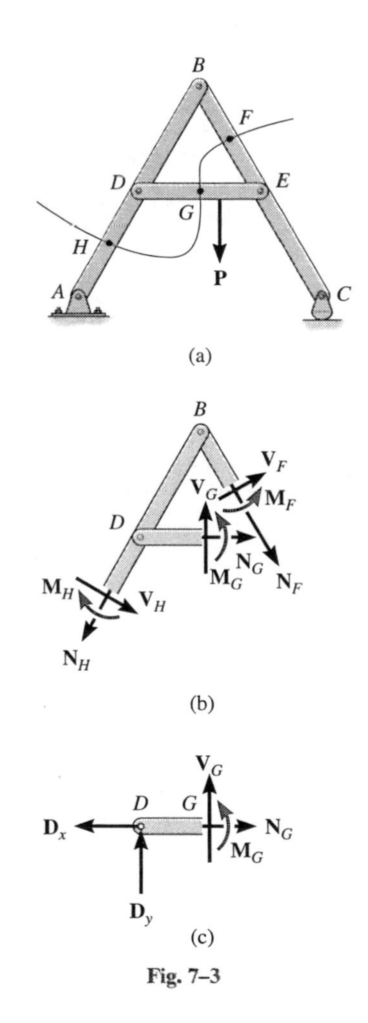

Fig. 7–3

In each case, the link on the backhoe is a two-force member. In the top photo it is subjected to both bending and axial load at its center. By making the member straight, as in the bottom photo, then only an axial force acts within the member.

PROCEDURE FOR ANALYSIS

The method of sections can be used to determine the internal loadings at a specific location in a member using the following procedure.

Support Reactions.

- Before the member is "cut" or sectioned, it may first be necessary to determine the member's support reactions, so that the equilibrium equations are used only to solve for the internal loadings when the member is sectioned.
- If the member is part of a frame or machine, the reactions at its connections are determined using the methods of Sec. 5.5.

Free-Body Diagram.

- Keep all distributed loadings, couple moments, and forces acting on the member in their *exact locations*, then pass an imaginary section through the member, perpendicular to its axis at the point where the internal loading is to be determined.
- After the section is made, draw a free-body diagram of the segment that has the least number of loads on it, and indicate the x, y, z components of the force and couple moment resultants at the section.
- If the member is subjected to a *coplanar* system of forces, only **N**, **V**, and **M** act at the section.
- In many cases it may be possible to tell by inspection the proper sense of the unknown loadings; however, if this seems difficult, the sense can be assumed.

Equations of Equilibrium.

- Moments should be summed at the section about axes passing through the *centroid* or geometric center of the member's cross-sectional area in order to eliminate the unknown normal and shear forces and thereby obtain direct solutions for the moment components.
- If the solution of the equilibrium equations yields a negative scalar, the assumed sense of the quantity is opposite to that shown on the free-body diagram.

EXAMPLE 7.1

Determine the resultant internal loadings acting on the cross section at C of the beam shown in Fig. 7–4*a*.

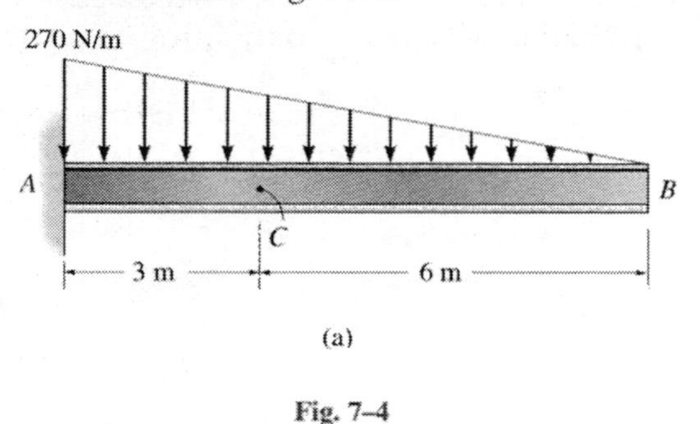

(a)

Fig. 7–4

Solution

Support Reactions. This problem can be solved in the most direct manner by considering segment CB of the beam, since then the support reactions at A do not have to be computed.

Free-Body Diagram. Passing an imaginary section perpendicular to the longitudinal axis of the beam yields the free-body diagram of segment CB shown in Fig. 7–4*b*. It is important to keep the distributed loading exactly where it is on the segment until *after* the section is made. Only then should this loading be replaced by a single resultant force. Notice that the intensity of the distributed loading at C is found by proportion, i.e., from Fig. 7–4*a*, $\mathbf{w}/6\text{ m} = (270\text{ N/m})/9\text{m}$, $\mathbf{w} = 180\text{ N/m}$. The magnitude of the resultant of the distributed load is equal to the area under the loading curve (triangle) and acts through the centroid of this area. Thus, $F = \frac{1}{2}(180\text{ N/m})(6\text{ m}) = 540\text{ N}$, which acts $1/3(6\text{ m}) = 2\text{ m}$ from C as shown in Fig. 7–4*b*.

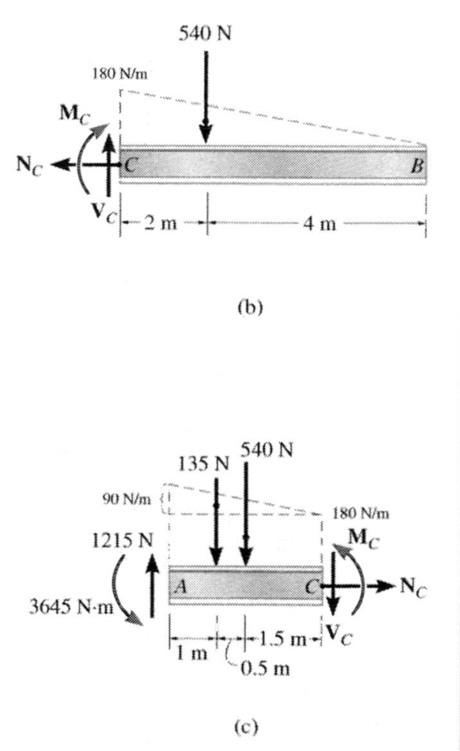

(b)

(c)

Equations of Equilibrium. Applying the equations of equilibrium we have

$\xrightarrow{+} \Sigma F_x = 0;$ $\quad -N_C = 0$

$N_C = 0$ *Ans.*

$+\uparrow \Sigma F_y = 0;$ $\quad V_C - 540\text{ N} = 0$

$V_C = 540\text{ N}$ *Ans.*

$\circlearrowleft + \Sigma M_C = 0;$ $\quad -M_C - 540\text{ N}(2\text{ m}) = 0$

$M_C = -1080\text{ N}\cdot\text{m}$ *Ans.*

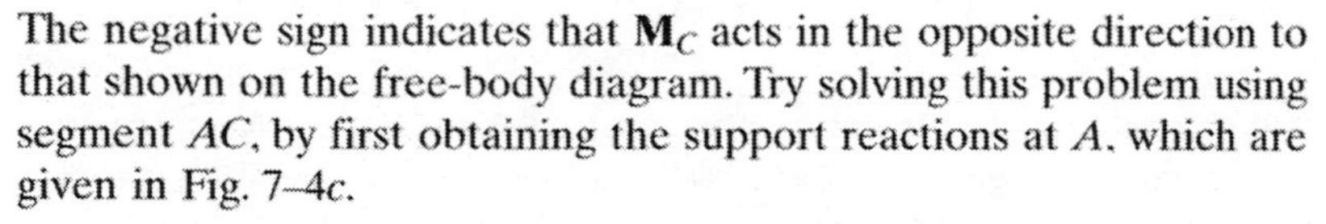
The negative sign indicates that $\mathbf{M}_C$ acts in the opposite direction to that shown on the free-body diagram. Try solving this problem using segment AC, by first obtaining the support reactions at A, which are given in Fig. 7–4*c*.

EXAMPLE 7.2

Determine the resultant internal loadings acting on the cross section at C of the machine shaft shown in Fig. 7–5a. The shaft is supported by bearings at A and B, which exert only vertical forces on the shaft.

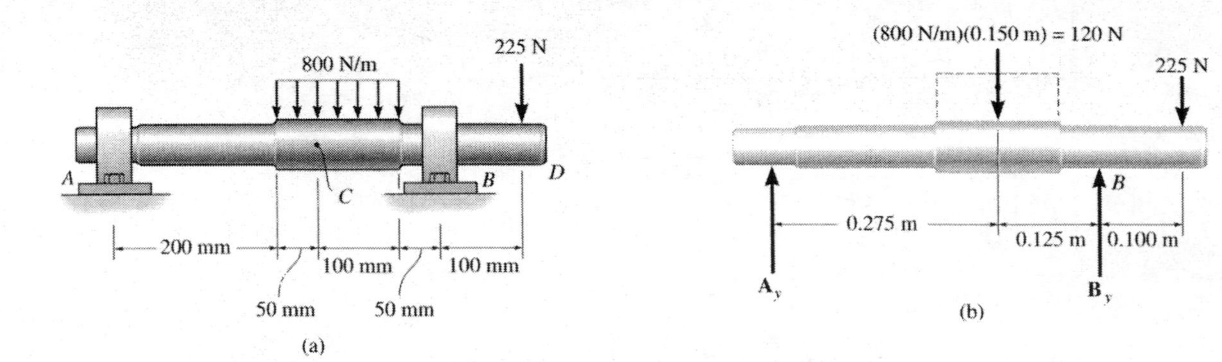

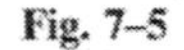
Fig. 7–5

Solution

We will solve this problem using segment AC of the shaft.

Support Reactions. A free-body diagram of the entire shaft is shown in Fig. 7–5b. Since segment AC is to be considered, only the reaction at A has to be determined. Why?

$$\circlearrowleft + \Sigma M_B = 0; \quad -A_y(0.400\text{ m}) + 120\text{ N}(0.125\text{ m}) - 225\text{ N}(0.100\text{ m}) = 0$$

$$A_y = -18.75\text{ N}$$

The negative sign for A_y indicates that $\mathbf{A}_y$ acts in the *opposite sense* to that shown on the free-body diagram.

Free-Body Diagram. Passing an imaginary section perpendicular to the axis of the shaft through C yields the free-body diagram of segment AC shown in Fig. 7–5c.

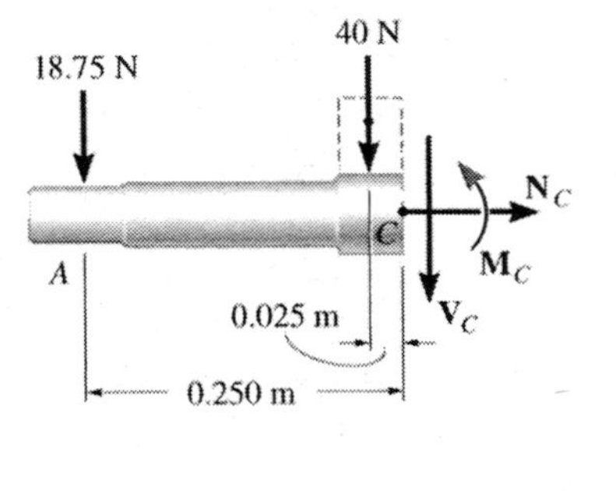

(c)

Equations of Equilibrium.

$$\overset{+}{\rightarrow} \Sigma F_x = 0; \quad N_C = 0 \qquad \textit{Ans.}$$

$$+\uparrow \Sigma F_y = 0; \quad -18.75\text{ N} - 40\text{ N} - V_C = 0$$

$$V_C = -58.8\text{ N} \qquad \textit{Ans.}$$

$$\circlearrowleft + \Sigma M_C = 0; \quad M_C + 40\text{ N}(0.025\text{ m}) + 18.75\text{ N}(0.250\text{ m}) = 0$$

$$M_C = -5.69\text{ N}\cdot\text{m} \qquad \textit{Ans.}$$

What do the negative signs for V_C and M_C indicate? As an exercise, calculate the reaction at B and try to obtain the same results using segment CBD of the shaft.

EXAMPLE 7.3

The hoist in Fig. 7–6*a* consists of the beam *AB* and attached pulleys, the cable, and the motor. Determine the resultant internal loadings acting on the cross section at *C* if the motor is lifting the 500-N (≈ 50-kg) load *W* with constant velocity. Neglect the weight of the pulleys and beam.

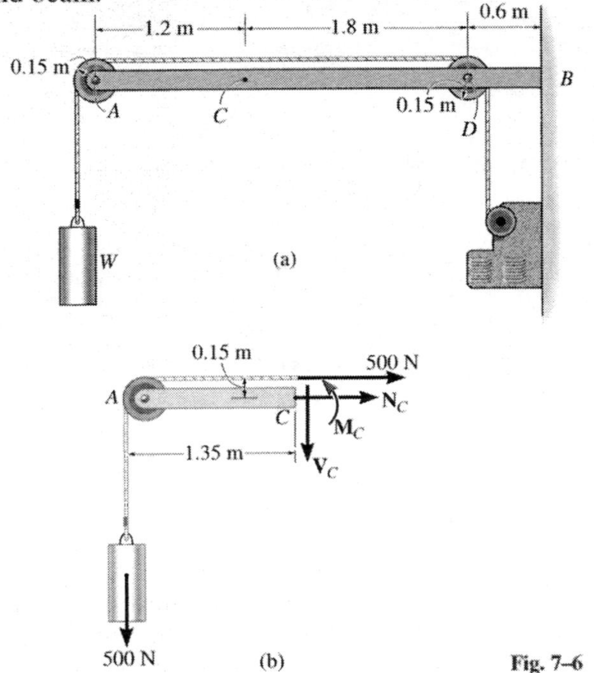

Fig. 7–6

Solution

The most direct way to solve this problem is to section both the cable and the beam at *C* and then consider the entire left segment.

Free-Body Diagram. See Fig. 7–6*b*.

Equations of Equilibrium.

$\overset{+}{\rightarrow} \Sigma F_x = 0;$ $\quad 500 \text{ N} + N_C = 0 \qquad N_C = -500 \text{ N}$ *Ans.*

$+\uparrow \Sigma F_y = 0;$ $\quad -500 \text{ N} - V_C = 0 \qquad V_C = -500 \text{ N}$ *Ans.*

$\curvearrowleft + \Sigma M_C = 0;$ $\quad 500 \text{ N } (1.35 \text{ m}) - 500 \text{ N } (0.15 \text{ m}) + M_C = 0$

$$M_C = -600 \text{ N} \cdot \text{m}$$ *Ans.*

As an exercise, try obtaining these same results by considering just the beam segment *AC*, i.e., remove the pulley at *A* from the beam and show the 500-N force components of the pulley acting on the beam segment *AC*. Also, this problem can be worked by first finding the reactions at *B*, ($B_x = 0$, $B_y = 1000$ N, $M_B = 2100$ N · m) and then considering segment *CB*.

EXAMPLE 7.4

Determine the resultant internal loadings acting on the cross section at G of the wooden beam shown in Fig. 7–7*a*. Assume the joints at A, B, C, D, and E are pin connected.

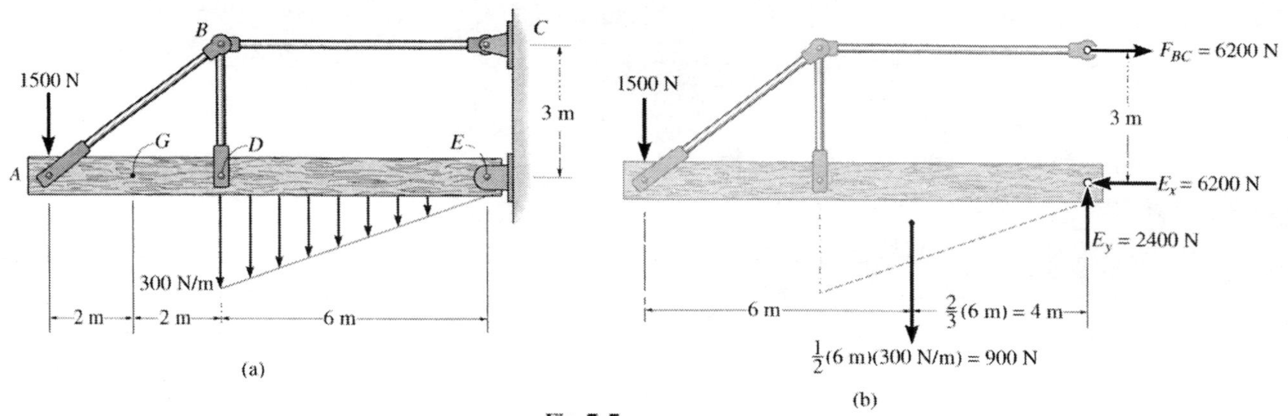

Fig. 7–7

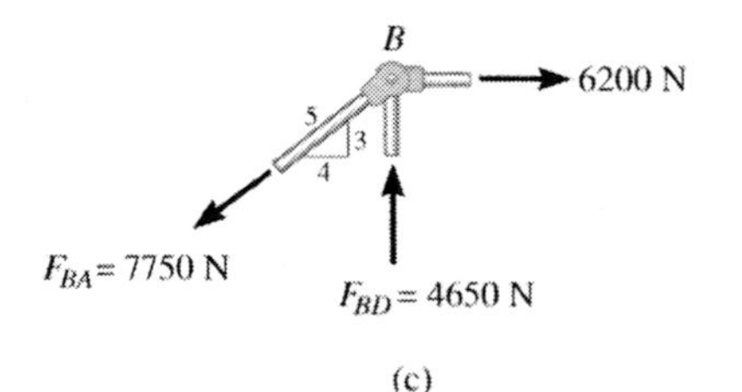

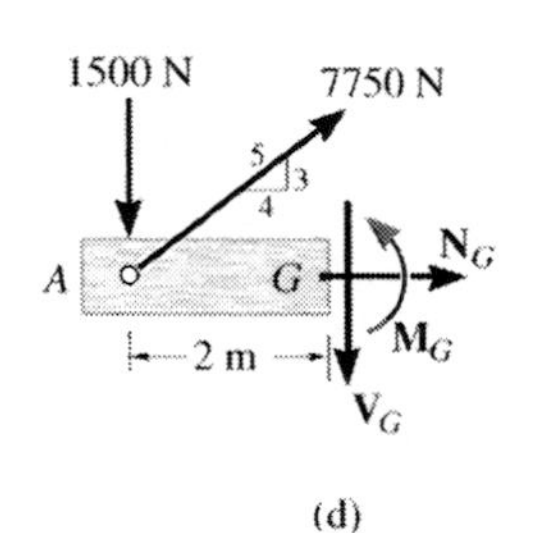

Solution

Support Reactions. Here we will consider segment AG for the analysis. A free-body diagram of the *entire* structure is shown in Fig. 7–7*b*. Verify the computed reactions at E and C. In particular, note that BC is a *two-force member* since only two forces act on it. For this reason the reaction at C must be horizontal as shown.

Since BA and BD are also two-force members, the free-body diagram of joint B is shown in Fig. 7–7*c*. Again, verify the magnitudes of the computed forces $\mathbf{F}_{BA}$ and $\mathbf{F}_{BD}$.

Free-Body Diagram. Using the result for $\mathbf{F}_{BA}$, the left section AG of the beam is shown in Fig. 7–7*d*.

Equations of Equilibrium. Applying the equations of equilibrium to segment AG, we have

$$\overset{+}{\rightarrow} \Sigma F_x = 0; \quad 7750\text{ N}(\tfrac{4}{5}) + N_G = 0 \qquad N_G = -6200\text{ N} \qquad \textit{Ans.}$$

$$+\uparrow \Sigma F_y = 0; \quad -1500\text{ N} + 7500\text{ N}(\tfrac{3}{5}) - V_G = 0$$

$$V_G = 3150\text{ N} \qquad \textit{Ans.}$$

$$\circlearrowleft + \Sigma M_G = 0; \quad M_G - (7750\text{ N})(\tfrac{3}{5})(2\text{ m}) + 1500\text{ N}(2\text{ m}) = 0$$

$$M_G = 6300\text{ N}\cdot\text{m} \qquad \textit{Ans.}$$

As an exercise, compute these same results using segment GE.

EXAMPLE 7.5

Determine the resultant internal loadings acting on the cross section at B of the pipe shown in Fig. 7–8a. The pipe has a mass of 2 kg/m and is subjected to both a vertical force of 50 N and a couple moment of 70 N · m at its end A. It is fixed to the wall at C.

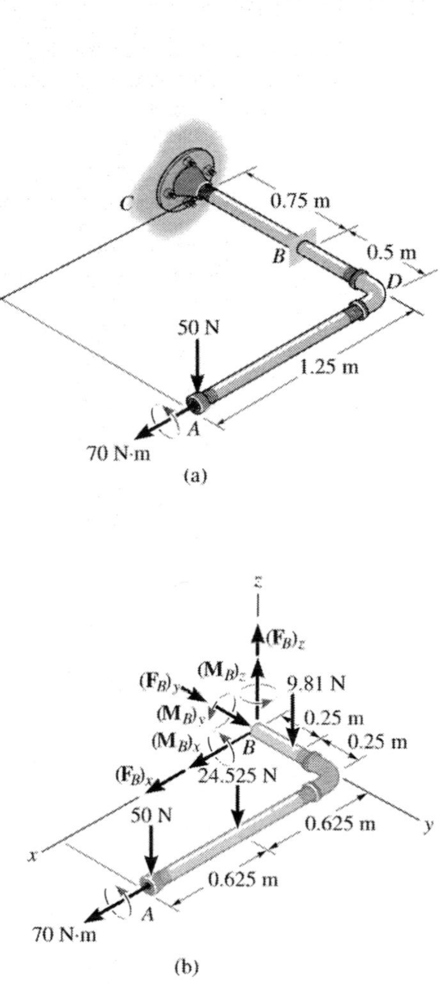

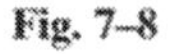
Fig. 7–8

Solution

The problem can be solved by considering segment AB, which does not involve the support reactions at C.

Free-Body Diagram. The x, y, z axes are established at B and the free-body diagram of segment AB is shown in Fig. 7–8b. The resultant force and moment components at the section are assumed to act in the positive coordinate directions and to pass through the *centroid* of the cross-sectional area at B. The weight of each segment of pipe is calculated as follows:

$$W_{BD} = (2\text{ kg/m})(0.5\text{ m})(9.81\text{ N/kg}) = 9.81\text{ N}$$
$$W_{AD} = (2\text{ kg/m})(1.25\text{ m})(9.81\text{ N/kg}) = 24.525\text{ N}$$

These forces act through the center of gravity of each segment.

Equations of Equilibrium. Applying the six scalar equations of equilibrium, we have*

$\sum F_x = 0;$ $\quad (F_B)_y = 0$ *Ans.*

$\sum F_y = 0;$ $\quad (F_B)_y = 0$ *Ans.*

$\sum F_z = 0;$ $\quad (F_B)_z - 9.81\text{ N} - 24.525\text{ N} - 50\text{ N} = 0$

$(F_B)_z = 84.3\text{ N}$ *Ans.*

$\Sigma(M_B)_x = 0;$ $\quad (M_B)_x + 70\text{ N}\cdot\text{m} - 50\text{ N}(0.5\text{ m}) - 24.525\text{ N}(0.5\text{ m}) - 9.81\text{ N}(0.25\text{ m}) = 0$

$(M_B)_x = -30.3\text{ N}\cdot\text{m}$ *Ans.*

$\Sigma(M_B)_y = 0;$ $\quad (M_B)_y + 24.525\text{ N}(0.625\text{ m}) + 50\text{ N}(1.25\text{ m}) = 0$

$(M_B)_y = -77.8\text{ N}\cdot\text{m}$ *Ans.*

$\Sigma(M_B)_z = 0;$ $\quad (M_B)_z = 0$ *Ans.*

What do the negative signs for $(M_B)_x$ and $(M_B)_y$ indicate? Note that the normal force $N_B = (F_B)_y = 0$, whereas the shear force is $V_B = \sqrt{(0)^2 + (84.3)^2} = 84.3\text{ N}$. Also, the torsional moment is $T_B = (M_B)_y = 77.8\text{ N}\cdot\text{m}$ and the bending moment is $M_B = \sqrt{(30.3)^2 + (0)^2} = 30.3\text{ N}\cdot\text{m}$.

*The *magnitude* of each moment about an axis is equal to the magnitude of each force times the perpendicular distance from the axis to the line of action of the force. The *direction* of each moment is determined using the right-hand rule, with positive moments (thumb) directed along the positive coordinate axes.

PROBLEMS

7-1. The column is fixed to the floor and is subjected to the loads shown. Determine the internal normal force, shear force, and moment at points A and B.

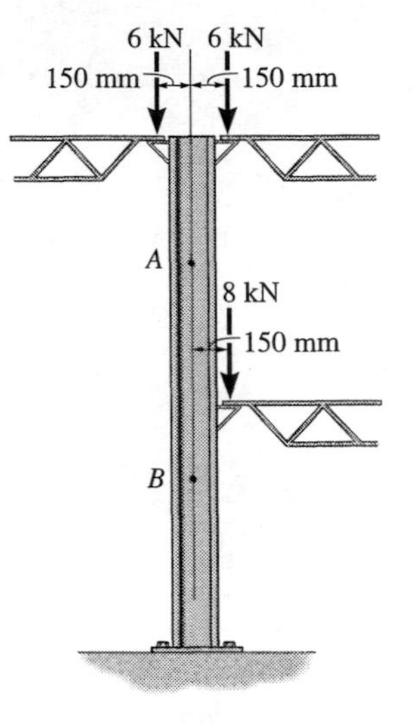

Prob. 7–1

7-2. The rod is subjected to the forces shown. Determine the internal normal force at points A, B, and C.

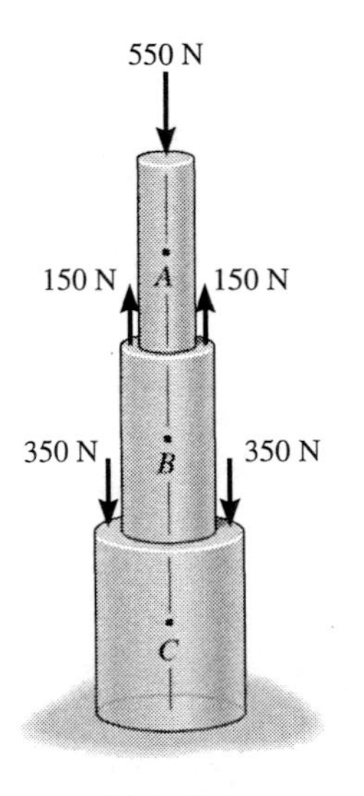

Prob. 7–2

7-3. The forces act on the shaft shown. Determine the internal normal force at points A, B, and C.

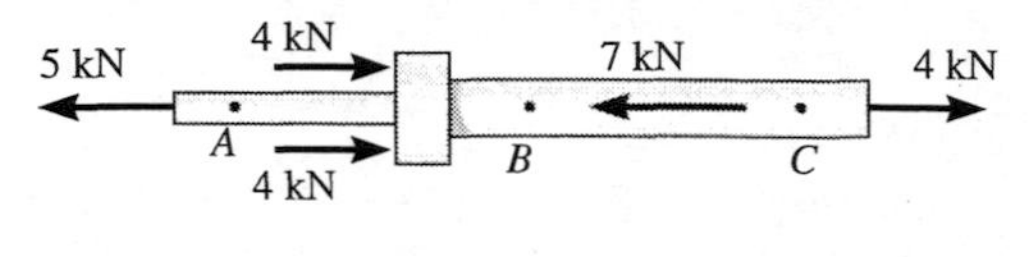

Prob. 7–3

***7-4.** The shaft is supported by the two smooth bearings A and B. The four pulleys attached to the shaft are used to transmit power to adjacent machinery. If the torques applied to the pulleys are as shown, determine the internal torques at points C, D, and E.

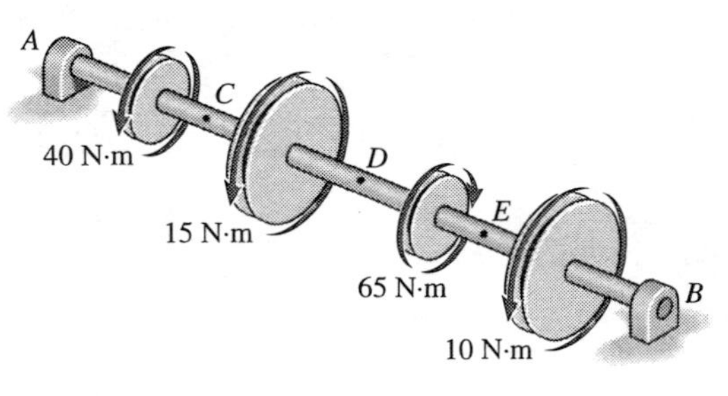

Prob. 7–4

7-5. The shaft is supported by a journal bearing at A and a thrust bearing at B. Determine the normal force, shear force, and moment at a section passing through (a) point C, which is just to the right of the bearing at A, and (b) point D, which is just to the left of the 3000-N force.

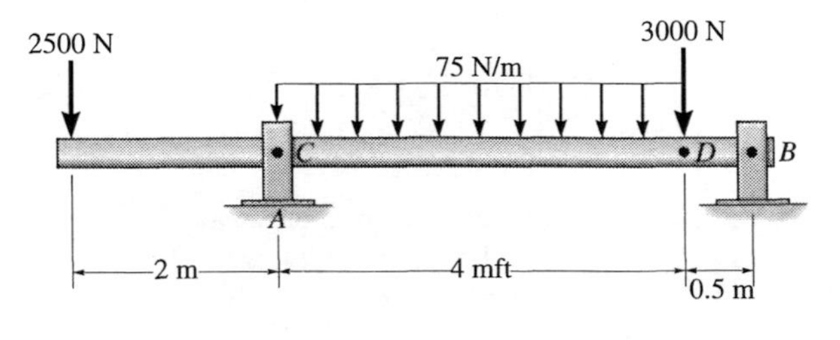

Prob. 7–5

7-6. Determine the internal normal force and shear force, and the bending moment in the beam at points C and D. Assume the support at B is a roller. Point C is located just to the right of the 8-kN load.

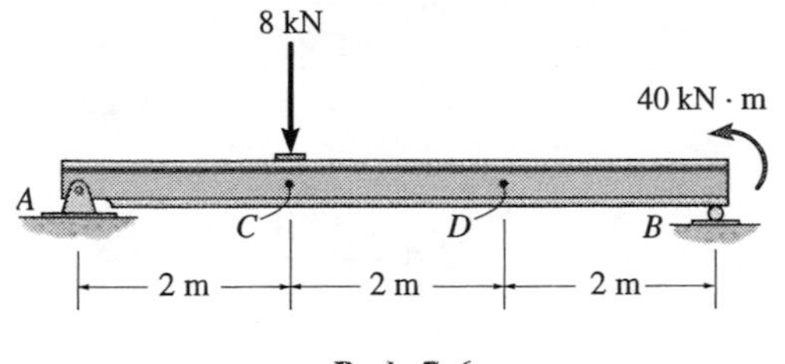

Prob. 7–6

7-7. Determine the shear force and moment at points C and D.

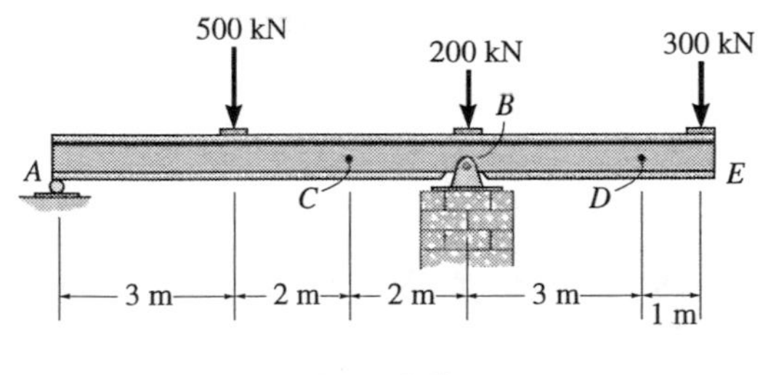

Prob. 7–7

***7-8.** Determine the normal force, shear force, and moment at a section passing through point C. Assume the support at A can be approximated by a pin and B as a roller.

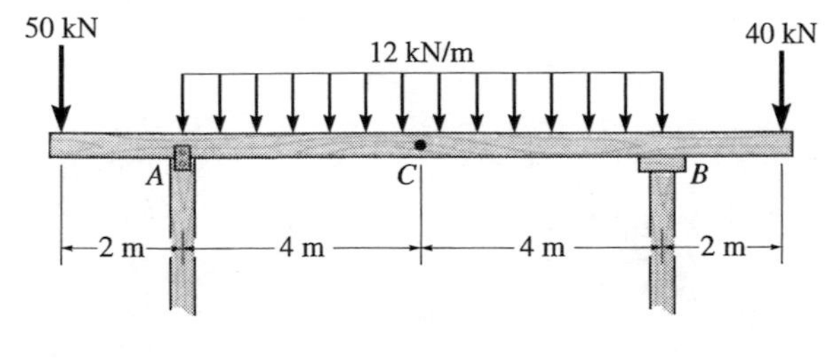

Prob. 7–8

7-9. Determine the normal force, shear force, and moment at a section passing through point D. Take $\mathbf{w} = 150$ N/m.

7-10. The beam AB will fail if the maximum internal moment at D reaches 800 N·m or the normal force in member BC becomes 1500 N. Determine the largest load w it can support.

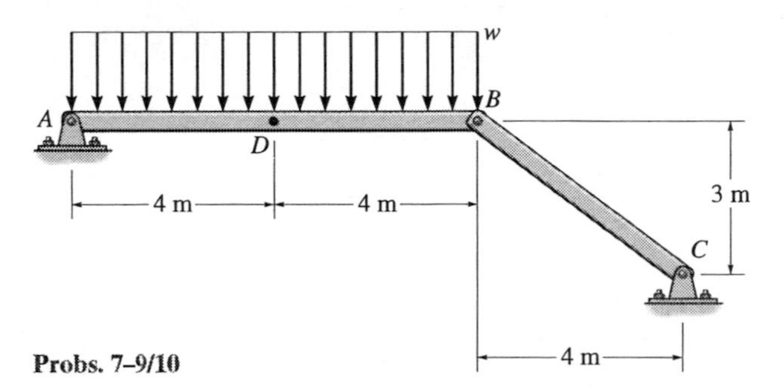

Probs. 7–9/10

7-11. Determine the shear force and moment acting at a section passing through point C in the beam.

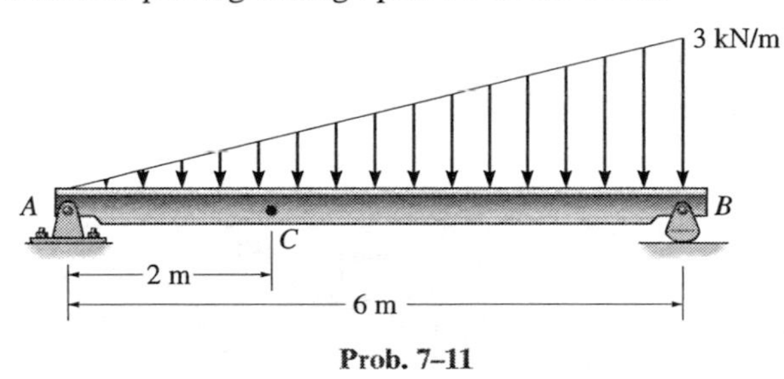

Prob. 7–11

***7-12.** The boom DF of the jib crane and the column DE have a uniform weight of 750 N/m. If the hoist and load weigh 1500 N, determine the normal force, shear force, and moment in the crane at sections passing through points A, B, and C. *Hint*: (Treat the boom tip, beyond the hoist, as weightless.)

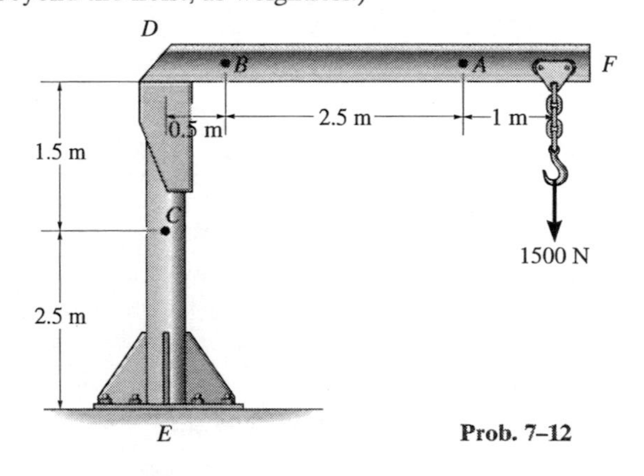

Prob. 7–12

7-13. Determine the internal normal force, shear force, and moment acting at point C and at point D, which is located just to the right of the roller support at B.

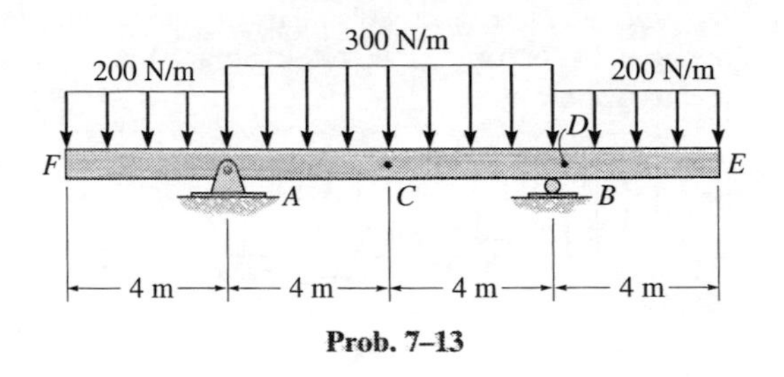

Prob. 7–13

7-14. Determine the resultant internal normal and shear force in the member at (a) section a–a and (b) section b–b, each of which passes through point A. The 500-N load is applied along the centroidal axis of the member.

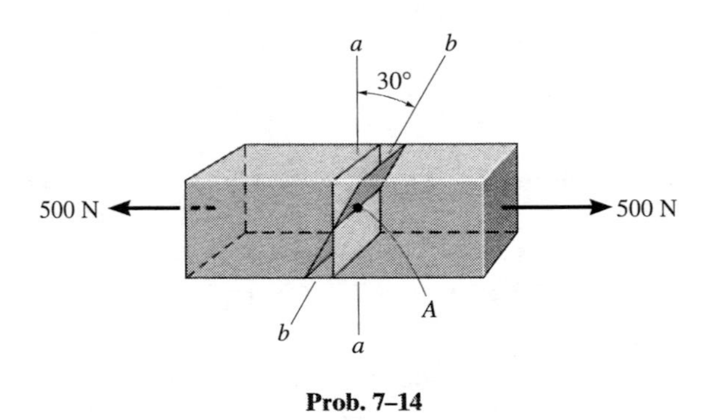

Prob. 7–14

7-15. Determine the normal force, shear force, and moment at a section passing through point E of the two-member frame.

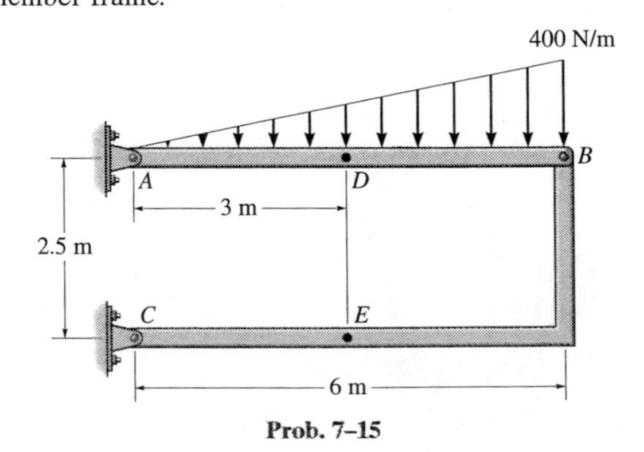

Prob. 7–15

***7-16.** The strongback or lifting beam is used for materials handling. If the suspended load has a weight of 2 kN and a center of gravity of G, determine the placement d of the padeyes on the top of the beam so that there is no moment developed within the length AB of the beam. The lifting bridle has two legs that are positioned at 45°, as shown.

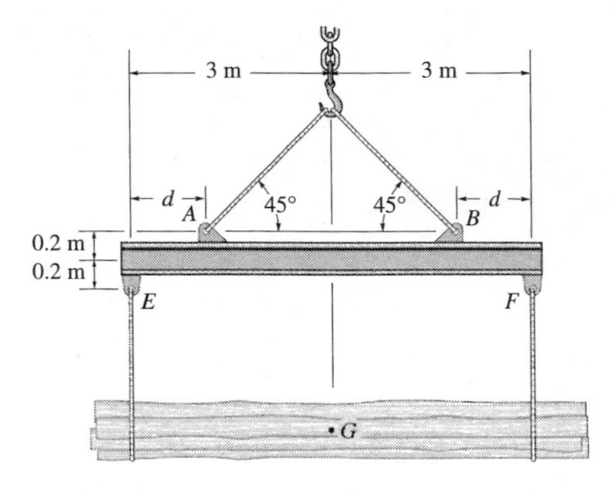

Prob. 7–16

7-17. Determine the normal force, shear force, and moment acting at a section passing through point C.

7-18. Determine the normal force, shear force, and moment acting at a section passing through point D.

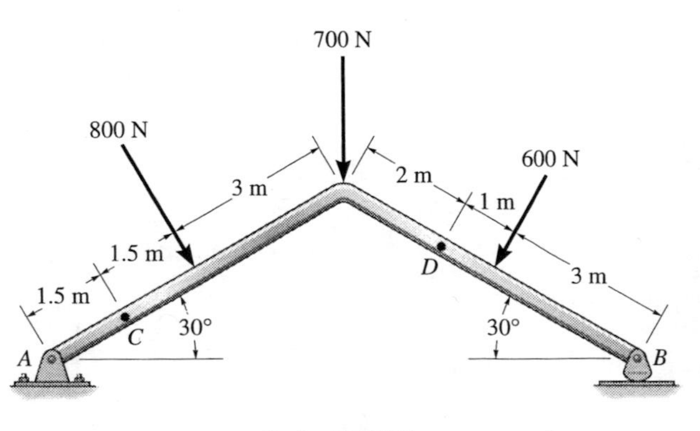

Probs. 7–17/18

7-19. Determine the normal force, shear force, and moment at a section passing through point C. Take $P = 8$ kN.

***7-20.** The cable will fail when subjected to a tension of 2 kN. Determine the largest vertical load P the frame will support and calculate the internal normal force, shear force, and moment at a section passing through point C for this loading.

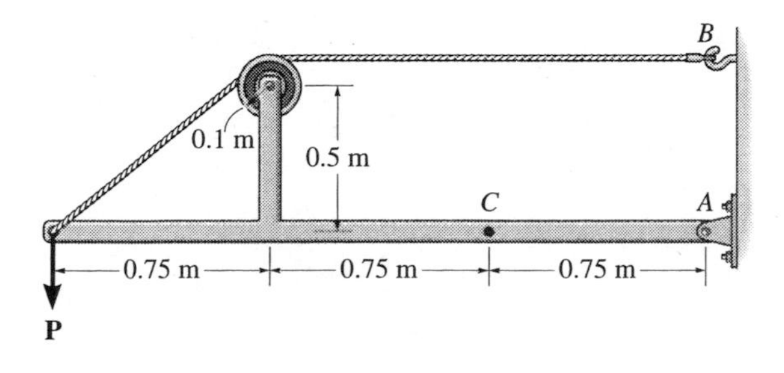

Probs. 7–19/20

7-21. Determine the internal normal force, shear force, and bending moment in the beam at point B.

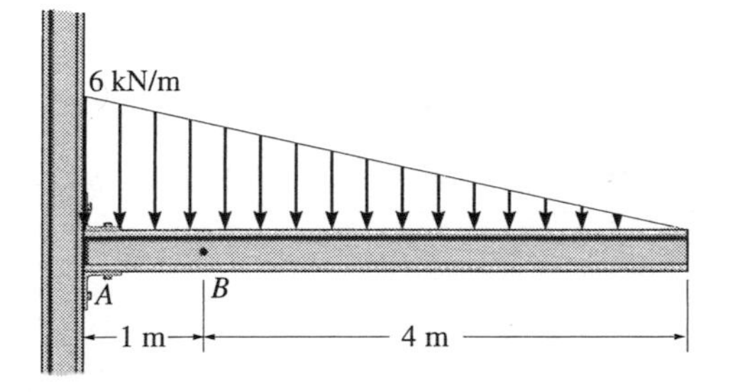

Prob. 7–21

7-22. Determine the ratio of a/b for which the shear force will be zero at the midpoint C of the beam.

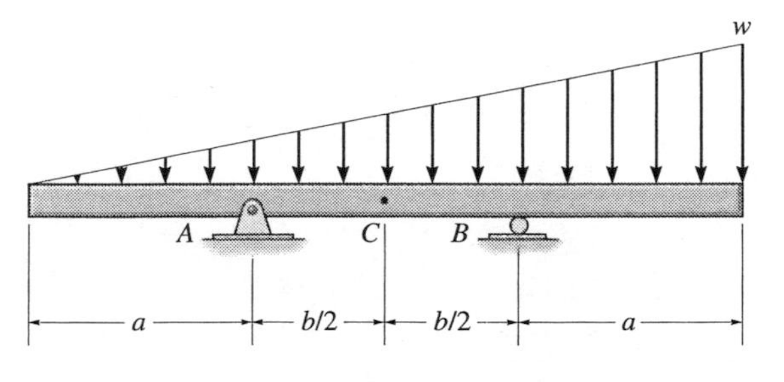

Prob. 7–22

7-23. Determine the internal normal force, shear force, and bending moment at point C.

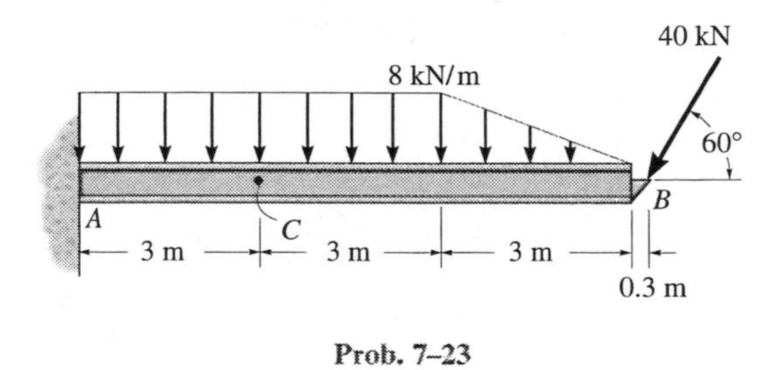

Prob. 7–23

***7-24.** The jack AB is used to straighten the bent beam DE using the arrangement shown. If the axial compressive force in the jack is 20 kN, determine the internal moment developed at point C of the top beam. Neglect the weight of the beams.

7-25. Solve Prob. 7–24 assuming that each beam has a uniform weight of 2400 N/m ($\approx$ 240 kg/m).

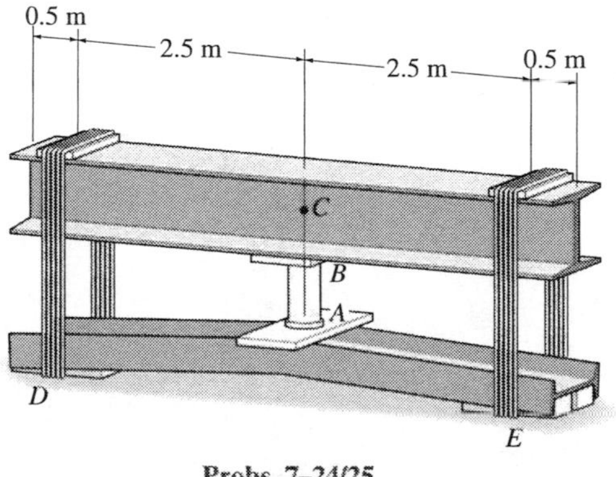

Probs. 7–24/25

7-26. Determine the normal force, shear force, and moment in the beam at sections passing through points D and E. Point E is just to the right of the 3-kN load.

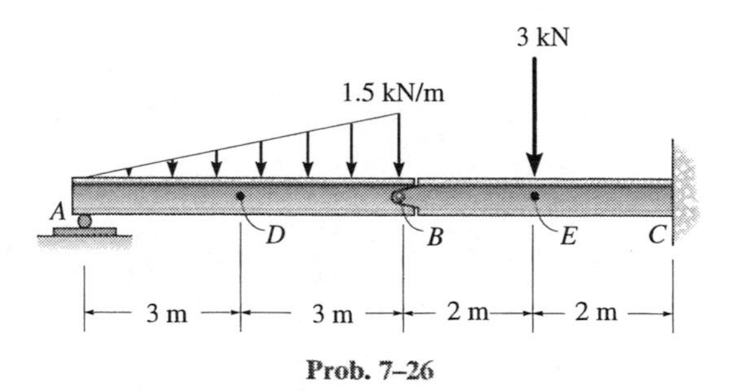

Prob. 7–26

7-27. Determine the internal normal force, shear force, and bending moment in the beam at points D and E. Point E is just to the right of the 20-kN load. Assume A is a roller support, the splice at B is a pin, and C is a fixed support.

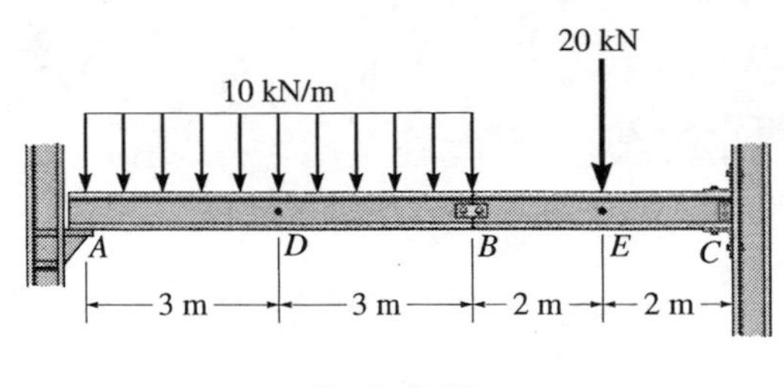

Prob. 7–27

7-28. Determine the internal normal force, shear force, and bending moment at points E and F of the frame.

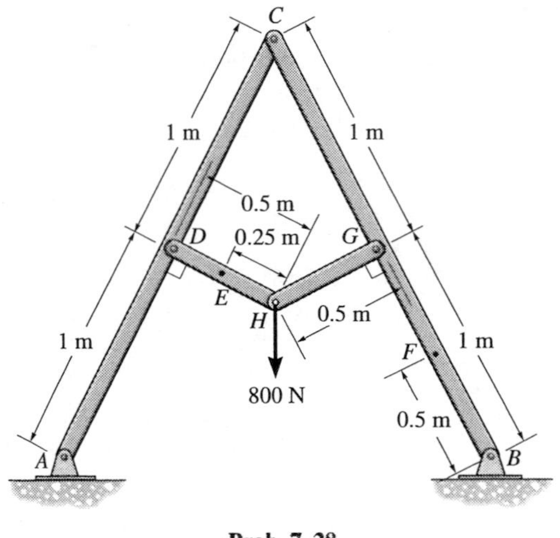

Prob. 7–28

***7-29.** The semicircular arch is subjected to a uniform distributed load along its axis of w_0 per unit length. Determine the internal normal force, shear force, and moment in the arch at $\theta = 45°$.

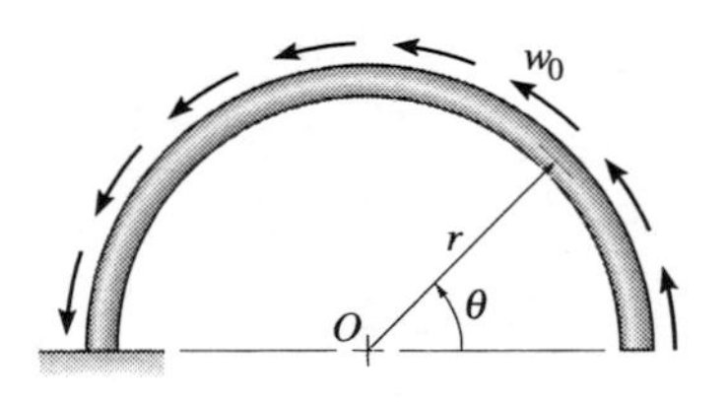

Probs. 7–29

7-30. Determine the x, y, z components of internal loading at a section passing through point C in the pipe assembly. Neglect the weight of the pipe. Take $\mathbf{F}_1 = \{80\mathbf{i} + 200\mathbf{j} - 300\mathbf{k}\}$ N and $\mathbf{F}_2 = \{250\mathbf{i} - 150\mathbf{j} - 200\mathbf{k}\}$ N.

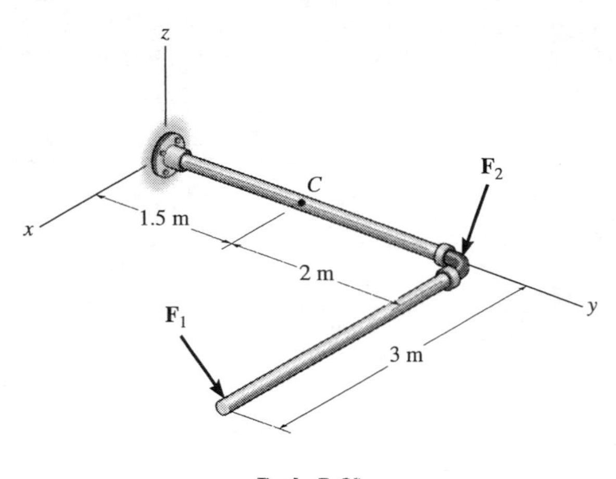

Prob. 7–30

***7-31.** Determine the x, y, z components of force and moment at point C in the pipe assembly. Neglect the weight of the pipe. The load acting at (0, 3.5 m, 3 m) is $\mathbf{F}_1 = \{-24\mathbf{i} - 10\mathbf{k}\}$ N and $\mathbf{M} = \{-30\mathbf{k}\}$ N · m and at point (0, 3.5 m, 0) $\mathbf{F}_2 = \{-80\mathbf{i}\}$ N.

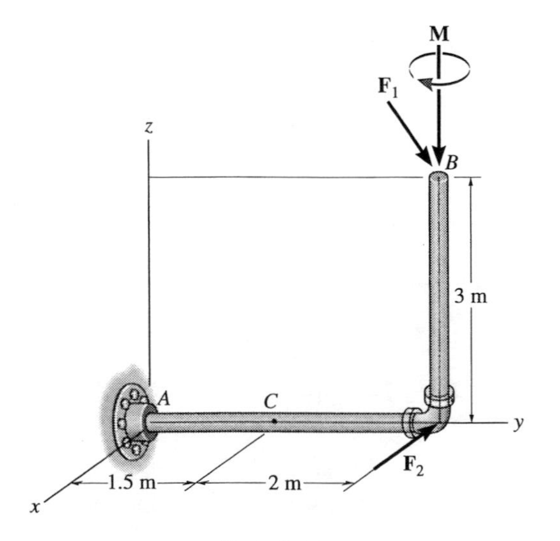

Prob. 7–31

APPENDICES

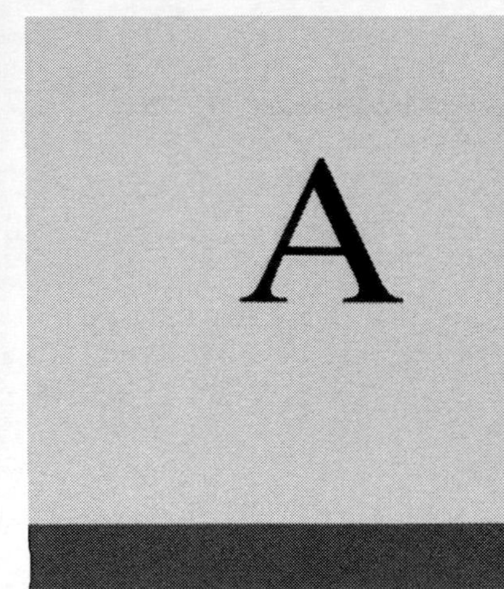

Mathematical Expressions

Quadratic Formula

If $ax^2 + bx + c = 0$, then $x = \dfrac{-b \pm \sqrt{b^2 - 4ac}}{2a}$

Hyperbolic Functions

$\sinh x = \dfrac{e^x - e^{-x}}{2}$, $\cosh x = \dfrac{e^x + e^{-x}}{2}$, $\tanh x = \dfrac{\sinh x}{\cosh x}$

Trigonometric Identities

$\sin^2\theta + \cos^2\theta = 1$

$\sin(\theta \pm \phi) = \sin\theta\cos\phi \pm \cos\theta\sin\phi$

$\sin 2\theta = 2\sin\theta\cos\theta$

$\cos(\theta \pm \phi) = \cos\theta\cos\phi \mp \sin\theta\sin\phi$

$\cos 2\theta = \cos^2\theta - \sin^2\theta$

$\cos\theta = \pm\sqrt{\dfrac{1 + \cos 2\theta}{2}}$, $\sin\theta = \pm\sqrt{\dfrac{1 - \cos 2\theta}{2}}$

$\tan\theta = \dfrac{\sin\theta}{\cos\theta}$

$1 + \tan^2\theta = \sec^2\theta \qquad 1 + \cot^2\theta = \csc^2\theta$

Power-Series Expansions

$\sin x = x - \dfrac{x^3}{3!} + \dfrac{x^5}{5!} - \dfrac{x^7}{7!} + \cdots$

$\cos x = 1 - \dfrac{x^2}{2!} + \dfrac{x^4}{4!} - \dfrac{x^6}{6!} + \cdots$

$\sinh x = x + \dfrac{x^3}{3!} + \dfrac{x^5}{5!} + \cdots$

$\cosh x = 1 + \dfrac{x^2}{2!} + \dfrac{x^4}{4!} + \cdots$

Derivatives

$\dfrac{d}{dx}(u^n) = nu^{n-1}\dfrac{du}{dx}$

$\dfrac{d}{dx}(uv) = u\dfrac{dv}{dx} + v\dfrac{du}{dx}$

$\dfrac{d}{dx}\left(\dfrac{u}{v}\right) = \dfrac{v\dfrac{du}{dx} - u\dfrac{dv}{dx}}{v^2}$

$\dfrac{d}{dx}(\sin u) = \cos u\dfrac{du}{dx}$

$\dfrac{d}{dx}(\cos u) = -\sin u\dfrac{du}{dx}$

$\dfrac{d}{dx}(\tan u) = \sec^2 u\dfrac{du}{dx}$

$\dfrac{d}{dx}(\cot u) = -\csc^2 u\dfrac{du}{dx}$

$\dfrac{d}{dx}(\sec u) = \tan u\sec u\dfrac{du}{dx}$

$\dfrac{d}{dx}(\csc u) = -\csc u\cot u\dfrac{du}{dx}$

$\dfrac{d}{dx}(\sinh u) = \cosh u\dfrac{du}{dx}$

$\dfrac{d}{dx}(\cosh u) = \sinh u\dfrac{du}{dx}$

Integrals

$$\int x^n\,dx = \frac{x^{n+1}}{n+1} + C, n \neq -1$$

$$\int \frac{dx}{a+bx} = \frac{1}{b}\ln(a+bx) + C$$

$$\int \frac{dx}{a+bx^2} = \frac{1}{2\sqrt{-ba}}\ln\left[\frac{\sqrt{a}+2\sqrt{-b}}{\sqrt{a}-x\sqrt{-b}}\right] + C, \quad a > 0, b < 0$$

$$\int \frac{x\,dx}{a+bx^2} = \frac{1}{2b}\ln(bx^2+a) + C$$

$$\int \frac{x^2\,dx}{a+bx^2} = \frac{x}{b} - \frac{a}{b\sqrt{ab}}\tan^{-1}\frac{x\sqrt{ab}}{a} + C$$

$$\int \frac{dx}{a^2-x^2} = \frac{1}{2a}\ln\left[\frac{a+x}{a-x}\right] + C, a^2 > x^2$$

$$\int \sqrt{a+bx}\,dx = \frac{2}{3b}\sqrt{(a+bx)^3} + C$$

$$\int x\sqrt{a+bx}\,dx = \frac{-2(2a-3bx)\sqrt{(a+bx)^3}}{15b^2} + C$$

$$\int x^2\sqrt{a+bx}\,dx = \frac{2(8a^2-12abx+15b^2x^2)\sqrt{(a+bx)^3}}{105b^3} + C$$

$$\int \sqrt{a^2-x^2}\,dx = \frac{1}{2}\left[x\sqrt{a^2-x^2} + a^2\sin^{-1}\frac{x}{a}\right] + C, \quad a > 0$$

$$\int x\sqrt{a^2-x^2}\,dx = -\frac{1}{3}\sqrt{(a^2-x^2)^3} + C$$

$$\int x^2\sqrt{a^2-x^2}\,dx = -\frac{x}{4}\sqrt{(a^2-x^2)^3} + \frac{a^2}{8}\left(x\sqrt{a^2-x^2} + a^2\sin^{-1}\frac{x}{a}\right) + C, a > 0$$

$$\int \sqrt{x^2 \pm a^2}\,dx = \frac{1}{2}\left[x\sqrt{x^2 \pm a^2} \pm a^2\ln(x+\sqrt{x^2 \pm a^2})\right] + C$$

$$\int x\sqrt{x^2 \pm a^2}\,dx = \frac{1}{3}\sqrt{(x^2 \pm a^2)^3} + C$$

$$\int x^2\sqrt{x^2 \pm a^2}\,dx = \frac{x}{4}\sqrt{(x^2 \pm a^2)^3} \pm \frac{a^2}{8}x\sqrt{x^2 \pm a^2} - \frac{a^4}{8}\ln(x+\sqrt{x^2 \pm a^2}) + C$$

$$\int \frac{dx}{\sqrt{a+bx}} = \frac{2\sqrt{a+bx}}{b} + C$$

$$\int \frac{x\,dx}{\sqrt{x^2 \pm a^2}} = \sqrt{x^2 \pm a^2} + C$$

$$\int \frac{dx}{\sqrt{a+bx+cx^2}} = \frac{1}{\sqrt{c}}\ln\left[\sqrt{a+bx+cx^2} + x\sqrt{c} + \frac{b}{2\sqrt{c}}\right] + C, c > 0$$

$$= \frac{1}{\sqrt{-c}}\sin^{-1}\left(\frac{-2cx-b}{\sqrt{b^2-4ac}}\right) + C, c < 0$$

$$\int \sin x\,dx = -\cos x + C$$

$$\int \cos x\,dx = \sin x + C$$

$$\int x\cos(ax)\,dx = \frac{1}{a^2}\cos(ax) + \frac{x}{a}\sin(ax) + C$$

$$\int x^2\cos(ax)\,dx = \frac{2x}{a^2}\cos(ax) + \frac{a^2x^2-2}{a^3}\sin(ax) + C$$

$$\int e^{ax}\,dx = \frac{1}{a}e^{ax} + C$$

$$\int xe^{ax}\,dx = \frac{e^{ax}}{a^2}(ax-1) + C$$

$$\int \sinh x\,dx = \cosh x + C$$

$$\int \cosh x\,dx = \sinh x + C$$

B Average Mechanical Properties of Typical Engineering Materials[a]

(SI Units)

Materials		Density (Mg/m^3)	Modulus of Elasticity (GPa)	Modulus of Rigidity (GPa)	Yield Strength (MPa) Tens.	Yield Strength (MPa) Comp.[b]	Yield Strength (MPa) Shear	Ultimate Strength (MPa) Tens.	Ultimate Strength (MPa) Comp.[b]	Ultimate Strength (MPa) Shear	% Elongation in 50 mm specimen	Poisson's Ratio	Coef. of Therm. Expansion (10^{-6})/°C
Metallic													
Aluminum Wrought Alloys	2014-T6	2.79	73.1	27	414	414	172	469	469	290	10	0.35	23
	6061-T6	2.71	68.9	26	255	255	131	290	290	186	12	0.35	24
Cast Iron Alloys	Gray ASTM 20	7.19	68.9	27	–	–	–	179	669	–	0.6	0.28	12
	Malleable ASTM A-197	7.28	172	68	–	–	–	276	372	–	5	0.28	12
Copper Alloys	Red Brass C83400	8.74	101	37	68.9	68.9	–	241	241	–	35	0.35	18
	Bronze C86100	8.83	103	38	345	345	–	655	655	–	20	0.34	17
Magnesium Alloy	[Am 1004-T61]	1.83	44.7	18	152	152	–	276	276	132	1	0.30	26
Steel Alloys	Structural A36	7.85	200	75	250	250	–	400	400	–	30	0.32	12
	Stainless 304	7.86	193	75	207	207	–	517	517	–	40	0.27	17
	Tool L2	8.16	200	78	703	703	–	800	800	–	22	0.32	12
Titanium Alloy	[Ti-6A1-4Y]	4.43	126	44	924	924	–	1,000	1,000	–	16	0.36	9.4
Nonmetallic													
Concrete	Low Strength	2.38	22.1	–	–	–	12	–	–	–	–	0.15	11
	High Strength	2.38	29.0	–	–	–	38	–	–	–	–	0.15	11
Plastic Reinforced	Kevlar 49	1.45	131	–	–	–	–	717	483	20.3	2.8	0.34	–
	30% Glass	1.45	72.4	–	–	–	–	90	131	–	–	0.34	–
Wood Select Structural Grade	Douglas Fir	0.47	13.1	–	–	–	–	2.1[c]	26[d]	6.2[d]	–	0.29[e]	–
	White Spruce	3.60	9.65	–	–	–	–	2.5[c]	36[d]	6.7[d]		0.31[e]	–

[a] Specific values may vary for a particular material due to alloy or mineral composition, mechanical working of the specimen, or heat treatment. For a more exact value reference books for the material should be consulted.

[b] The yield and ultimate strengths for ductile materials can be assumed equal for both tension and compression.

[c] Measured perpendicular to the grain.

[d] Measured parallel to the grain.

[e] Deformation measured perpendicular to the grain when the load is applied along the grain.

C Geometric Properties of An Area and Volume

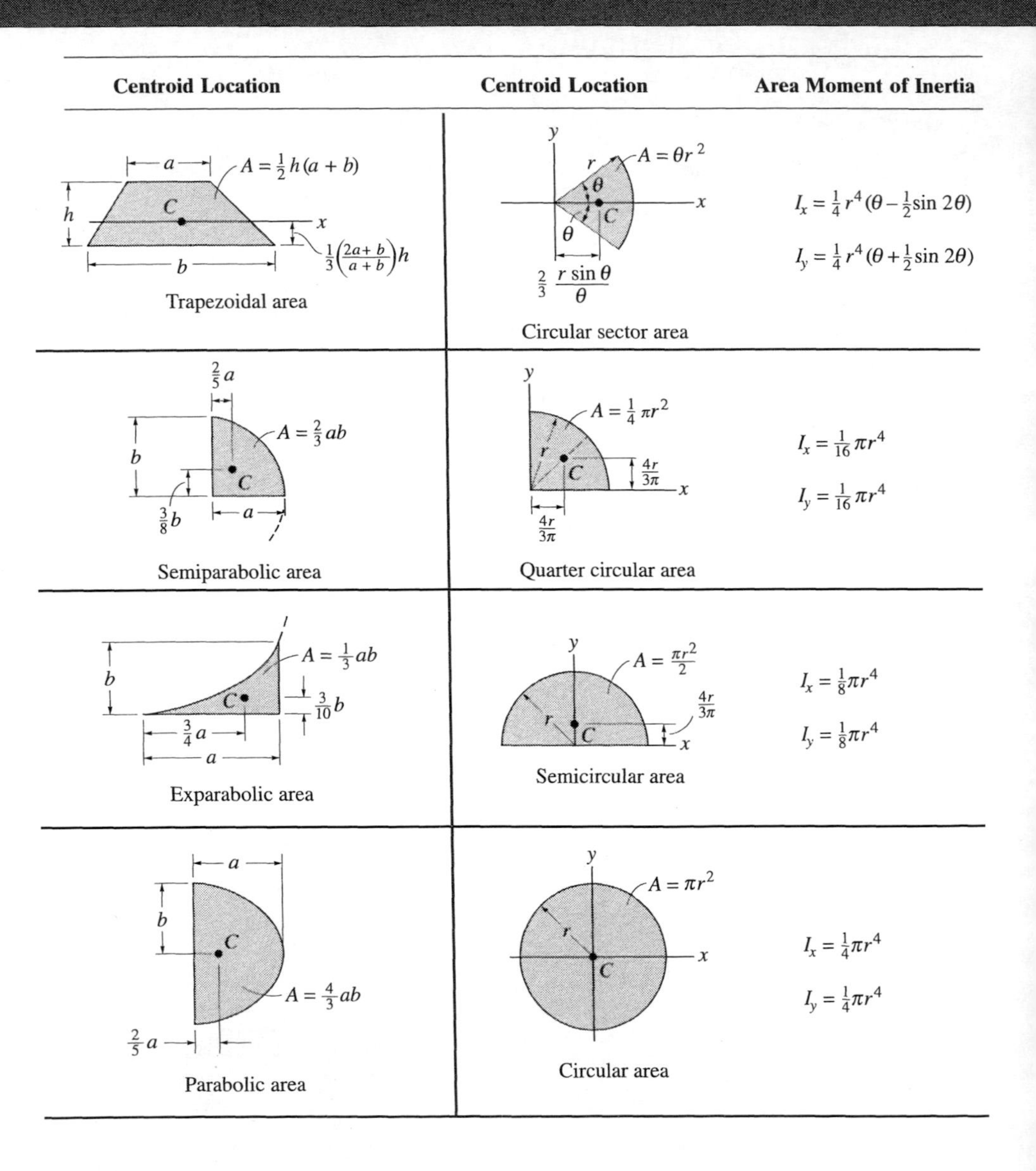

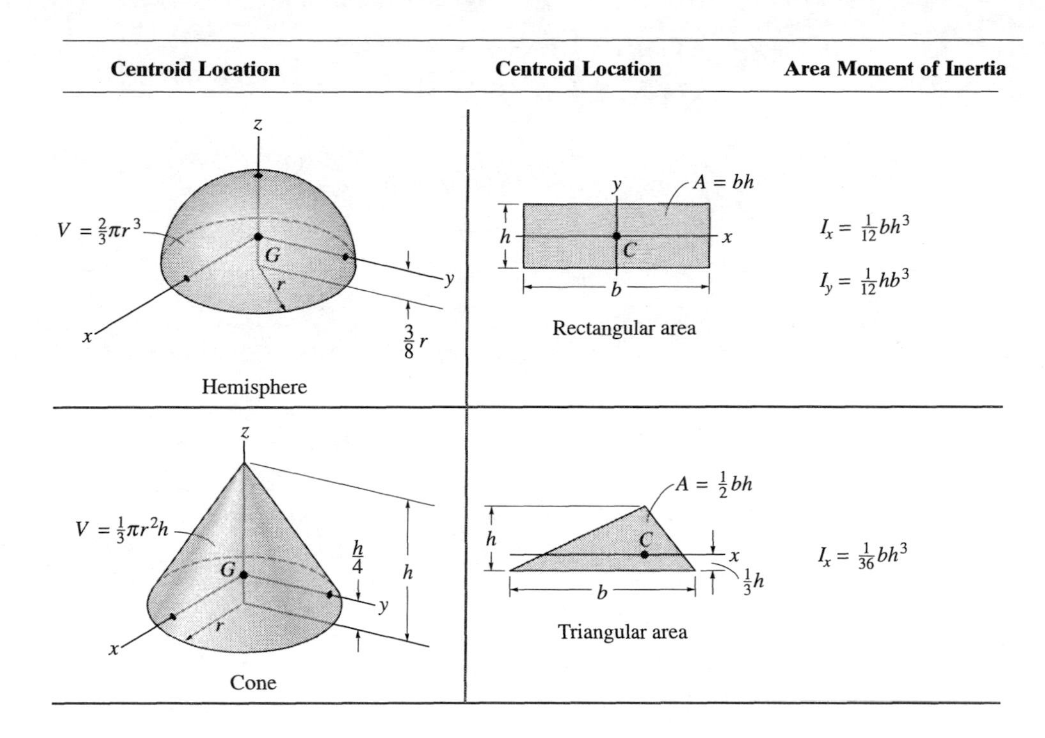
Centroid Location
Centroid Location
Area Moment of Inertia
z
$V = \frac{2}{3}\pi r^3$
G
r
y
x
$\frac{3}{8}r$
Hemisphere
y
$A = bh$
h
C
x
b
Rectangular area
$I_x = \frac{1}{12}bh^3$
$I_y = \frac{1}{12}hb^3$
z
$V = \frac{1}{3}\pi r^2 h$
G
$\frac{h}{4}$
h
y
r
x
Cone
$A = \frac{1}{2}bh$
h
C
x
$\frac{1}{3}h$
b
Triangular area
$I_x = \frac{1}{36}bh^3$

D Properties of Wide-Flange Sections

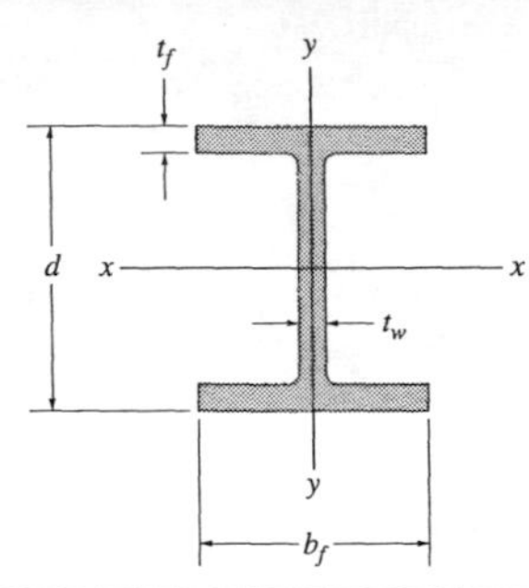

Wide-Flange Sections or W Shapes   SI Units

Designation	Area A	Depth d	Web thickness t_w	Flange width b_f	Flange thickness t_f	$x-x$ axis I	$x-x$ axis S	$x-x$ axis r	$y-y$ axis I	$y-y$ axis S	$y-y$ axis r
mm × kg/m	mm^2	mm	mm	mm	mm	10^6 mm^4	10^3 mm^3	mm	10^6 mm^4	10^3 mm^3	mm
W610 × 155	19 800	611	12.70	324.0	19.0	1 290	4 220	255	108	667	73.9
W610 × 140	17 900	617	13.10	230.0	22.2	1 120	3 630	250	45.1	392	50.2
W610 × 125	15 900	612	11.90	229.0	19.6	985	3 220	249	39.3	343	49.7
W610 × 113	14 400	608	11.20	228.0	17.3	875	2 880	247	34.3	301	48.8
W610 × 101	12 900	603	10.50	228.0	14.9	764	2 530	243	29.5	259	47.8
W610 × 92	11 800	603	10.90	179.0	15.0	646	2 140	234	14.4	161	34.9
W610 × 82	10 500	599	10.00	178.0	12.8	560	1 870	231	12.1	136	33.9
W460 × 97	12 300	466	11.40	193.0	19.0	445	1 910	190	22.8	236	43.1
W460 × 89	11 400	463	10.50	192.0	17.7	410	1 770	190	20.9	218	42.8
W460 × 82	10 400	460	9.91	191.0	16.0	370	1 610	189	18.6	195	42.3
W460 × 74	9 460	457	9.02	190.0	14.5	333	1 460	188	16.6	175	41.9
W460 × 68	8 730	459	9.14	154.0	15.4	297	1 290	184	9.41	122	32.8
W460 × 60	7 590	455	8.00	153.0	13.3	255	1 120	183	7.96	104	32.4
W460 × 52	6 640	450	7.62	152.0	10.8	212	942	179	6.34	83.4	30.9
W410 × 85	10 800	417	10.90	181.0	18.2	315	1 510	171	18.0	199	40.8
W410 × 74	9 510	413	9.65	180.0	16.0	275	1 330	170	15.6	173	40.5
W410 × 67	8 560	410	8.76	179.0	14.4	245	1 200	169	13.8	154	40.2
W410 × 53	6 820	403	7.49	177.0	10.9	186	923	165	10.1	114	38.5
W410 × 46	5 890	403	6.99	140.0	11.2	156	774	163	5.14	73.4	29.5
W410 × 39	4 960	399	6.35	140.0	8.8	126	632	159	4.02	57.4	28.5
W360 × 79	10 100	354	9.40	205.0	16.8	227	1 280	150	24.2	236	48.9
W360 × 64	8 150	347	7.75	203.0	13.5	179	1 030	148	18.8	185	48.0
W360 × 57	7 200	358	7.87	172.0	13.1	160	894	149	11.1	129	39.3
W360 × 51	6 450	355	7.24	171.0	11.6	141	794	148	9.68	113	38.7
W360 × 45	5 710	352	6.86	171.0	9.8	121	688	146	8.16	95.4	37.8
W360 × 39	4 960	363	6.48	128.0	10.7	102	578	143	3.75	58.6	27.5
W360 × 33	4 190	349	5.84	127.0	8.5	82.9	475	141	2.91	45.8	26.4

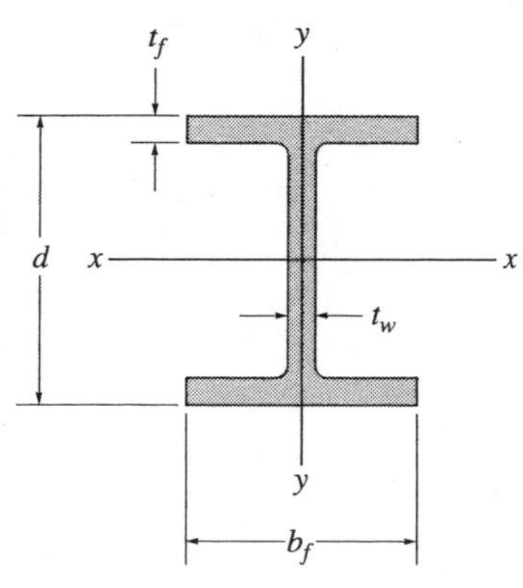

Wide-Flange Sections or W Shapes SI Units

Designation	Area A	Depth d	Web thickness t_w	Flange width b_f	Flange thickness t_f	$x-x$ axis I	$x-x$ axis S	$x-x$ axis r	$y-y$ axis I	$y-y$ axis S	$y-y$ axis r
mm × kg/m	mm^2	mm	mm	mm	mm	10^6 mm^4	10^3 mm^3	mm	10^6 mm^4	10^3 mm^3	mm
W310 × 129	16 500	318	13.10	308.0	20.6	308	1 940	137	100	649	77.8
W310 × 74	9 480	310	9.40	205.0	16.3	165	1 060	132	23.4	228	49.7
W310 × 67	8 530	306	8.51	204.0	14.6	145	948	130	20.7	203	49.3
W310 × 39	4 930	310	5.84	165.0	9.7	84.8	547	131	7.23	87.6	38.3
W310 × 33	4 180	313	6.60	102.0	10.8	65.0	415	125	1.92	37.6	21.4
W310 × 24	3 040	305	5.59	101.0	6.7	42.8	281	119	1.16	23.0	19.5
W310 × 21	2 680	303	5.08	101.0	5.7	37.0	244	117	0.986	19.5	19.2
W250 × 149	19 000	282	17.30	263.0	28.4	259	1 840	117	86.2	656	67.4
W250 × 80	10 200	256	9.40	255.0	15.6	126	984	111	43.1	338	65.0
W250 × 67	8 560	257	8.89	204.0	15.7	104	809	110	22.2	218	50.9
W250 × 58	7 400	252	8.00	203.0	13.5	87.3	693	109	18.8	185	50.4
W250 × 45	5 700	266	7.62	148.0	13.0	71.1	535	112	7.03	95	35.1
W250 × 28	3 620	260	6.35	102.0	10.0	39.9	307	105	1.78	34.9	22.2
W250 × 22	2 850	254	5.84	102.0	6.9	28.8	227	101	1.22	23.9	20.7
W250 × 18	2 280	251	4.83	101.0	5.3	22.5	179	99.3	0.919	18.2	20.1
W200 × 100	12 700	229	14.50	210.0	23.7	113	987	94.3	36.6	349	53.7
W200 × 86	11 000	222	13.00	209.0	20.6	94.7	853	92.8	31.4	300	53.4
W200 × 71	9 100	216	10.20	206.0	17.4	76.6	709	91.7	25.4	247	52.8
W200 × 59	7 580	210	9.14	205.0	14.2	61.2	583	89.9	20.4	199	51.9
W200 × 46	5 890	203	7.24	203.0	11.0	45.5	448	87.9	15.3	151	51.0
W200 × 36	4 570	201	6.22	165.0	10.2	34.4	342	86.8	7.64	92.6	40.9
W200 × 22	2 860	206	6.22	102.0	8.0	20.0	194	83.6	1.42	27.8	22.3
W150 × 37	4 730	162	8.13	154.0	11.6	22.2	274	68.5	7.07	91.8	38.7
W150 × 30	3 790	157	6.60	153.0	9.3	17.1	218	67.2	5.54	72.4	38.2
W150 × 22	2 860	152	5.84	152.0	6.6	12.1	159	65.0	3.87	50.9	36.8
W150 × 24	3 060	160	6.60	102.0	10.3	13.4	168	66.2	1.83	35.9	24.5
W150 × 18	2 290	153	5.84	102.0	7.1	9.19	120	63.3	1.26	24.7	23.5
W150 × 14	1 730	150	4.32	100.0	5.5	6.84	91.2	62.9	0.912	18.2	23.0

Answers to Selected Problems

Chapter 1

1–1. **a)** 4.66 m, **b)** 55.6 s, **c)** 4.56 kN, **d)** 2.77 Mg

1–2. **a)** 0.000431 kg = 0.431 g,
b) $35.3(10^3)$ N = 35.3 kN,
c) 0.00532 km = 5.32 m

1–4. **a)** $(430 \text{ kg})^2 = 0.185 \text{ Mg}^2$,
b) $(0.002 \text{ mg})^2 = 4\ \mu\text{g}^2$,
c) $(230 \text{ m})^3 = 0.0122 \text{ km}^3$

1–6. **a)** $W = 98.1$ N,
b) $W = 4.90$ mN,
c) $W = 44.1$ kN

1–7. **a)** (354 mg)(45 km)/0.0356 kN = 0.447 kg · m/N,
b) (0.00453 Mg)(201 ms) = 0.911 kg · s,
c) 435 MN/23.2 mm = 18.8 GN/m

1–9. **a)** $m = \dfrac{W}{g} = 2.04$ g,
b) $m = \dfrac{W}{g} = 15.3$ Mg,
c) $m = \dfrac{W}{g} = 6.12$ Gg,

1–10. $F = 7.41(10^{-6})$ N = 7.41 μN

Chapter 2

2–20. $F_R = 546$ N, $\theta = 253°$

2–21. $\theta = 29.1°$, $F_1 = 275$ N

2–22. $F_R = 1.03$ kN, $\theta = 87.9°$

2–23. $\mathbf{F}_1 = \{-15.0\mathbf{i} - 26.0\mathbf{j}\}$ kN,
$\mathbf{F}_2 = \{-10.0\mathbf{i} + 24.0\mathbf{j}\}$ kN

2–25. $F_R = 867$ N, $\theta = 108°$

2–26. $F_R = 19.2$ N, $\theta = 2.37°$

2–27. $\theta = 68.6°$, $F_B = 960$ N

2–29. $F_{1x} = 141$ N, $F_{1y} = 141$ N, $F_{2x} = -130$ N,
$F_{2y} = 75$ N

2–30. $F_R = 217$ N, $\theta = 87.0°$

2–31. $F_{1x} = -2$ kN, $F_{1y} = 0$, $F_{2x} = 3200$ N,
$F_{2y} = -2400$ N, $F_{3x} = 1800$ N, $F_{3y} = 2400$ N,
$F_{4x} = -3000$ N, $F_{4y} = 0$, $F_R = 0$

2–33. $\theta = 54.3°$, $F_A = 686$ N

2–34. $F_R = 1.23$ kN, $\theta = 6.08°$

2–35. $\mathbf{F}_1 = \{90\mathbf{i} - 120\mathbf{j}\}$ N, $\mathbf{F}_2 = \{-275\mathbf{j}\}$ N,
$\mathbf{F}_3 = \{-37.5\mathbf{i} - 65.0\mathbf{j}\}$ N, $F_R = 463$ N

2–37. $F_R = 161$ kN, $\theta = 38.3°$

2–38. $F = 2.03$ kN, $F_R = 7.87$ kN

Chapter 3

3–3. If A · (B × C) = 0, then the volume equals zero, so that **A**, **B**, and **C** are coplanar.

3–5. ↻+ $M_P = 2.37$ kN · m ↺

3–6. ↻+ $M_O = 2.88$ kN · m ↻

3–7. ↻+ $M_P = 3.15$ kN · m ↻

3–9. ↻+ $M_P = 3.15$ kN · m ↺

3–10. ↻+ $(M_{F_1})_O = 24.1$ N · m ↻,
↻+ $(M_{F_2})_O = 14.5$ N · m ↻

3–11. $M_O = 2.42$ kN · m ↻

3–13. ↻+ $(M_{F_1})_B = 825$ N · m ↻,
↻+ $(M_{F_2})_B = 400$ N · m ↻,
↻+ $(M_{F_3})_B = 8$ N · m ↻

3–14. ↻+ $M_B = 108.8$ N · m ↺, ↻+ $M_C = 173.2$ N · m ↺

3–15. ↻+ $M_A = 237.5$ N · m ↺

3–17. $M_O = 28.1$ N · m ↺, $\theta = 88.6°$,
$(M_A)_{max} = 32.0$ N · m ↺

3–18. **a)** ↺+ $(M_A)_{max} = 412$ N · m, $\theta = 76.0°$
b) ↺+ $(M_A)_{min} = 0$, $\theta = 166°$

3–19. ↻+ $M_O = 120$ N · m ↻, ↻+ $M_O = 520$ N · m ↻

3–21. **a)** $M_A = 13.0$ N · m **b)** $F = 35.2$ N

3–22. ↻+ $(M_{F_1})_A = 433$ N · m ↻,
↻+ $(M_{F_2})_A = 1.30$ kN · m ↻,
↻+ $(M_{F_3})_A = 800$ N · m ↻,

3–23. $\theta = 8.05°$

3–25. $F_A = 115.5$ N

3–27. $F = 4$ kN

3–28. $\mathbf{M}_O = \{260\mathbf{i} + 180\mathbf{j} + 510\mathbf{k}\}$ N · m

3–29. $\mathbf{M}_O = \{440\mathbf{i} + 220\mathbf{j} + 990\mathbf{k}\}$ N · m

3–31. $\mathrm{M}_P = \{-116\mathrm{i} + 16\mathrm{j} - 135\mathrm{k}\}$ kN·m
3–32. $\mathrm{M}_O = \{-128\mathrm{i} + 128\mathrm{j} - 257\mathrm{k}\}$ N·m
3–33. $\mathrm{M}_B = \{-37.6\mathrm{i} + 90.7\mathrm{j} - 155\mathrm{k}\}$ N·m
3–35. $\mathbf{M}_C = \{-3.54\mathbf{i} - 12.8\mathbf{j} - 22.2\mathbf{k}\}$ N·m
3–36. $\mathrm{M}_A = \{-16.0\mathrm{i} - 32.1\mathrm{k}\}$ N·m
$\mathbf{M}_A = \{-16.0\mathbf{i} - 32.1\mathbf{k}\}$ N·m
3–37. $F_{AB} = 185.6$ N
3–39. $\mathrm{M}_B = \{10.6\mathrm{i} + 13.1\mathrm{j} + 29.2\mathrm{k}\}$ N·m
3–40. $\mathrm{M}_O = \{373\mathrm{i} - 99.9\mathrm{j} + 173\mathrm{k}\}$ N·m
3–41. $\mathrm{M}_R = \{-1.90\mathrm{i} + 6.00\mathrm{j}\}$ kN·m
3–42. $(\mathrm{M}_{Oa})_P = \{218\mathrm{j} + 163\mathrm{k}\}$ N·m
3–44. $(\mathrm{M}_R)_{Oa} = \{26.1\mathrm{i} - 15.1\mathrm{j}\}$ N·m
3–45. **a)** $(M_{AB})_1 = 72.0$ N·m, $(M_{AB})_2 = (M_{AB})_3 = 0$
b) $(M_{AB})_2 = (M_{AB})_3 = 0, (M_{AB})_1 = 72.0$ N·m
3–46. $M_x = 66.6$ N·m
3–48. $M_y = 0.277$ N·m
3–49. $\mathbf{M}_y = \{-66.67\mathbf{j}\}$ N·m
3–50. $M_x = 15.0$ N·m, $M_y = 4.00$ N·m,
$M_z = 36.0$ N·m
3–52. $M_x = 3.75$ N·m
3–53. $M_z = 109$ N·cm
3–54. $|M_{CA}| = 226$ N·m
3–55. $M_C = 18.3$ kN·m ↺
3–56. $M_C = 100$ N·m ↺
3–57. $M_C = 17.6$ kN·m ↺
3–59. $F = 133$ N, $F = 800$ N
3–60. $T = 0.909$ kN
3–61. $N = 26.0$ N
3–63. $F = 167$ N
Resultant couple can act anywhere.
3–64. $d = 2.03$ m
3–66. $\mathbf{M}_C = \{12.6\mathbf{k}\}$ N·m, $M_C = 12.6$ N·m
3–67. $\mathrm{M}_C = \{-360\mathrm{i} + 380\mathrm{j} + 320\mathrm{k}\}$ kN·m
3–68. $\mathrm{M}_C = \{-411\mathrm{i} - 257\mathrm{j} - 651\mathrm{k}\}$ kN·m
3–69. $\mathrm{M}_R = \{11.0\mathrm{i} - 49.0\mathrm{j} - 40.0\mathrm{k}\}$ kN·m
$M_R = 64.2$ N·m, $\alpha = 80.1°$, $\beta = 140°$, $\gamma = 129°$
3–70. $M_R = 59.9$ N·m, $\alpha = 99.0°$, $\beta = 106°$, $\gamma = 18.3°$
3–71. $\alpha = 155°$, $\beta = 115°$, $\gamma = 90°$
3–73. $d = 342$ mm

Chapter 4

4–1. $C_y = 586$ N, $F_A = \sqrt{(103.528)^2 + (400)^2} = 413$ N
4–2. $F_A = 120$ N, $F_B = 144.9$ N, $F_C = 37.5$ N
4–3. $F_H = 288.9$ N, $T_B = 328.9$ N
4–4. $F_{CD} = 975$ N, $A_x = 487.4$ N, $A_y = 155.8$ N
4–6. $(N_A)_r = 397.7$ N, $(N_A)_s = 396.5$ N
4–7. $N_B = 10.5$ N, $A_x = 42.0$ N, $A_y = 10.5$ N
4–8. $W_B = 314.29$ N
4–10. $F_B = 6.37765$ N $= 6.38$ N,
$A_x = 3.19$ N, $A_y = 2.48$ N
4–11. $F_{BC} = 574$ N, $A_x = 1.08$ kN, $A_y = 637$ N
4–12. $A_x = 1462$ N, $F_B = 1.66$ kN
4–14. $D_x = 0, D_y = 1.65$ kN, $M_D = 1.40$ kN·m,
$(M_D)_{max} = 3.00$ kN·m

4–15. $x = 2.5$ m, $A_x = N_B = 4.17$ kN, $A_y = 5.00$ kN
$x = 1$ m, $A_x = N_B = 1.67$ kN, $A_y = 5.00$ kN

4–16. $F_B = 105$ N

4–17. $h = 4.731$ m

4–18. $N_A = 408.1$ N, $F_B = 251.2$ N

4–19. $B_x = 989$ N, $A_x = 989$ N, $B_y = 186$ N

4–20. $T = 5$ kN, $T_{BC} = 16.4$ kN, $F_A = 20.6$ kN

4–22. $R_A = 204.67$ kN, $R_B = 625.33$ kN

4–23. $C_x = 1333.3$ N, $C_y = 2888.9$ N

4–24. $N_A = 8.76$ kN, $N_B = 4.64$ kN, $W = 18.96$ kN

4–26. $F_2 = 724$ N, $F_1 = 1.45$ kN, $F_A = 1.75$ kN

4–27. $d = \frac{3a}{4}$

4–28. $N_B = 2.11$ N, $F_A = 2.81$ N

4–30. $k = 336.8$ N/m

4–31. $R_C = 255.6$ N, $R_B = 47.8$ N, $R_A = 104$ N

4–33. $F_A = 15$ kN, $M_A = 24.74$ kN

4–34. $A_x = -80$ N, $A_y = 40$ N, $A_z = 0$
$(M_A)_y = 11\ \text{N}\cdot\text{m}$, $(M_A)_z = -8\ \text{N}\cdot\text{m}$

4–35. $N_C = 375$ N, $N_A = N_B = 188$ N

4–37. $P = 245$ N, $A_y = 0$, $B_z = 245$ N, $A_z = 245$ N
$B_x = 368$ N, $A_x = 123$ N

4–38. $B_z = 312$ N, $M_{B_y} = 104\ \text{N}\cdot\text{m}$, $B_x = 180$ N,
$A_x = 480$ N, $B_y = 0$, $A_z = 831$ N

4–39. $A_y = 168$ N, $A_z = 368$ N, $B_x = -358$ N
$B_y = -168$ N, $C_x = 358$ N, $C_z = -168$ N

4–40. $N_A = 16.5$ kN, $N_B = 42.3$ kN
When the wheels at A are locked, **the mine car moves.**
When both wheels at A and B are locked, **the mine car does not move.**

4–41. $F_C = 27.4$ N, $N_C = 309$ N

4–42. Yes, the pole will remain stationary.

4–44. $P = 75$ N

4–45. $P = 5$ N
The ladder will remain in contact with the wall.

4–46. $N_C = 4000$ N, $N_B = 4805$ N

4–48. The ladder will not slip.

4–49. $P = \frac{M_0}{\mu_s r a}(b - \mu_s c)$

4–50. $\mu_s \geq \frac{b}{c}$

4–52. **a)** $P = 30\ \text{N} < 39.8$ N No,
b) $P = 70\ \text{N} > 39.8$ N Yes

4–53. **a)** $P = 30\ \text{N} < 34.26$ N No,
b) $P = 70\ \text{N} > 34.26$ N Yes

4–54. Since $P_{Req'd} = 6000\ \text{N} < 7659.57$ N
It is possible to pull the load without slipping or tipping.

4–56. $P = 416.67$ N

4–57. $P = 500$ N

4–58. $m = 54.9$ kg

4–60. **a)** $W = 1272$ N, **b)** $W = 1440$ N

4–61. Dresser: $F = 90$ N
Man: $\mu_m = 0.15$

4–62. Dresser: $F = 121.45$ N
Man: $\mu_m = 0.195$

4–64. $d = 72$ mm

4–65. $\theta = 16.7°$, $\phi = 42.6°$

4–66. $1 < 10.99$ Therefore car A will not move.

4–68. $\theta = 16.7°$, $P = 0.287W$

4–69. $(F_B)_{\max} = 1157.06\ \text{kN} > 571.45$ N
Slipping occurs at A.

4–70. $\theta = 11.0°$

4–72. $\mu_s = 0.268$

4–73. $L = 1.118$ m

4–74. 1.02°

4–75. $k_B = 2.5$ kN/m

4–76. $P = 500$ N, $B_z = 200$ N, $B_x = -178.57$ N
$A_x = 678.57$ N, $By_x = 0$, $A_z = 200$ N

4–77. $F_{BD} = 171$ N, $F_{BC} = 145$ N

4–78. $T = 1.01$ kN, $F_D = 982$ N

4–79. $N_{\min} = 561$ N

4–81. $T_{BA} - 715$ N, $T_{BC} = 104$ kN, $D_x = 490$ N,
$D_y = 654$ N, $D_z = 2.29$ kN,

Chapter 5

5–1. Joint B: $F_{BA} = 286$ kN (T), $F_{BC} = 808$ kN (T)
Joint C: $F_{CA} = 571$ kN (C), $C_y = 571$ kN
Note: The support reactions A_x and A_y can be determined by analyzing Joint A using the results obtained above.

5–2. Joint B: $F_{BA} = 286$ kN (T), $F_{BC} = 384$ kN (T)
Joint C: $F_{CA} = 271$ kN (C), $C_y = 271.43$ kN
Note: The support reactions A_x and A_y can be determined by analyzing Joint A using the results obtained above.

5–3. Joint A: $F_{AD} = 849$ kN (C), $F_{AB} = 600$ kN (T)
Joint B: $F_{BD} = 400$ kN (C), $F_{BC} = 600$ kN (T)
Joint D: $F_{DC} = 1.41$ MN (T), $F_{DE} = 1.60$ MN (C)

5–5. Joint A: $F_{AE} = 8.94$ kN (C), $F_{AB} = 8.00$ kN (T)
Joint B: $F_{BC} = 8.00$ kN (T), $F_{BE} = 8.00$ kN (C)
Joint E: $F_{EC} = 8.94$ kN (T), $F_{ED} = 17.9$ kN (C)
Joint D: $F_{DC} = 8.00$ kN (T), $D_x = 16.0$ kN
Note: The support reactions C_x and C_y can be determined by analyzing Joint C using the results obtained above.

5–6. Joint A: $F_{AE} = 372$ N (C), $F_{AB} = 332$ N (T)
Joint B: $F_{BC} = 332$ N (T), $F_{BE} = 196$ N (C)
Joint E: $F_{EC} = 558$ N (T), $F_{ED} = 929$ N (C)
Joint D: $F_{DC} = 582$ N (T)

5–7. Joint B: $F_{BC} = 3$ kN (C), $F_{BA} = 8$ kN (C)
Joint A: $F_{AC} = 1.46$ kN (C), $F_{AF} = 4.17$ kN (T)
Joint C: $F_{CD} = 4.17$ kN (C), $F_{CF} = 3.12$ kN (C)
Joint E: $F_{EF} = 0$, $F_{ED} = 13.1$ kN (C)
Joint D: $F_{DF} = 5.21$ kN (T)

5–9. Joint C: $F_{CB} = 8.00$ kN (T), $F_{CD} = 6.93$ kN (C)
Joint D: $F_{DE} = 6.93$ kN (C), $F_{DB} = 4.00$ kN (T)
Joint B: $F_{BE} = 4.00$ kN (C), $F_{BA} = 12.0$ kN (T)
Note: The support reactions at support A and E can be determined by analyzing Joints A and E respectively using the results obtained above.

5–10. Joint A: $F_{AG} = 47.1$ kN (C), $F_{AB} = 33.3$ kN (T)
Joint B: $F_{BG} = 0$, $F_{BC} = 33.3$ kN (T)
Joint D: $F_{DE} = 94.3$ kN (C), $F_{DC} = 66.7$ kN (T)
Joint E: $F_{EC} = 66.7$ kN (T), $F_{EG} = 66.7$ kN (C)
Joint C: $F_{CG} = 47.1$ kN (T)

5–11. Joint A: $F_{AG} = 117.9$ kN (C), $F_{AB} = 83.3$ kN (T)
Joint B: $F_{BC} = 83.3$ kN (T), $F_{BG} = 50$ kN (T)
Joint D: $F_{DE} = 165$ kN (C), $F_{DC} = 116.7$ kN (T)
Joint E: $F_{EC} = 116.7$ kN (T), $F_{EG} = 116.7$ kN (C)
Joint C: $F_{CG} = 47.1$ kN (T)

5–13. $F_{GB} = 30$ kN (T), Joint A: $F_{AF} = 20$ kN (C),
$F_{AB} = 22.4$ kN (C)
Joint B: $F_{BF} = 20$ kN (T), $F_{BC} = 20$ kN (T)
Joint F: $F_{FC} = 28.3$ kN (C), $F_{FE} = 0$
Joint E: $F_{ED} = 0$, $F_{EC} = 20.0$ kN (T)
Joint D: $F_{DC} = 0$

5–14. Joint A: $F_{AB} = 33$ kN (C), $F_{AF} = 7.93$ kN (T)
Joint B: $F_{BF} = 23.3$ kN (T), $F_{BC} = 23.3$ kN (C)
Joint F: $F_{FC} = 4.71$ kN (C), $F_{FE} = 11.3$ kN (T)
Joint E: $F_{EC} = 30$ kN (T), $F_{ED} = 11.3$ kN (T)
Joint C: $F_{CD} = 37.7$ kN (C)

5–15. Joint A: $F_{AB} = 37.7$ kN (C), $F_{AF} = 19$ kN (T)
Joint B: $F_{BF} = 26.7$ kN (T), $F_{BC} = 26.7$ kN (C)
Joint F: $F_{FC} = 18.9$ kN (T), $F_{FE} = 5.67$ kN (T)
Joint E: $F_{ED} = 5.67$ kN (T), $F_{EC} = 0$
Joint C: $F_{CD} = 18.9$ kN (C)

5–16. $F_{HG} = 29.0$ kN (C), $F_{BC} = 20.5$ kN (T),
$F_{HC} = 12.0$ kN (T)

5–17. $F_{GF} = 29.0$ kN (C), $F_{CD} = 23.5$ kN (T),
$F_{CF} = 7.78$ kN (T)

5–19. $F_{KJ} = 13.3$ kN (T), $F_{BC} = 14.9$ kN (C),
$F_{CK} = 0$

5–20. $F_{KJ} = 112.5$ kN (T), $F_{CD} = 93.75$ kN (C),
$F_{CJ} = 31.25$ kN (C), $F_{DJ} = 0$

5–21. $F_{JI} = 7.5$ kN (T), $F_{EI} = 25$ kN (C)

5–23. $F_{FG} = 8.08$ kN (T), $F_{CD} = 8.47$ kN (C),
$F_{CF} = 0.770$ kN (T)

5–24. $F_{GF} = 67.1$ kN (C), $F_{GB} = 67.1$ kN (T)

5–25. $F_{BG} = -200\sqrt{L^2 + 9}$,
$F_{BC} = -200L$, $F_{HG} = 400L$

5–27. AB, BC, CD, DE, HI, and GI are zero-force members.
Joint E: $F_{JE} = 9.38$ kN (C), $F_{GF} = 5.625$ kN (T)

5–28. $F_{BC} = 10.4$ kN (C), $F_{HG} = 9.16$ kN (T),
$F_{HC} = 2.24$ kN (T)

5–29. $F_{CD} = 11.2$ kN (C),
Joint G: $F_{CF} = 3.21$ kN (T)
$F_{GH} = 9.155$ kN (T), $F_{CG} = 6.80$ kN (C)

5–31. $F_{GJ} = 20$ kN (C)

5–32. $F_{GC} = 10$ kN (T)

5–33. $F_{GF} = 1.78$ kN (T), $F_{CD} = 2.23$ kN (C),
$F_{CF} = 0$

5–34. **a)** $P = 25.0$ N, **b)** $P = 33.3$ N, **c)** $P' = 33.33$ N,
$P = 11.1$ N

5–35. $F_P = 59.4$ N, $F_A = 852$ N

5–37. $R_E = 177$ N, $R_A = 128$ N

5–38. $P = 40.0$ N, $x = 240$ mm

5–39. $P = 21.8$ N, At A, $R_A = 2P = 43.6$ N,
At B, $R_B = 2P = 43.6$ N, At C, $R_C = 6P = 131$ N

5–41. $A_y = 9.59$ kN, $B_y = 8.54$ kN,
$C_y = 2.93$ kN, $C_x = 9.20$ kN

5–42. $P = 743$ N

5–43. $A_y = 300$ N, $A_x = 300$ N

For pin C,
$C_x = F_{BC} \sin 45° = 300$ N,
$C_y = F_{BC} \cos 45° = 300$ N

5–45. $B_y = 1.33$ kN, $B_x = 5.00$ kN
For pin A and C, $A_x = C_x = 5.00$ kN,
$A_y = C_y = 6.67$ kN
From FBD **(b)**, $M_D = 10.0$ kN · m,
$D_y = 8.00$ kN, $D_x = 0$

5–46. $C_x = 7.5$ kN, $C_y = 10$ kN

5–47. $A_x = 4.20$ kN, $B_x = 4.20$ kN, $A_y = 4.00$ kN,
$B_y = 3.20$ kN, $C_x = 3.40$ kN, $C_y = 4.00$ kN

5–49. $T = 100$ N, $\theta = 14.6°$

5–50. $x = 3.30$ m

5–51. Pulley E: $T = 350$ N, Member ABC: $A_y = 700$ N,
$A_x = 1.88$ kN
At D: $D_x = 1.70$ kN, $D_y = 1.70$ kN

5–53. $A_x = 80$ kN, $A_y = 80$ kN, $B_y = 1.33$ kN,
$B_x = 336$ kN, $C_x = 416$ kN, $C_y = 53.3$ kN

5–54. From FBD **(a)**, $F_{AB} = 9.23$ kN, $C_x = 2.17$ kN,
$C_y = 7.01$ kN
From FBD **(b)**, $D_x = 0$, $D_y = 1.96$ kN,
$M_D = 2.66$ kN · m

5–55. $C_y = 350$ N, $C_x = 166.7$ N
$B_x = 666.7$ N, $B_y = 150$ N

5–57. $C_x = D_x = 1600$ N, $C_y = D_y = 1067$ N,
$B_y = 266.7$ N, $B_x = 800$ N, $E_x = 0$,
$E_y = 266.7$ N, $A_x = 1600$ N

5–58. $F_E = 3.64F$

5–59. $A_y = 657$ N, $C_y = 229$ N, $C_x = 0$,
$B_x = 0$, $B_y = 429$ N

5–61. $m = 366$ kg, $F_A = 2.93$ kN

5–62. $F_{AD} = 1796.3$ N, $M = 376.3$ N · m

5–63. $P = 168.85$ N

5–65. From FBD **(a)**, $A_y = 34.0$ N, $A_x = 0$
From **(b)**, $C_y = 6.54$ kN, $C_x = 0$
From **(c)**, $x = 292$ mm, $B_y = 1.06$ N, $B_x = 0$

5–66. $F_{DE} = 1.07$ kN

5–67. From FBD **(b)**, $C_y = 1.33$ kN, $B_y = 549$ N,
From FBD **(a)**, $C_x = 2.98$ kN, $A_y = 235$ N,
$A_x = 2.98$ kN, $B_x = 2.98$ kN

5–69. $F = 47.12$ N

5–70. From FBD **(a)**, $F_{AC} = 6.28$ N
FBD **(b)**, $F_{AD} = 8.58$ kN

5–71. $D_y = 2.5$ kN, $B_y = 12$ kN, $A_y = 1.5$ kN
$A_x = 0$

5–72. $P = \dfrac{kL}{2\tan\theta\sin\theta}(2 - \csc\theta)$

5–73. $F_{AD} = 990$ N (C), $F_{AB} = 700$ N (T),
$F_{DB} = 495$ N (C), $F_{DC} = 1.48$ kN (C),
$F_{CB} = 1.05$ kN (T)

5–74. $F_{HD} = 7.07$ kN (C), $F_{CD} = 50$ kN (T),
$F_{GD} = 5$ kN (T)

5–75. $F_{HB} = 21.2$ kN (C), $F_{BC} = 50$ kN (T),
$F_{HI} = 35$ kN (C)

5–77. $B_y = 115.47$ N, $A_x = 92.31$ N, $A_y = 519.27$ N,
$M_A = 2308$ N · m,

5–78. $B_x = 84.9$ kN, $B_y = 84.9$ kN, $A_x = 84.9$ kN,
$A_y = 265$ kN, $M_A = 953$ kN · m,

Chapter 6

6–2. $\bar{x} = 3.20$ cm, $\bar{y} = 3.20$ cm, $T_A = 1.707$ N
$T_C = 1.707$ N, $T_B = 5.12$ N

6–3. $\bar{x} = \dfrac{(n+1)}{2(n+2)}a$, $\bar{y} = \dfrac{n+1}{2(2n+1)}h$

6–5. $\bar{y} = \dfrac{4b}{3\pi}$, $\bar{x} = \dfrac{4a}{3\pi}$

6–6. $\bar{x} = \dfrac{\pi}{2}a$, $\bar{y} = \dfrac{\pi}{8}a$

6–7. $\bar{y} = 2.80$ m, $\bar{x} = 6.00$ m

6–9. $\bar{x} = \bar{y} = 0$, $\bar{z} = \dfrac{4}{3}$ m

6–10. $\bar{z} = \dfrac{3}{8}a$

6–11. $\bar{z} = \dfrac{5}{6}h$

6–13. $\bar{x} = 0.4a$

6–14. $\bar{z} = 2.50$ m

6–15. $\bar{y} = 2.67$ m

6–17. $\bar{y} = 154$ mm

6–18. $\bar{y} = 11.9$ mm

6–19. $\bar{x} = \dfrac{\frac{2}{3}r\sin^3\alpha}{\alpha - \frac{\sin 2\alpha}{2}}$

6–20. $\bar{y} = 2.00$ cm

6–22. $\bar{x} = 77.2$ mm, $\bar{y} = 31.7$ mm

6–23. $\bar{y} = 135$ mm

6–24. $\bar{y} = 102.4$ mm

6–26. $h = 323$ mm

6–27. $\bar{z} = 128$ mm
6–28. $\bar{x} = -1.14$ cm, $\bar{y} = 1.71$ cm, $\bar{z} = -0.857$ cm
6–30. $\bar{x} = 47.4$ mm, $\bar{y} = 29.9$ mm
6–31. $\bar{z} = 101$ mm
6–32. $\bar{z} = 58.1$ mm
6–34. $\bar{z} = 0.70$ m
6–35. $h = 2.00$ m
6–37. $F_R = 27$ kN, $x = 2.11$ m
6–38. $F_R = 15$ kN, $x = 3.889$ m
6–39. $F_R = 13.5$ kN, $x = 6.00$ m
6–41. $b = 1.5$ m, $a = 2.92$ m
6–42. $F_R = 107$ kN $\leftarrow$, $h = 1.60$ m
6–43. $F_R = 1.87$ MN, $x = 3.66$ m
6–45. $F_R = 133$ kN, $\bar{y} = 750$ m, $\bar{x} = 0$
6–46. $\bar{x} = 0$, $\bar{y} = 2.40$ m, $F_R = 42.7$ kN, $B_y = C_y = 12.8$ kN, $A_y = 17.1$ kN
6–47. $F_R = 7.62$ kN, $\bar{y} = 3.00$ m, $\bar{x} = 2.74$ m
6–48. $I_x = 39.0\ \text{m}^4$
6–49. $I_y = 8.53\ \text{m}^4$
6–50. **a)** $I_x = 23.8\ \text{m}^4$ **b)** $I_x = 23.8\ \text{m}^4$
6–52. **a)** $I_x = 1.07\ \text{m}^4$ **b)** $I_x = 1.07\ \text{m}^4$
6–53. $I_x = \dfrac{2}{15}bh^3$
6–54. $I_x = 1.54\ \text{cm}^4$
6–56. $I_x = \dfrac{2}{7}bh^3$
6–57. $I_y = \dfrac{2}{15}hb^3$
6–58. $I_x = 10.7\ \text{cm}^4$
6–60. $I_y = 2.44\ \text{m}^4$
6–61. $I_x = 0.571\ \text{cm}^4$
6–62. $I_y = 1.07\ \text{cm}^4$
6–63. $\bar{y} = 2.00$ cm, $I_{x'} = \Sigma(I_{x'})_i = 64.0\ \text{cm}^4$
6–64. $\bar{x} = 3.00$ cm, $I_{y'} = \Sigma(I_{y'})_i = 136\ \text{cm}^4$
6–66. $I_{x'} = 49.5(10^6)\ \text{mm}^4$
6–67. $I_x = 1.217(10^3)\ \text{cm}^4$, $I_y = 367.8\ \text{cm}^4$
6–68. $I_{x'} = 95.9(10^6)\ \text{mm}^4$
6–70. $\bar{y} = 80.7$ mm, $\bar{I}_{x'} = 67.6(10^6)\ \text{mm}^4$
6–71. $\bar{x} = 61.6$ mm, $\bar{I}_{y'} = 41.2(10^6)\ \text{mm}^4$
6–72. $\bar{y} = 0.181$ m, $I_{x'} = 4.23(10^{-3})\ \text{m}^4$
6–74. $\bar{y} = 22.5$ mm, $I_{x'} = 34.4(10^6)\ \text{mm}^4$
6–75. $I_{y'} = 122(10^6)\ \text{mm}^4$
6–76. $I_x = 648\ \text{cm}^4$
6–78. $\bar{y} = 2$ cm, $I_{x'} = 128\ \text{cm}^4$
6–79. $I_x = 503\ \text{cm}^4$
6–80. $\bar{I}_{x'} = \frac{1}{12}a^3b\sin^3\theta$
6–82. $\bar{y} = 53.0$ mm, $I_{x'} = 3.67(10^6)\ \text{mm}^4$
6–83. $I_{x'} = 30.2(10^6)\ \text{mm}^4$
6–84. $\bar{y} = 91.7$ mm, $I_{x'} = 216(10^6)\ \text{mm}^4$
6–85. $\bar{I}_{x'} = \frac{1}{36}bh^3$, $\bar{I}_{y'} = \frac{1}{36}hb(b^2 - ab + a^2)$
6–86. 90.5 mm
6–87. 0.4 m
6–88. $I_{xy} = \dfrac{3}{16}b^2h^2$
6–89. $\bar{z} = 0.422$ mm, $\bar{x} = \bar{y} = 0$
6–90. $I_x = 246\ \text{cm}^4$, $I_y = 61.5\ \text{cm}^4$
6–91. 10.8 kN, 2.26 m
6–93. $\bar{x} = 3.30$ cm, $\bar{y} = 3.30$ cm
6–94. $\bar{x} = -0.262$ cm, $\bar{y} = -0.262$ cm
6–95. $0.0954d^4$
6–95. $I_y = 0.0954d^4$
6–96. $I_y = 0.1874d^4$

Chapter 7

7–1. $V_A = 0$, $N_A = 12.0$ kN, $M_A = 0$, $V_B = 0$, $N_B = 20.0$ kN, $M_B = 1.20$ kN·m
7–2. $N_A = 550$ N, $N_B = 250$ N, $N_C = 950$ N
7–3. $N_A = 5.00$ kN, $N_C = 4.00$ kN, $N_B = 3.00$ kN
7–5. $M_C = 5$ kN·m, $N_C = 0$, $V_C = 1.33$ kN, $M_D = 0.98$ kN·m, $N_D = 0$, $V_D = 1.03$ kN
7–6. $N_C = 0$, $V_C = -4.0$ kN, $M_C = 8$ kN·m, $N_D = 0$, $V_D = -4.0$ kN, $M_D = 48$ kN·m
7–7. $N_C = 0$, $V_C = -386$ kN, $M_C = -428.6$ kN·m, $N_D = 0$, $V_D = 300$ kN, $M_D = -300$ kN·m
7–9. $N_D = -800$ N, $V_D = 0$, $M_D = 1.20$ kN·m
7–10. $\mathbf{w} = 100$ N/m
7–11. $M_C = 5.33$ kN·m, $V_C = 2$ kN
7–13. $N_D = 0$, $V_D = 800$ N, $M_D = -1.60$ kN·m, $N_C = 0$, $V_C = 0$, $M_D = 800$ N·m
7–14. **a)** $N_a = 500$ N, $V_a = 0$ **b)** $N_b = 433$ N, $V_b = 250$ N
7–15. $N_E = -1.92$ kN, $V_E = 800$ N, $M_E = 2.40$ kN·m
7–17. $N_C = -406$ N, $V_C = 903$ N, $M_C = 1.35$ kN·m
7–18. $N_D = -464$ N, $V_D = -203$ N, $M_D = 2.61$ kN·m
7–19. $N_C = -30$ kN, $V_C = -8$ kN, $M_C = 6$ kN·m
7–21. $N_B = 0$, $V_B = 9.6$ kN, $M_B = -12.8$ kN·m

7–22. $\frac{a}{b} = \frac{1}{4}$

7–23. $N_C = 20.0 \text{ kN}, \; V_C = 70.6 \text{ kN}, \; M_C = -302 \text{ kN} \cdot \text{m}$

7–25. $M_C = -17.8 \text{ kN} \cdot \text{m}$

7–26. $N_D = 0, V_D = 0.375 \text{ kN}, \; M_D = 3.375 \text{ kN} \cdot \text{m},$
$N_E = 0, V_E = -6 \text{ kN}, \; M_E = -6 \text{ kN} \cdot \text{m}$

7–27. $N_D = 0, V_D = 0, \; M_D = 45 \text{ kN} \cdot \text{m},$
$N_E = 0, V_E = -50 \text{ kN}, \; M_E = -60 \text{ kN} \cdot \text{m}$

7–28. $V_E = 0, \; N_E = 894 \text{ N}, \; M_E = 0, \; V_F = 447 \text{ N},$
$N_F = 224 \text{ N}, \; M_F = 224 \text{ N} \cdot \text{m}$

7–30. $C_x = -170 \text{ N}, C_y = -50 \text{ N}, C_z = 500 \text{ N},$
$M_{C_x} = 1 \text{ kN} \cdot \text{m}, M_{C_y} = -900 \text{ N} \cdot \text{m},$
$M_{C_z} = -260 \text{ N} \cdot \text{m}$

D

E

F

G

H

I

T

U

V

W

XYZ

Simply Supported Beam Slopes and Deflections

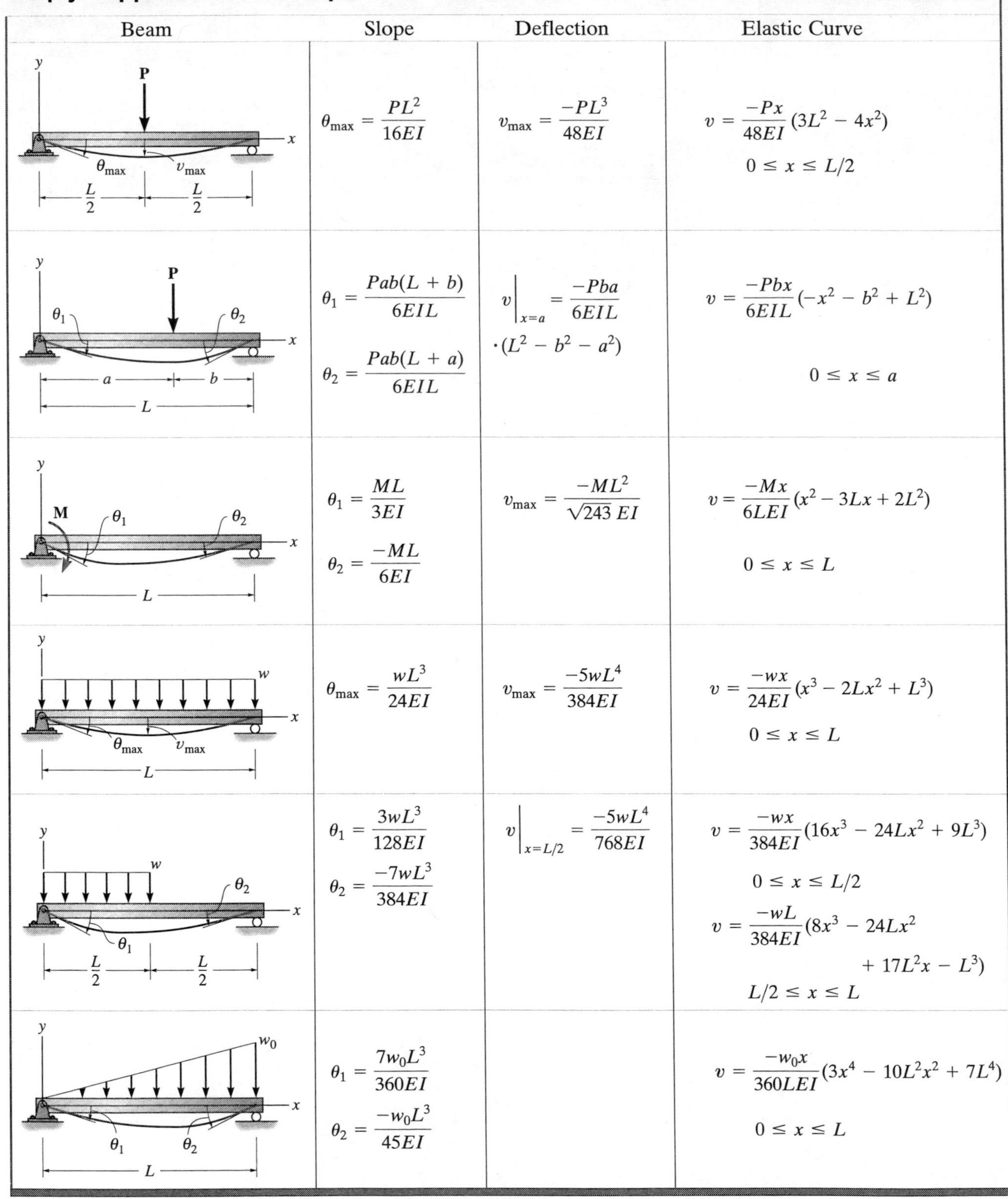

Beam	Slope	Deflection	Elastic Curve
	$\theta_{max} = \dfrac{PL^2}{16EI}$	$v_{max} = \dfrac{-PL^3}{48EI}$	$v = \dfrac{-Px}{48EI}(3L^2 - 4x^2)$ $0 \le x \le L/2$
	$\theta_1 = \dfrac{Pab(L+b)}{6EIL}$ $\theta_2 = \dfrac{Pab(L+a)}{6EIL}$	$v\Big\rvert_{x=a} = \dfrac{-Pba}{6EIL}$ $\cdot(L^2 - b^2 - a^2)$	$v = \dfrac{-Pbx}{6EIL}(-x^2 - b^2 + L^2)$ $0 \le x \le a$
	$\theta_1 = \dfrac{ML}{3EI}$ $\theta_2 = \dfrac{-ML}{6EI}$	$v_{max} = \dfrac{-ML^2}{\sqrt{243}\,EI}$	$v = \dfrac{-Mx}{6LEI}(x^2 - 3Lx + 2L^2)$ $0 \le x \le L$
	$\theta_{max} = \dfrac{wL^3}{24EI}$	$v_{max} = \dfrac{-5wL^4}{384EI}$	$v = \dfrac{-wx}{24EI}(x^3 - 2Lx^2 + L^3)$ $0 \le x \le L$
	$\theta_1 = \dfrac{3wL^3}{128EI}$ $\theta_2 = \dfrac{-7wL^3}{384EI}$	$v\Big\rvert_{x=L/2} = \dfrac{-5wL^4}{768EI}$	$v = \dfrac{-wx}{384EI}(16x^3 - 24Lx^2 + 9L^3)$ $0 \le x \le L/2$ $v = \dfrac{-wL}{384EI}(8x^3 - 24Lx^2 + 17L^2x - L^3)$ $L/2 \le x \le L$
	$\theta_1 = \dfrac{7w_0L^3}{360EI}$ $\theta_2 = \dfrac{-w_0L^3}{45EI}$		$v = \dfrac{-w_0x}{360LEI}(3x^4 - 10L^2x^2 + 7L^4)$ $0 \le x \le L$

Cantilevered Beam Slopes and Deflections

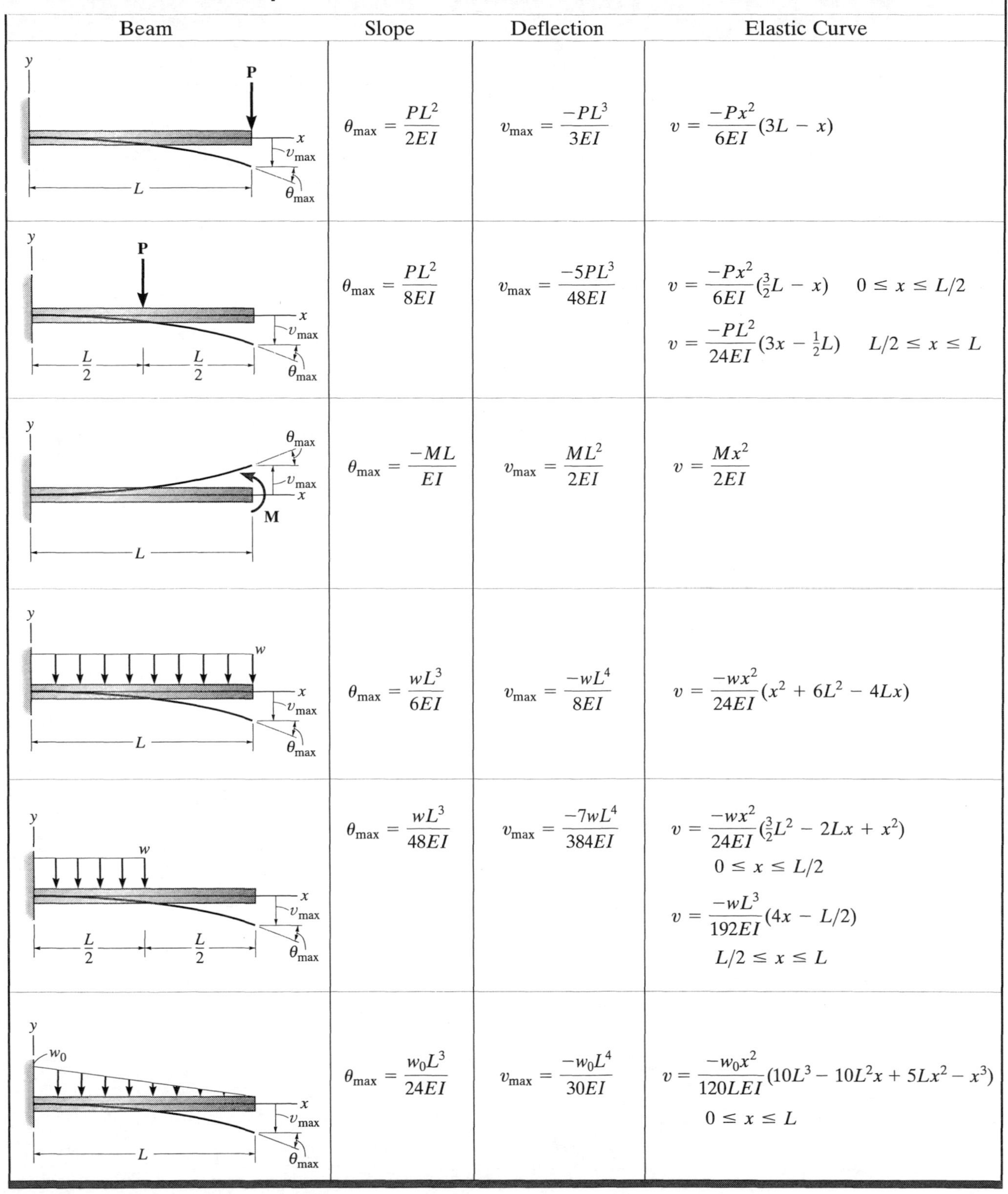

Beam	Slope	Deflection	Elastic Curve
	$\theta_{max} = \dfrac{PL^2}{2EI}$	$v_{max} = \dfrac{-PL^3}{3EI}$	$v = \dfrac{-Px^2}{6EI}(3L - x)$
	$\theta_{max} = \dfrac{PL^2}{8EI}$	$v_{max} = \dfrac{-5PL^3}{48EI}$	$v = \dfrac{-Px^2}{6EI}(\tfrac{3}{2}L - x) \quad 0 \le x \le L/2$ $v = \dfrac{-PL^2}{24EI}(3x - \tfrac{1}{2}L) \quad L/2 \le x \le L$
	$\theta_{max} = \dfrac{-ML}{EI}$	$v_{max} = \dfrac{ML^2}{2EI}$	$v = \dfrac{Mx^2}{2EI}$
	$\theta_{max} = \dfrac{wL^3}{6EI}$	$v_{max} = \dfrac{-wL^4}{8EI}$	$v = \dfrac{-wx^2}{24EI}(x^2 + 6L^2 - 4Lx)$
	$\theta_{max} = \dfrac{wL^3}{48EI}$	$v_{max} = \dfrac{-7wL^4}{384EI}$	$v = \dfrac{-wx^2}{24EI}(\tfrac{3}{2}L^2 - 2Lx + x^2)$ $0 \le x \le L/2$ $v = \dfrac{-wL^3}{192EI}(4x - L/2)$ $L/2 \le x \le L$
	$\theta_{max} = \dfrac{w_0L^3}{24EI}$	$v_{max} = \dfrac{-w_0L^4}{30EI}$	$v = \dfrac{-w_0x^2}{120LEI}(10L^3 - 10L^2x + 5Lx^2 - x^3)$ $0 \le x \le L$